CALCULUS:
An Intuitive and Physical Approach

By the same author

Morris Kline and Irvin W. Kay, *Electromagnetic Theory and Geometrical Optics*
    (Interscience Monograph in Pure and Applied Mathematics), Wiley, New York,
    1965.

Morris Kline, *Mathematics, a Cultural Approach*, Addison-Wesley, Reading, Mass.,
    1962.

Morris Kline, *Mathematics and the Physical World*, T. Y. Crowell Co., New York,
    1959.

Morris Kline, *Mathematics in Western Culture*, Oxford University Press, New York,
    1953.

Part One

CALCULUS:

An Intuitive and Physical Approach

MORRIS KLINE   PROFESSOR OF MATHEMATICS

COURANT INSTITUTE OF MATHEMATICAL SCIENCES

NEW YORK UNIVERSITY

John Wiley and Sons, Inc.   *New York · London · Sydney*

Library of Congress Catalog Card Number: 66-26748
Printed in the United States of America

Preface

Intuitive Approach! (handwritten)

excess (handwritten)

Anyone who adds to the plethora of introductory calculus texts owes an explanation, if not an apology, to the mathematical community. I believe that an introductory course in the calculus should present the subject intuitively and should relate it as closely as possible to science. A text for such an approach is not available.

In this book the justification of the theorems and techniques is consistently intuitive; that is, geometrical, physical, and heuristic arguments and generalizations from concrete cases are employed to convince. The approach is especially suitable for the calculus because the subject grew out of physical and geometrical problems. These problems tell us what functions we should take up, what concepts we want to formulate, and what techniques we should develop. In view of the fact that the human mind learns intuitively and that time does not permit both an intuitive and a rigorous presentation in elementary calculus, it seems to me that the approach adopted is the correct one.

The intuitive approach is explained to the student so that he will know what kind of evidence is being used to support arguments. Thus he is told that a graph of a typical function may not represent all functions. On the other hand, he is also told that the elementary functions are well behaved except at isolated points and that he can usually trust his intuition. As he works with the ideas of the calculus, he will sharpen his intuition. If he continues with mathematics, he will learn the analytical foundations and proofs that guard against the failings of intuition.

The use of an intuitive approach in the first treatment of a subject is not an innovation. Arithmetic is learned intuitively in elementary school and then the logic of it is learned gradually through the work in algebra. Geometry is learned intuitively in junior high school and then the formal deductive approach is presented in senior high school. A difficult subject such as the calculus, therefore, should certainly be introduced by an intuitive approach.

This approach has many merits beyond that of being the only feasible one. Every pedagogue today champions discovery, but few teach it. How does one discover in mathematics? By thinking in physical and geometrical terms, by conjecturing or guessing, by formulating hypotheses and testing them, and by generalizing on specific cases. Physical problems that call for the creation of mathematics set the stage for discovery. That the intuitive approach may lead to errors is granted, but "truth emerges more readily from error than from confusion." The student must be allowed to make mistakes, for if he makes no mistakes, he will not progress.

After the basic material has been covered, the need for rigor is motivated, and the last two chapters of Part 2 of this book do offer an introduction to precise language and proof. These chapters are intended as a transition to advanced calculus.

One alternative to an intuitive approach is a rigorous treatment. In my opinion, a rigorous first course in the calculus is ill advised for numerous reasons. First, it is too difficult for the students. Beginners are asked to learn a mass of concepts so subtle that they defied the best mathematicians for two hundred years. Even Cauchy, the founder of rigor, gave formulations that are crude compared to what the current rigorous presentations ask students to absorb. And Cauchy, despite his concern for rigor, missed the distinctions between continuity and differentiability and between convergence and uniform convergence. Before one can appreciate a precise formulation of a concept or theorem, he must know what idea is being formulated and what exceptions or pitfalls the wording is trying to avoid. Hence he must be able to call upon a wealth of experience acquired before tackling the rigorous formulation. Furthermore, having students master a polished deductive organization does not teach them how to think and how to do mathematics, for thinking and doing are not deductive processes. How can discovery take place when students are asked to work with ideas that are already overladen with sophistication and refinement? Finally, the rigorous approach is misleading. Because the introductory calculus course is the student's first contact with higher mathematics, he obtains the impression that real mathematics is deductive and that good mathematicians think deductively.

Rigor has its place in mathematics education. It is a check on the creations and it permits an aesthetic (as well as an anaesthetic) presentation. But it is also to some extent gilt on the lily and an interdiction against the inclusion of functions which rarely occur in practice and which must even be invented with Weierstrassian ingenuity. A rigorous first course in calculus reminds one of the words of Samuel Johnson; "I have found you an argument but I am not obliged to find you an understanding." Even if the rigorous material is understood, its value is limited. As Henri Lebesgue pointed out: "Logic makes us reject certain arguments but it cannot make us believe any argument."

The reasons often given for a rigorous presentation—that students must learn what a real proof is or that students should not be asked to unlearn later what they have already been taught—are hollow. One cannot give the whole truth at once in any subject. Even we, as teachers, do not face the whole truth for, in fact, the whole question of what is rigorous in mathematics was never so much up in the air as it is now. At any rate, what may seem ideally right and efficient is pedagogically intolerable.

There is also the alternative of compromising on rigor by offering precise definitions and proofs in some portions of the text and intuitive or pseudo-rigorous arguments in others. This alternative seems to me to have almost all of the disadvantages of a rigorous presentation and the additional one of confusing the student about what proof really is.

The second essential respect in which this book differs from current ones is that the relationship of mathematics to science is taken seriously. The present trend to separate mathematics from science is tragic. There are chapters of mathematics that have value in and for themselves. However, the calculus divorced from applications is meaningless. We should also keep in mind that most of the students taking calculus will be scientists and engineers, and these students must learn how to use mathematics. But the step from mathematics to its applications is not simple and straightforward and it creates difficulties for the student from the time he is called upon to solve verbal problems in algebra. The mathematics courses fail to teach students how to formulate physical problems mathematically. The science and engineering courses, on the other hand, assume that students know how to translate physical problems into mathematical language and how to make satisfactory idealizations. The gap between mathematics and science instruction must be filled, and we can do so to our own advantage because thereby we give meaning and motivation to the calculus.

In this book real problems are used to motivate the mathematics, and the latter, once developed, is applied to genuine physical problems—the magnificent, impressive, and even beautiful problems tendered by nature. I have selected those that do *not* require a background in physics. However, if the student is to think properly even about familiar concepts, such as weight, force, velocity, acceleration, light, and work, the book must say a little about them and about the physical laws that are involved. It does. To relegate physical problems only to the exercises is, in my opinion, ineffective in teaching students how to apply mathematics. If the student is not informed about the physics of a problem, all he can do in tackling an exercise is to apply a formula mechanically or guess what technical process is called for, do it, and check his answer. If the book does not supply an answer and if the student's result is off by a factor of 1000, he will not realize it because he has no judgment about what to expect.

I have tried to incorporate several other features that may contribute to the pedagogy. In many instances I have deliberately made false starts so as to have the student realize that correct methods and correct proofs are almost always preceded by groping and to have students appreciate why we finally take one course rather than another. I wish to dispel the impression that good mathematicians are able to proceed directly to the right conclusion because strict logic or a God-given insight guides them. I have given full details on the mathematical steps in the hope that the book will be readable. The style is informal.

The pace of the first few chapters of Part 1 has been deliberately made slow. It is well known that calculus students are still struggling with elementary algebra. By keeping the opening algebra simple, I trust that the calculus ideas will stand forth. In later chapters the algebra becomes more difficult.

The order of the mathematical concepts and topics was chosen so that applications could be introduced almost from the beginning. However, no artificial or complicated arrangement was necessary. Differentiation and antidifferentiation are the key concepts in the first thirteen chapters and then summation is introduced. The early introduction of applications should permit good correlation with physics courses if these are taken concurrently. The concept of differentials was deliberately delayed until Chapter 12 of Part 1. Most books do stress that the derivative is a limit of a quotient, but often present differentials early. No matter how much the student is cautioned that the derivative is not a quotient, if he is allowed to work almost at once with the quotient of the differentials, he tends to forget the true meaning of the derivative.

Beyond the matter of the proper approach, there are a few other points that may warrant comment. Despite my own preference for a course in analytic geometry which precedes the calculus, I have included the former. This is a concession to the current fad. Some work with vectors is included, but I have not done much with the differentiation and integration of vector functions. I believe that this topic requires a new way of thinking and that we should not try to teach two major classes of techniques at the same time. The calculus of scalar functions is the basic one, and this should be mastered first. Apropos of the inclusion of vector analysis, the present trend to include this topic, linear algebra, probability, and differential equations in a three- or four-semester analytic geometry and calculus course, seems to me to be attempting the impossible.

Any book should be adjustable to the needs of a particular course. Most of the applications are in separate sections, and therefore the number of those that need to be included is optional. Even whole chapters, such as Chapter 13 of Part 1 on further techniques of integration, Chapter 16 of Part 1 on further physical applications of the definite integral, and Chapter 19 of Part 2 on polar parametric equations, can be omitted. The last two chapters of Part 2 (Chapters 24 and 25), the introduction to rigor, can be omitted or, on the other hand, they can be read before the chapters on solid analytic geometry and functions of two or more variables.

I wish to express my thanks to the publishers for their generous support of this approach to the calculus and for their efficient handling of the production.

New York   *Morris Kline*
November 1966

Contents

Contents for Part Two

Why Calculus?

1. *The Historical Motivations for the Calculus.* Each branch of mathematics has been developed to attack a class of problems that could not be solved at all or yielded to a solution only after great efforts. Thus elementary algebra was created to find answers to simple physical problems which in mathematical form called for solving first, second, and higher degree equations with one or two unknowns. Plane and solid geometry originated in the need to find perimeters, areas, and volumes of common figures and to state conditions under which two figures, say two triangles, are congruent or have the same shape—that is, are similar. Trigonometry, introduced by astronomers, enabled man to determine the sizes and distances of heavenly bodies.

In high school algebra and trigonometry we usually learn the fundamentals of another branch of mathematics, called coordinate or analytical geometry. Thus we learn to graph linear equations such as $x + 2y = 5$, to represent a circle of radius R by an equation of the form $x^2 + y^2 = R^2$, and to determine which curves correspond to such equations as $y = \sin x$ and $y = \cos x$. The primary purpose of relating equations and curves is to enable us to use the equations in the study of such important curves as the paths of projectiles, planets, and light rays. Of course, each of the above-mentioned branches of mathematics has also helped to treat problems of the physical and social sciences which arose long after the motivating questions had been disposed of.

During the seventeenth century, when modern science was founded and began to expand apace, a number of new problems were brought to the fore. Because the mathematicians of that century, like those of most great periods, were the very physicists and astronomers who raised the questions, they responded at once to the problems. Let us see what some of these problems were.

Seventeenth-century scientists were very much concerned with problems of motion. The heliocentric theory created by Nicolaus Copernicus (1473–1543) and Johannes Kepler (1571–1630) introduced the concepts of the earth rotating on its axis and revolving around the sun. The earlier theory of planetary motion, dating back to Ptolemy (c. A.D. 150), which presupposed an earth absolutely fixed in space and, indeed, in the center of the universe, was discarded. The adoption of the theory involving an earth in motion invalidated the laws and explanations of motion that had been accepted since Greek times. New insights were needed into such phenomena as the motion of a projectile shot from a cannon and an answer to the question of why objects stay with the moving earth seemed called for. Furthermore, Kepler had shown on the basis of observations that the path of each planet around the sun is an ellipse, although no theoretical explanation of why the planets move on such paths had been offered. However, the notion that all bodies in the universe attract one another in accordance with the force of gravitation became prominent, and scientists decided to investigate whether the motions of planets around the sun and of moons around planets could be deduced from the proper laws of motion and gravitation. The motion of celestial bodies became the dominant scientific study.

All of these motions—those of objects near the surface of the earth and those of the heavenly bodies—take place with variable velocity, and many involve variable acceleration. Although the difficulties in handling variable velocities and accelerations may not be apparent at the moment, the branches of mathematics that existed before the calculus was created were not adequate to treat them. We shall see later precisely what the difficulties are and how they are surmounted. In pre-calculus courses students often work on problems involving variable velocity—for example, the motion of a body falling to earth—but the intricacy is circumvented there by one dodge or another.

The second major problem of the seventeenth century was the determination of tangents to various curves (Fig. 1-1). This question is of some interest

| Figure 1-1 | Figure 1-2 |

as a matter of pure geometry, but its deeper significance is that the tangent to a curve at a point represents the *direction* of the curve at the point. Thus, if a projectile moves along a curve, the direction in which the projectile is headed at any point on its path is the direction of the tangent at that point. To determine whether the projectile will strike its target head on or merely at a glancing angle, we must know in which direction the projectile is moving at that point on its path at which it strikes the target. To determine the course of a light ray after it strikes the surface of a lens, we must know the angle that the light ray makes with the lens, that is, the angle (Fig. 1-2) between the light ray and the tangent to the lens. The invention of the telescope and microscope in the seventeenth century stimulated great interest in the action of lenses. Incidentally, the study of the behavior of light was, next to the study of motion, the most active scientific field in that century. It may now be apparent why the question of finding the tangent to a curve was a major one.

A third class of problems besetting the seventeenth-century scientists may be described as maxima and minima problems. The motion of cannon balls was studied intensively from the sixteenth century onward. In fact, the mathematicians Nicolò Tartaglia (1500–1557) and Galileo Galilei (1564–1642) made significant progress in this investigation even before the calculus was applied to it. One of the important questions about the motion of cannon balls and other kinds of projectiles was the determination of the maximum range. As the angle of elevation of a cannon (angle *A* in Fig. 1-3) is varied,

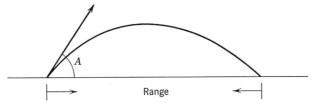

Figure 1-3

the range—that is, the horizontal distance from the cannon to the point at which the projectile again reaches the ground—also varies. The question is, at what angle of elevation is the range a maximum? Another maximum and minimum problem of considerable importance arises in planetary motion. As a planet moves about the sun, its distance from the sun varies. A basic question in this area is, what are the maximum and minimum distances of the planet from the sun? Some simple maxima and minima problems can be solved by the methods of elementary algebra and elementary geometry, but the most important problems are beyond the power of these branches.

Still another class of problems in the seventeenth century concerned the lengths of curves and the areas and volumes of figures bounded by curves and surfaces. Elementary mathematics suffices to determine the areas and volumes of simple figures, principally figures bounded by line segments and by portions of planes. However, when curves or curved surfaces are involved, elementary geometry is almost helpless. For example, the shape of the earth is an oblate spheroid, that is, a sphere somewhat flattened on the top and bottom (Fig. 1-4). The calculation of the volume of this figure cannot be performed with elementary geometry; it can be done with the calculus. Euclidean geometry does have a method, called the method of exhaustion, for treating a very limited number of area and volume problems involving curves and surfaces, respectively. This method is difficult to apply and, moreover, involves concepts that can with considerable justification be regarded as belonging to the calculus, although the Greeks did not formulate them in modern terms. In any case, the method of exhaustion could not cope with the variety and difficulty of the area and volume problems that appeared in the seventeenth century. Closely related to these problems were those of finding the center of gravity of a body and the gravitational attraction exerted by, say, the earth on the moon. The relation may not be evident at the moment, but we shall see that the same method solves both types of problem.

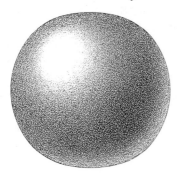

Figure 1-4

The efforts to treat the four classes of problem that we have thus far briefly described led mathematicians to methods which we now embrace under the term calculus. Of course, similar problems continue to be important in our time; otherwise the calculus would have only historical value. In fact, once a mathematical method or branch of any significance is created, many new uses are found for it that were not envisioned by its creators. For the calculus this has proved to be far more the case than for any other mathematical creation; we shall examine later a number of modern applications. Moreover, the most weighty developments in mathematics since the seventeenth century employ the calculus. Indeed, it is the basis of a number of branches of mathematics which now comprise its most extensive portion. The calculus has proved to be the richest lode that the mathematicians have ever struck.

2. The Creators of The Calculus.   Like almost all branches of mathematics, the calculus is the product of many men. In the seventeenth century Pierre de Fermat (1601–1665), René Descartes (1596–1650), Blaise Pascal (1623–1662), Gilles Persone de Roberval (1602–1675), Bonaventura Cavalieri (1598–1647), Isaac Barrow (1630–1677), James Gregory (1638–1675), Christian Huygens (1629–1695), John Wallis (1616–1703), and, of course Isaac Newton (1642–1727) and Gottfried Wilhelm Leibniz (1646–1716) all contributed to it. Newton and Leibniz are most often mentioned as the creators of the calculus. This is a half-truth. Without deprecating their contributions, it is fair to say, as Newton himself put it, that they stood on the shoulders of giants. They saw more clearly than their predecessors the generality of the methods that were gradually being developed and, in addition, added many theorems and processes to the stock built up by their predecessors.

Even Newton and Leibniz did not complete the calculus. Throughout the eighteenth century new results were obtained by, for example, James Bernoulli (1654–1705), his brother John Bernoulli (1667–1748), Michel Rolle

(1652–1719), Brook Taylor (1685–1731), Colin Maclaurin (1698–1746), Leonhard Euler (1707–1783), Jean Le Rond d'Alembert (1717–1783), and Joseph-Louis Lagrange (1736–1813). Moreover, the final clarification of the concepts of the calculus was achieved only in the nineteenth century by, among others, Bernhard Bolzano (1781–1848), Augustin-Louis Cauchy (1789–1857), and Karl Weierstrass (1815–1897). We shall find many of these great names attached to theorems that we shall be studying.*

3. *The Nature of the Calculus.* The word *calculus* comes from the Latin word for pebble, which became associated with mathematics because the early Greek mathematicians of about 600 B.C. did arithmetic with the aid of pebbles. Today a calculus can mean a procedure or set of procedures such as division in arithmetic or solving a quadratic equation in algebra. However, most often the word means the theory and procedures we are about to study in the differential and integral calculus. Usually we say *the calculus* to denote the differential and integral calculus as opposed to other calculi.

The calculus utilizes algebra, geometry, trigonometry, and some coordinate geometry (which we shall study in this book). However, it also introduces some new concepts, notably the derivative and the integral. Fundamental to both is the limit concept. We shall not attempt to describe the notion of limit and how it is used to formulate the derivative and integral, because a brief explanation may be more confusing than helpful. Nevertheless, we do wish to point out that the calculus in its introduction and utilization of the limit concept marks a new stage in the development of mathematics.

The proper study of the calculus calls for attention to several features. The first is the theory, which leads to numerous theorems about the derivative and the integral. The second feature is the technique; to use the calculus, one must learn a fair amount of technique in differentiation and integration. The third feature is application. The calculus was created in response to scientific needs, and we should study many of the applications to gain appreciation of what can be accomplished with the subject; these applications also give insight into the mathematical ideas.

The theory of the calculus, which depends primarily on the limit concept, is rather sophisticated. Complete proofs of all the theorems are difficult to grasp when one is beginning the study of the subject. Our approach to the theory attempts to surmount this hurdle. Many of our proofs are complete. However, other proofs are made by appealing to geometric evidence; that is, we use curves or other geometric figures to substantiate our assertions. The geometric evidence does not necessarily consist of complete geometric proofs, so that we cannot say that we are *proving* geometrically. Nevertheless, the arguments are quite convincing. For example, we can be certain even

---

* The history of the calculus is very well presented in Carl B. Boyer, *The Concepts of the Calculus*, Dover Publications, New York, 1959.

without geometric proof that the bisector of angle *A* (Fig. 1-5) divides the isosceles triangle *ABC* into two congruent triangles.

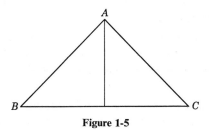

Figure 1-5

This approach, which will become clearer when we begin considering specific cases, is called the intuitive approach. It is recommended for several reasons. The first, as already suggested, is pedagogical. A thoroughly sound, deductive approach to the calculus, one which the modern mathematician would regard as logically rigorous, is meaningless before one understands the ideas and the purposes to which they are put. One should always try to understand new concepts and theorems in an intuitive manner before studying a formal and rigorous presentation of them. The logical version may dispose of any lingering doubts and may be aesthetically more satisfying to some minds, but it is not the road to understanding.

The rigorous approach, in fact, did not become available until about 150 years after the creation of the calculus. During these years mathematicians built up not only the calculus but also differential equations, differential geometry, the calculus of variations, and many other major branches of mathematics that depend on the calculus. In achieving these results the greatest mathematicians thought in intuitive and physical terms.

The second reason for adopting the intuitive approach is that we wish to have time for some techniques and for applications. Were we to study the rigorous formulations of limit, derivative, integral, and allied concepts, we would not have time for anything else. These concepts can be carefully and most profitably studied in more advanced courses in the calculus after one has some appreciation of what they mean in geometrical and physical terms and of what one wishes to do with them. As for the applications, the calculus more than any other branch of mathematics was created to solve major physical problems, and one should certainly learn what the calculus accomplishes in this connection.

After we have become reasonably familiar with the ideas, techniques, and uses of the calculus, we shall consider in the last two chapters how the intuitive approach may be strengthened by a more rigorous one.

The Derivative

1. *The Concept of Function.* Before considering any ideas of the calculus itself, we shall review a concept that is, no doubt, largely familiar—the concept of a function.

If an object moves in a straight line—for example, a ball rolls along a floor—the time during which it moves, measured from the instant it starts its motion, is a variable. In the case of the ball, the time continually increases. The distance the object moves, measured from the point at which it starts to move, is also a variable. The two variables are related. The distance the ball travels depends on the time the ball has been in motion. By the end of 1 second it may have moved 50 feet, by the end of 2 seconds, 100 feet, and so on. The relation between distance and time is a function. Loosely stated for the moment, a function is a relation between variables.

There are, of course, thousands of functions. If the ball were started on its journey with a different speed, the relation between distance traveled and time in motion would be different. All kinds of motions take place around us, and for each of them there is a function or relation between distance traveled and time in motion. The idea of a relation between variables is not confined to motion. The national debt of this country varies as time varies, and the relation between these variables is also a function. If money is allowed to accumulate interest in a bank, the amount in the account increases with time. Here, too, we have a function. Obviously, many other examples could be cited.

The notion of a function as used in the calculus is more restricted than we have thus far indicated. The statement that a person's obligation to society increases with his age expresses a function, the variables of which are obligation and age. However, it is not possible to measure the extent of this obligation in numbers. The calculus is concerned only with variables whose values can be expressed numerically. Thus time, distance, and money accumulating in a bank are variables whose various values can be measured and therefore can be expressed as numbers.

The most effective mathematical representation of a function is what we shall call a *formula*. Suppose that an object is dropped and falls straight down. The time during which it falls continually increases as does the

7

distance that it falls. The formula

(1) $$s = 16t^2,$$

whose correctness we shall establish later, expresses the relation between the two variables if the resistance of air is neglected. In this formula t is the number of seconds the object falls measured from the instant it starts to fall and s is the number of feet it falls measured from the point at which it is dropped. (The letter s is used to represent space because the Latin word for it is *spatium*.) The formula thus says that when $t = 2$, then $s = 16 \cdot 2^2$ or 64. For each value that we may substitute for t there is a corresponding value of s. This example not only illustrates a formula but also possesses a property which is important for the functions that the calculus treats. For each value we may choose for t there is no more than one value of s. We say that s is a single-valued function of t.

When written in the form (1), that is, when solved for s, formula (1) shows how s depends on t or expresses s as a function of t. Then t is called the *independent* variable and s, the *dependent* variable.

Formula (1) also tells us something about how t depends on s, for example, when $s = 64$, we find that t can be $+2$ or -2. To express more clearly the dependence of t on s, we can solve (1) algebraically for t and obtain

(2) $$t = \pm \sqrt{\frac{s}{16}}.$$

Formula (2) expresses t as a function of s, so that s is the independent variable and t is the dependent variable. Here we can say that t is a double-valued function of s or we can say that there are two functions,

$$t = \sqrt{\frac{s}{16}} \quad \text{and} \quad t = -\sqrt{\frac{s}{16}},$$

each of which is single-valued. Because the techniques of the calculus apply to single-valued functions, we use either one or the other of these two functions, depending on the physical problem.

2. The Graph or Curve of a Function. We learn in algebra that formulas may be pictured as curves. The powerful method of interpreting formulas geometrically is known as coordinate or analytic geometry. This subject was created in the early part of the seventeenth century by René Descartes (1596–1650) and Pierre de Fermat (1601–1665) to expedite the study of functions, which were just beginning to be used, and to study geometric problems by algebraic means.

The main idea of coordinate geometry is that a function relating two variables, such as $y = x^2$ or $y = x^2 + 6x$, can be represented geometrically by a curve and, conversely, that a curve can be represented by a function, although it may not be single-valued. It is customary to speak of the function as the equation of the curve.

The basic device of coordinate geometry is a coordinate system, that is, a scheme that locates points in a plane by means of a pair of numbers. The most important coordinate system is the one that utilizes two mutually perpendicular lines (Fig. 2-1), called the x- and y-axes. These lines intersect

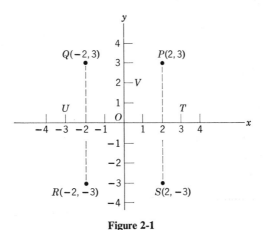

Figure 2-1

at some point O, called the origin. Along the x-axis, which is usually taken to be a horizontal line, we assign to each point its distance from the origin O. This distance is taken to be positive if the point lies to the right of O and negative if it lies to the left. Thus point T, which is 3 units to the right of O, has the number 3 or $+3$ assigned to it, whereas point U, which is 3 units to the left of O, has the number -3 assigned to it. Likewise numbers that represent their distances from O are assigned to points on the y-axis, but in this case points above O are assigned positive numbers and points below O, negative numbers. It is customary and usually convenient to use the same unit of distance in assigning numbers to points on both axes.

We are now able to locate or describe the positions of points in relation to the axes. Consider point P in Fig. 2-1. To reach it from O we can travel 2 units to the right along the x-axis and 3 units up in the direction of or parallel to the y-axis. Point P is located by the numbers 2 and 3, which are usually written as (2, 3), the first number indicating the distance along the x-axis and the second, the distance parallel to the y-axis. The two numbers are called the coordinates of P; the first is called the abscissa and the second, the ordinate.

The coordinates of point Q in Fig. 2-1 are $(-2, 3)$; the minus sign enters because we must travel 2 units to the left to reach Q. Similarly, the coordinates of R are $(-2, -3)$ and the coordinates of S are $(2, -3)$.

Our method of attaching coordinates to points assigns two coordinates to each point. Accordingly, point T on the x-axis in Fig. 2-1 has the coordinates $(3, 0)$ and point V on the y-axis has the coordinates $(0, 2)$.

The coordinates of a point may be interpreted in a different way. The abscissa or x-coordinate is the distance of the point from the y-axis, and the ordinate or y-coordinate is the distance from the x-axis. Of course the proper sign must be attached to these distances. The coordinate system we have examined is called the rectangular Cartesian system. The word Cartesian honors Descartes who introduced it, although in cruder form, and the word rectangular refers to the fact that the axes meet at right angles.

With the help of the rectangular Cartesian coordinate system we can obtain curves that represent or picture formulas. Thus to obtain the curve corresponding to $s = 16t^2$ we first introduce the usual horizontal and vertical axes of a rectangular coordinate system. We may as well label these axes t and s instead of x and y to remind us of the letters we are actually using for the variables in our formula. We can now graph the formula $s = 16t^2$ by making a table of values. Thus when $t = 0$, $s = 0$; when $t = 1$, $s = 16$; and so forth. The table then reads:

t	0	1	2	3
s	0	16	64	144

Because the s-values are large, we use a smaller unit of length on the s-axis than on the t-axis. We now plot the points $(0, 0)$, $(1, 16)$, $(2, 64)$, ... , and join them by a smooth curve (Fig. 2-2). In the present case there is no need to include negative values of t in the table because we see that for each negative value of t, say -2, the s-value is the same as that for the corresponding positive value of t. Geometrically this means that the curve rises to the left in precisely the same way as to the right. The full curve in Fig. 2-2 is called a *parabola*.

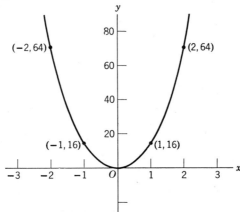

Figure 2-2

The graph of a formula, that is, the curve corresponding to a formula, is a useful picture of how the variables in the formula behave. Thus we see in Fig. 2-2 that *s* not only increases as *t* increases from 0 onward through positive values but does so much more rapidly than *t*. We must, however, be careful to distinguish the curve from the *physical* situation. The motion described by $s = 16t^2$ is that of an object that falls straight down. There is a correspondence between the physical happening and the curve, but the latter is usually not a picture of the physical motion. It is also important to note that both the formula and the curve differ in another essential respect from the physical motion. An object that is dropped from a point near the surface of the earth may fall for, say, 5 seconds and then hit the earth. The physical motion, then, is represented by the formula and the curve only for the values of *t* from 0 to 5. However, the mathematical formula and mathematical curve have meaning for every positive and negative value of *t*.

The function $s = 16t^2$ is especially simple in that to *each* value of *t* that we may select there is a corresponding value of *s*. The concept of a function does not require this. Consider, for example, the function

(3) $$y = \frac{1}{x - 2}.$$

For each value of *x* other than 2, there is a definite value of *y*. For $x = 2$ the expression on the right side becomes 1/0, which is meaningless because division by 0 is not defined.* Hence this function is defined or, as the mathematician says, this function exists for each value of *x* other than 2. The graph of the function is shown in Fig. 2-3. There is no point on the graph corresponding to $x = 2$.

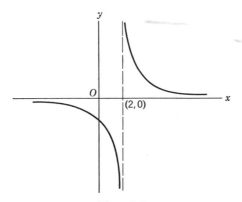

Figure 2-3

---

* Let us recall why a quantity such as *a*/0 is not defined. Suppose first that *a* is not 0. Were there a number of *b* such that $a/0 = b$, then by multiplying both sides of this equation by 0 we would have $a = 0 \cdot b$. However, $0 \cdot b$ cannot equal *a*, for *a* is not 0. If *a* is 0, by the same steps we obtain $0 = 0 \cdot b$; now the trouble is that *b* can be any number. Because there is no unique answer to 0/0, the expression is meaningless.

As another example, let us consider the function

(4) $$y = \sqrt{1 - x},$$

wherein we mean the positive square root. When x is greater than 1, the radicand is negative, and the square root of a negative number is a complex number. In elementary calculus we prefer not to deal with complex numbers. Hence we restrict the values of x to 1 and numbers algebraically less than 1; that is, the permissible values of x are the positive numbers less than or equal to 1, 0, and all negative numbers. The graph of the permissible x- and y-values is shown in Fig. 2-4.

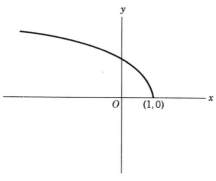

Figure 2-4

Thus the concept of a function does not require that there be a y-value for each value of x, but it does require a y-value for each value of x in some collection or set of x-values. The technical word for the collection of x-values for which the y-values exist is *domain*; the collection of corresponding y-values is called the *range* of the function.

Let us consider next the function

(5) $$y = \frac{x^2 - 4}{x - 2}.$$

The temptation in studying this function is to use algebra at once and write

$$y = \frac{x^2 - 4}{x - 2} = \frac{(x + 2)(x - 2)}{x - 2},$$

and now one almost naturally cancels the factor $x - 2$ in numerator and denominator and obtains

(6) $$y = x + 2.$$

There seems to be nothing wrong about yielding to temptation and, in fact, one seems to gain a lot by doing so, contrary to all the moralists: the function (6) is much simpler than (5).

Nevertheless, there is a vital distinction between (5) and (6). To arrive at (6) we canceled the factor $x - 2$ in numerator and denominator. What this operation really amounts to is dividing numerator and denominator by $x - 2$. However, division by $x - 2$ is legitimate except when $x = 2$. Hence the steps from (5) to (6) are correct except when $x = 2$. Let us look at (5) when $x = 2$. The numerator and denominator are each 0, and what we obtain for y is 0/0. Now, division by 0 is meaningless, and therefore y in (5) has no value at $x = 2$. On the other hand the function in (6) has a very definite value when $x = 2$, namely $y = 4$. Thus the two functions (5) and (6) differ in their behavior at $x = 2$.

Let us look at the graphs of the two functions. To graph (5) we must calculate the y-values for various x-values. For this purpose we can use the simpler function (6), which is the same as (5) except at $x = 2$. We find that the graph of (6), which is a first degree equation in x and y, is a straight line; this is shown in Fig. 2-5*b*. Then the graph of (5) must also be the same straight line *except* at $x = 2$. At $x = 2$ the function (5) has no value, and therefore there is no point on the graph corresponding to $x = 2$. The graph of (5) then consists of two half lines or rays emanating from point P of Fig. 2-5*a*, but point P itself is *not* part of the graph.

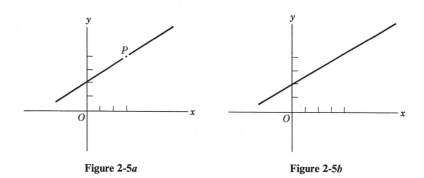

Figure 2-5*a*   Figure 2-5*b*

The distinction we have drawn between the functions (5) and (6) may seem to be much ado about nothing, but let us withhold judgment and undertake a further study of (5). What can we say about the behavior of that function as x takes on values closer and closer to 2? For values of x close to 2, other than 2 itself, the function (6) has the same values as (5), and we see from (6) that as x takes on values closer and closer to 2, the y-values come closer and closer to 4. Hence the same must be true of the function (5). We say that the number 4 is the *limit* of the y-values in (5) as x approaches 2. We shall explain the notion of limit and its implications more fully later, as we probe more deeply into the calculus. We should note at this point, however, that although a function is not defined, that is, it has no value, at a given value of x, the value $x = 2$ in (5), the values of the function may approach a given number

Limits

more and more closely as the values of x approach that given value of x. In other words, a function may approach a limit even when it has no value.

Exercises

1. Sketch the graphs of the following functions by the method of plotting points:

(a) $y = 3x^2$.

(b) $y = \sqrt{1 - x^2}$.

(c) $y = -\sqrt{1 - x^2}$.

(d) $y = \dfrac{1}{x - 3}$.

(e) $y = x^3$.

(f) $y = \dfrac{1}{x^2}$.

(g) $y = \dfrac{x^2 - 9}{x - 3}$.

(h) $y = \dfrac{x^3 - 1}{x - 1}$.

(i) $y = x^2 - 7x$.

(j) $y = -x^2$.

(k) $y = -x^2 + 7x$.

(l) $y = -x^2 - 7x$.

(m) $y = \sqrt{x^2}$.

2. There is of course no obligation to use y and x as the symbols for the dependent and independent variables, respectively. We may use k and h. Sketch the following functions:

(a) $k = \dfrac{16h + h^2}{h}$.

(b) $k = \dfrac{h^3}{h}$.

(c) $k = \dfrac{9h + h^3}{h}$.

(d) $k = \dfrac{9h^2 + h^3}{h}$.

(e) $k = \dfrac{(h - 1)^2}{h - 1}$.

3. Average and Instantaneous Speed. The primary concept of the calculus deals with the rate of change of one variable with respect to another. Let us approach an understanding of this concept by discussing the notion of speed, the very concept with which Newton started. By speed we usually understand the rate of change of distance with respect to time. Thus, if a person travels 90 miles in 3 hours, his speed, he says, is 30 mi/hr (miles per hour). He has, of course, divided the distance traveled by the time during which he has traveled that distance to obtain the speed. This speed is more properly called the *average* speed or the *average* rate of change of distance with respect to time.

Of course, the person who travels at the average speed of 30 mi/hr does not necessarily travel at that fixed speed throughout the 3 hours. He may slow down or speed up at various times during the 3 hours. For many purposes, however, it suffices for people to know the average speed at which they have traveled or can expect to travel on some journey.

However, the average speed is not the significant quantity in many daily happenings and scientific phenomena. If a person traveling in an automobile strikes a tree, it is not his average speed during the time he has traveled from the starting point to the tree but his speed at the *instant of collision* that determines whether he will survive the accident. Likewise, when a bullet strikes a target it is the speed of the bullet at the *instant it strikes* rather than its average speed over the time it has been traveling that determines what damage the bullet will do. Many other more agreeable examples of speed at an instant will be encountered later.

In contrasting average speed with instantaneous speed we have implicitly utilized a distinction between interval and instant, which is vital for what follows. An average speed is one that concerns what happens over an *interval* of time—3 hours, 5 seconds, one half second, and so forth. The interval may be small or large, but it does represent the passage of a definite amount of time. We use the word instant, however, to state the fact that something happens so fast that no time elapses. The event is momentary. When we say, for example, that it is 3 o'clock, we refer to an instant, a precise moment. If the lapse of time is pictured by length along a line, then an interval is represented by a line segment, whereas an instant corresponds to a point. The notion of an instant, although it is also used in everyday life, is strictly a mathematical idealization.

Our ways of thinking about real events do cause us to speak in terms of instants and of speed at an instant, but closer examination shows that the concept of speed at an instant presents difficulties. Average speed, which is simply the distance traveled during some *interval* of time divided by that amount of time, is easily calculated. Suppose, however, that we try to carry over this process to instantaneous speed. The distance an automobile travels in one instant is 0 and the time that elapses during one instant is also 0. Hence the distance divided by the time is 0/0, which is meaningless. Thus, although instantaneous speed is a physical reality, there seems to be a difficulty in calculating it, and unless we can calculate it, we cannot work with it mathematically.

Let us see if we can devise some method of calculating instantaneous speed. If an object travels at a constant speed, say 30 mi/hr or 44 ft/sec (feet per second), there is no problem. We can take its speed at each instant to be, for example, 44 ft/sec. Suppose, however, that an object moves with variable speed and we wish to determine its instantaneous speed, say, exactly 3 seconds after it has been in motion. A practical beginning might be to calculate the average speed during the fourth second of the motion. This average speed would tell us something about the speed at the end of the third second. Of course, during the fourth second the object would have changed its speed, because it is moving with variable speed, and the average for the fourth second might not be the speed we seek. This average would be an approximation.

We can improve this approximation if we calculate the average speed for the half second from 3 to $3\frac{1}{2}$ seconds. This average should be a better approximation because even though the object is moving with a variable speed the average is not so likely to differ in a half second as in a full second from the speed which the object possesses at the end of the third second. Nevertheless, even the average speed during the half second is only an approximation to the speed at the end of the three seconds.

The way to obtain better approximations is now indicated. We could calculate the average speed over a quarter second from 3 to $3\frac{1}{4}$. This average should be better than the average over a half second because there is less time in which the object's speed can depart from the speed at the end of the third second. Still better approximations would be obtained by calculating the average speed for one eighth of a second from 3 to $3\frac{1}{8}$, then for one sixteenth of a second from 3 to $3\frac{1}{16}$, and so on.

Let us suppose that our calculations of average speeds yielded the following table:

Time interval after 3 seconds	1	$\frac{1}{2}$	$\frac{1}{4}$	$\frac{1}{8}$	$\frac{1}{16}$	$\frac{1}{32}$	$\cdots$
Average speed	100	96.5	96.3	96.1	96.05	96.01	$\cdots$

This table suggests that, as the time intervals over which the average speeds are computed become smaller and smaller, the average speeds get closer and closer to 96. However, as the time intervals, which begin at the end of the third second, become smaller and smaller and indeed approach 0 in size, the average speeds represent the speed of the moving object for a time interval closer and closer to the end of the third second. Would it not then be reasonable to take the number approached by these average speeds, namely 96, to be the speed precisely at the end of the third second? Physically this seems most advisable. After all, as the intervals of time measured from the end of the third second become very small, the average speeds in those intervals cannot differ much from what the object possessed at the end of the third second, for the object does not have much time to change its speed. Indeed, because the intervals of time are approaching 0, the object has less and less time to change its speed from what it possessed at the end of the third second.

This indication of how the speed at an instant might be determined is the kernel of the mathematical method of obtaining instantaneous rates. Before we attempt to make the method more precise and more efficient, let us note a very important point. The average speeds over the various time *intervals* are easy to compute. An average speed is simply the distance traveled over an interval of time divided by the interval of time. However, the instantaneous speed, the speed at the end of the third second, is *not* obtained by dividing a distance by a time interval. It is obtained *by observing the number that the average speeds approach*—the number 96 in our illustration. In mathematical language we say that the number 96 is the *limit* of the average speeds as the time intervals over which the average speeds are computed approach 0. Hence the instantaneous speed is obtained by a totally new process, namely, by finding the limit of average speeds. By this process we avoid the meaningless expression 0/0 which we would have to face if we tried to compute the instantaneous speed as distance traveled divided by time of travel. Also, as we have already seen, it makes excellent sense from the physical standpoint to choose this limit to be the speed at the end of the third second.

Exercises

1. Suppose that in order to obtain the speed of an object at the end of the third second of its motion you calculated the average speed during the third second, then during the time interval from $2\frac{1}{2}$ to 3, then during the time interval $2\frac{3}{4}$ to 3, and so on. Would you expect the average speeds to come closer and closer to the speed at the end of the third second? Why?   *Ans.* Yes.

2. Suppose that the average speeds of a moving object for smaller and smaller intervals of time after the third second prove to be 129, 128.5, 128.2, 128.05, ... What would you expect the speed at the end of the third second to be?
                                        Ans. 128 ft/sec.

The indication above of how instantaneous speed might be calculated was, of course, sketchy. We presumed that we knew the average speeds for smaller and smaller intervals of time, and from them we determined the instantaneous speed. Given a real problem, how do we know these average speeds? We could calculate them if we knew the distance the objects travels as a function of the time it travels. In other words, we must know the formula that relates distance and time traveled.

Let us see how the formula can be used to calculate average speeds and then instantaneous speed. We shall take the case of a ball that is dropped near the surface of the earth. The relevant formula is $s = 16t^2$. The formula presupposes that the time t is measured in seconds from the instant the ball starts to fall and the distance s in feet is measured from the point at which the ball is dropped. (Just how such formulas are obtained will be a later concern.)

We shall seek the speed at the end of the fourth second of fall, that is, the speed at the instant $t = 4$. We have already pointed out that we cannot obtain this speed in the same manner in which we calculate the average speed over some interval of time because it is meaningless to divide the zero distance traveled at $t = 4$ by the zero time elapsed. We therefore start with the calculation of the average speed *during the fifth second*. Although this average does yield the desired instantaneous speed, it yields an approximation. At the beginning of the fifth second, that is, when $t = 4$, the distance covered by the falling body is obtained by substituting 4 for t in the formula $s = 16t^2$. This distance is then $16 \cdot 4^2$ or 256. The distance covered by the end of the fifth second, that is, when $t = 5$, is $16 \cdot 5^2$ or 400. Hence the distance covered during the fifth second is $400 - 256$ or 144, and the average speed during the fifth second is

$$\frac{144}{1} \quad \text{or} \quad 144 \text{ ft/sec.}$$

As we have already stated, the average speed during the fifth second is not the speed at $t = 4$ itself, for during the fifth second the speed of the body keeps changing. Hence the quantity 144 can be no more than an approximation of the instantaneous speed. We may, however, improve the approximation by calculating the average speed in the interval of time from 4 to 4.1 seconds, for during this interval the average speed can, on physical grounds, be expected to approximate more closely the speed actually possessed by the body at $t = 4$. We therefore repeat the procedure of the preceding paragraph, this time using the values 4.1 and 4 for t. Thus for $t = 4.1$, $s = 16(4.1)^2 = 16(16.81) = 268.96$. For $t = 4$ we know that $s = 256$. Hence the distance traveled during the 0.1 second from $t = 4$ to $t = 4.1$ is $268.96 - 256$ or 12.96, and the average speed during the interval $t = 4$ to $t = 4.1$ seconds is then

$$\frac{12.96}{0.1} = 129.6.$$

We note that the average speed during this tenth of a second is quite different from the value 144 for the fifth second.

Of course, the average speed during the interval $t = 4$ to $t = 4.1$ is not the speed at $t = 4$, because even during one tenth of a second the speed of the falling body changes and the average is not the value at $t = 4$. We can obtain a still better approximation to the speed at $t = 4$ if we calculate the average speed during the one one-hundredth of a second from $t = 4$ to $t = 4.01$, because the speed during this short interval of time near $t = 4$ ought to be almost equal to that at $t = 4$. Hence we again apply our previous procedure. For $t = 4.01$, $s = 16(4.01)^2 = 16(16.0801) = 257.2816$. For $t = 4$ we know that $s = 256$. Thus the distance traveled during the 0.01 of a second from $t = 4$ to $t = 4.01$ is $257.2816 - 256$ or 1.2816. Then the average speed during the interval $t = 4$ to $t = 4.01$ is

$$\frac{1.2816}{0.01} = 128.16.$$

We could continue this process. The speed during the interval $t = 4$ to $t = 4.01$ is not the exact speed at $t = 4$, because the speed of the falling body changes even in one one-hundredth of a second. We could therefore calculate the average speed in the interval $t = 4$ to $t = 4.001$ and expect this average to be even closer to the speed at $t = 4$ than the preceding ones. (The result is 128.016 ft/sec.) Of course, no matter how small the interval over which the average speed is calculated, the result is *not* the speed at the instant $t = 4$. However, we now see that the average speeds for the intervals of time 1, 0.1, 0.01, and 0.001 are 144, 129.6, 128.16, and 128.016, respectively. These numbers seem to be approaching, or getting closer to, the fixed number 128. Hence we take 128 to be the speed of the falling body at $t = 4$. This number is the *limit* of the set of average speeds. We should note again that the instantaneous speed is not defined as the quotient of distance and time. Rather it is the limit approached by average speeds as the intervals of time over which they are computed approach zero.

Two objections to what we have done may occur. First, what right have we to take the number approached by the average speeds to be the speed at $t = 4$? The answer, as we have already implied, is that mathematicians have adopted a definition that makes good physical sense. They argue that the smaller the interval of time starting at $t = 4$ for which the average speeds are computed, the closer the behavior of the falling body must be to that at $t = 4$. Hence the number approached by average speeds over the smaller and smaller intervals of time starting at $t = 4$ should be the speed at $t \doteq 4$. Because mathematics seeks to represent physical phenomena, it naturally adopts definitions that seem to be in accord with physical facts. It can then expect the results obtained by mathematical reasoning and calculations to fit the physical world.

The second possible objection to our definition of instantaneous speed is a more practical one. Apparently, we must calculate average speeds over many intervals of time and attempt to discern what number these average speeds seem to be approaching. However, there appears to be no guarantee that the fixed number chosen is the correct one. Thus, if in our above calculations we had obtained only the average speeds 114, 129.6, and 128.16, we might have decided that these speeds were approaching the number 128.15; this result would be in error by 0.15 ft/sec. The answer to this objection is that we can generalize the entire process of obtaining the instantaneous speed so that it can be carried out more quickly and with certainty. We shall describe this new method in the next section.

Exercises

1. Distinguish between the change in distance that results when an object moves for some interval of time and the rate of change of distance compared to time in that interval.

2. Suppose that an object falls a distance s given by $s = 16t^2$. What is the change in distance, or distance traveled, from $t = 3$ to $t = 5$? What is the average rate of change of distance compared to time in that time interval? What is the average speed in that time interval?   *Ans.* 256 ft; 128 ft/sec; 128 ft/sec.

3. Distinguish between average speed and instantaneous speed.

4. What mathematical concept is used to obtain instantaneous speed from average speed?

5. If the distance s, in feet, that a body falls in t seconds is given by the formula $s = 16t^2$, calculate the following:

   (*a*) The average speed of the body during the first 5 seconds of fall.

                                                                                              Ans. 80 ft/sec.

   (*b*) The average speed during the fifth second of fall.

   (*c*) The instantaneous speed at the end of the fifth second of fall.   *Ans.* 160 ft/sec

6. In the text we calculated the instantaneous speed at $t = 4$ of an object falling according to the formula $s = 16t^2$ by first calculating average speed over intervals of time following $t = 4$; that is, we calculated average speeds over the intervals 4 to 5, 4 to 4.1, 4 to 4.01, and so on. Calculate the instantaneous speed at $t = 4$ by working with average speeds over the time intervals 3 to 4, 3.9 to 4, 3.99 to 4, and so on.

7. If at some instant during its motion an object has the speed of 30 mi/h, will the object travel 30 miles in the next hour?   *Ans.* Not necessarily.

4. *The Method of Increments.* We have already stated that we can formulate the process of calculating instantaneous speed in such a way as to avoid tedious calculation and at the same time be certain of the limit that the average speeds approach. To examine this method, let us again ·calculate the instantaneous speed of a dropped body at the end of the fourth second of fall, that is, at the instant $t = 4$. The formula that relates distance fallen and time of travel is, of course,

$$(7) \qquad\qquad\qquad\qquad s = 16t^2.$$

Again we can calculate at once the distance fallen by the end of the fourth second. This distance, which we denote by s_4, is $16 \cdot 4^2$ or

$$(8) \qquad\qquad\qquad\qquad s_4 = 256.$$

The generality of our new process consists in calculating the average speed not over a specific interval of time, such as 0.1 of a second, but over an arbitrary interval of time. We introduce a quantity h that is to represent any interval of time beginning at $t = 4$ and extending before or after $t = 4$. The quantity h is called an *increment* in t because it is some additional interval of time. If h is positive, it represents an interval after $t = 4$; if it is negative, it denotes an interval before $t = 4$.

To calculate the average speed in the interval 4 to $4 + h$ seconds, we must first find the distance traveled in this interval of time. We therefore substitute $4 + h$ for t in (7) and obtain the distance fallen by the body in $4 + h$ seconds.

This distance is denoted by $s_4 + k$, where s_4 is the distance the body falls in four seconds and k is the additional distance fallen, or the *increment* in distance, in the interval of h seconds. Thus

$$s_4 + k = 16(4 + h)^2.$$

We multiply $4 + h$ by itself and obtain

$$s_4 + k = 16(16 + 8h + h^2).$$

Application of the distributive axiom of algebra, that is, multiplying through by 16, yields

(9) $$s_4 + k = 256 + 128h + 16h^2.$$

To obtain k, the distance traveled in the interval of h seconds, we have but to subtract (8) from (9). The result is

(10) $$k = 128h + 16h^2.$$

The average speed in the interval of h seconds is the distance traveled in that time divided by the time, that is k/h. Let us therefore divide both sides of (10) by h. Then

(11) $$\frac{k}{h} = \frac{128h + 16h^2}{h}.$$

When h is *not* zero, it is correct to divide the numerator and denominator on the right-hand side of (11) by h. The result is

(12) $$\frac{k}{h} = 128 + 16h.$$

Hence (12) is also a correct expression for the average speed when h is not zero.

To obtain the instantaneous speed at $t = 4$, we must determine the number approached by the average speeds as the interval h of time over which these speeds are computed becomes smaller and smaller. We can readily obtain it from (12). If h decreases, $16h$ must also decrease; when h is close to zero, $16h$ is also close to zero. In view of (12), then, the fixed number that the average speed approaches is 128. This number is taken to be the instantaneous speed at $t = 4$.

The process we have just examined, called the *method of increments*, is basic to the calculus. It is subtler than it appears at first sight. We should not expect to appreciate its finer points on first contact, any more than one gets to know another person well on the basis of one meeting. As a step in the right direction, however, we shall make one or two observations.

First, we wish to determine the speed at $t = 4$. Because h is the increment in time beyond $t = 4$ and k/h is the average speed in this interval, we may think that to determine the speed at $t = 4$ we should let h be 0 in (11).

However, when $h = 0$, we see from the right side that the numerator and denominator are 0, so that we obtain 0/0. This result should no longer surprise us. We have already recognized that we cannot get instantaneous speed by dividing the 0 distance traveled at an instant by the 0 time that an instant amounts to. However, if we agree to consider average speeds, then h is not 0 and the right side of (11) is a meaningful expression. Moreover, when h is not 0, it is correct to divide numerator and denominator by h and to obtain the simpler expression in (12) for the average speeds. This latter expression happens to be especially simple, and therefore we can determine from it the limit approached by the average speeds as h approaches 0, namely, the number 128. The difference between (11) and 1(2) is precisely the difference between the function

$$y = \frac{x^2 - 4}{x - 2}$$

and the function

$$y = x + 2,$$

which we discussed in Section 2.

For the rather elementary function $s = 16t^2$, instead of finding the limit of k/h in (12) by letting h approach 0, we may let h be 0 in (12); the result then is also 128. This agreement between the value of the right side of (12) when h is 0 and the number approached by k/h as h gets closer to 0 will appear in a number of fairly simple functions. However, let us not lose sight of the fact that we seek the limit of k/h as h approaches 0 rather than the value of k/h when h is 0. Indeed, k/h has no value when $h = 0$. If the two values, the limit of k/h and the value of the expression for k/h when $h = 0$, happen to be the same in some cases, as in (12), one is lucky, but let us not press this luck too hard.* The reader who wishes to tempt fate may substitute 0 for h in simplified expressions such as (12). However, he is urged to indulge his teacher and the author and consider the limit of k/h as h approaches 0. This limit, which Bishop George Berkeley (1685–1753) once criticized by calling it the ghost of departed quantities, is very real and is the number we seek.

The main point that emerges from this section is the possibility of finding instantaneous speed by a general process—the method of increments. No tedious arithmetical calculations are necessary, nor is there any doubt about the limit approached by the average speeds.

To appreciate what the method of increments achieves, we may consider a somewhat crude analogy. Suppose that a marksman seeks to hit a particular spot on a target. Even though he is a good shooter, he is not likely to hit the given spot squarely but will hit all around it and indeed come close. A

---

* We could pursue the point further and learn just when the limit approached by k/h as h approaches 0 must agree with the "value" of k/h when h is 0. But to do so would involve a long digression into theory which at the moment is of secondary importance. We shall return to this point in Chapter 24.

bystander observing the location of the hits can readily determine the exact spot at which the marksman is aiming by noting the concentration of the hits. This process of inferring the precise location at which the marksman is aiming is analogous to determining the instantaneous speed from a knowledge of the average speeds. We note the number the average speeds are approaching by examining (11) or the simplified form (12), and this limit is taken to be the instantaneous speed.

Exercises

1. Describe in your own words the essence of the method of increments.

2. Suppose that the fall of an object is described by the formula $s = 16t^2$. Use the method of increments to calculate the following:

(*a*) The instantaneous speed at the end of the third second of fall.

Ans. 96 ft/sec.

(*b*) The instantaneous speed at the end of the fifth second of fall.

(*c*) The instantaneous speed when $t = 6$. *Ans.* 192 ft/sec.

3. Suppose that the formula that relates the height above the ground and the time of travel of a ball thrown up into the air is $s = 128t - 16t^2$.

(*a*) How high is the ball when $t = 3$? *Ans.* 240 ft.

(*b*) What is the average speed during the fourth second of flight?

(*c*) Calculate the instantaneous speed when $t = 3$. *Ans.* 32 ft/sec.

4. For each of the following functions find the number or limit approached by the numerator, by the denominator, and by the entire function as h approaches 0:

(*a*) $\dfrac{3h^2}{h^2}$. *Ans.* 0, 0, 3.

(*d*) $\dfrac{3h^3 + 3h^2 + h}{h}$.

(*b*) $\dfrac{h^2}{2h^2}$. *What do they mean by approach*

(*e*) $\dfrac{h^2}{h}$. *Ans.* 0, 0, 0.

(*c*) $\dfrac{3h^2 + h}{h}$. *Ans.* 0, 0, 1.

(*f*) $\dfrac{3h^2}{h}$.

lim
contant

5. Find the limit as h approaches 0 of $h/(\sqrt{h + 4} - 2)$. *Suggestion:* multiply the numerator and denominator by $\sqrt{h + 4} + 2$. *Ans.* 4.

6. (*a*) Is the function $(3h^2 + h)/h$ identical with the function $3h + 1$?

(*b*) Can we use the latter function in place of the former to determine the number approached by the former as h approaches 0? Justify your answer.

5. A Matter of Notation.

The method of increments, which we examined in Section 4, begins by giving an increment h to the value of the independent variable. An increment h in this variable causes an increment k to occur in the dependent variable. We then calculate k/h—the average rate of change of one variable with respect to the other—and finally obtain the limit approached by k/h as h approaches 0.

We have used h and k to denote the increments in t and s, respectively, and we could very well continue to use these symbols to denote increments throughout the calculus. However, history has something else to say on this matter. It has been customary since the days of Euler to use Δt (pronounced delta t) for the increment in t and Δs for the increment in s. These symbols are both bad and good. The notation Δt is *not* a product of Δ and t, but must be taken as a whole. It means a change in the value of t, that is, some numerical change. Thus if t is increased from 3 to 4, then $\Delta t = 1$. If t increases from 3 to $3\frac{1}{2}$, $\Delta t = \frac{1}{2}$. If t decreases from 3 to $2\frac{1}{2}$, $\Delta t = -\frac{1}{2}$. Thus Δt has the same meaning as h. Likewise, Δs has the same meaning as k.

It is, of course, more awkward to write Δt instead of h and Δs instead of k. There is, however, a slight advantage in that Δt denotes explicitly an increment in t and Δs, an increment in s; that is, we do not have to remember to which variable the increment refers. Like better men before us, we shall bow to history and use Δt and Δs.

Let us repeat the calculation of the preceding section in this new notation; that is, we shall calculate the speed at the end of the fourth second of an object that falls according to the formula $s = 16t^2$. The method of increments calls for first calculating the average speed in an interval of time Δt bordering on the fourth second. When $t = 4$, the value of s, which we denote by s_4, is 256; that is,

(13) $s_4 = 256.$

If we increase the value of t by some amount Δt, the new value is $4 + \Delta t$. The new value of s is denoted by $s_4 + \Delta s$. Then

(14) $s_4 + \Delta s = 16(4 + \Delta t)^2 = 256 + 128\Delta t + 16(\Delta t)^2.$

By subtracting (13) from (14) we obtain

(15) $\Delta s = 128\Delta t + 16(\Delta t)^2.$

The quantity Δs is, of course, the distance traveled in the time Δt. To obtain the average speed in the interval of time Δt, we must calculate $\Delta s/\Delta t$. Division of both sides of (15) by Δt yields

(16) $\dfrac{\Delta s}{\Delta t} = 128 + 16\,\Delta t.$

To obtain the instantaneous speed at $t = 4$, we seek the limit of $\Delta s/\Delta t$ as the values of Δt become smaller and indeed approach 0 in value. However, as Δt approaches 0, $16\Delta t$ also approaches 0, so that the right-hand side of (16) approaches 128. Hence the instantaneous speed at $t = 4$, which is the limit of the average speed as the increment Δt approaches 0, is 128.

It is desirable to have some short notation for the statement that we have evaluated the limit of $\Delta s/\Delta t$ as the values of Δt approach 0. We can express it in the abbreviated form

(17)
$$\lim_{\Delta t \to 0} \frac{\Delta s}{\Delta t}.$$

Here lim is an abbreviation for limit, the arrow symbolizes approach, and the whole expression means the limit of $\Delta s/\Delta t$ as Δt approaches 0. In this notation what we showed in the calculation above is that

$$\lim_{\Delta t \to 0} \frac{\Delta s}{\Delta t} = 128.$$

Even the notation in (17) is somewhat lengthy. Hence mathematicians replace it by a still briefer one. Newton used $\dot s$. Leibniz used ds/dt; that is,

$$\lim_{\Delta t \to 0} \frac{\Delta s}{\Delta t} = \dot s = \frac{ds}{dt}.$$

The three notations are identical on meaning, but all fall short of perfection. Newton's symbolism is concise but poor because the dot above the s is often overlooked. Leibniz's notation suggests that the limit is a quotient, whereas the limit of average speeds definitely is *not* a quotient. In fact, the very idea of using the limit of average speeds for the instantaneous speed is to avoid the meaningless quotient $0/0$. Leibniz's symbol ds/dt must be taken in its entirety. Nevertheless, Leibniz's notation, properly understood, does remind us that the limit, although not itself a quotient, is obtained from a quotient, that is, average speed. Moreover, it does show the independent and dependent variables. We shall see later that there is some additional merit in Leibniz's notation.

Exercises

1. Give the argument that convinces you that, as the values of Δt approach 0, $16\Delta t$ also approaches 0.
2. If $s = 16t^2$, how much is Δs when $t = 3$ and $\Delta t = 1$? When $t = 4$ and $\Delta t = 1$? When $t = 4$ and $\Delta t = \frac{1}{2}$?   *Ans.* 112; 144; 68.
3. Use the delta notation to calculate the instantaneous speed at the end of the fifth second of an object that falls according to the formula $s = 16t^2$.
4. Use the delta notation to calculate the instantaneous speed at the instant $t = t_1$ of an object that falls according to the formula $s = 16t^2$. *Ans.* $32t_1$.
5. An object dropped near the surface of the moon falls to the surface in accordance with the formula $s = 2.6t^2$. Use the delta notation to calculate the speed of the object at the end of the fourth second.
6. An object dropped near the surface of the sun falls to the surface in accordance with the formula $s = 432t^2$. Use the delta notation to calculate the speed of the object at the end of the fifth second.   *Ans.* 4320 ft/sec.
7. Consider the function $s = t^2$. At $t = 2$ and for $\Delta t = 0.1$, $\Delta s/\Delta t$ is a good approximation to $\dot s$. How could you improve this approximation to $\dot s$?

8. Calculate the instantaneous speed of the following relations between distance and time at the instant indicated:

(a) $s = 4t^2$ at $t = 3$.   *Ans.* 24.   (c) $s = 3t^2$ at $t = 0$.   *Ans.* 0.

(b) $s = \frac{1}{4}t^2$ at $t = 3$.   (d) $s = \frac{5}{2}t^2$ at $t = 2$.

9. Is a limit a variable or a constant?

10. Is a limit an exact value or an approximate value?

6. *The Method of Increments Applied to* $y = ax^2$.   It is characteristic of mathematics to seek to generalize a process which has proved useful in a number of particular situations and so make it applicable to a whole class of problems.   For example, in elementary algebra we learn first to solve particular quadratic equations such as $x^2 - 4 = 0$ and $x^2 - 5x + 8 = 0$ by special methods such as factoring and completing the square.   However, by considering the general quadratic equation $ax^2 + bx + c = 0$ and by deriving the quadratic formula

$$x = \frac{-b \pm \sqrt{b^2 - 4ac}}{2a}$$

we can subsequently write down the solutions of any quadratic equation.

In the few examples of the calculation of instantaneous speed that we have thus far explored we calculated this speed for the formula $s = 16t^2$ at various values of t.   However, the formula for the motion of a body is not always $s = 16t^2$.   Also, one would hope that the calculus is more widely applicable than merely to the calculation of instantaneous speeds.   Science is concerned with thousands of rates of change; the rate of change of air pressure with respect to altitude, the rate of change of the altitude of an airplane with respect to velocity, and the rate of change of temperature with respect to time or to altitude are a few familiar examples.   Let us investigate then a generalization of what we have been doing in finding instantaneous speed.   Instead of the symbols t and s for our variables, let us use x and y, without specifying what x and y may stand for physically.   Furthermore instead of, the particular function $s = 16t^2$, let us work with

(18) $$y = ax^2,$$

where a is some constant whose value is not specified but plays the role that 16 does in $s = 16t^2$.   Finally, instead of calculating the instantaneous speed, which is the instantaneous rate of change of s with respect to t, we shall calculate the instantaneous rate of change of y with respect to x.

To calculate the instantaneous rate of change of y with respect to x means, of course, to calculate the rate of change at a value of x as opposed to an average rate of change over some interval of x-values.   The word instantaneous really does not apply, because x need not represent time.   However, the word is used because in the original and in many current applications of the calculus the independent variable represents values of time.

To compute the instantaneous rate of change of y with respect to x we use the method of increments and the customary Δx and Δy for the increments of x and y. Also, the rate of change is always computed at a value of x, and to be general we let this be x_1. We compute first the value of y when x has the value x_1. This value of y, which we shall call y_1, is obtained by substituting x_1 for x in (18). Then

$$(19) \qquad\qquad y_1 = ax_1{}^2.$$

We now consider a change or increment Δx in the value of x, so that the new value of x is $x_1 + \Delta x$. To compute the new value of y, which we denote by $y_1 + \Delta y$, we must substitute the new value of x in (18). Then

$$y_1 + \Delta y = a(x_1 + \Delta x)^2.$$

Because

$$(x_1 + \Delta x)^2 = x_1{}^2 + 2x_1 \, \Delta x + (\Delta x)^2,$$

it follows that

$$(20) \qquad\qquad y_1 + \Delta y = ax_1{}^2 + 2ax_1 \, \Delta x + a(\Delta x)^2.$$

Our next step is to determine the change Δy in y which results from the change Δx in x by subtracting (19) from (20). Thus

$$(21) \qquad\qquad \Delta y = 2ax_1 \, \Delta x + a(\Delta x)^2.$$

To arrive at the average rate of change of y in the interval Δx, we must find $\Delta y / \Delta x$. Accordingly, we divide both sides of (21) by Δx and obtain

$$(22) \qquad\qquad \frac{\Delta y}{\Delta x} = \frac{2ax_1 \, \Delta x + a(\Delta x)^2}{\Delta x}.$$

To secure the rate of change of y compared to x at the value x_1 of x we must determine the limit of the right side of (22) as Δx approaches 0. We are fortunate in that we can divide the numerator and denominator of (22) by Δx and obtain

$$(23) \qquad\qquad \frac{\Delta y}{\Delta x} = 2ax_1 + a \, \Delta x.$$

As Δx becomes smaller and approaches 0, the quantity $a \, \Delta x$, which is merely a constant times Δx, also approaches 0, and the quantity $\Delta y / \Delta x$ approaches the value $2ax_1$. This last quantity is the limit approached by the average rates of change, $\Delta y / \Delta x$, and so is the rate of change of y with respect to x at the value x_1 of x. Just to check our result, we note that when $a = 16$ and $x_1 = 4$, the quantity $2ax_1$ is 128, which is the limit that we obtained in the special case.

Thus the instantaneous rate of change of y with respect to x at the value x_1 of x is $2ax_1$. We have already indicated the notation for the instantaneous speed. Now we merely change the notation for the variables. The following

(24)
$$\lim_{\Delta x \to 0} \frac{\Delta y}{\Delta x} = 2ax_1,$$

(25)
$$\dot{y} = 2ax_1,$$

(26)
$$\frac{dy}{dx} = 2ax_1$$

are then equivalent statements.

To speak of the instantaneous rate of change of y with respect to x at the value x_1 of x is lengthy. Hence we call this rate the *derivative* of y with respect to x and, when necessary, specify "at x_1." The process of applying the method of increments to obtain the derivative is called *differentiation*.

We should note the significance of what we have accomplished so far. We have proved that the derivative of $y = ax^2$ at the value x_1 of x is $2ax_1$. Hence, given any function that is a special case of $y = ax^2$, we can write down at once the derivative of this function. We do not have to go through the entire method of increments. Thus, given $s = 16t^2$, the value of the derivative at t_1 is $2 \cdot 16 \cdot t_1$. If t_1 were 4, the value of the derivative would be $2 \cdot 16 \cdot 4$ or 128.

As another example let us consider the relation of the area of a circle to the radius. The formula that expresses the function is, of course,

(27)
$$A = \pi r^2.$$

In relation to $y = ax^2$, here A plays the part of y, r plays the part of x, and the constant π is the value of a. If we use the notation $\dot{A}$ for the derivative, formula (25) tells us that at $r = r_1$

(28)
$$\dot{A} = 2\pi r_1.$$

The result (28) has a simple geometrical meaning (Fig. 2-6). It says that the instantaneous rate of change of the area of a circle with respect to the radius at any given value of the radius is the circumference. More loosely stated, the rate at which the area increases when r increases is the size of the circumference. This result is very reasonable. When the radius r_1 is increased by an amount Δr, the area A of the circle increases by an amount ΔA. We may think intuitively of ΔA as a thin band whose area is approximately the circumference $2\pi r_1$ times the width Δr. The ratio $\Delta A / \Delta r$ is then approximately $2\pi r_1$. This average rate of

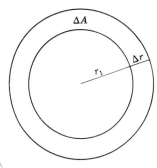

Figure 2-6

change of area with respect to the radius comes closer to $2\pi r_1$ as Δr approaches 0. The circumference $2\pi r_1$ is the instantaneous rate at which the area increases at the given value r_1 or r.

Exercises

1. Calculate the derivatives of the following functions at the specified values of the independent variable:

(a) $y = 16x^2$ at $x = x_1$ *Ans.* $32x_1$. (e) $A = \pi r^2$ at $r = 5$.   *Ans.* 10π.

(b) $y = 16x^2$ at $x = 4$. (f) $s = 2.6t^2$ at $t = 5$.

(c) $y = bx^2$ at $x = 4$.   *Ans.* $8b$. (g) $y = -2x^2$ at $x = 4$. *Ans.* -16.

(d) $s = 16t^2$ at $t = 5$. (h) $y = \frac{1}{2}x^2$ at $x = x_1$.

2. The functions in the following items relate distance and time. Calculate the instantaneous speed at the specified value of t.

(a) $s = 16t^2$ at $t = 6$.   *Ans.* 192 ft/sec.

(b) $s = 10t^2$ at $t = 3$.

(c) $s = \dfrac{g}{2} t^2$ at $t = t_1$.   *Ans.* gt_1 ft/sec.

3. A man lays out a circular area of radius 100 feet. If he increases the radius by 10 feet, how much does he increase the area? When $r_1 = 100$ and $\Delta r = 10$, how much is ΔA?   *Ans.* 2100π ft; 2100π ft.

4. Determine the derivative of $y = x^2$ at $x = x_1$ by the method of increments or any other legitimate method. Compare the results with that for $y = ax^2$. Does the comparison suggest any general statement about the effect on the derivative of the constant factor a in the function?

5. Find the rate of change of the area A of a square with respect to a side s at a given value s_1 of the side. Is the result intuitively reasonable?   *Ans.* $\dot{A} = 2s_1$.

6. The area of a rectangle is given by the formula $A = lw$, where l and w are the length and width, respectively. Suppose that l is kept fixed. Find the rate of change of A with respect to w at a given value of w. Interpret the result geometrically.

7. The Derived Function. We have found that the derivative of $y = ax^2$ at the value x_1 of x is $2ax_1$; in symbols

(29) $$\dot{y} = 2ax_1.$$

The derivative is, of course, the rate of change of y with respect to x at a value of x. However, by using the letter x_1 for the value of x at which we calculated (29), we actually accomplished more than we intended. The value x_1 of x is *any* value of x. Its value is not limited. Hence we can say that at any value of x the derivative $\dot{y}$ of $y = ax^2$ is $2ax$; that is,

(30) $$\dot{y} = 2ax.$$

By writing (30) instead of (29) we merely emphasize that x_1 is really any value of x. Because for each value of x there is a corresponding value of the derivative $\dot{y}$, we have in (30) a new function. The independent variable is x, and the dependent variable is $\dot{y}$. We might prefer to use a more conventional symbol for the dependent variable. We cannot use y because it already denotes ax^2 in the present context. We could use z or some other letter. However, there is really no objection to using $\dot{y}$ (or dy/dx) if we remember that, in addition to denoting the derivative of y with respect to x, it also denotes the dependent variable in the function $\dot{y} = 2ax$. Sometimes, however, we do use a special symbol for the dependent variable $\dot{y}$. Thus for the function $s = 16t^2$ the derived function is $\dot{s} = 32t$. The symbol often used for $\dot{s}$ is v, the first letter of the word velocity, because $\dot{s}$ does give physically the instantaneous speed or instantaneous velocity. (We shall distinguish between speed and velocity later.)

To distinguish the derivative at a value of x from the function that arises when we consider the various values of the derivative as x changes, we call the function the *derived function*. Thus $\dot{y} = 2ax$ is the derived function of $y = ax^2$. Sometimes the word derivative is used to denote the function, and this is permissible if no confusion results.

When we discussed the concept of a function, we pointed out that it does not require that there be a y-value for each value of x. There need be a y-value only for the values of x in some domain. The same remark applies to derived function. In the case of $\dot{y} = 2ax$ there is a value of $\dot{y}$ for each value of x. Let us, however, consider the function $y = 1/(x - 2)$. As we pointed out, this function has no value or does not exist for the value 2 of x. Therefore, the derived function does not exist at $x = 2$ because the derivative at $x = 2$ depends, by its very definition, on the value of the original function at $x = 2$. Thus a derived function, like any function, has a domain and a range, and the domain need not include all values of x.

Exercises

1. Suppose that an object falls in accordance with the formula $s = 5t^2$. Find the formula for the speed at any time t.   *Ans. $v = 10t$.*

2. State in words what the following represent symbolically:

    (a) $\dot{s} = 32t$.   (c) $\dot{v} = -32$.
    (b) $\dot{s} = 5t$.   (d) $\dot{y} = 4x$.

3. State at once what the derived functions are for the following functions:

(a) $s = 3t^2$.	*Ans. $\dot{s} = 6t$.*	(g) $y = -3x^2$.	*Ans. $\dot{y} = -6x$.*	
(b) $s = -3t^2$.		(h) $y = 27x^2$.		
(c) $s = \frac{7}{2}t^2$.	*Ans. $\dot{s} = 7t$.*	(i) $y = \frac{4}{3}x^2$.	*Ans. $\dot{y} = \frac{8}{3}x$.*	
(d) $y = 8x^2$.		(j) $y = -\frac{15}{2}x^2$.		
(e) $y = x^2$.	*Ans. $\dot{y} = 2x$.*	(k) $y = 0.03x^2$.	*Ans. $\dot{y} = 0.06x$.*	
(f) $y = -x^2$.		(l) $y = \sqrt{2}x^2$.		

8. *The Differentiation of Simple Monomials.* We have seen that by considering the general function $y = ax^2$ we could determine the derivative at once; therefore we can now find the derivative of all functions of that form without going through the method of increments each time. To be able to utilize other particular functions as readily in applications we may as well treat general forms. Because we shall find later that our applications will involve functions such as $y = 3x$ and $y = 5x$, let us determine the derivative of functions of the form $y = bx$ (Fig. 2-7).

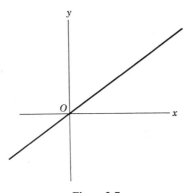

Figure 2-7

This function is so simple that we may be able to see on an intuitive basis what the derivative should be. Let us consider a special case. If an automobile travels at the constant speed of 30 mi/hr, the formula that relates distance traveled (in miles) and time of travel (in hours) is $s = 30t$. However, if the automobile travels at a constant speed, its speed at each instant is the same. . In other words, its instantaneous rate of change of distance with respect to time is 30. Then the derivative of $s = 30t$ should be 30. What then should we expect the derivative of $y = bx$ to be? The answer should be b.

Let us use the method of increments to establish our conjecture. Let x_1 be the value of x at which we calculate the derivative. Then

$$(31) \qquad\qquad y_1 = bx_1.$$

In accordance with the method of increments we let x change to $x_1 + \Delta x$. Then

$$(32) \qquad y_1 + \Delta y = b(x_1 + \Delta x) = bx_1 + b\,\Delta x.$$

If we subtract (31) from (32), we obtain

$$(33) \qquad\qquad \Delta y = b\,\Delta x.$$

To obtain the average rate of change of y with respect to x in the interval Δx we divide both sides of (33) by Δx. Then

(34)
$$\frac{\Delta y}{\Delta x} = b.$$

The instantaneous rate of change of y with respect to x at $x = x_1$ is the limit of the average rate of change as Δx approaches 0. However, (34) shows that as Δx decreases the average rate of change remains constant. It is always b. What limit do the values of $\Delta y/\Delta x$ approach? Since the average rate is always b no matter how small Δx is, these average rates for various values of Δx do better than come closer and closer to b. They have the value b. Hence the number they "approach" is b. In other words, the limit is b so that

(35)
$$\dot{y} = b.$$

This result is the derivative at $x = x_1$. Because this $\dot{y}$ is independent of x_1, that is, it is the same for all values of x, it is also the derived function. It does seem a bit peculiar to refer to $\dot{y} = b$ as a function because there appears to be no independent variable; nor does $\dot{y}$ vary. However, it is convenient to think of $\dot{y} = b$ as a function which for each value of x yields $\dot{y} = b$. Once can, if he so wishes, write the function as $\dot{y} = bx^0$, and because, by definition of the zero exponent, x^0 is always 1, we have of course $\dot{y} = b$.

Now let us consider the function $y = c$, where c is a constant. An example is $y = 3$ (Fig. 2-8). What is the derivative of $y = c$ at any given value x_1 of x? This function, too, is so simple that we can foresee the answer. If y is a constant for all values of x, then certainly its instantaneous rate of change at any value of x is 0.

Figure 2-8

Of course, the method of increments yields this result almost at once. If x_1 is the value of x at which we wish to calculate the derivative, then at $x = x_1$

(36)
$$y_1 = c.$$

If we allow x to change by an amount Δx, then at the value $x_1 + \Delta x$, y becomes $y_1 + \Delta y$. Because y does not change with x, when $x = x_1 + \Delta x$,

(37)
$$y_1 + \Delta y = c.$$

By subtracting (36) from (37) we have

$$\Delta y = 0.$$

Then

$$\frac{\Delta y}{\Delta x} = 0,$$

and the limit of $\Delta y/\Delta x$ as Δx approaches 0 must be 0 because an expression that is always 0 as Δx varies certainly comes closer and closer to 0. Then

(38) $$\dot{y} = 0.$$

Thus if $y = c$, the derivative $\dot{y}$ at any value of x is 0 and the derived function is 0.

Exercises

1. Find the derived functions of the following functions:

   (a) $y = 2x^2$. *Ans.* $\dot{y} = 4x$. (d) $d = -9t$
   (b) $y = -2x^2$. (e) $y = 7$. *Ans.* $\dot{y} = 0$.
   (c) $y = 3x$. *Ans.* $\dot{y} = 3$. (f) $s = 6$.

2. Apply the method of increments to find the derived function of the function $y = ax^3$. *Ans.* $\dot{y} = 3ax^2$.

3. We found that the instantaneous rate of change of the area of a circle with respect to the radius at a given value of the radius is the circumference of the circle. What is your guess as to the instantaneous rate of change of the volume of a sphere with respect to the radius at a given value of the radius? Apply the result of Exercise 2 to the formula for the volume of a sphere, $V = \frac{4}{3}\pi r^3$ and see if your guess was correct.

4. When $y = ax^2$, the $\dot{y} = 2ax$; when $y = ax^3$, then you should have found in Exercise 2 that $\dot{y} = 3ax^2$. Now suppose that $y = ax^4$. What would you expect $\dot{y}$ to be? Verify your conjecture by applying the method of increments to $y = ax^4$. *Ans.* $\dot{y} = 4ax^3$.

5. Suppose that an object moves along the arc of a circle of radius 5 and that arc length and central angle are as shown in Fig. 2-9. How much is $ds/d\theta$ if θ is measured in radians?

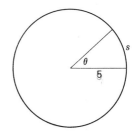

Figure 2-9

6. The speed of an object that is dropped and falls toward the earth from some point near the surface is given by the formula $v = 32t$. By definition the instantaneous acceleration is the instantaneous rate of change of speed with respect to time at any given value of t. Find the acceleration in the present case. *Ans.* $\dot{v} = 32$.

7. Express the following statements in symbols:

    (*a*) The instantaneous rate of change of y with respect to x is n times y.

    (*b*) The rate of change of y with respect to x at a value of x is a constant times x.

                                                  Ans. $\dot{y} = kx.$

    (*c*) The rate of change of y with respect to x at a value of x is proportional to x.

    (*d*) The rate of change of the area of a circle with respect to the radius is proportional to the radius.   *Ans.* $\dot{A} = kr.$

8. Criticize the following argument. The derivative of any function is defined at a value of x. The function is constant at that value of x. Hence the derivative is 0 because the derivative of a constant is 0.

9. *The Differentiation of Simple Polynomials.* The functions which occur in actual scientific work do not usually consist of single terms such as $3x^2$ or $5t$, that is, monomials. For example, the formula that represents the height above the ground of a ball that is thrown up with an initial speed of 100 ft/sec is $s = 100t - 16t^2$. To find the derivative, that is, the instantaneous rate of change, of such functions at various values of t, or to find the derived function, we must treat polynomials, that is, functions that are a sum or difference of two or more monomials. Let us see what the method of increments yields for polynomials.

    We shall determine the instantaneous speed at time t_1 of the object whose height is given by

(39) $$s = 100t - 16t^2.$$

At time t_1 the value of s is given by

(40) $$s_1 = 100t_1 - 16t_1^2.$$

If t now changes to the value $t_1 + \Delta t$, then by (39) the new value of s is

$$s_1 + \Delta s = 100(t_1 + \Delta t) - 16(t_1 + \Delta t)^2.$$

or

(41) $$s_1 + \Delta s = 100t_1 + 100\,\Delta t - 16t_1^2 - 32t_1\,\Delta t - 16(\Delta t)^2.$$

Subtraction of (40) from (41) yields

$$\Delta s = 100\,\Delta t - 32t_1\,\Delta t - 16(\Delta t)^2.$$

To obtain the average speed in the interval Δt, we divide both sides by Δt. Then

$$\frac{\Delta s}{\Delta t} = \frac{100\,\Delta t - 32t_1\,\Delta t - 16(\Delta t)^2}{\Delta t}.$$

Because Δt is not 0, we may divide numerator and denominator of the right-hand fraction by Δt and obtain

$$\frac{\Delta s}{\Delta t} = 100 - 32t_1 - 16\,\Delta t.$$

To obtain the instantaneous speed we must determine the limit of $\Delta s/\Delta t$ as Δt approaches 0. The terms 100 and $32t_1$ do not vary as Δt changes. However, the term $16 \Delta t$ approaches 0 as Δt approaches 0. Hence

$$\dot{s} = 100 - 32t_1.$$

The derived function, which gives the formula for the speed, is then

(42) $$\dot{s} = 100 - 32t.$$

The result (42) should be compared with the original function (39). If in (39) we had differentiated the term $100t$ as a separate function, we would have obtained 100. Likewise, if we had differentiated $16t^2$ as a separate function, we would have obtained $32t$. We see from (42) that the derived function of the difference of the two functions gives rise to the difference of their derived functions. It would appear then that the derived function of the difference of any two functions is the difference of their derived functions, and presumably the derived function of a sum of two functions is the sum of their derived functions. Of course, we have not proved that this result holds generally; for the present we shall use it in connection with simple polynomials. When in doubt, we can, of course, resort to the method of increments applied to the entire function, as we did in deriving (42).

Exercises

1. Prove that if $y = ax^2 + bx + c$, $\dot{y} = 2ax + b$.
2. Show that $y = x^2 + 5$ and $y = x^2$ have the same derived function. Can you give any heuristic argument for this result?   *Ans.* $\dot{y} = 2x$.
3. If an object is thrown downward with an initial speed of 100 ft/sec, the distance that it falls in t seconds is given by the formula $s = 100t + 16t^2$. Determine the formula for the speed at any time t. Calculate the speed of the object at the end of the fourth second of fall.
4. The temperature T at a point x feet above sea level is $T = 55 - 0.004x°$. What is the rate of change of temperature with respect to altitude at (a) sea level, (b) 100 feet above sea level, and (c) 1000 feet above? What physical significance do you attach to the fact that the rate of change is negative?
    Ans. (a) -0.004; (b) -0.004; (c) -0.004.
5. In one kind of chemical reaction two separate substances combine to form a third substance, much as hydrogen gas and oxygen gas combine to form water vapor. Suppose that the third substance amounts to x grams after t minutes and that $x = 18t - 3t^2$. What is the rate in g/min (grams per minute) at which the third substance is produced after the following time intervals?

(a) 2 minutes.   *Ans.* 6 g/min.
(b) 3 minutes.
(c) 4 minutes.   *Ans.* -6 g/min.
(d) Is there any question about the physical significance of the answer to part (c)?

6. Find by any method the derived functions of the following functions:

(*a*) $s = 10t^2 - 32t$.

                    Ans. $\dot{s} = 20t - 32$.

(*b*) $s = 10t^2 + 7$.

(*c*) $s = 4t^2 + 16t + 8$.

                    Ans. $\dot{s} = 8t + 16$.

(*d*) $s = 16t - 4t^2 + 8$.

(*e*) $y = x^2 - 7x + 12$.

(*f*) $y = -x^2 + 14x - 12$.

(*g*) $y = -7x + 2$.

(*h*) $y = 3\sqrt{2}x^2 + \sqrt{3}x$.

10. *The Second Derivative.* We have seen so far that, given the formula that relates the distance and time traveled by an object, we can calculate the speed or the instantaneous rate of change of distance with respect to time. Thus, when

(43) $$s = 16t^2,$$

then at any time t

(44) $$\dot{s} = 32t.$$

We have already pointed out that the derivative calculated at an arbitrary time t is itself a function of t which is called the derived function. Then (44) is the derived function in which t is the independent variable and $\dot{s}$ is the dependent variable. Here $\dot{s}$ represents speed, and, as already noted, it is customary to use the letter v (the first letter of velocity) in place of $\dot{s}$. Then

$$v = 32t.$$

Now the speed v is a function of t, and we can ask for the instantaneous rate of change of v with respect to t. This rate has important physical meaning. It is the instantaneous acceleration.

Acceleration, as used in ordinary discourse, does not mean the instantaneous rate of change of speed with respect to t. Usually it means the average acceleration. Thus, if an automobile increases its *speed* from 44 ft/sec (30 mi/hr) to 50 ft/sec in 2 seconds, its average acceleration is 3 ft/sec for each second. One writes this as 3 ft/sec² merely for brevity. Of course, the exponent in sec² does not mean the square of a number, because it refers to the unit of time. As in the case of speed, it is often the instantaneous acceleration rather than the average acceleration that matters. Thus, if the brakes of an automobile are applied suddenly, the automobile suffers an instantaneous deceleration, which is a negative acceleration. Unfortunately, the passengers do not receive the same deceleration and they continue to move forward.

If the speed of an object is given as a function of time, we can find the instantaneous acceleration because it is the instantaneous rate of change of speed with respect to time. Thus, if

(45) $$v = 32t,$$

then in view of what we learned about the derivatives of functions of the form $y = bx$, we know that

(46) $$\dot{v} = 32.$$

There is nothing really new mathematically in obtaining the derivative or the derived function of formulas such as (45). However, we may wish to call attention to the fact that the acceleration is the derived function of a function which is itself the derived function of still another function; that is, the acceleration is the derived function of the speed function which is the derived function of the distance function. To indicate this, we use the notation

$$\ddot{s} \quad \text{or} \quad \frac{d^2s}{dt^2}$$

for the acceleration. The functions denoted by either symbol are called the *second derived function* of $s = 16t^2$ or, if we should be calculating $\ddot{s}$ or d^2s/dt^2 at a particular value of t, we speak of these values of $\ddot{s}$ or of d^2s/dt^2 as the *second derivative* of $s = 16t^2$ at the value of t in question. Thus in place of (46) we can write

(47) $$\ddot{s} = 32 \quad \text{or} \quad \frac{d^2s}{dt^2} = 32.$$

Here the second derived function happens to be a constant; hence its value at any given value of t is always 32.

The notation just introduced for the second derivative applies, of course, regardless of what letters we use for the variables. If we use x and y, the second derived function of y with respect to x is denoted by

$$\ddot{y} \quad \text{or} \quad \frac{d^2y}{dx^2}.$$

Exercises

1. Suppose that an object falls according to the formula $s = 16t^2 + 100t$.
    (a) Calculate the second derived function $\ddot{s}$.   *Ans.* $\ddot{s} = 32$.
    (b) Calculate d^2s/dt^2.
    (c) Calculate the function that gives the acceleration at any time t.
                                                                            Ans. $\dot{v} = 32$.
    (d) Calculate the acceleration at the instant $t = 3$.
    (e) Calculate the derived function of the velocity as a function of time.
                                                                            Ans. $\dot{v} = 32$.
2. Suppose that the height of an object above the ground at time t is given by $s = 100t - 16t^2$. Answer the same questions raised in Exercise 1.
                                        Ans. $\ddot{s} = d^2s/dt^2 = \dot{v} = -32$.
3. Write in symbols: the acceleration of an object is proportional to its speed.

4. What is the second derived function of $y = bx$?   *Ans.* $\ddot{y} = 0.$

5. Calculate the second derived functions of the following functions:

(*a*) $s = -16t^2.$ *Ans.* $\ddot{s} = -32.$ (*g*) $y = 8x - 10.$

(*b*) $s = -16t^2 + 100t.$ (*h*) $y = \sqrt{5}x^2 - 7x.$

(*c*) $y = -t^2 + 100t.$ (*i*) $y = 3\sqrt{5}x^2 - 7x.$

            Ans. $d^2y/dt^2 = -2.$

(*d*) $y = -3t^2 + 100t + 50.$ *Ans.* $\ddot{y} = 6\sqrt{5}.$

(*e*) $y = 4x^2 + 8x.$ (*j*) $s = 16t^2 - 100t + 3.$

(*f*) $y = -4x^2 - 8x + 20.$

            Ans. $d^2y/dx^2 = -8.$

The Antiderived Function
or the Integral

1. *The Integral.* Suppose that we are given the derived function

(1) $$\dot{s} = 32t$$

and are obliged to find the original function, that is, the function which relates s and t. How can we do so? Of course, in the case of (1) we happen to know that the original function is $s = 16t^2$, but, generally, given a derived function we might not know beforehand what the original function is. For example, we might be given that

$$\dot{s} = 7t^2 - 3t$$

or

$$\dot{y} = \tfrac{1}{3}x^3 - 7x,$$

and in these cases it is not clear how to find the respective original functions.

Before we bother to look into the problem of finding the original function, we may well ask why we should entertain such a task. The answer is that when we formulate physical problems mathematically the given physical information usually leads to derived functions, and the primary objective in solving the physical problems is to find the original functions. Indeed, our knowledge of the many formulas that govern physical phenomena is most often obtained by finding the original functions corresponding to given derived functions, and we shall see later that the basic use of the calculus is to start with the derived function and find the original one.

Let us start with the problem of finding the original function corresponding to (1) and let us suppose for the moment that we do not know the answer. We do know that there is some formula relating s and t such that $\dot{s} = 32t$. We can ask ourselves, what do we do in going from a formula to its derived function? Having answered this question, perhaps we can reverse the process. In Chapter 2 we learned that when $y = ax^2$ then $\dot{y} = 2ax$. Evidently, $\dot{y}$ can be obtained from y by taking the quantity 2, which appears as the exponent in the original function, multiplying it into the coefficient a, and then reducing the exponent by 1. Hence, if we start with $2ax$ and wish to obtain the original function, we should increase the exponent of x by 1, thus obtaining $2ax^2$, and then divide the whole term by the new exponent 2. We then obtain ax^2.

Let us apply this method to $\dot{s} = 32t$, which is a special case of $\dot{y} = 2ax$. We increase the exponent by 1, obtain $32t^2$, and then divide the latter quantity by the new exponent 2 to obtain $16t^2$. Then $s = 16t^2$ is a function whose derived function is $\dot{s} = 32t$. Thus for derived functions of the form $\dot{y} = 2ax$ we can obtain the original function.

We have overlooked one point. It is true that if $y = ax^2$ then $\dot{y} = 2ax$. However, it is also true that if $y = ax^2 + C$, where C is any constant, then $\dot{y}$ is still $2ax$. In other words, a constant term that may be present in the original function does not contribute to or show up in the derived function. Hence, given $\dot{y} = 2ax$, we do know that the term ax^2 belongs in the original function but we do not know whether this function should also contain a constant term and, if it should, we have no information as to the value of this constant term. All we can say is that if

(2) $$\dot{y} = 2ax$$

then

(3) $$y = ax^2 + C,$$

and, unless we know more about the original function, we cannot say how much C is. For the moment let us recognize the necessity of including this C in the original function and not pursue the question of what we might do about determining it.* What appears to be an unfortunate circumstance will soon be seen to be a considerable advantage.

As an example of the use of our result, let us find the original function for which

$$\dot{y} = 8x.$$

If we increase the exponent by 1, we obtain $8x^2$, and, if we then divide by 2, we obtain $4x^2$. Thus

$$y = 4x^2 + C.$$

The process of going from the derived function to the original function is called *antidifferentiation* or *integration*. The original function is called the *primitive function*, the *antiderived function*, or the *indefinite integral* of the given derived function. We most often use the third term and even shorten it to *integral*.

Before we can make use of antidifferentiation or integration, we must be able to carry it out for at least a few types of functions. Suppose we are given

---

* We have not shown that there may not be functions even more complicated than (3) whose derived function is $2ax$. It is certainly conceivable that other functions may exist. We shall return to this point later and prove that if two functions have the same derived function over an interval of x-values then these two functions can differ at most by a constant.

that the instantaneous acceleration, that is, the instantaneous rate of change of speed with respect to time, of some moving object is

$$\dot{v} = 32; \tag{4}$$

Which formula relates v and t? (We know that the independent variable is t because $\dot{v}$ is acceleration.) Formula (4) should remind us of the formula

$$\dot{y} = b, \tag{5}$$

which, as we found earlier, is the derived function of $y = bx$. Hence the integral of $\dot{v} = 32$ should be $v = 32t$. Furthermore, in view of the possibility that there may be a constant term in the original function, we must say that

$$v = 32t + C. \tag{6}$$

Hence we can find the integrals of derived functions such as (4).

Let us note that we can use the same process to go from (4) to (6) as in going from $32t$ to $16t^2$. The quantity 32 in (4) can be thought of as $32t^0$. If we now increase the exponent by 1 and divide $32t$ by the new exponent, which is 1, we obtain $32t$.

Exercises

1. Find the primitive function or integral of the following derived functions:

(a) $\dot{s} = 2t$.   *Ans.* $s = t^2 + C$.

(b) $\dot{y} = 5$.

(c) $\dot{s} = -32t$.

   Ans. $s = -16t^2 + C$.

(d) $\dot{v} = -32$.

(e) $\dot{y} = x$.   *Ans.* $y = \dfrac{x^2}{2} + C$.

(f) $\dot{y} = 3x$.

(g) $\dot{v} = 32t$.   *Ans.* $v = 16t^2 + C$.

2. Remembering that the derived function of the sum (or difference) of two functions is the sum (or difference) of the derived functions, find the integrals of the following derived functions:

(a) $\dot{s} = 32t + 100$.

   Ans. $s = 16t^2 + 100t + C$.

(b) $\dot{s} = 32t - 100$.

   Ans. $s = 16t^2 - 100t + C$.

(c) $\dfrac{ds}{dt} = -16t + 50$.

(d) $\dot{y} = 3x + 7$.

(e) $\dot{y} = \sqrt{2}x - 7$.

   Ans. $y = \dfrac{\sqrt{2}}{2}x^2 - 7x + C$.

(f) $\dfrac{dy}{dx} = -\sqrt{2}x + 8$.

(g) $\dot{y} = 50 - 3x$.

(h) $\dot{y} = 50x - 3$.

(i) $\dot{y} = 100 - 32x$.

   Ans. $y = 100x - 16x^2 + C$.

(j) $\dot{s} = 96 - 6t$.

   Ans. $\dot{s} = 96t - 3t^2 + C$.

(k) $\dot{s} = 50 - \sqrt{2}t$.

(l) $\dot{s} = \sqrt{2}t + 50$.

(m) $\dot{s} = \frac{1}{3}t - \frac{1}{4}$.

   Ans. $s = \frac{1}{6}t^2 - \frac{1}{4}t + C$.

(n) $\dot{s} = -2.5t + 3.2$.

(o) $\dot{y} = \sqrt{12}t + 5$.

(p) $\dot{y} = \sqrt{24}x - 5\sqrt{3}$.

2. Straight Line Motion in One Direction.   The simplest problem in which
the calculus and antidifferentiation in particular prove to be effective is
vertical motion near the surface of the earth. Before we investigate this
problem, it is important to understand how mathematics is employed in
physical problems. Mathematics proper can give us facts about numbers
and geometrical figures. However, the concepts of speed, acceleration, mass,
force, light, sound, molecularstructure, and kinetic energy are not part of
mathematics but of physics, chemistry, or some other science. Hence the
axioms and theorems of mathematics can tell us nothing about these concepts.
To deduce conclusions about them, we must have physical facts or what the
physicist calls laws or principles. To these physical facts, which generally
are quantitative statements, we can apply the processes of mathematics.
Thus it is the combination of physical principles and mathematics that makes
possible the fruitful application of mathematics to physical problems. The
meaning and the accomplishments of the collaboration of mathematics and
physics will become clearer as we advance further into the subject of the
calculus.

     For vertical motion near the earth's surface, Galileo obtained a basic
physical principle: if one *neglects air resistance*, all objects fall to earth with
the same acceleration, which is a constant. Specifically, all objects near the
surface of the earth are subject to a downward acceleration of 32 ft/sec². In
symbols,

(7) $a = 32$.

This acceleration is caused by the gravitional attraction of the earth.

     Let us consider our first physical problem and try to find out how long it
takes an object dropped from a point 400 feet above the earth's surface to
reach the surface. To solve this problem it seems reasonable that we must
find the function that relates the distance and the time traveled by the
object.

     Before we tackle any physical problem, it is well to be certain that the signs
of the quantities involved are correctly chosen. We know in the present case
that the object has a downward acceleration of 32 ft/sec². Should we take
this acceleration to be positive or negative? The answer depends on what
direction we choose as positive for the distance traveled. Suppose that we
choose the downward direction to be the positive one for distance. Now let
us see what happens if we take the acceleration to be positive. If an object is
dropped, it starts out with 0 speed. Because the acceleration is positive—and
acceleration means a change in speed—the object acquires more and more
positive speed as it falls. A positive speed causes the distance to increase
with time and, if the distance is 0 at the start, the distance traveled is positive.
To sum up, if we wish the downward direction for distance to be the positive
one, then a downward acceleration should be taken as positive.

Let us choose the downward direction to be the positive one for distance and accordingly write

(8)
$$a = 32.$$

We know that by antidifferentiation we can proceed from the acceleration to the speed and from the speed to the distance traveled. Hence let us carry out these antidifferentiations or integrations. To remind ourselves that instantaneous acceleration is the instantaneous rate of change of speed with respect to time let us rewrite (8) as

(9)
$$\dot{v} = 32.$$

In Section 1 we learned that by antidifferentiation we can write

(10)
$$v = 32t + C.$$

The presence of the unknown quantity C seems to be an obstacle but actually is not. If an object is dropped, it leaves the hand with zero speed. This means that if time is measured from the instant the object leaves the hand, then, when $t = 0$, $v = 0$. Let us use this information in (10). Substitution of 0 for t and 0 for v gives

$$0 = 32 \cdot 0 + C$$

or

$$C = 0.$$

Hence the correct formula for speed is

(11)
$$v = 32t.$$

Instantaneous speed is, of course, the instantaneous rate of change of distance with respect to time. To state this explicitly, we rewrite (11) as

(12)
$$\dot{s} = 32t.$$

By using antidifferentiation we can state that

(13)
$$s = 16t^2 + C.$$

We must use some physical information to determine the constant of integration. If we agree to measure distance from the point at which the object is dropped and if, as we have already agreed, we measure time from the instant the object is dropped, then $s = 0$ when $t = 0$. Substitution of these values in (13) gives

$$0 = 16 \cdot 0^2 + C$$

or

$$C = 0.$$

Then

(14)
$$s = 16t^2$$

is the formula that gives the distance (in feet) the body falls in t seconds.

To answer the original question of how long it takes the object to fall 400 feet, we have but to substitute 400 for s in (14) and calculate the corresponding value of t. It so happens that there are two answers; $t = 5$ and $t = -5$. Of course, both are correct mathematical answers, but only the positive one answers the *physical* problem.

The preceding example shows how the constants C that arise in integration can be determined in a given physical problem. The information we used to determine both constants concerned values of v and s at $t = 0$. These values of v and s at $t = 0$ are called *initial* values for the obvious reason.

Before considering other applications, let us note that we could have proceeded differently in the problem above. We could have insisted that the upward direction be the positive direction for s. However, the acceleration is downward. As we have already pointed out, a downward acceleration means a downward speed and a downward distance covered with increasing time. If the positive direction for distance is to be upward, the downward distance that the object falls is in the negative direction. We can take care of the signs if we agree to start with the fact that a or $\dot{v}$ is -32; that is

$$\dot{v} = -32.$$

Then by antidifferentiation

$$v = -32t + C.$$

Now it is still true that $v = 0$ when $t = 0$, because at $t = 0$ a dropped object has 0 speed. Then $C = 0$ and

$$v = -32t$$

or

$$\dot{s} = -32t.$$

By antidifferentiation

(15) $$s = -16t^2 + C.$$

To determine this C, we must first establish the origin for s. Suppose that we agree to measure s from the ground. Moreover, the upward direction has been chosen as positive. Then, since the object is dropped from a point 400 feet above the ground, at $t = 0$, $s = 400$. If we substitute these values in (15), we have

$$400 = -16 \cdot 0^2 + C$$

or

$$C = 400.$$

The final formula is

(16) $$s = -16t^2 + 400.$$

We must, however, be careful about how we describe this result. The variable s is *not* the distance traveled by the object. This distance is $16t^2$.

The quantity $400 - 16t^2$ is the original height of the object measured from the ground upward minus the distance fallen by the object in time t (Fig. 3-1). Thus s is the *height above the ground* at time t. To call attention to this meaning of s, we can write (16) as

(17) $h = -16t^2 + 400,$

where h denotes height above the ground.

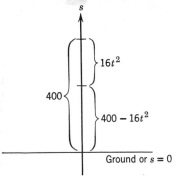

Figure 3-1

To answer the original question of how long it takes the object to fall 400 feet, we must now say that when the object hits the ground $h = 0$. If we substitute 0 for h in (17), we see that the equation for t becomes precisely the same as the one obtained from (14), namely, $16t^2 = 400$. The positive value of t, $t = 5$, is still the correct answer to the physical problem because t is measured from the instant the object begins to fall.

In this second method we introduced a negative acceleration and consequently a negative speed. It is customary when the sign of the speed enters significantly into a problem to use the word *velocity* in place of speed. A velocity can be positive or negative. The word speed is then used to denote the numerical value of the velocity without regard to sign. In the second method the velocity is always negative for t greater than 0. The word acceleration, however, is used to cover positive and negative rates of change of velocity.

To practice the use of the correct sign and the proper determination of the constants of integration, we shall solve the problem in a third way. We choose the downward direction as positive for the distance (as in the first method) but measure distance from the surface of the earth (as in the second method). Because we have chosen the downward direction as positive for the distance, we must choose the downward direction as positive for the acceleration, because a positive acceleration downward produces a positive velocity downward, if the initial velocity is 0, and a positive velocity downward produces a positive distance downward. Then

$$\dot{v} = 32$$

and

$$v = 32t + C.$$

Again $v = 0$ when $t = 0$ and therefore $C = 0$. Then

$$v = \dot{s} = 32t$$

and

(18) $$s = 16t^2 + C.$$

Now we must introduce the initial value of s. We have agreed to measure distance from the surface of the earth, and to take the downward direction to be positive. Because the object is 400 feet above the surface when it is dropped, we must say that when $t = 0$, $s = -400$. Then from (18) we have

$$-400 = 0 + C$$

and the correct formula is

(19) $s = 16t^2 - 400.$

Again we ask, what does s represent? This time, too, s does *not* represent the distance fallen by the object. It still falls $16t^2$ feet in t seconds, but the quantity $16t^2 - 400$ is the height above the ground (Fig. 3-2). This height is -400 at $t = 0$ and *increases* as t increases.

Figure 3-2

To solve the original problem of determining how long it takes the object to reach the earth, we now argue that when the object reaches the earth $s = 0$. Then from (19) we see that t again satisfies the equation $16t^2 = 400$. The positive root is still the correct physical answer.

We see from the examples already considered that the occurrence of the constant of integration is not a disadvantage but may even be an advantage. It permits us to adjust the formulas for velocity and distance to the specific situation we wish to describe.

With the same mathematical theory we can also tackle a class of problems in which an object is not just dropped but is thrown downward and then continues to fall under the acceleration of gravity. To throw an object downward as opposed to dropping it means that when the object leaves the hand it already has some velocity. Suppose, for example, that an object is thrown downward with a velocity of 100 ft/sec from a height of 1000 feet. Let us find the formula for the distance traveled in time t. Suppose that we choose the downward direction of distance as positive. We know that as soon as the object is released by the hand it possesses a downward acceleration due to gravity of 32 ft/sec². This downward acceleration generates a downward velocity, and the downward velocity causes the object to move downward. Because we have chosen the downward direction of distance as positive, we must start with

(20) $$a = \dot{v} = 32.$$

Then by antidifferentiation

(21) $$v = 32t + C.$$

The essential change in treating objects that are thrown downward as opposed to objects that are dropped comes in the next step. Suppose that we agree to measure time from the instant the object leaves the hand. Then at $t = 0$, $v = 100$. We substitute these values in (21) and obtain

$$100 = 32 \cdot 0 + C$$

or

$$C = 100.$$

Then from (21) we have

(22) $$v = 32t + 100.$$

We should compare this result with (11). To obtain the distance traveled we note that $v = \dot{s}$, so that

$$\dot{s} = 32t + 100.$$

Then by antidifferentiation

(23) $$s = 16t^2 + 100t + C.$$

To determine the constant of integration we must decide what our origin for distance is to be. Let us agree that distance is to be measured from the point at which the object is released. Then, at $t = 0$, $s = 0$. If we substitute these values in (23), we see that $C = 0$, and the formula for the distance traveled downward is

(24) $$s = 16t^2 + 100t.$$

We can now answer such questions as how long it takes the object to fall a given distance or how far it falls in a given time.

The rather simple problems discussed in this section show how the process of antidifferentiation or integration enables us to start with physical information about derived functions and produce useful formulas. We shall consider weightier examples subsequently.

Exercises

1. An object is dropped from the top of the Empire State Building, which is 1000 feet high. Derive the formula for the distance the object falls in time t. Then calculate the time it takes the object to reach ground and the velocity with which it hits the ground.   *Ans.* $s = 16t^2$; $5\sqrt{10}/2$ sec; $80\sqrt{10}$ ft/sec.

2. Suppose that an object is dropped from the tenth floor of a building whose roof is 50 feet above the point of release. Derive the formula for the position of the object t seconds after its release if distance is measured from the *roof*, the positive direction of distance is downward and time is measured from the instant the object is dropped. What is the distance fallen by the object in t seconds?

3. An object is dropped from a stationary balloon which is 1000 feet above the ground. Derive the formula for the position of the object after t seconds if the distance is measured from the ground, the positive direction is upward, and time is measured from the instant the object is dropped.

   Ans. $s = -16t^2 + 1000.$

4. Suppose that an object is dropped from a height of 1000 feet at 10 seconds after 12 o'clock. Derive the formula for the position of the object in t seconds if distance is measured from the starting point, the positive direction is downward, and time is measured from 12 o'clock.

5. Suppose that an object is thrown downward so that as it leaves the hand it has a speed of 100 ft/sec. Derive the formula for the distance fallen in t seconds after it is thrown if the distance is measured from the starting point and the downward direction is chosen positive.   *Ans.* $s = 16t^2 + 100t.$

6. Suppose that an object is set into straight line motion along the ground by giving it an initial speed of 100 ft/sec. If we suppose that the ground is smooth and flat, there is no horizontal acceleration. Derive the formula for the distance traveled in t seconds.

7. An object that is dropped from a point 500 feet above the surface of the moon falls to the surface with a constant acceleration of 5.3 ft/sec². If the distance is measured from the surface and the upward direction is positive, derive the formula for the position of the object (i.e., its height above the surface) after t seconds. Incidentally, the moon has no atmosphere and therefore air resistance does not enter into motions near the surface.

   Ans. $s = -(5.3/2)t^2 + 500.$

8. Suppose that an object is thrown downward from the roof of a building that is 200 feet high and that the initial speed is 50 ft/sec. Derive the formula for the height above the ground if the distance is taken positive in the upward direction.

9. An object is dropped from a height of 1000 feet. What is its velocity when it hits the ground?   *Ans.* $80\sqrt{10}$ ft/sec.

10. An object dropped near the surface of the earth acquires the velocity $v = 32t$ in t seconds. Suppose that it falls for T seconds. Is it correct to take the arithmetic mean of the initial and final velocities as the equivalent constant velocity in order to calculate the distance traveled?

11. A train runs at a velocity of 45 mi/hr along a straight track. When the brakes are applied, the deceleration (negative acceleration) is $1\frac{1}{3}$ ft/sec². For how long and how far from the station should the brakes be applied so that the train stops at the station?   *Ans.* 49.5 sec; 1633.5 ft.

12. Water drops flow out from a small opening at the rate of one drop per second and fall vertically with an acceleration of 32 ft/sec². Determine the distance between two successive drops exactly 1 second after the second one has left the opening.

$s = 0$
$t = 0$
$v = 100$

stop $t = ?$
$s = \frac{1}{4}$
$v = 0$

13. The landing velocity of an airplane (i.e., the velocity at which it touches the ground) is 100 mi/hr. It decelerates at a constant rate and comes to a stop after traveling $\frac{1}{4}$ mile along a straight landing strip. Find the deceleration.

Ans. 20,000 mi/hr^2.

14. With what velocity must a body be projected downward in order to catch up in 10 seconds with a body that has already fallen 100 feet from rest and from the same point.

15. If an object moves along a circle of radius R, its position can be described by specifying the angle θ through which it has rotated (Fig. 3-3). The derivative of θ with respect to t is called the angular velocity and is usually denoted by ω; that is, $\dot{\theta} = \omega$. The derivative of the angular velocity with respect to t is called the angular acceleration and is usually denoted by α; that is, $\ddot{\theta} = \dot{\omega} = \alpha$. The linear distance covered by the object is $s = R\theta$ if θ is measured in radians. Answer the following questions concerning circular motion:

Figure 3-3

(*a*) What is the linear velocity?   *Ans.* $R\dot{\theta}$.

(*b*) What is the linear acceleration?

(*c*) Find the constant angular acceleration of an object moving along a circle if starting from rest it makes 3600 revolutions during the first 2 minutes.   *Ans.* π rad/sec^2.

(*d*) The end of a shaft rotates about the other end with a constant acceleration. It starts from rest and makes 12.5 revolutions in the first 5 seconds. What is its angular velocity at the end of the fifth second?

(*e*) The initial angular velocity of a wheel turning about a fixed axle is 2π rad/sec. After 10 revolutions the wheel is brought to rest by friction in the bearings. Find angular deceleration on the assumption that it is constant.   *Ans.* 0.1π rad/sec^2.

(*f*) A wheel of radius 1 foot starts from rest and rotates with a constant acceleration. After 10 minutes any point on the rim of the wheel has a linear velocity of $v = 100$ ft/sec. Find the linear velocity of the point and angular velocity of the wheel after 15 seconds.

Ans. $\frac{5}{2}$ ft/sec; $\frac{5}{2}$ rad/sec.

3. *Up and Down Motion.* Among straight line motions, that of an object projected upward is very important physically and of considerable interest mathematically. Let us seek the formulas that govern such motions. We shall continue to restrict ourselves to motions near the surface of the earth and to neglect air resistance, so that we may use the fact that the acceleration of gravity is constant and equal to 32 ft/sec^2. It is convenient to measure distance from the surface of the earth and to take the upward direction as positive. However, the acceleration is downward, which gives the object a downward speed and, in turn, causes the object to fall downward. To ensure that the distance traveled *by reason of this acceleration* is recorded as downward, we must regard the acceleration as negative. We start then with the basic fact that

(25) $a = \dot{v} = -32.$

Then by antidifferentiation

(26) $v = -32t + C.$

If an object is projected upward, it must have an initial velocity upward; that is, if we measure time from the instant it is projected upward, at the instant $t = 0$ the object must be given an upward or positive velocity. Let us suppose that this velocity is 128 ft/sec. Then, at $t = 0$, $v = 128$. If we substitute these values in (26), we find that

$$128 = -32 \cdot 0 + C$$

or

$$C = 128,$$

so that

(27) $v = -32t + 128.$

We have in (27) the formula for the velocity of the moving object at any time t. To find the height reached by the object, that is, the distance traveled upward, at any time t, we use the fact that the velocity is the instantaneous rate of change of distance with respect to time. Hence v is $\dot{s}$, and by anti-differentiation applied to (27) we obtain

(28) $s = -16t^2 + 128t + C.$

To establish the value of C we may use the physical fact that, when $t = 0$, the object is on the ground. Because we have agreed to measure distance from this surface, $s = 0$ at $t = 0$. Thus from (28)

$$0 = -16 \cdot 0^2 + 128 \cdot 0 + C.$$

Then $C = 0$ and

(29) $s = -16t^2 + 128t.$

We have derived formula (29) by considering what happens when the object travels upward. However, we know from experience that the object reaches some highest point and then falls downward. Does formula (29) apply to the falling motion? We started with the fact that the acceleration is -32 ft/sec². This acceleration applies at every instant that the object is in the air because gravity acts constantly on an object in motion, to produce a downward acceleration of 32 ft/sec². Hence this fact applies to the upward and downward motion. We also used the fact that the object is projected upward with an initial velocity of 128 ft/sec. Surprisingly, this velocity also applies throughout the motion. If we ignore for the moment the effect of gravity, only the velocity of 128 ft/sec operates. Now Newton's first law of motion, an axiom of physics thoroughly grounded in experience, states that if an object is at rest and no force acts it remains at rest and if it is in motion and no force acts it continues to move indefinitely in a straight line at a constant speed. If an object is set into upward motion at 128 ft/sec and gravity does not act, the object continues to move upward *indefinitely* at 128 ft/sec. The correctness of Newton's first law of motion can be appreciated if we think of what happens when an object is projected horizontally along a smooth surface such as ice. Gravity does not affect the horizontal motion, and therefore the object keeps skimming along the ice. If there were no air resistance and if the ice were ideally smooth, the object would move indefinitely at the velocity with which it was projected.

In vertical motion, however, gravity does act to produce the acceleration of -32 ft/sec² and, accordingly, the velocity of $-32t$ ft/sec. Hence the object moves upward at 128 ft/sec while gravity produces a downward velocity of $32t$ ft/sec; that is, at any instant of time during the upward *and* downward motion the object is impelled upward with a speed of 128 ft/sec and downward at $32t$ ft/sec. The *net* velocity then is $-32t + 128$. Hence formula (27) holds at each instant of the motion.

What about (29)? Because (27) is the correct expression for the velocity during the downward as well as the upward motion and because the velocity is the rate of change of distance with respect to time, the integral of the velocity function should give the distance traveled downward. The function in (29) thus represents the upward and downward motion. What, however, does s represent? For some interval of t-values starting at $t = 0$, the object rises and the corresponding s-values represent distance traveled or height above the ground. At some value of t (which happens to be 4 here) the object reaches a maximum height and then, because the net velocity becomes negative, the object moves downward. The distance traveled during the downward motion is a negative distance, which, added to the positive distance already covered by the object, gives the *net height* of the object above the ground. Then s represents the height of the object above the ground.

To be certain that we understand the meaning of s in (29), let us look at Fig. 3-4. We see from (27) that v is positive from $t = 0$ to $t = 4$. Hence in this interval the object moves upward, and during this motion the value of s is both the distance traveled and the height above the ground. At $t = 4$, v is 0. At this instant the object begins its downward motion. From $t = 4$ to $t = 5$, for example, the object falls some distance, and this negative distance, when added to the positive distance already covered, gives the net height of the object above the ground.

Thus (29) does hold for the upward and downward motion, provided we remember that s is not distance traveled throughout the motion but the height above the ground. With formula (29) available, we can answer all kinds of questions about the motion.

One question of interest is the maximum height attained by an object that is thrown or shot up into the air. This question is easily answered. Let

Figure 3-4

us consider the motion represented by formula (29), namely,

$$(30) \qquad\qquad s = -16t^2 + 128t.$$

We happen to know the maximum height in this case; it is shown in Fig. 3-3. Let us suppose, however, that we do not know it and therefore seek a method of finding it. The problem of finding the maximum height could be answered if we knew at what instant of time, that is, at what value of t, the object attains maximum height because we could then substitute this value of t in (30). But we seem to lack this information. However, we do know but have not yet utilized the formula for velocity, namely,

$$(31) \qquad\qquad v = -32t + 128.$$

A distinctive fact about the velocity of the object at the instant it attains maximum height is that the velocity is 0; for the object rises until its velocity is 0 and then falls. Hence we substitute 0 for v in (31) and solve

$$0 = -32t + 128$$

for t. We see then that, when the object is at maximum height, $t = 4$. We now substitute this value of t in (30) and obtain

$$s = -16 \cdot 4^2 + 128 \cdot 4 = 256.$$

Thus the maximum height attained by the object is 256 feet.

We should note that to solve the problem of maximum height we used a physical argument, namely, that the velocity of the object is 0 at the maximum point. We may indeed be convinced that this physical fact is correct. Nevertheless, we must go outside of mathematics to obtain it. Although some physical information must enter into all applications of mathematics to physical science, it is desirable to prove by mathematical means as much as we can because we are then more certain of our facts. We shall see later, when studying maxima and minima, that we can prove *by mathematical means* that the velocity is 0 at the highest point of the object's path.

Exercises   *Tues*

1. For the motion represented by formula (29), what is the height above the ground at $t = 5$? What is the distance traveled by the object from $t = 0$ to $t = 5$?
   Ans. 240 ft; 272 ft.

2. Suppose that an object is projected upward from the ground with a velocity of 160 ft/sec. Choose the upward direction to be the positive one for height above the ground and derive the formulas for the velocity at any time t and for the height above the ground at any time t.

3. The height of a ball which is thrown up from the ground with a velocity of 192 ft/sec is given by the formula $s = +192t - 16t^2$. Find t when $s = 512$. What physical significance do the two answers have?   *Ans.* $t = 4.8$.

4. The height of a ball which is thrown upward from the ground with a velocity of 144 ft/sec is given by the formula $s = 144t - 16t^2$. Find the velocity when $t = 9$ and interpret the result physically.

5. If a gun is capable of firing a bullet at the speed of 1000 ft/sec and if the gun is fired straight up, how high will the bullet go?   *Ans.* 15,625 ft.

6. Because man is preparing for activities on the moon, it may be worthwhile to consider this question: Suppose that a ball is thrown up from the surface of the moon with a velocity of 96 ft/sec. How high will it go and how long will it take to reach that maximum height? The acceleration due to gravity near the surface of the moon is 5.3 ft/sec².

7. A stone is thrown upward from the ground with an initial velocity of 96 ft/sec. (*a*) How long does it take to reach the ground again? (*b*) What velocity does it have at the instant it returns to the ground?   *Ans.* 6 sec; −96 ft/sec.

8. A stone is thrown upward from the surface of a planet where the acceleration due to gravity (the attraction of that planet) is g ft/sec². The initial velocity is v_0 and distance upward is taken to be positive. Find the formulas for the velocity and the height above the ground.   *Ans.* $v = v_0 - gt$; $s = v_0 t - \dfrac{gt^2}{2}$.

9. A bullet is shot straight up and returns to earth in 20 seconds. What is its initial velocity?

10. Suppose that an object is thrown upward with an initial velocity of 200 ft/sec and that the upward direction is taken to be positive for height above the ground. However, time is measured from the instant 5 seconds before the object is thrown up. Derive the formula for the height above the ground at any time t.

11. Suppose that an object is thrown upward with an initial velocity of 200 ft/sec and that another one is thrown upward 5 seconds later with an initial velocity of 300 ft/sec. When and where do they meet?
    Ans. 2.3 sec after second object is thrown.

12. Calculate the velocity with which an object must be shot straight up in order to just reach a height of 1000 feet. By just reaching the specified height we mean that the velocity of the object should be 0 at that height.

13. Calculate the minimum ejection velocity with which a shell must be fired to strike a target 1000 feet high and directly overhead.   *Ans.* $80\sqrt{10}$ ft/sec.

14. Show that an object thrown up into the air near the surface of the earth with a velocity V will rise to a maximum height of $V^2/64$.

15. A subway train travels 400 feet between two stations. It starts from rest and accelerates at the rate of 8 ft/sec^2 until its velocity reaches 20 ft/sec. It then moves at this constant velocity for a while and then decelerates to rest at the rate of 12 ft/sec^2. Find the total time between the stations.

16. A rocket is shot straight up into the air to a height of 10 miles at which point its velocity is 120 mi/hr (176 ft/sec). Its fuel is now exhausted, and therefore the rocket receives no further acceleration from the fuel. Assuming that the acceleration due to gravity is still 32 ft/sec^2, write a formula for the subsequent velocity of the rocket and for its height above the ground. *Suggestion:* Choose the instant at which the rocket reaches the 10-mile height as the zero point for time.   *Ans.* $v = -32t + 176$; $s = -16t^2 + 176t + 52{,}800$.

17. (*a*) A ball is thrown straight up into the air from the roof of a building with a velocity of 96 ft/sec. Write a formula for its subsequent height above the roof as a function of time.   *Ans.* $s = -16t^2 + 96t$.

(*b*) If the roof is 112 feet above the ground, how long after it is thrown up does the ball reach the ground?

18. (*a*) A ball is thrown straight up into the air from the roof of a building with a velocity of 96 ft/sec. If the roof is 112 feet above the ground, write a formula for the height of the ball above the ground.

Ans. $s = 96t - 16t^2 + 112$.

(*b*) How long after it is thrown up does the ball reach the ground?

Ans. 7 sec.

19. Suppose that an object which travels along a horizontal straight road at a velocity of 88 ft/sec starts to lose velocity, that is, decelerates at the rate of 11 ft/sec^2. What distance does it travel by the time it comes to rest? The answer, incidentally, is the minimum distance in which one can stop a car that is traveling at 60 mi/hr. Actually, it takes about 1 second before a person who decides to apply the brakes actually does so. Hence the car travels another 88 feet between the instant the decision is made and the instant at which the car comes to rest.

20. Suppose that a ball is thrown up with a velocity of 128 ft/sec. Decide on the basis of experience or intuition whether it takes as much, more, or less time for the ball to travel from the starting point to the maximum height as it does to travel from that position to the ground. Now obtain the answer mathematically.

21. A motorist is traveling at a constant speed v_0 and is approaching a traffic light. He wishes to stop the car at the light. However, his reaction time, that is, the time it takes him to put his foot on the brakes, is τ and the maximum deceleration of the braked car is a. What is the minimum distance from the light in which he can bring his car to a stop?   *Ans.* $\frac{1}{2}(v_0^2/a) + v_0\tau$.

22. The traffic department of a town wishes to put a warning sign reading "Slow Down, Stoplight Ahead" sufficiently in advance of the stoplight for oncoming motorists to have time to slow down and stop at the light. If automobiles can decelerate at the rate of 5 ft/sec² and if the maximum speed allowed on the road is 30 mi/hr (44 ft/sec), how far in advance of the light should the warning sign be placed to permit motorists to stop in time?

23. A subway train travels over a distance s in t seconds. It starts from rest (zero velocity) and ends at rest. In the first part of its journey it moves with constant acceleration f and in the second part with constant deceleration (negative acceleration) r. Show that $s = [fr/(f + r)]t^2/2$.

24. A bomber releases a bomb while flying vertically *upward* at a velocity of 1500 ft/sec at a height of 10,000 feet. (The bomb when released also has an upward velocity of 1500 ft/sec.)

    (a) How long after it is released will it take the bomb to reach the ground?
    Ans. 106 sec.

    (b) Immediately after releasing the bomb the bomber flies away horizontally at the rate of 1200 ft/sec. How far away from the point at which the bomb strikes the ground is the plane when the bomb strikes?

25. In a chemical reaction two substances are combining to form a third one. The rate $\dot{x}$ at which the third substance is being formed in grams/min is given by the function $\dot{x} = 9 - \frac{1}{2}t^2$ when the reaction has been underway for t minutes. How much substance is formed in 4 minutes? *Ans.* $25\frac{1}{3}$ g.

26. A body is dropped from a height of 100 yards. After falling for 2 seconds a second body is projected vertically upward from a point on the earth directly below and with a velocity of 40 yd/sec (yards per second). Find the time and height at which the two bodies meet.
    Ans. Approx. 3.3 sec after first body is dropped; approx. 42 yd.

27. A balloon is ascending with a velocity of 20 ft/sec when a stone is dropped from it. The stone reaches the ground in 6 seconds. Find the height of the balloon when the stone was dropped. (When dropped from the balloon, the stone has the upward velocity of the balloon.)

28. Show that a body thrown upward has the same speed when passing a given point on the upward and the downward motions.

29. A body is thrown into the air with an initial velocity of v_0 ft/sec. What initial velocity is required to double the maximum height previously attained?
    Ans. $\sqrt{2}v_0$ ft/sec.

4. Motion Along an Inclined Plane. Motion along a straight line is not confined to vertical or horizontal paths. Trains and automobiles move up and down hills, and airplanes rising or descending from a field follow essentially straight line paths. Such paths are studied under the concept of motion along an inclined plane. We shall consider how the calculus helps to study the motion of objects down or up inclined planes.

If an object M is placed on a smooth inclined plane (Fig. 3-5), we know that it will slide down. To obtain quantitative information about the motion, we must know something about its acceleration, velocity, or the distance it

Figure 3-5

moves. The force that causes the motion, as in the case of objects that fall straight down, is gravity. Gravity pulls straight down, whereas the object slides down the plane. Hence we are obliged to look into the question of how a force which acts in one direction can be effective in another direction.

Forces are peculiar animals. Suppose an object rests on a horizontal smooth table at P (Fig. 3-6). If a force of magnitude or numerical value F_1 pulls it toward S and another force of magnitude F_2 pulls it toward T, the object actually moves along the diagonal PQ of the parallelogram determined by the two forces. That is, the two sides of the parallelogram which determine it are the side of length F_1 in the direction of F_1 and the side of length F_2 in the direction of F_2, both starting at P, which is the point of application of the two forces. The magnitude F of the total or resultant force is the length of the diagonal PQ. Why do the combined forces behave in this way? The only answer is that this is what we find to be the case in experimenting with forces. We cannot quarrel with nature, but we can be grateful that we can describe the action of forces by a simple mathematical law.

Forces are a prime example of what are known as vectors, that is, entities that have magnitude and direction. When we obtain the effect of two forces by using the parallelogram law, we say that we *add* the forces. This meaning of the word "add" differs from that used to describe the addition of two numbers. In fact, as the parallelogram law implies, a force of 3 poundals and a force of 4 poundals (a poundal is one unit of force) do not generally add

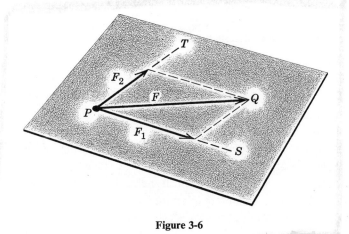

Figure 3-6

up to 7 poundals. The mathematicians have reasons for using the word "add" in combining forces, but the reasons are irrelevant here. It is important to note, however, that the statement that forces are being added means that they are being combined under the parallelogram law.

The most important case of the addition of two forces is that in which they are at right angles to each other (Fig. 3-7). Here the parallelogram becomes a rectangle, and the resultant of magnitude F is the diagonal of the rectangle.

Let us return to our object at P on the inclined plane (Fig. 3-8). Gravity acts on this object and pulls straight down. We can think of this force of gravity of magnitude F as the resultant of two forces—one of magnitude F_1 which is directed down the plane and the other of magnitude F_2 which is directed perpendicular to the plane. These summands or components of the

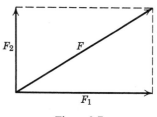

Figure 3-7

gravitational force are determined by dropping perpendiculars from the endpoint Q of F onto the plane and onto the line perpendicular to the plane, so that F is the diagonal of the rectangle determined by F_1 and F_2. Thus we can think of the force whose magnitude is F as having been replaced by the

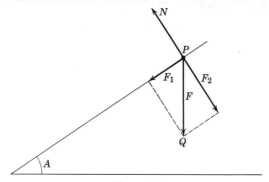

Figure 3-8

forces with magnitudes F_1 and F_2. Now F_2 is the magnitude of the force with which gravity presses the object against the inclined plane. The plane resists this force; that is, the plane, because it is rigid, does not permit the object to move into or perpendicular to the plane. This reaction of the plane, denoted by N in Fig. 3-8 offsets or exactly counteracts F_2. Hence the force which causes the object to slide down the plane is the other component or summand of the gravitational force, the one with magnitude F_1.

How large is F_1? Suppose that the plane is inclined at angle A to the horizontal (Fig. 3-9). Then the angle at Q is also A, and therefore

(32) $$F_1 = F \sin A.$$

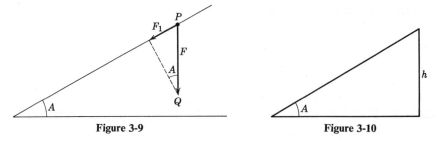

Figure 3-9   **Figure 3-10**

To obtain the numerical value of F_1, we must make use of one more physical fact. The force that the earth's gravity exerts on an object is called the weight of the object. Each of us is constantly being pulled toward the earth by the earth's gravitational force, and the magnitude of this force is the person's weight. Thus F in (32) is the weight of the object on the inclined plane.

We know as a physical fact that when an object is allowed to fall straight down, the force of gravity or the weight of the object gives it an acceleration of 32 ft/sec². Because the force acting on the object along the inclined plane is $F \sin A$, it would seem reasonable that the acceleration given to the object would be $32 \sin A$. We are assuming, in other words, that the force is proportional to the acceleration. Let us make the physical assumption; later, when we have had occasion to look further into this relation between force and acceleration, we shall see that it is correct.* What we have decided then is that the acceleration a of an object sliding down a plane inclined at an angle A to the horizontal is

(33) $a = 32 \sin A.$

We are now in a position to answer some questions about motion down an inclined plane. Suppose that an object is placed on a plane inclined at an angle A to the horizontal (Fig. 3-10). What velocity does it acquire after sliding for 10 seconds? We know that $a = \dot{v}$. Hence

$$\dot{v} = 32 \sin A.$$

Now $32 \sin A$ is a constant for a given inclined plane. Hence

$$v = (32 \sin A)t + C = 32t \sin A + C.$$

Because the object starts with 0 velocity, $v = 0$ when $t = 0$. Hence $C = 0$ and

(34) $v = 32t \sin A.$

Thus after 10 seconds the object acquires a velocity of $320 \sin A$ ft/sec. Given the value of A, we can of course find $\sin A$.

---

* The reader who already knows Newton's second law of motion, $F = ma$, where m is the mass of the object and a the acceleration, will see at once the correctness of the assumption.

We can also find how far the object travels in 10 seconds. If we let s be the distance traveled down the plane in t seconds, $v = \dot{s}$. By (34)

$$\dot{s} = 32t \sin A.$$

Again we must remember that $32 \sin A$ is a constant, and integration yields

$$s = 16t^2 \sin A + C.$$

If s is measured from the point at which the object begins to slide, $s = 0$ when $t = 0$ and therefore $C = 0$. Thus

(35) $$s = 16t^2 \sin A$$

is the formula for the distance traveled in t seconds. We can now calculate s for any value of t.

Handwritten annotations:
$a = \dot{s} = 16$
$\dot{s} = 16t$
$s = 8t^2$

$\frac{200}{} = t^2$
$25 = t^2$
$5 = t$

Exercises

1. Suppose that an object starts from rest and slides 200 feet down a hill whose inclination is 30°. How long does it take to slide this distance and what velocity does the object acquire?   *Ans.* 5 sec; 80 ft/sec.

2. Suppose that an object starts from rest and slides down a hill whose inclination is 30°. The object slides from a height of 100 feet above the horizontal ground to the ground. How long does it take to slide down the hill and what velocity does the object acquire?

3. Answer the questions of Exercise 2 if the conditions are the same except for the fact that the inclination of the hill is 15°.   *Ans.* 10 sec approx.; 80 ft/sec.

4. If a plane is inclined at an angle of 90° to the horizontal, that is, if $A = 90°$, the motion down the plane of a body which starts from rest should be the same as that of a body which is dropped and falls vertically. Do formulas (33), (34), and (35) reduce to the formulas for the latter kind of motion when $A = 90°$?

5. (*a*) Suppose that an object is allowed to slide down an inclined plane from a point which is h feet above the horizontal ground, and that the object slides l feet along the plane to the ground. How long does it take to slide this distance?   *Ans.* $l/4\sqrt{h}$.

   (*b*) Under the conditions of part (*a*), what velocity does the object acquire?   *Ans.* $8\sqrt{h}$.

   (*c*) Is there anything remarkable about the answer to part (*b*)?

6. (*a*) Suppose that an object slides down two different inclined planes from a height of h feet above a horizontal plane to the horizontal plane itself. One inclined plane slopes gradually and is l_1 feet long; the other is steep and l_2 feet long. Show that the respective times of descent t_1 and t_2 satisfy the equation $t_1/t_2 = l_1/l_2$.

   (*b*) Under the conditions of part (*a*), compare the velocities acquired at the bottoms of the two paths.   *Ans.* Equal.

7. An object slides down an inclined plane OP' (Fig. 3-11) starting from rest at 0. Show that the point Q reached in the time t_1 required to fall straight down to P lies on a circle with OP as diameter.

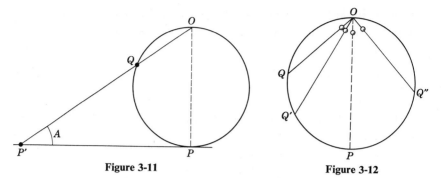

Figure 3-11   **Figure 3-12**

8. In Fig 3-12, OQ, OQ', OP, ... are pieces of straight wire all emanating from O and lying in one vertical plane. A bead is slipped on each wire at O, and all are released simultaneously to slide down their respective wires. Show that at any instant of time the beads lie on a circle. *Suggestion:* Use the result of Exercise 7.

9. Find the straight line path for which the time required for an object to slide from O to some point of the curve C is least (Fig. 3-13). *Suggestion:* Use the result of Exercise 8. *Ans.* The path OQ for which the circle on OQ has O as its highest point and is tangent to C.

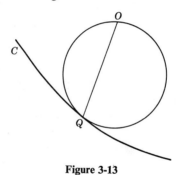

Figure 3-13

10. Suppose that an object slides down a hill whose inclination is A and that at the instant it starts to slide it has a velocity of v_0 ft/sec. Derive the formula for the distance the object slides in time t.

APPENDIX*

The Coordinate Geometry
of Straight Lines

A1. The Need for Geometrical Interpretation. Thus far in our work on the calculus we have dealt with formulas. It is a wise procedure in all

---

* The appendix may be omitted by readers familiar with the elements of coordinate geometry.

mathematical work to try to think in geometrical as well as algebraic (or analytical) terms. The geometrical mode of thinking not only helps us to understand what we are doing algebraically but may also suggest new results. Moreover, as we noted in Chapter 1, we intend to base some of our theorems on geometric evidence.

The way to associate geometrical figures with formulas has already been indicated in Chapter 2. We use the technique of coordinate geometry to associate a curve with a formula. Our method of doing this so far has been to make a table of x- and y-values which satisfy the formula, plot a point on a rectangular Cartesian coordinate system for each pair of x- and y-values, and join these points by a smooth curve. This method is crude and laborious; it can be replaced by more effective ones. In this Appendix we begin a deeper and more systematic study of the relation between formulas and the curves representing them or, as one also says in coordinate geometry, between equations and curves.

A2. The Distance Formula. Before we can take up the main task of co-ordinate geometry—the interpretation of given formulas as curves and the attachment of the proper formula to a given curve—we must acquire a few subsidiary ideas. The first is a formula or algebraic expression for the distance between two points in terms of the coordinates of these points.

To denote two specific points and at the same time to indicate that they can be any two points, we use the notation (x_1, y_1) for one point and (x_2, y_2) for the other. The subscripts 1 and 2 distinguish the points. Suppose, then, that P_1 with coordinates (x_1, y_1) and P_2 with coordinates (x_2, y_2) are the two points (Fig. 3A-1). If we draw the horizontal line through P_1 and the vertical

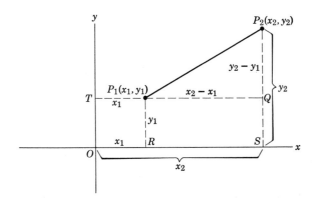

Figure 3A-1

line through P_2, they intersect at a point Q. We see at once that P_1P_2 is the hypotenuse of the right triangle P_1QP_2. Moreover, we see from the figure that

$$QP_2 = SP_2 - SQ = SP_2 - RP_1 = y_2 - y_1.$$

Also,

$$P_1Q = TQ - TP_1 = x_2 - x_1.$$

Hence by the Pythagorean theorem

$$(P_1P_2)^2 = (x_2 - x_1)^2 + (y_2 - y_1)^2,$$

and therefore

(1) $$P_1P_2 = \sqrt{(x_2 - x_1)^2 + (y_2 - y_1)^2}.$$

We take the positive square root because the distance is usually taken to be positive. Formula (1) gives the distance between two points in terms of their coordinates.

Our proof of the distance formula begged a question. Suppose that one or both of the points has negative coordinates. Would formula (1) still be correct in such cases? Let us take P_1 to be in the third quadrant (Fig. 3A-2) and see if (1) is still correct.

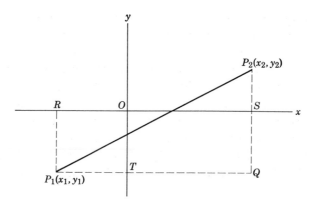

Figure 3A-2

Previously we found that QP_2 is $y_2 - y_1$. We see in Fig. 3A-2 that now QP_2 is $QS + SP_2$ and we want QP_2 to be the actual sum of the positive lengths SP_2 and QS. Now SP_2 is y_2. However, the actual length of QS is the length of P_1R. If we took y_1 to be the length of P_1R, we would have a negative quantity, because y_1 here represents a negative number. Hence we take the positive length of QS to be $-y_1$. Then

$$QP_2 = SP_2 + QS = y_2 - y_1.$$

Likewise the length P_1Q is the sum of the positive lengths P_1T and TQ. Because x_1 is negative, we take $-x_1$ to represent the positive length P_1T. Then

$$P_1Q = TQ + P_1T = x_2 - x_1.$$

We see then that our results for QP_2 and P_1Q are the same as the previous ones, and formula (1) holds.

Exercises

1. Show that in finding the distance between two points it does not matter which point we denote by P_1 and which by P_2.
2. Find the distance between the points whose coordinates are the following:
   (*a*) (3, 2) and (5, 7).   *Ans.* $\sqrt{29}$.   (*d*) (−7, −5) and (−1, −3).
   (*b*) (−3, 2) and (5, 7).   (*e*) (1, 2) and (1, −2).   *Ans.* 4.
   (*c*) (−3, −1) and (−4, 2).

   Ans. $\sqrt{10}$.

3. Show that the coordinates of the midpoint of the line segment joining (x_1, y_1) and (x_2, y_2) are $\left(\dfrac{x_1 + x_2}{2}, \dfrac{y_1 + y_2}{2}\right)$.

A3. The Slope of a Straight Line.   In our everyday experience we use the notion of the slope of a hill. What we mean by the slope is the number of feet we travel up, which is called the rise, divided by the number of feet of horizontal travel, which is called the run. Thus if we walk from P to Q (Fig. 3A-3) and rise 6 feet while moving horizontally 2 feet, we say that the slope is 6/2 or 3. This notion of slope is utilized to specify the slope of any line with respect to the horizontal or x-axis.

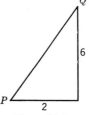

Figure 3A-3

Consider the line through P_1 and P_2 of Fig. 3A-4 and, in particular, the segment P_1P_2. The rise is QP_2 and the run is P_1Q. Then the slope is QP_2/P_1Q. We found in deriving formula (1) that $QP_2 = y_2 - y_1$ and $P_1Q = x_2 - x_1$. Then the slope of the segment P_1P_2, which is usually denoted by m, is

(2) $$m = \frac{y_2 - y_1}{x_2 - x_1}.$$

Suppose that we take any other two points, say R_1 and R_2 on the line P_1P_2. Would the slope of the segment R_1R_2 be the same as the slope of P_1P_2? Triangles R_1SR_2 and P_1QP_2 are similar because the corresponding sides are parallel. Hence $QP_2/P_1Q = SR_2/R_1S$. Thus the slope of R_1R_2 is the same as that of P_1P_2. This means that any two segments of a line have the same slope, and therefore we can speak of the slope of a line and mean by it the slope of any segment of that line. Then formula (2) gives the slope of the line.

Let us note that it does not matter which of the two points determining the segment is called P_1 and which P_2. For, if we interchange (x_1, y_1) and (x_2, y_2) in (2), we change the signs of numerator and denominator but not the sign of the fraction.

To distinguish lines which "fall" as x increases from lines which rise as x increases we make a slight extension of the usual notion of slope. We

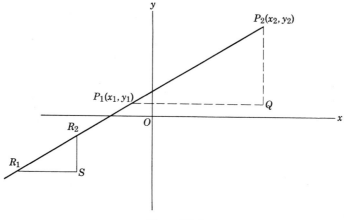

Figure 3A-4

continue to use formula (2) for the value of the slope. However, as we can see from Fig. 3A-5, although $y_2 - y_1$ is positive, the quantity $x_2 - x_1$ is negative. Hence formula (2) gives a negative slope for a line which falls to the right or as x increases. Let us note that here too it does not matter which point we call (x_1, y_1) and which (x_2, y_2). If P_1 and P_2 are interchanged, $x_2 - x_1$ becomes positive, but $y_2 - y_1$ becomes negative and therefore the ratio remains the same.

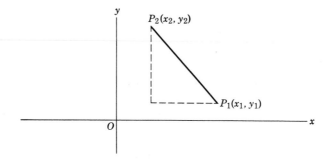

Figure 3A-5

There are two exceptional cases of slope. If a line is parallel to the y-axis, $x_2 - x_1 = 0$ and the slope of the line is not defined. If the line is parallel to the x-axis, formula (2) yields the slope 0.

Exercises

1. Draw the line joining the two given points and calculate its slope:

    (*a*) (3, 4) and (5, 7).   *Ans.* $\frac{3}{2}$.   (*d*) (−3, 7) and (5, 2).

    (*b*) (−1, 2) and (5, 7).   (*e*) (−3, 7) and (−5, −2). *Ans.* $\frac{9}{2}$.

    (*c*) (3, 7) and (5, 2).   *Ans.* $-\frac{5}{2}$.   (*f*) (3, 7) and (3, 10).

A4. *The Inclination of a Line.* An alternative method of describing the slope of a line with respect to the horizontal or x-axis utilizes the angle which the line makes with the axis. This angle of inclination is the counterclockwise angle whose initial side is the x-axis taken in the positive direction and whose terminal side lies on the line itself taken in the upward direction. Figure 3A-6 shows 4 lines in different positions with respect to the x-axis, and the angle of inclination A of each of these lines is indicated. We note that angle A can vary from 0 to 180°. These extreme values are assigned as the inclination of a line which is parallel to the x-axis.

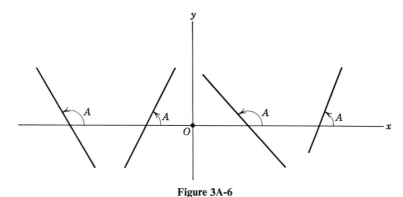

Figure 3A-6

The slope of a line indicates how it lies in relation to the x-axis; it gives the direction of the line. So does the angle of inclination. These two methods of specifying direction are related. The slope of a line, according to (2), is

$$m = \frac{y_2 - y_1}{x_2 - x_1}.$$

If the line rises to the right as in (*a*) of Fig. 3A-7, the slope is positive and is the ratio QP_2/P_1Q. However, this ratio is also tan A. Hence*

(3) $$m = \tan A.$$

If the line falls to the right as in (*b*) of Fig. 3A-7, the slope is still QP_2/P_1Q but the ratio is negative. The ratio of the positive lengths QP_2 and QP_1 is tan B. However, because $A = (180 - B)$,

(4) $$\tan A = \tan (180 - B) = -\tan B.$$

Then tan A is negative and still gives the slope. Thus formula (3) still holds.

If the angle of inclination A of a line is given, we can always find the slope by finding the tangent of the angle. If A is acute, we merely look up its tangent in a table of trigonometric ratios. If A is obtuse, we look up the tangent of the supplementary angle B, and, as (4) shows, tan $A = -\tan B$.

---

* Strictly speaking, formula (3) is correct only if we use the same unit of distance on the x and y axes.

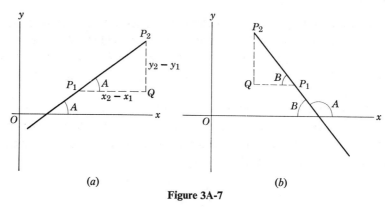

(a)   (b)

Figure 3A-7

Conversely, if the slope is specified, we know tan A. We can now use trigonometric tables to find the angle A. If the tangent value is positive, angle A is the acute angle found directly in the table. If the tangent value is negative, say -3, then, because we have the identity (4), we find the angle B whose tangent value is $+3$, and the identity (4) tells us that $180 - B$ is the angle whose tangent value is -3. Hence $180 - B$ is the angle of inclination A of the line whose slope is -3.

Exercises

1. Find the slope of the line whose angle of inclination is the following:

(a) $30°$.   *Ans.* $\sqrt{3}/3$.   (g) $0°$.   *Ans.* 0.

(b) $45°$.   (h) $\pi/4$.

(c) $70°$.   *Ans.* 2.7.   (i) $\pi/3$.   *Ans.* $\sqrt{3}$.

(d) $110°$.   (j) $\pi/2$.   *Ans.* Undefined.

(e) $120°$.   *Ans.* $-\sqrt{3}$.   (k) π.

(f) $170°$.

2. Find the angle of inclination of the line whose slope is the following:

(a) 1.   *Ans.* $\pi/4$.   (e) $-\frac{1}{2}$.   *Ans.* $153° 26'$.

(b) $\dfrac{\sqrt{3}}{3}$.   (f) -0.7270.

                                                      (g) 2.748.   *Ans.* $70°$.

(c) $\sqrt{3}$.   *Ans.* $\pi/3$.   (h) 0.

(d) $\frac{1}{2}$.   (i) -2.748.   *Ans.* $110°$.

3. Find the angle of inclination of the line through the following points:

(a) $(1, 1)$ and $(4, 4)$.   *Ans.* $\pi/4$.   (d) $(-5, -7)$ and $(1, 1)$.

(b) $(-4, 4)$ and $(-1, 1)$.   (e) $(3, 2)$ and $(3, 7)$.   *Ans.* $\pi/2$.

(c) $(1, 1)$ and $(5, 7)$.   *Ans.* $56° 19'$.

A5. Slopes of Parallel and Perpendicular Lines.   If two lines are parallel, as are the lines p and q in each pair of Fig. 3A-8, their angles of inclination are equal because they are what in plane geometry are called corresponding

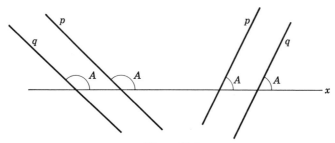

Figure 3A-8

angles of parallel lines. If two angles are equal, their tangent values are the same. Hence if two lines are parallel, their slopes are equal.

Conversely, if two lines, say p and q, have the same slope, then by (3) the tangents of their respective angles of inclination are equal. Moreover, given the tangent of an angle, there is just one angle between 0 and 180° which has this tangent value. Then the angles of inclination of the two lines are equal, and by the theorem of plane geometry which states that if the corresponding angles of two lines are equal the lines are parallel, the lines p and q must be parallel. Hence we have proved the following theorem:

Theorem: If two lines are parallel, their slopes are equal, and conversely if two lines have equal slopes, then the lines are parallel.

Now let us consider two lines p and q which are perpendicular (Fig. 3A-9). According to a theorem of plane geometry, which states that an exterior

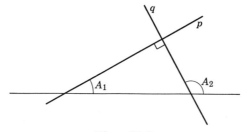

Figure 3A-9

angle of a triangle is equal to the sum of the two remote interior angles, we have that

$$A_2 = A_1 + 90°.$$

Then

$$\tan A_2 = \tan (A_1 + 90°) = -\cot A_1 = -\frac{1}{\tan A_1}.$$

Thus the slope m_2 of q is the negative reciprocal of the slope m_1 of p, that is, $m_2 = -1/m_1$.

Conversely, if we start with two lines p and q (Fig. 3A-10) whose slopes are the negative reciprocals of each other and if we let A_2 and A_1 be the angles of

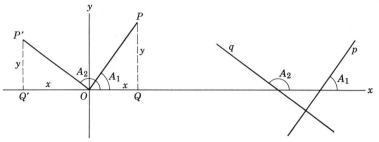

Figure 3A-10

inclination of these lines, we know that

(5)
$$\tan A_2 = -\frac{1}{\tan A_1} = -\cot A_1.$$

We now ask what, in view of (5), is the relation between A_2 and A_1? Because angles of inclination cannot be larger than 180°, one of the angles must be acute and the other obtuse. Suppose that A_2 is the larger angle. Let us take OP parallel to p and OP' parallel to q. Then, if we suppose that A_1 is $A_2 - 90°$, Fig. 3A-10, in which $OP = OP'$, shows that (5) holds for this A_1. Moreover, there is no other acute angle with the same cotangent value as A_1. Hence the only A_1 which satisfies (5) is $A_2 - 90°$. Geometrically this means that, because A_1 and A_2 are angles of inclination, the lines p and q are perpendicular to each other. Thus we have proved the following theorem:

Theorem: If two lines are perpendicular to each other, their slopes are negative reciprocals of each other and conversely.

Exercises

1. Show that the line through $(1, 2)$ and $(7, 3)$ is parallel to the line through $(-4, -3)$ and $(8, -1)$.   *Ans.* $m = \frac{1}{6}$ for both.

2. Show that the line joining $(1, 4)$ and $(3, 7)$ is perpendicular to the line through $(1, -4)$ and $(4, -6)$.

3. What is the inclination of a line which is perpendicular to the line through the points $(2, 1)$ and $(5, 4)$?   *Ans.* 135°.

4. What is the inclination of a line which is perpendicular to a line whose slope is 2?

5. What is the inclination of any line perpendicular to the line through the points $(2, 1)$ and $(-5, 7)$?

A6.   The Angle Between Two Lines.   If two lines are not parallel, they intersect at some angle, say θ. As Fig. 3A-11 shows that there are really two different angles formed at the intersection, one of which is the supplement of the other. To be specific about which angle we mean, we take the upward direction of each line as the positive direction on the line and take the angle between the positive directions as the angle between the two lines.

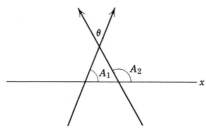

Figure 3A-11

Now let A_2 and A_1 be the inclinations of the two lines, with A_2 the greater inclination. We see from Fig. 3A-11 that

$$A_2 = \theta + A_1$$

or

$$\theta = A_2 - A_1.$$

Then

$$\tan \theta = \tan (A_2 - A_1).$$

We learn in trigonometry an identity for the tangent of the difference of two angles. According to this identity

$$\tan \theta = \frac{\tan A_2 - \tan A_1}{1 + \tan A_2 \tan A_1}.$$

If we now let m_2 be $\tan A_2$ and m_1 be $\tan A_1$, we have the following theorem:

Theorem: If m_2 and m_1 are the slopes of two lines, the tangent of the angle θ between the two lines is given by the formula

(7)
$$\tan \theta = \frac{m_2 - m_1}{1 + m_1 m_2}.$$

The quantity m_2 must be taken to be the slope of the line with the larger inclination.

Exercises

1. Find the angle between two lines:
   (a) Whose slopes are 3 and 4.
   Ans. 4° 24′.
   (b) Whose inclinations are 30 and 135°.
   (c) Whose slopes are 3 and −2.
   Ans. 45°.
2. Find the angle between the line through (1, 3) and (5, 7) and the line through (1, 3) and (−2, 7).

A7. The Equation of a Straight Line.   We come now to the main concern of coordinate geometry, namely, relating equations and curves. We begin with

the straight line, which, incidentally, is also spoken of as a curve in coordinate
geometry.

To know a line implies that one knows some facts which determine that
line. Thus if we know a point (x_1, y_1) on a line and the slope of the line, the
line is fixed or unique. Suppose, then, that we have any line and that we know
the slope m of that line and the coordinates (x_1, y_1) of some point on that
line (Fig. 3A-12). Let (x, y) be the coordinates of *any* other point on the line.
Then by (2) we have that

$$m = \frac{y - y_1}{x - x_1}$$

or

(8) $$y - y_1 = m(x - x_1).$$

Equation (8) is the equation of the line because the coordinates (x, y) of *any*
point on the line satisfy the equation. Moreover, any point not on the line
does not satisfy the equation because such a point, say (x_2, y_2) in Fig. 3A-12,
and (x_1, y_1) determine a line with a different slope. Equation (8) is known as
the *point-slope equation* of a straight line.

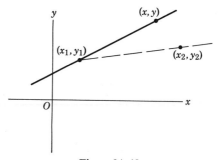

Figure 3A-12

To become more familiar with the notion of an equation of a curve, let us
consider an example of (8). Suppose that we are told that a line goes through
the point (3, 2) and has a slope of 4. Then (3, 2) are the (x_1, y_1) of (8) and
$m = 4$. According to (8) the equation of the line is

$$y - 2 = 4(x - 3).$$

We know from the derivation of (8) that if x and y are the coordinates of
any point on the line, the x and y must satisfy the equation. Let us take an
x and y, say $x = 6$ and $y = 5$. If we substitute 6 for x and 5 for y, we obtain

$$5 - 2 \overset{?}{=} 4(6 - 3).$$

Now we see that the left side of the equation does not equal the right side.
Hence (6, 5) are *not* the coordinates of a point on the line. On the other hand,
the coordinates (5, 10) do satisfy the equation and therefore do represent a
point on the line.

The equation of a curve, then, *is an equation involving x and y which is satisfied by the coordinates of any point on the curve but is not satisfied by the coordinates of any point not on the curve.*

Equation (8) gives the equation of a straight line, if we know one point on the line and its slope. There is a special case of (8) which is often used. Suppose that the known point is a point on the y-axis (Fig. 3A-13) and its coordinates are $(0, b)$. The quantity b is called the y-intercept of the line. Then equation (8) becomes

(9) $$y = mx + b.$$

Equation (9) is known as the *slope-intercept equation* of a straight line.

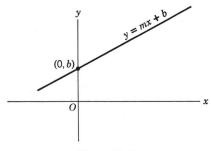

Figure 3A-13

A straight line is also determined if two points on the line are fixed. Suppose that the two points are (x_1, y_1) and (x_2, y_2). Then by (2) we know that

$$m = \frac{y_2 - y_1}{x_2 - x_1}.$$

We now know a point on the line and its slope. Then by equation (8) the equation of the line is

$$y - y_1 = \frac{y_2 - y_1}{x_2 - x_1}(x - x_1)$$

or, in the more symmetrical form obtained by dividing both sides by $(x - x_1)$,

(10) $$\frac{y - y_1}{x - x_1} = \frac{y_2 - y_1}{x_2 - x_1}$$

Equation (10) is known as the *two-point form of the equation* of the straight line. For the moment we exclude the possibility that $x_2 = x_1$.

Exercises

1. (a) Find the equation of the line which passes through the point $(1, 2)$ and has a slope of 5. *Ans.* $y - 2 = 5(x - 1)$.

(b) Does the point with coordinates $(2, 3)$ lie on the line?

2. Find the equation of the line:

    (*a*) Passing through (2, 3) and (7, −5).   *Ans.* $y - 3 = -\frac{8}{5}(x - 2)$.

    (*b*) Passing through (0, 5) and having the slope −2.

    (*c*) Passing through (3, 0) and having the slope 2.   *Ans.* $y = 2(x - 3)$.

    (*d*) Whose y-intercept is 5 and has the slope −4.

3. Show that the three points whose coordinates are (3, 6), (4, 7), and (5, 8) lie on one straight line.   *Ans.* $y = x + 3$.

4. Find the equation of the line:

    (*a*) Passing through (3, 4) and parallel to the line whose slope is 2.

                              Ans. $y - 4 = 2(x - 3)$.

    (*b*) Passing through (4, 2) and perpendicular to the line whose slope is 2.

5. Find the tangent of the angle between $y = 3x + 7$ and $y = -2x + 5$.   *Ans.* 1.

Let us rewrite equations (8), (9), and (10) so that the terms are in the order: the term containing x, the term containing y, and the term containing only constant or known quantities; then each of these equations takes the form

$$(11) \qquad\qquad Ax + By + C = 0.$$

Thus equation (8) when written in this form is

$$mx - y - mx_1 - y_1 = 0.$$

Here $A = m$, $B = -1$, and $C = -mx_1 - y_1$. We see then that the equation of any line is of the form (11) and we note that (11) is an equation of the first degree in x and y.

The converse is also true, that is, an equation of the first degree in x and y represents a straight line. To prove this, suppose that we start with $B \neq 0$. Then (11) can be written in the form

$$y = -\frac{A}{B}x - \frac{C}{A}.$$

If we compare this equation with (9), we see that it represents a straight line with slope $m = -A/B$ and y-intercept $b = -C/A$.

If $B = 0$ and $A \neq 0$ in (11), it reads

$$Ax + 0y + C = 0$$

or

$$x = -\frac{C}{A}.$$

Where are all the points for which $x = -C/A$? Because all the points have the same x-coordinate, they must lie on the line parallel to the y-axis and at a distance $-C/A$ to the right or to the left depending on whether $-C/A$ is positive or negative.

Thus we have proved the following theorem:

Theorem: The equation of any straight line can be written in the form

$$(12) \qquad\qquad Ax + By + C = 0$$

and every equation of the form (12) in which $A \neq 0$ or $B \neq 0$ represents a straight line.

The first degree equation in x and y is also called a linear equation because it represents the straight line.

Exercises

1. Find the slope and the y-intercept of the straight line whose equation is the following:
    (a) $2x + 3y + 5 = 0$.   (b) $3x - 4y = 7$.
           Ans. $-\frac{2}{3}$; $-\frac{5}{3}$.   (c) $3x + 4y = 0$.   *Ans.* $-\frac{3}{4}$; 0.
2. Describe the line whose equation is $y = 3$.
3. Find the equation of the line passing through $(1, 2)$ and parallel to the line $3x + y + 7 = 0$.   *Ans.* $3x + y - 5 = 0$.
4. Find the equation of the line passing through $(5, -1)$ and perpendicular to the line $3x + y + 7 = 0$.
5. Show that if the line $Ax + By + C = 0$ passes through the origin, then $C = 0$.
6. Find the condition that the lines $Ax + By + C = 0$ and $ax + by + c = 0$ be parallel.   *Ans.* $Ab = aB$.
7. Show that the lines $3x + 2y = 7$ and $2x - 3y = 7$ are perpendicular.
8. What is the inclination of the line $3x + 2y = 7$?
9. Find the tangent of the angle between $3x + 2y = 5$ and $x - 7y = 6$.
                                              Ans. 2.09.
10. If we take any point (x, y) on any straight line, then by the distance formula $x^2 + y^2 = r^2$ where r is the distance from (x, y) to the origin. Accordingly, the equation of the straight line should be $x^2 + y^2 = r^2$ because the coordinates of any point on the line satisfy the equation. What is wrong with this argument?

A8. The Distance from a Point to a Line.   A formula that is occasionally useful is the one which shows us how to obtain the distance from a known point (x_1, y_1) to a known line $Ax + By + C = 0$. What we wish to calculate, then, is the distance PR of Fig. 3A-14. There seems to be no direct method of finding PR but, if we introduce the point S which has the same x-value as P and lies on the line $Ax + By + C = 0$, we can find the distance PS. The x-value of S is x_1, and because S lies on the line, the y-value of S, namely y_2, must satisfy the equation

$$Ax_1 + By_2 + C = 0.$$

Then

$$y_2 = -\frac{A}{B} x_1 - \frac{C}{B}.$$

Now $PS = y_1 - y_2$ so that

$$PS = y_1 - \left(-\frac{A}{B} x_1 - \frac{C}{B}\right) = y_1 + \frac{A}{B} x_1 + \frac{C}{B}.$$

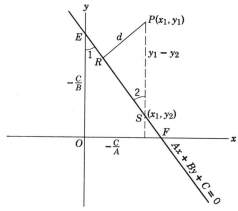

Figure 3A-14

If we could obtain some additional fact about triangle PRS, we might be able to use it and the value of PS to obtain what we want, that is, PR. We note that the given line cuts the x- and y-axes at F and E, respectively, and so forms the triangle FOE. Moreover, because PS is parallel to EO, $\angle 1 = \angle 2$, and both triangles FOE and PRS are right triangles. Hence the two triangles are similar. Then

$$(13) \qquad\qquad \frac{PR}{PS} = \frac{OF}{EF}.$$

We can, however, find OF and EF. OF is the x-intercept of our line, and because $y = 0$ at F, we have only to set $y = 0$ in $Ax + By + C = 0$ to find that the abscissa of F, $OF = -C/A$. Likewise $OE = -C/B$. Then $EF = \sqrt{(C/A)^2 + (C/B)^2}$. We now know PS, OF, and EF in (13). If we substitute their values, we have

$$PR = \frac{OF \cdot PS}{EF} = \frac{-\dfrac{C}{A}\left(y_1 + \dfrac{A}{B}x_1 + \dfrac{C}{B}\right)}{\sqrt{\dfrac{C^2}{A^2} + \dfrac{C^2}{B^2}}}.$$

A little algebra simplifies the result. We factor out the C^2 from the radical and cancel it and the C above. Then we add the fractions in the radical and take out AB. The result thus far is

$$PR = \frac{-\dfrac{1}{A}\left(y_1 + \dfrac{A}{B}x_1 + \dfrac{C}{B}\right)}{\dfrac{1}{AB}\sqrt{A^2 + B^2}}.$$

Inversion of $1/AB$ and multiplication yields

$$(14) \qquad\qquad PR = \frac{Ax_1 + By_1 + C}{\sqrt{A^2 + B^2}}.$$

We have neglected the minus sign, which usually is not of interest.

Let us note that (14) is easy to remember. The numerator is the result of substituting the coordinates (x_1, y_1) of the given point into $Ax + By + C$. The denominator is the square root of the sum of the squares of the co-efficients of x and y.

The above proof fails when the line goes through the origin, but formula (14) is still correct. We shall not bother with a proof for this special case.

Exercises

1. Find the distance in the following cases:

 (*a*) From the point (2, 1) to the line $4x - 3y + 15 = 0$.   *Ans.* 4.

 (*b*) From the point (3, 2) to the line $4x - y + 2 = 0$.

 (*c*) From the point $(-1, 3)$ to the line $4x + 2y = 0$.   *Ans.* $\sqrt{5}/5$.

 (*d*) From the point (2, 7) to the line $3x + 4y - 2 = 0$.

A9. Equation and Curve. We have already pointed out that the main concern of coordinate geometry is to associate curves with equations and equations with curves. Thus far we have carried out this task for straight lines. We shall study the relation of curve and equation for more complicated cases throughout the book. For the present, however, we shall resort when necessary to the method introduced in Chapter 2 for finding the curve of a function, namely, making a table of values of x and y and plotting the corresponding points.

CHAPTER FOUR

The Geometrical Significance of the Derivative

1. The Derivative as Slope. We have mentioned the desirability of thinking geometrically as well as algebraically in order to help us understand what we are doing. Let us, therefore, attempt to find a geometrical meaning for the derivative.

To pursue this objective, let us review the process of finding the derivative of

$$y = x^2 \tag{1}$$

at the value x_0 of x and let us interpret each step geometrically. We introduce a rectangular Cartesian coordinate system (Fig. 4-1) in which, as usual, the positive x-axis is directed to the right and the positive y-axis is directed upward. The function $y = x^2$ is then pictured geometrically by the parabola shown in the figure. The first step in obtaining the derivative at x_0 is to calculate the y-value at x_0. This value is given by

$$y_0 = x_0{}^2. \tag{2}$$

The choice of x_0 and the corresponding y_0 places us at some point, say P on the curve. We now let the value of x change to $x_0 + \Delta x$ and denote the corresponding value of y by $y_0 + \Delta y$. Then by substituting $x_0 + \Delta x$ in (1) we have

$$y_0 + \Delta y = (x_0 + \Delta x)^2 = x_0{}^2 + 2x_0\Delta x + (\Delta x)^2. \tag{3}$$

Because $y_0 + \Delta y$ is the value of y corresponding to the value $x_0 + \Delta x$ of x, the point whose coordinates are $(x_0 + \Delta x, y_0 + \Delta y)$ is some new point, say Q, on the curve. In accordance with the method of increments, we now subtract (2) from (3). Then

$$\Delta y = 2x_0\Delta x + (\Delta x)^2. \tag{4}$$

The quantity Δy is the difference in the ordinates of P and Q; geometrically it is the length RQ. The quantity Δx is the length PR.

We now obtain the average rate of change of y with respect to x in the interval Δx by dividing both sides of (4) by Δx. Then

$$\frac{\Delta y}{\Delta x} = 2x_0 + \Delta x. \tag{5}$$

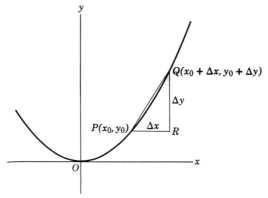

Figure 4-1

The quantity $\Delta y/\Delta x$ has an important geometrical interpretation. In coordinate geometry we learn that the slope of a line is given by (see formula (2) of the Appendix to Chapter 3)

$$m = \frac{y_2 - y_1}{x_2 - x_1}.$$

In this formula (x_1, y_1) and (x_2, y_2) are the coordinates of any two points on the line. Now Δy is the difference in the y-values of P and Q in Fig. 4-1. Likewise Δx is the difference in the x-values of P and Q. Hence

$$\frac{\Delta y}{\Delta x} = \text{slope of secant } PQ.$$

To obtain the derivative $\dot{y}$ at x_0, we must now let Δx approach 0 and then determine the limit of $\Delta y/\Delta x$. When Δx becomes smaller, this means geometrically that Q moves along the curve toward P. Thus, for some smaller value of Δx than shown in Fig. 4-1, Q might move to Q' (Fig. 4-2).

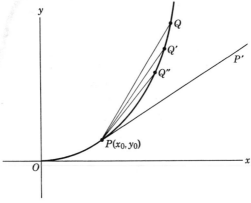

Figure 4-2

Of course, when Δx becomes smaller, Δy also becomes smaller, as we can see geometrically or from (4). For the Δx and Δy that correspond to Q', $\Delta y / \Delta x$ is the slope of the secant line PQ'.

Algebraically the limit of $\Delta y / \Delta x$ is $2x_0$; that is,

(6)
$$\dot{y} = 2x_0.$$

As Δx approaches 0, the points Q, Q', Q'', ... approach P. Geometrically, the lines PQ, PQ', PQ'', ... seem to approach a fixed line, namely, the line through P which just touches the curve at P, the line PP' in the figure. That is, the line PP' seems to be the limit of the lines PQ, PQ', ... Because for each choice of Δx, $\Delta y / \Delta x$ is the slope of one of the secants through P and $\dot{y}$ is the limit of $\Delta y / \Delta x$, then $\dot{y}$ should be the slope of the limit approached by the secants, that is, the slope of PP'. To be specific, when x_0 is 1, then $\dot{y}$ is 2 and the slope of the line PP' is 2.

2. *The Concept of Tangent to a Curve.* We propose to pursue more carefully the nature of the line PP' which is the limit of the secants PQ, PQ', PQ'', ... The line PP' just touches the curve $y = x^2$ at (x_0, y_0); that is, it has only point P in common with the curve. For if it cut the curve in some point, say $\bar{Q}$, near P, $P\bar{Q}$ would be one of the secant lines. The fact that PP' is the limit of secant lines PQ as Q approaches P and that PP' has only point P in common with the curve near P, suggests that we take PP' to be the tangent to the curve at P. Moreover, we learn from the argument in Section 1 that *the slope of the tangent at (x_0, y_0) is the derivative of the function evaluated at* x_0.

We have, then, not only obtained a geometric meaning for the derivative, but have introduced a new definition of tangent, namely that it is the limit of secants through the point P of tangency. One might ask, how does this notion of tangent square with the notion used in Euclidean geometry in which the tangent to a curve is a line which has only one point in common with a curve and does not cross the curve? The answer is that the present notion generalizes the older Euclidean notion. This generalization is needed to treat the variety of curves with which the calculus deals. Consider, for example, the line PS of Fig. 4-3. It has two points in common with the curve, namely, P and S. Yet intuitively we feel that it is a tangent at P. It would not be a tangent in the Euclidean sense because it has two points in common with the

Figure 4-3

curve. It is a tangent in our more general
sense because it is the limiting line of the
secants PQ as Q approaches P.

Again, the horizontal line through P of
Fig. 4-4 is not a tangent in the Euclidean
sense because it crosses the curve at P. It
is a tangent under the more general definition because it is the limiting line of the
secants PQ as Q approaches P.

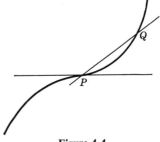

Figure 4-4

Let us see if our geometrical interpreta-
tion of the derivative holds up. The derivative of $y = x^2$ at $x_0 = -2$, in view
of (6), is -4. According to Fig. 4-5, the line through $(-2, 4)$ on the curve
with slope of -4 does seem to be the tangent to the curve at the point
$(-2, 4)$.

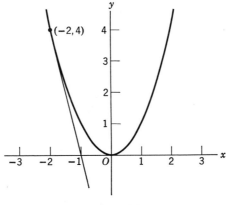

Figure 4-5

3. *Application of the Derivative as the Slope.*   From the standpoint of application the fact that the derivative at any value x_0 of x is the slope of the tangent at the point (x_0, y_0) of the curve is very significant. First, the derivative
solves the purely geometrical problem of finding the tangent to a curve at any
point on that curve. Because the derivative gives the slope of the tangent line
and because we have a point on that line, we know the line precisely.

Second, we often have to consider the physical situation of an automobile
or a train climbing a hill. It is important to know the slope of the path or

Figure 4-6

curve at any point. We define the slope
of the curve at a point to be the slope of
the tangent to the curve at that point.
This definition is quite reasonable. The
slope of the curve at P in Fig. 4-6 is
approximated, although poorly, by the
slope of PQ. However, as Q approaches

P, the slope of the line *PQ* approximates the slope of the curve better and better. Hence the slope of the curve at *P* should be the slope of the tangent at *P*.

To understand how useful this definition of the slope of a curve can be, let us consider the roadway of a bridge which is shown as the arc *AOB* in Fig. 4-7. For the purpose of our illustration we can assume that this arc is part of the parabola $y = -x^2$. The slope of the curve at $x = -2$ is given by the derivative. Because the derived function of $y = -x^2$ at an arbitrary value of *x* is $-2x$, the derivative at $x = -2$ is $+4$. This then is the slope of the roadway at $x = -2$; that is, at $x = -2$ the roadway rises at the rate of 4 feet for every foot of horizontal distance. This rate of climb is totally impractical, because no automobile or truck has the power to climb at such a rate. Our example thus makes the general point that the derivative enables us to calculate the slope of an inclined roadway and to determine whether the slope is or is not too steep for the vehicles that are to use that road.

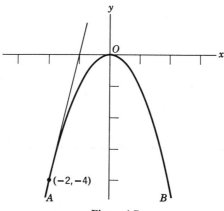

Figure 4-7

There is another use for the tangent to a curve and hence for the derivative. Suppose that an object moves along a curve. Then the direction in which the object is moving, when at any point on the curve, is taken to be the direction of the tangent to the curve at that point. The reasonableness of this definition of direction of motion is readily seen from Fig. 4-2. If the object at *P* were to move directly to *Q*, we would surely take *PQ* to be its direction of motion. If, instead, the object were to move from *P* directly to *Q'*, we would take *PQ'* to be its direction of motion. The more the object tends to follow the curve, the closer its direction of motion approaches the direction of the tangent at *P*. Hence for an object which moves along the curve, the direction of its motion when at *P* is the direction of the tangent at *P*.

The fact that we can find the slope of the tangent to a curve enables us, then, to find the slope of a roadway or the direction in which an object is moving at a point of a curvilinear path.

There is another use for the interpretation of the derivative as the slope of the curve of the formula. In Chapter 3 we found, for example, that the formula which represents the height above the ground of an object that is thrown up with an initial velocity of 128 ft/sec is given by

(7) $$h = -16t^2 + 128t.$$

The graph of this formula, obtained by point-for-point plotting, is shown in Fig. 4-8. We know now that the slope of this curve at any point P is the value of the derivative of formula (7) at the abscissa of P. However, the derivative of (7) is the velocity of the object at the point P. Hence the velocity can be interpreted geometrically as the slope of the curve representing the relation between height above the ground and time.

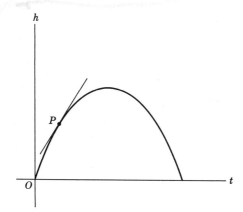

Figure 4-8

We should note that the curve in Fig. 4-8 is not a picture of the physical motion, which would be straight up and down. Nevertheless, the curve does show how the height varies with time, and its slope shows how the velocity changes. It is often convenient, as in Fig. 4-8, to use a different unit for length on the y-axis from that on the x-axis. In such cases the slope of the graph will not agree with the value of the derivative. Nevertheless, the knowledge that the slope is the velocity is still helpful.

To solve some problems involving the tangent to a curve at a point, it is desirable to employ the equation of the tangent. Let us consider the tangent to $y = 2x^2$ at $x = 3$ and $y = 18$. We know that the slope of this tangent is the value of the derivative $\dot{y}$ at $x = 3$. The slope at any value of x is

$$\dot{y} = 4x$$

and the slope at $x = 3$ is 12. Because at $x = 3$, $y = 18$, the tangent passes through the point $(3, 18)$. We have then the slope of the tangent line and the coordinates of one point on that line. To find the equation of the tangent, we can use the point-slope form of the equation of a straight line, namely,

$$y - y_1 = m(x - x_1).$$

In the present case we obtain

$$y - 18 = 12(x - 3)$$

or

$$y = 12x - 18.$$

Exercises

1. Draw carefully the graph of $y = x^2$ and from it find the slope of the tangent at the point $(3, 9)$. Does your measurement of the slope agree with the value of $\dot{y}$ at $x = 3$?   *Ans. m = 6.*

2. Calculate the slope of the tangent to the curve of the following formulas:
   (a) $s = 4t^2$ at $t = 2$.   *Ans. 16.*   (c) $y = -x^2 + 6x$ at $x = 2$.
   (b) $y = 2x^2$ at $x = 1$.   *Ans. 2.*
   (d) $y = -x^2 + 6x$ at $x = 3$.
   Draw the graph in each case and see if the calculation agrees with the visual estimate of the slope of the tangent.

3. Find the angle of inclination of the tangent to the curve of the following:
   (a) $y = x^2$ at $x = 3$.   *Ans. 80° 32′.*   (d) $y = -x^2$ at $x = 0$.
   (b) $y = 16x^2$ at $x = 2$.   (e) $y = -x^2 + 6x$ at $x = 3$.
   (c) $y = x^2$ at $x = -2$.   *Ans. 0°.*
   Ans. 104° 2′.

4. Suppose that an object is moving along a curve whose equation is $y = -4x^2 + 16x$ and is at the point whose abscissa is 3. Specify the direction of motion of the object in terms of the slope and the angle of inclination of the tangent.
   Ans. −8; 97° 7′.

5. Suppose that an object moving along the curve whose equation is $y = -4x^2 + 16x$ strikes a (vertical) wall whose equation is $x = +2$. Would you describe the direction of impact as head-on or glancing?

6. Find the equation of the tangent to the curve whose equation is the following:
   (a) $y = x^2$ at $x = -3$.   (b) $y = x^2 - 6x$ at $x = 2$.
   Ans. y = -6x - 9.

7. Suppose that a path up a hill can be represented by the function $y = \frac{1}{100}x^2$ for x in the interval 0 to 6.
   (a) What is the slope of the hill at $x = 3$?   *Ans. $\frac{3}{50}$.*
   (b) Is the slope steeper at $x = 3$ or at $x = 5$?

8. Prove that no two tangents of the curve $y = x^2$ are parallel.

9. Find the slope of the tangent to the curve $y = x^3$ at $x = 0$, $x = 1$, and $x = -1$. (We found in Chapter 2, Section 8, Exercise 2, that the derived function of $y = x^3$ is $3x^2$.) Draw the curve and the tangents. Note that the tangent crosses the curve at $x = 0$.   *Ans. 0, 3, 3.*

10. Find a point on the curve $y = x^3$ at which the tangent is parallel to the tangent at $x = 4$.

11. Given a function whose graph for the domain from a to b is shown in Fig. 4-9, describe the variation in the value of the derivative as the values of x vary from a to b.

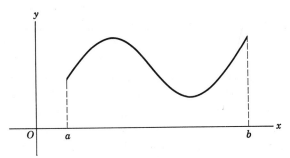

Figure 4-9

12. Suppose that the height above the surface of the earth of some object which moves along a vertical path varies during the time interval from 0 to b as shown in Fig. 4-10. When was the velocity greatest? Least? Zero?

Ans. At 0; at $t = b$; at maximum point.

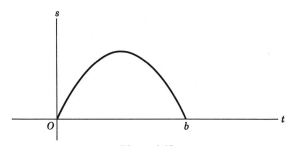

Figure 4-10

13. Show geometrically that the functions $y = x^2$ and $y = x^2 + 5$ must have the same derived function.

14. Express the following statements in symbols:

(*a*) The slope of a curve at any point equals the abscissa of that point.

Ans. $\dot{y} = x$.

(*b*) The ordinate of a curve at any point is a constant times the square of the slope at that point.

(*c*) At any point P of a curve the slope is equal to one half of the slope of the line joining P to the origin. *Ans.* $\dot{y} = y/2x$.

4. *The Equation of the Parabola.* Because we intend to make intensive use of the parabola in a variety of applications, let us establish a few facts about that curve. Geometrically a parabola is defined as the set of all points which are equidistant from a fixed point and a fixed line. Thus in Fig. 4-11 F is the given fixed point and d is the given fixed line. Then P is a point on the

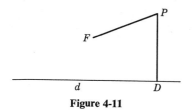

Figure 4-11

parabola if and only if *PF = PD*. The fixed point is called the *focus,* and the fixed line is called the *directrix.*

To apply the methods of the calculus to the parabola we need the equation of the parabola, that is, the functional relation between the coordinates x and y of all points on the parabola. Experience shows that we can make the equation as simple as possible if we make the following choice of axes. We choose the perpendicular line from the focus to the directrix as the y-axis (Fig. 4-12) and the x-axis as the line which passes halfway between the focus and the directrix. With this choice of axes and if $2p$ is the (fixed) distance between the focus and the directrix, the coordinates of the focus become $(0, p)$ and the equation of the directrix is $y = -p$.

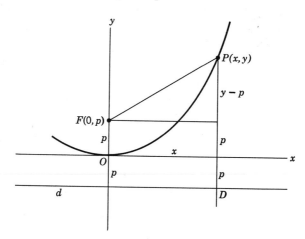

Figure 4-12

Now let the coordinates of any point P on the parabola be (x, y). According to the definition of the parabola

(8) $$PF = PD.$$

The length PF is the hypotenuse of a right triangle whose sides have length $y - p$ and x. Then

$$PF = \sqrt{x^2 + (y - p)^2}.$$

The length PD is seen from the figure to be $y + p$. Then, in view of (8),

$$\sqrt{x^2 + (y - p)^2} = y + p.$$

We could stop at this point and rightly maintain that we have the equation of the parabola, but a little algebra simplifies the result. If we square both sides, we obtain

$$x^2 + (y - p)^2 = (y + p)^2$$

or

$$x^2 + y^2 - 2py + p^2 = y^2 + 2py + p^2.$$

We subtract equal quantities from both sides and obtain

(9)
$$y = \frac{1}{4p} x^2.$$

Equation (9) is the equation of the parabola. We should note that there is not one parabola but an indefinite number of them. Each choice of a value of p, which means each choice of a distance from focus to directrix, determines a different parabola.

If we did not happen to know what a parabola looks like, we chould choose a value of p and sketch the curve. Figure 4-12 shows the general appearance of a parabola. Each such curve is symmetric about a line which is called the *axis* of the parabola. This axis happens to be the y-axis when the coordinate system is chosen as in Fig. 4-12. The point at which the axis cuts the parabola, the point O in Fig. 4-12, is called the *vertex* of the parabola.

Exercises

1. Suppose that the focus and directrix lie as shown in Fig. 4-13 and that the axes are chosen as shown. Guess what the equation of the parabola is and then derive it in the manner indicated in the text.   *Ans.* $x = (1/4p)y^2$.

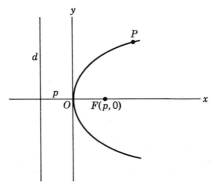

Figure 4-13

2. Suppose that the focus and the directrix lie as shown in Fig. 4-14 and that the axes are chosen as shown. Guess what the equation of the parabola is and then derive it in the manner indicated in the text. *Suggestion*: Remember that p is positive and that the y-values of the points P are negative. Hence, for example, the distance PD is $-y + p$.   *Ans.* $y = -(1/4p)x^2$.

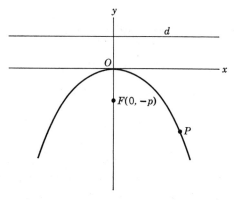

Figure 4-14

3. Suppose that the equation of a parabola is $y = \frac{1}{12}x^2$. What are the coordinates of the focus and what is the equation of the directrix?

4. Suppose that the equation of a parabola is $y = \frac{1}{12}x^2$. What is the width of the parabola at the height of the focus? This width is called the *latus rectum*. Can you generalize the result for any parabola whose equation is $y = (1/4p)x^2$?

   Ans. 4p.

5. Given the focus and the directrix of a parabola and the axes as shown in Fig. 4-15, derive the equation of the parabola. Now that you have the answer, compare the position of the parabola with that in Fig. 4-12 and see if you can derive the answer from the equation $y = (1/4p)x^2$.   *Ans.* $y = [(1/4p)x^2] - p$.

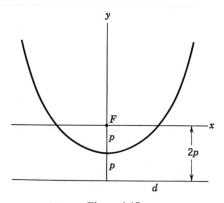

Figure 4-15

6. Suppose that the coordinate axes are chosen so that the focus of a parabola has the coordinates $(4, 0)$ and the directrix has the equation $y = -8$ (Fig. 4-16). Find the equation of the parabola.   *Ans.* $y = \frac{1}{16}x^2 - \frac{1}{2}x - 3$.

7. Describe in words how:

   (a) $y = x^2 + 6$ differs from $y = x^2$.   (c) $y = (x + 6)^2$ differs from $y = x^2$.

   (b) $y = 3x^2$ differs from $y = x^2$.

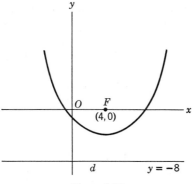

Figure 4-16

8. **(a)** Prove that the tangent at any point of the parabola $y = x^2/4p$ cuts the
x-axis halfway between the origin and the abscissa of the point of tangency.
   (b) Using this result give a construction for the tangent to a parabola at a given
point.

9. A high voltage cable is supported by two towers 2800 feet apart and 348 feet
high. The cable hangs in approximately the shape of a parabola, and the
lowest point on the cable is 200 feet above the ground. Find the equation of
the parabola.   *Ans.* $y = 37x^2/490,000.$

10. A parabolic arch supports a bridge over a roadway. The width of the roadway
is 50 feet and the center of the arch is 25 feet above the center of the roadway.
A truck 10 feet high wishes to pass under the arch and plans to keep its right-
hand wheels 2 feet from the right-hand edge of the roadway. Is there enough
overhead clearance for the truck?

11. A ship wishes to sail along a path which will keep it equidistant from a battery
of guns located at F (Fig. 4-17) and along the shore 30 miles away. Write an
equation for the path that the ship should take.
       Ans. $y = x^2/60$ if origin is midway and x-axis is parallel to shore.

Figure 4-17

12. Prove that the foot of the perpendicular from the focus to any tangent of a
parabola lies on the tangent to the vertex. *Suggestion*: If two lines are perpendicular to each other, the slope of one is the negative reciprocal of the slope of
the other.

13. Prove that the point of intersection of two tangents to a parabola which are
perpendicular to each other lies on the directrix.

14. In Fig. 4-18 the length QT, which is described as the projection of PT on the axis of the parabola, is called the subtangent. The line PR, which is perpendicular to the tangent at P, is called the normal to the parabola at P and the length QR, which is the projection of PR on the axis, is called subnormal. (*a*) Prove that the vertex bisects the subtangent of any tangent to the parabola. Hence describe a method of constructing the tangent at P. (*b*) Prove that the length of the subnormal is $2p$.

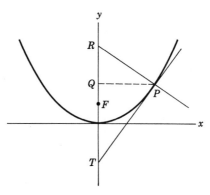

Figure 4-18

5. Physical Applications of the Derivative as Slope.

One of the most important uses of the parabola is to concentrate light, sound, and radio waves in a particular direction. Let us see first what this means. Suppose that a source of light, say a flashlight bulb with nothing surrounding it, is placed at some point in space and that by feeding electric current to it somehow the bulb is lit. Then light rays emanate from the bulb and spread out into space uniformly in all directions. This light is not concentrated at all. We know, however, that by using a reflector which partially surrounds this bulb we obtain a strong beam in one direction. Such reflectors are used, for example, in powerful searchlights and in automobile headlights. What shape should the reflector have in order to reflect in one direction all the rays that strike it?

It seems evident on physical grounds that a surface of revolution should be sought. For suppose that the source of light is placed at F (Fig. 4-19) and the reflector is placed below and about F so as to reflect the light in the upward direction FF'. Now suppose that a ray making some angle A with the upwardly directed line FF' leaves F and strikes the point P on the surface and that at P the surface is so shaped that the reflected ray takes the upward course PD. Consider next another ray leaving F and making the same angle A with FF'. If the surface is a surface of revolution about the axis FF', this ray strikes the surface at some point P' at the same level as P. Moreover, because the shape of the surface at P' is the same as at P, this ray is also reflected directly upward. What we want then is a surface of revolution generated by revolving the curve OPQ of Fig. 4-19 about the line OFF'. If

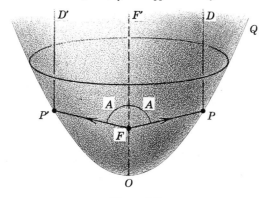

Figure 4-19

OPQ is correctly designed, the whole surface will direct the reflected light upward.

Our problem reduces then to choosing the shape of the curve *OPQ*, so that light rays from *F* striking various points on this curve are all reflected upward. To design *OPQ* correctly, we must know how light rays behave when they strike a reflecting surface. The relevant behavior of light rays is embodied in the *law of reflection*. Suppose for the moment that *MN* is a *flat* reflecting miror (Fig. 4-20) and that a light ray emanating from *F* strikes the mirror at *P*. Then the reflected ray takes the path *PD* for which $\angle 1 = \angle 2$. Alternatively stated, if we introduce the perpendicular or normal *PR* to mirror at *P*, the reflected ray takes the path for which $\angle 3 = \angle 4$. Of course, the equality of angles 1 and 2 is equivalent to the equality of angles 3 and 4. In physics $\angle 3$ is called the angle of incidence and $\angle 4$ is the angle of reflection, so that the law of reflection states that the angle of incidence equals the angle of reflection. Where convenient, we can also call $\angle 1$ the angle of incidence and $\angle 2$ the angle of reflection.

Now suppose that we reintroduce the curve *OPQ* (Fig. 4-21) and the light ray *FP* that strikes the curve at *P*. At *P* the curve behaves as though it were

Figure 4-20

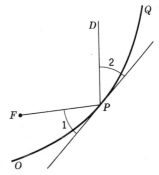

Figure 4-21

replaced by the tangent at *P*. This behavior is to be expected for only a very little bit of the curve at *P* has anything to do with the reflection of the ray *FP*. What does count about the curve at *P* is the direction in which it is going, so to speak, or the angle that it makes with *FP*. However, at *P* the direction of the curve is the direction of the tangent. In other words, for the purpose of studying the reflection of light, at each point a curve may be replaced by its tangent.

What do we want now? We know that at *P* the reflected light ray takes the path which makes $\sphericalangle 2 = \sphericalangle 1$. We want to fix the curve so that the reflected ray takes the upward path *PD*. Hence we must choose a curve *such that the line FP makes the same angle with the tangent at P as the upward direction PD makes with the tangent at P*. If the curve is so chosen, the light ray *FP* is automatically reflected in the upward direction.

To find the proper curve we could set up in mathematical terms the condition we have just described and then try to determine the curve. This problem can be solved, but it is also wise to see if some known curve possesses this property. Actually, the Greeks discovered that the parabola reflects light rays issuing from the focus, so that the reflected rays all travel out parallel to the axis of the parabola. We shall prove that the parabola does this, that is, we shall prove that for the parabola *OPQ* (Fig. 4-22) the lines *FP* and *PD*, when *PD* is parallel to the axis *OF*, make equal angles with the tangent at *P* or that $\sphericalangle 1 = \sphericalangle 2$.

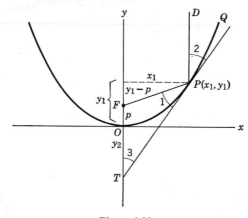

Figure 4-22

The proof is straightforward. We choose the *x*- and *y*-axes as shown in Fig. 4-22. We see, first, that $\sphericalangle 3 = \sphericalangle 2$ because *PD* is parallel to the *y*-axis. Hence we should prove that $\sphericalangle 1 = \sphericalangle 3$. We can prove this if we can prove that *FP* = *FT*. Let us try to do this.

If we designate (x_1, y_1) to be the coordinates of *P* and if the coordinates of the focus are, as usual, $(0, p)$, we see that *FP* is the hypotenuse of a right triangle whose arms are $y_1 - p$ and x_1. Then

(10) $\qquad FP = \sqrt{x_1{}^2 + (y_1 - p)^2} = \sqrt{x_1{}^2 + y_1{}^2 - 2y_1 p + p^2}.$

However, because (x_1, y_1) is a point on the parabola, by (9)

(11) $\qquad\qquad\qquad x_1{}^2 = 4py_1.$

If we substitute this value of $x_1{}^2$ in (10), we obtain

(12) $\qquad\qquad\qquad FP = y_1 + p.$

Now let us obtain an expression for FT. We see from Fig. 4-22 that

(13) $\qquad\qquad FT = FO + OT = p + OT.$

However, OT is the y-value of the point at which the tangent at P cuts the y-axis; that is, OT is the y-intercept of the tangent. Let us therefore find the equation of the tangent at P and find its y-intercept. To find the equation of the tangent, we use the point-slope form of the equation of a line; this calls for the slope of the tangent. The slope of the tangent is the derivative of the curve at (x_1, y_1). The equation of the curve is

$$y = \frac{1}{4p} x^2.$$

Because the derived function of $y = ax^2$ is $\dot{y} = 2ax$, in our case

$$\dot{y} = \frac{1}{2p} x,$$

and at (x_1, y_1)

$$\dot{y} = \frac{1}{2p} x_1.$$

Then the equation of the tangent is

$$y - y_1 = \frac{x_1}{2p} (x - x_1),$$

where x and y refer to *coordinates of points on the tangent*. The y-intercept of the tangent is the point at which $x = 0$. Hence the y-value of T, say y_2, is

$$y_2 - y_1 = \frac{x_1}{2p} (0 - x_1) = -\frac{x_1{}^2}{2p}$$

or

$$y_2 = y_1 - \frac{x_1{}^2}{2p}.$$

However, in view of (11)

$$y_2 = y_1 - 2y_1 = -y_1.$$

Now y_1 is a positive quantity and therefore y_2 is negative as indeed it should be. We are, however, interested in the *geometric* length OT and therefore we may say that

$$OT = y_1.$$

Then by (13)

(14) $$FT = p + y_1.$$

If we now compare (12) and (14), we see that we have proved that $FP = FT$. Then $\measuredangle 3 = \measuredangle 1$ and therefore $\measuredangle 1 = \measuredangle 2$. Thus we have proved an important geometrical property of the parabola. The line from the focus to any point P on the parabola and the line through P and parallel to the axis make equal angles with the tangent. Then, because light rays obey the physical law that the angle of incidence must equal the angle of reflection, a light ray issuing from F and striking the parabola at P takes the direction PD. The point P is any point on the parabola. Hence *all* rays from F travel after reflection in the direction of the axis of the parabola.

If a surface is formed by rotating the arc OPQ of the parabola about its axis, we obtain what is called a paraboloid of revolution, and all rays issuing from P and striking any point on the paraboloid travel out parallel to the axis of the paraboloid. The paraboloid is such a powerful concentrator of light, sound, and radio waves that its use has become very widespread. It is used not only in the reflectors of flashlights and searchlights but in hundreds of different types of radio antennas.

Exercises

1. Where does the calculus enter into the proof of the reflection property of the parabola?
2. Review the proof of the reflecting property of the parabola and determine whether it also establishes that the parabola is the only curve which reflects rays from a point source into a parallel beam of rays.
3. Prove that if the chord (Fig. 4-23) joining the points of tangency of two tangents to a parabola goes through the focus, the tangents are perpendicular to each other. *Suggestion*: Use the reflection property of the parabola.

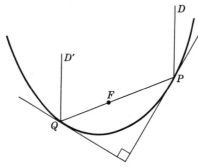

Figure 4-23

Our knowledge of the calculus enables us to solve another physical problem of considerable significance—the problem of determining the shape of the cable of a bridge when the weight of the load (the roadway) per horizontal foot is constant. The cable is assumed to be perfectly flexible (that is, it offers no resistance to bending) and inelastic (that is, it does not stretch or contract). Both properties are possessed, for example, by a piece of ordinary rope. The weight of the cable itself is assumed to be negligible compared to the load. This is physically not quite correct, but it is a useful idealization with which to start the study of the shapes of cables of bridges.

Consider the cable $Q'APQ$ shown in Fig. 4-24. Because the cable supports the roadway, there is tension in the cable. Let us first satisfy ourselves that at any point on the cable the tension that any part of the cable exerts on an adjoining part is along the cable. Specifically we should see that the tension exerted by the arc QP on the rest of the cable has the direction of the tangent at P. Intuitively this fact is rather obvious, for if the pull at P were not along the tangent the cable would bend (because it is perfectly flexible) inward or outward. Nevertheless, we may consider a supporting argument.

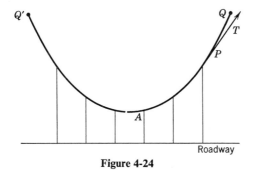

Figure 4-24

Suppose that the cable were made up of short rods (Fig. 4-25) which were linked at the joints and that the rods were free to move at the joints. At any point within any rod the tension is merely along the rod, because one part of a rod can pull another part of the same rod only along the rod. At a joint such as P the pull of the rod PR on the rod PQ is along PR, whereas the pull of the rod PQ on the rod PR is along PQ. The two rods make an angle with each other at P, and the two pulls are in different directions. We now imagine that the rods are made smaller and smaller and that of course more joints are introduced to connect adjacent rods. As the rods become smaller, the shape of the whole chain of rods approaches that of the original, completely flexible cable and the directions of the pulls or tensions within a rod or at a joint of two rods approaches that of the tangent to the flexible cable at the corresponding point.

Figure 4-25

Now let us consider any section of the flexible cable, say the section from
A to P in Fig. 4-26. Because the pull at A by the section to the left of A is
tangential to the cable, at A the pull or tension is horizontal and to the left.
This tension is some constant which we shall denote by T_0. The tension on
AP at P exerted by the section PQ of the cable is along the tangent at P.
Let us call the magnitude of this tension T. Because this tension also has a
direction, namely, the direction of the tangent at P, it is represented geometrically by a directed line segment or a vector. We shall let θ be the angle
which the direction of the tension (or the tangent) at P makes with the
horizontal.

There is one more force acting on the section AP of the cable, namely, the
pull of that portion of the roadway which extends from O to P' (Fig. 4-26).
Because the roadway is assumed to have the same weight per horizontal foot
along its entire length, then, if w is the weight per horizontal foot, the load
supported by the arc AP is wx, where x is the abscissa of P. (We are here
using the fact that the y-axis passes through A.) The pull of this load is
actually distributed along AP, but all the pulls are downward, and we need
to know only that there is a total downward pull on AP amounting to wx.

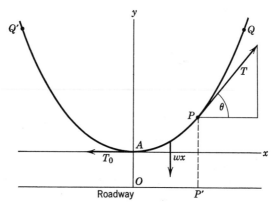

Figure 4-26

Thus there are three forces acting on AP: the horizontal pull T_0 to the left,
the downward pull wx of the load, and the tension or pull T tangential at P.
Because the arc AP is at rest or in equilibrium, the three forces must somehow
offset one another, for if there were some net force the cable would move or
bend under the action of that force. Alternatively, we may say that the
horizontal forces must offset one another and that the vertical forces must do
likewise. The tension T is equivalent to a horizontal and a vertical tension
acting simultaneously, for a tension is a force and, as we saw in Section 4
of Chapter 3, any force may be replaced by the proper horizontal and vertical
components. Specifically, the tension of magnitude T (Fig. 4-27) is equivalent

to the combined action of the horizontal component $T \cos \theta$ and the vertical component $T \sin \theta$.

The horizontal component $T \cos \theta$ must offset the only other horizontal force that is acting, namely, T_0. Hence

(15) $$T \cos \theta = T_0.$$

Figure 4-27

The vertical component $T \sin \theta$ of the tension must offset the only other vertical force that is acting, namely, wx. Hence

(16) $$T \sin \theta = wx.$$

If we divide (16) by (15), we obtain

(17) $$\tan \theta = \frac{w}{T_0}\, x.$$

Now $\tan \theta$ is the slope of the tangent line at P, and this slope is $\dot{y}$ where $\dot{y}$ is the derived function of whatever function represents the shape of the cable. Thus

$$\dot{y} = \frac{w}{T_0}\, x.$$

By antidifferentiation we obtain

$$y = \frac{w}{2T_0}\, x^2 + C$$

To fix the constant C we can choose the x-axis so as to pass through the point A of Fig. 4-26. Then $y = 0$ when $x = 0$, so that $C = 0$. Thus

$$y = \frac{w}{2T_0}\, x^2. \tag{18}$$

We note the important result that the shape of the cable must be parabolic. We have of course used the fact that the load must be the same for each horizontal foot. Later we shall study the shape of a cable when the load is differently distributed.

Let us note one or two implications of the result (18). Although the equation seems to involve two unknown quantities w and T_0, only their ratio is involved. We can in fact write the equation as $y = kx^2$ where $k = w/2T_0$. To determine the equation of the parabola, we need to know only the value of k, which we can find if we know the coordinates of one point through which the parabola must go.

Suppose that we do specify the coordinates of one point (Fig. 4-28), say the point $(2, 3)$. Because the curve is symmetric with respect to the y-axis, the point $(-2, 3)$ must also be on the curve. Moreover, the lowest point of the cable must be the origin if (18) is presupposed. Hence to specify the

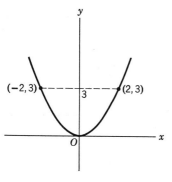

Figure 4-28

coordinates of one point means really that the width from $(-2, 3)$ to $(2, 3)$ and the depth, 3, are specified. We know, however, that the cable must have an equation of the form $y = kx^2$, and there is only one parabola of this form through a given point. Hence it would seem that if we fix one point, that is, fix the width and depth, there is no freedom to choose the load that the cable will support. However, this is not true. The quantity $k = w/2T_0$. Fixing k fixes only the ratio of w to T_0. If we increase w, the load per horizontal foot, then T_0 must increase in the same ratio. To sum up, if the width of a cable and the depth at that width are specified, there is only one shape for the cable regardless of the load, provided only that the load is constant over each horizontal foot.

Exercises

1. With reference to the derivation of the equation of the cable, (*a*) does the horizontal component of the tension T vary from point to point on the cable? (*b*) Does the vertical component of the tension T vary from point to point on the cable?   *Ans.* (*a*) No; (*b*) Yes.

2. Assuming that w, the load per horizontal foot, is given, calculate the tension T at any point on the parabola $y = (w/2T_0)x^2$. *Suggestion*: Square (15), square (16), and add. Then use the equation of the parabola to eliminate T_0 from the expression for T.   *Ans.* $T = (wx/2y)\sqrt{x^2 + 4y^2}$.

3. Find the tension at the points at which the cable of a suspension bridge is attached to the towers, if the width of the cable between the two points of attachment is 120 feet (Fig. 4-29), the depth of the cable is 15 feet and the cable supports a roadway whose weight of 150 tons is uniformly distributed horizontally. *Suggestion*: Use the result in Exercise 2.   *Ans.* $75\sqrt{5}$ tons.

Figure 4-29

4. Consider the cable described in Exercise 3. Because it passes through the point $(60, 15)$, the equation of the cable is $y = x^2/240$. Using the result of Exercise 2, study the variation of the tension T along the cable. At what point or points is the tension greatest and at what point is the tension least?

Ans. Greatest at $(\pm 60, 15)$; least at $(0, 0)$.

5. We have required in our derivation of the equation of the cable that the weight of the roadway per horizontal foot be constant. Can the roadway itself be curved?

6. *Further Discussion of the Derivative as the Slope.* In Sections 1 and 2 of this chapter we showed that, given a function, it is reasonable to take the derivative at a given value x_0 of x to be the slope at x_0 of the tangent to the curve representing that function. The argument rested on the geometrical interpretation of Δx, Δy, $\Delta y/\Delta x$, and then the limit of $\Delta y/\Delta x$ as Δx approaches 0. However, in our geometrical interpretation (see Fig. 4-1) we took Δx as a positive increment so that Q lay above P. We may recall that in our original discussion of speed at an instant we pointed out that we could calculate the speed at the instant $t = 3$, say, by taking average speeds over intervals following $t = 3$ and shrinking to 0 or over intervals preceding $t = 3$ and shrinking to 0. That is, we arrive at the same limit for $\Delta s/\Delta t$, whether the quantity Δt is positive or negative. The same argument applies to Δx. Let us examine geometrically what a negative Δx implies.

Suppose that the function is again $y = x^2$ and that the value of x at which we consider the derivative is $x = 3$. Let the point P of Fig. 4-30 be the point $(3, 9)$. If now we take Δx to be some negative quantity, the point $(3 + \Delta x, 9 + \Delta y)$ might be the point Q which lies below P. It is still true that $\Delta y/\Delta x$ represents the slope of PQ. As Δx becomes numerically smaller (although algebraically larger), the point Q moves toward P, and of course $\Delta y/\Delta x$ continues to represent the slope of PQ. Our concept of the derivative requires that $\Delta y/\Delta x$ should approach the same limit at $x = 3$ when Δx goes through negative values as when it goes through positive values. Then geometrically our concept of the derivative requires that the secants QP approach the same line as Q approaches P from below as from above, because we took the tangent at P to be the line whose slope at P is the derivative.

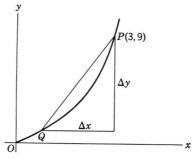

Figure 4-30

Let us consider, however, the curve shown in Fig. 4-31. As Q approaches P, the secants QP approach a limiting line at P, namely PR. As Q' approaches P, the secants $Q'P$ approach another limiting line at P, namely PS. The lines PR and PS are not the same, and therefore we do *not* speak of a tangent at P.

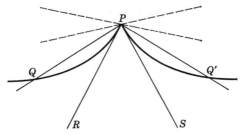

Figure 4-31

Put otherwise, a point traveling toward P from Q has one direction of motion as it reaches P, namely RP, whereas a point traveling toward P from Q' has another direction of motion as it reaches P, namely SP. Let us note also that if we had been content to take as our definition of tangent a line which has one point in common with the curve (cf. Section 2), any of the broken lines shown in the figure would have had to be accepted as a tangent.

The fact that the secants through P approach different limiting lines means in algebraic terms that if we calculated the limit of $\Delta y/\Delta x$ at the x-value or abscissa of P, we would obtain a different limit for $\Delta y/\Delta x$ when Δx approaches 0 through negative values than when Δx approaches 0 through positive values. Just as we say that there is no tangent at P, so we must say that the function which represents the curve has no derivative at P.

Exercises

1. By $|x|$ we mean the positive value of x, whether the value of x in question be negative or positive. Thus $|-3| = 3$ and $|3| = 3$. Graph $y = |x|$ for negative and positive x. What can you say about the existence of a tangent at negative values of x? At positive values of x? At $x = 0$?

   Ans. Tangent exists everywhere except at (0, 0).

2. Does $y = |x|$ have a derivative at $x = 0$?

3. Graph the function $y = \frac{1}{2}(x + |x|)$. At what values of x does the derivative exist and what is the value of the derivative when it does exist?

   Ans. For $x < 0$, $\dot{y} = 0$; for $x > 0$, $\dot{y} = 1$.

The Differentiation and Integration of Powers of x

1. Introduction. So far our work in the calculus has involved only simple functions of the form $y = ax^2 + bx + c$. The calculus would be rather limited and uninteresting if it were confined to these functions. To increase its applicability we must consider more complicated functions. In this chapter we shall study the differentiation and integration of functions of the form $y = x^n$.

2. The Functions x^n for Positive Integral n. We start with the function $y = x^n$. For the present we consider only the case when n is a positive integer, and our purpose is to find $\dot{y}$. Before we attempt this task, let us consider what we already know about special cases. When $n = 1$, we have

$$y = x \quad \text{and} \quad \dot{y} = 1.$$

When $n = 2$, we have

$$y = x^2 \quad \text{and} \quad \dot{y} = 2x.$$

When $n = 3$ (see Chapter 2, Section 8, Exercise 2),

$$y = x^3 \quad \text{and} \quad \dot{y} = 3x^2.$$

If we study these special cases, we find that the exponent in the function becomes a coefficient in the derived function and the exponent of the derived function is one less than it is in the original function. We would guess then that when

$$y = x^n \quad \text{then} \quad \dot{y} = nx^{n-1}.$$

Let us see if we can prove that this is correct.

To find the derived function we must first find the derivative at some fixed value of x. When we wish to find the derivative of a function which we do not know how to differentiate, we usually resort to the method of increments.

Let x_0 be the value of x at which we seek the derivative. Then

(1) $$y_0 = x_0{}^n.$$

We change x_0 by some amount Δx to the value $x_0 + \Delta x$. The corresponding value of y is denoted by $y_0 + \Delta y$. Then

(2) $$y_0 + \Delta y = (x_0 + \Delta x)^n.$$

We seek next the increase in y, that is Δy. This results from subtracting (1) from (2). Then

(3) $$\Delta y = (x_0 + \Delta x)^n - x_0{}^n.$$

The method of increments now calls for finding the average rate of change of y with respect to x in the interval Δx. We therefore divide both sides of (3) by Δx to obtain

(4) $$\frac{\Delta y}{\Delta x} = \frac{(x_0 + \Delta x)^n - x_0{}^n}{\Delta x}.$$

We must now find the limit of $\Delta y / \Delta x$ as Δx approaches 0.

The natural thing to try is to expand $(x_0 + \Delta x)^n$ by means of the binomial theorem. Let us recall that

(5)

$$(a + b)^n = a^n + na^{n-1}b + \frac{n(n-1)}{2} a^{n-2}b^2 + \cdots + c_{n-1}ab^{n-1} + c_n b^n.$$

We have used c_{n-1} and c_n as coefficients in the last two terms instead of writing them out explicitly because, as we shall see in a moment, their precise values do not matter.

If we now apply (5) to $(x_0 + \Delta x)^n$ and substitute the expansion in (4), the terms $x_0{}^n$ cancel and we are left with

(6)

$$\frac{\Delta y}{\Delta x} = \frac{nx_0^{n-1} \Delta x + \dfrac{n(n-1)}{2} x_0^{n-2}(\Delta x)^2 + \cdots + c_{n-1}x_0(\Delta x)^{n-1} + c_n(\Delta x)^n}{\Delta x}.$$

Now Δx is not 0, and so we may divide the numerator and the denominator by Δx. Then

(7) $$\frac{\Delta y}{\Delta x} = nx_0^{n-1} + \frac{n(n-1)}{2} x_0^{n-2}(\Delta x) + \cdots + c_{n-1}x_0(\Delta x)^{n-2} + c_n(\Delta x)^{n-1}.$$

To determine the limit of $\Delta y / \Delta x$ as Δx approaches 0 we rewrite (7) as

(8) $$\frac{\Delta y}{\Delta x} = nx_0^{n-1} + \Delta x\left[\frac{n(n-1)}{2} x_0^{n-2} + \cdots + c_{n-1}x_0(\Delta x)^{n-3} + c_n(\Delta x)^{n-2}\right].$$

There are $n - 1$ terms in the bracket. Suppose that for a given value of Δx, the value of the largest term is A. Then the value of all the terms is at most $(n - 1)|A|$. As Δx approaches 0 in value, the absolute value of each term in the bracket cannot increase because Δx is the only variable quantity. In fact, for values of Δx less than 1, the quantities $(\Delta x)^2$, $(\Delta x)^3$, and so on are smaller than Δx, and these powers of Δx decrease in value even more than Δx. The bracket is itself multiplied by Δx, and therefore the value of the product is at most $\Delta x(n - 1)\,|A|$. As Δx approaches 0, this product must also approach 0. Then the limit of the right side of (8) is nx_0^{n-1}. That is,

$$(9) \qquad \dot{y} = \lim_{\Delta x \to 0} \frac{\Delta y}{\Delta x} = nx_0^{n-1}.$$

The proof of (9) holds for every value x_0 of x. Hence we have proved a general result which is sufficiently significant to be recognized as a theorem.

Theorem: If
$$y = x^n,$$

then the derived function is

$$(10) \qquad \dot{y} = nx^{n-1}$$

when n is a positive integer.

We shall call the result (10) the *power rule*.

We now consider the inverse process; that is, given that

$$(11) \qquad \dot{y} = nx^{n-1}$$

we seek the original function or integral of $\dot{y}$. We know that $y = x^n$ is one function whose derived function is given by (11), and in view of what we had to say in Chapter 3 about the possible presence of a constant we must now state that

$$y = x^n + C.$$

However, generally we are not given the derived function in the form of (11), but in the form

$$(12) \qquad \dot{y} = x^n.$$

To find y we have but to observe that in differentiating x^n we multiply the coefficient, which is 1, by the exponent and reduce the exponent by 1. Hence to find the integral we increase the exponent by 1 and divide by the *new* exponent. This result, too, we set out as a theorem.

Theorem: If
$$\dot{y} = x^n,$$

then

$$(13) \qquad y = \frac{x^{n+1}}{n + 1} + C$$

when n is a positive integer or zero.

Exercises

1. The proof of the power rule is valid for positive integral values of n. Why is it necessary to impose this limitation?

2. Is it true for $n = 0$ that if $y = x^n$ then $\dot{y} = nx^{n-1}$? *Ans.* Yes.

3. In using the method of increments we encounter the function $\Delta y / \Delta x$. What are the independent and dependent variables in this function?

4. For each of the following functions find the derived function:

(*a*) $y = x^6$.   *Ans.* $\dot{y} = 6x^5$.   (*d*) $y = x^{10}$.

(*b*) $y = x$.   (*e*) $y = 7$.   *Ans.* $\dot{y} = 0$.

(*c*) $y = x^5$.   *Ans.* $\dot{y} = 5x^4$.

5. For each of the following derived functions find the integral:

(*a*) $\dot{y} = x^3$.   *Ans.* $y = \dfrac{x^4}{4} + C$.   (*c*) $\dot{y} = 1$.   *Ans.* $y = x + C$.

(*b*) $\dot{y} = x$.   (*d*) $\dot{y} = x^6$.

6. Show that the rate of change of the volume of a cube with respect to the edge is three times the area of any face.

3. *A Calculus Method of Finding Roots.*   The ability to differentiate $y = x^n$ will serve us in many applications. Here we discuss how Newton used it to devise a method of obtaining the nth root of a number. Let us suppose that we wish to obtain $\sqrt[3]{5}$. The number that we seek then is the quantity $x_0 = \sqrt[3]{5}$. Then $x_0^3 = 5$ or $x_0^3 - 5 = 0$. We shall consider how to approximate x_0. This means that we shall consider values of $x^3 - 5$ such that $x^3 - 5$ may not exactly equal 0 but may come close to 0. In other words, let us study the function $y = x^3 - 5$ and see what we can learn about values of x that come close to making y zero.

We graph the function $y = x^3 - 5$ (Fig. 5-1). The point $(\sqrt[3]{5}, 0)$ is, of course, the point at which the graph cuts the x-axis. We note that if we take a point P on the curve and near $(\sqrt[3]{5}, 0)$, the tangent to the curve at P cuts the x-axis at a point Q whose abscissa should be close to $(\sqrt[3]{5}, 0)$. Hence let us find the equation of the tangent at P and then determine its x-intercept.

Suppose that the coordinates of P are (x_1, y_1). Then the slope of the tangent at P is the derivative of $y = x^3 - 5$ at x_1. This slope is $\dot{y} = 3x_1^2$.

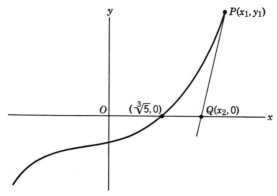

Figure 5-1

Because the tangent goes through (x_1, y_1), the equation of the tangent is

$$y - y_1 = 3x_1{}^2(x - x_1).$$

We agreed earlier that we would find the x-intercept of the tangent. Hence we set $y = 0$ and solve for the x-intercept, which we shall denote by x_2. Then

$$-y_1 = 3x_1{}^2(x_2 - x_1)$$

or

(14)
$$x_2 = \frac{-y_1}{3x_1{}^2} + x_1.$$

This number x_2 is then an approximation to $\sqrt[3]{5}$. In view of the fact that y_1 is a y-value on the curve, we know that $y_1 = x_1{}^3 - 5$, and we can rewrite (14) as

$$x_2 = -\frac{x_1}{3} + \frac{5}{3x_1{}^2} + x_1$$

or

(15)
$$x_2 = \frac{1}{3}\left(2x_1 + \frac{5}{x_1{}^2}\right).$$

If we examine Fig. 5-2, we see that had we taken the point P' whose coordinates are (x_2, y_2) in place of P, the approximation would have been a

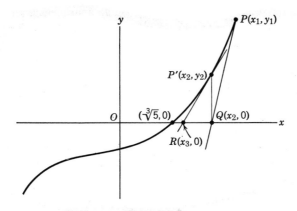

Figure 5-2

better one because the tangent at P' cuts the x-axis at R which is closer to $\sqrt[3]{5}$ than Q is. There is, however, no need to redo the whole derivation with (x_2, y_2) in place of (x_1, y_1). Because the point (x_1, y_1) was any point on the curve, the result (15) is quite general. If in (15) we substitute x_2 for x_1 and write x_3 for the x-value of R, we obtain

(16)
$$x_3 = \frac{1}{3}\left(2x_2 + \frac{5}{x_2{}^2}\right).$$

This value x_3, which is the abscissa of the point R, is a better approximation to $\sqrt[3]{5}$ than x_2.

Now we can repeat the argument of the preceding paragraph. If we substitute x_3 for x_2 in (16), we obtain a still better approximation x_4. The process can be continued as long as necessary to secure the approximation that is desired. Thus if we want an approximation to 3 decimal places and find that the next approximation after a given one no longer affects the third decimal place, we know that we have the right approximation.

The method that we employ to obtain better and better approximations to $\sqrt[3]{5}$ in effect solves approximately the equation $x^3 - 5 = 0$. The method can be used to solve more complicated equations approximately.

Exercises

1. Using formula (15), calculate an approximate value of $\sqrt[3]{5}$ correct to 3 decimal places. $\qquad$ *Ans.* 1.710.

2. Suppose that instead of $\sqrt[3]{5}$ we seek $\sqrt[3]{a}$. How is formula (15) altered to generalize from 5 to a?

3. Derive a formula, analogous to (15), which would furnish an approximate value

   of $\sqrt{5}$. $\qquad$ *Ans.* $x_2 = \dfrac{1}{2}\left(x_1 + \dfrac{5}{x_1}\right)$.

4. Generalize the result of Exercise 3 to obtain an approximate formula for $\sqrt{a}$. Note that the answer gives a very useful method for finding square roots.

   $$Ans.\ x_2 = \frac{1}{2}\left(x_1 + \frac{a}{x_1}\right).$$

5. Use Newton's method to obtain a general formula analogous to (15) for $\sqrt[n]{a}$.

   $$Ans.\ x_2 = \frac{1}{n}\left\{(n-1)x_1 + \frac{a}{x_1^{n-1}}\right\}.$$

6. Suppose that you had to find one or more solutions of $x^3 - 7x + 5 = 0$. Do you think Newton's method applies to this equation? If so, describe the method.

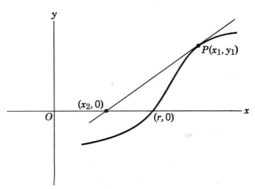

Figure 5-3

Important

7. Suppose that you apply Newton's method to find an approximation to the abscissa r where the function graphed in Figure 5-3 cuts the x-axis and suppose that you start at the point P or (x_1, y_1). Is the approximate value x_2 necessarily a better approximation to r than x_1? Although criteria for the success of Newton's method can be given, it is just as well at this stage to draw the graph of the function and to rely upon geometric evidence as to whether the successive approximations $x_2, x_3, \ldots$ approach the root.

4. Differentiation and Integration of x^n for Fractional Values of n.

We have so far restricted the value of n in $y = x^n$ to positive integral values of n. However, functions such as $y = x^{1/2}$, $y = x^{2/3}$, and other fractional powers of x are also useful, and therefore it is desirable to know how to find their derivatives. Before we consider this question let us note a few facts about the meaning of such functions.

The function $y^2 = x$ has real values only for positive values of x and for $x = 0$. For positive values of x there are two values of the function, a positive and a negative value. We take the symbols $x^{1/2}$ or $\sqrt{x}$ to stand for the positive value. For each value of x, positive or negative, the function $x^{1/3}$ or $\sqrt[3]{x}$ has 3 values if we include complex numbers. Another way of saying this is that if $y = x^{1/3}$, then $y^3 = x$, and that to each value of x there are 3 values of y. However, whether x is positive or negative there is just one value of $x^{1/3}$ which is real. If x is positive, the real value of $x^{1/3}$ is positive; thus $\sqrt[3]{8} = 2$. If x is negative, the real value of $x^{1/3}$ is negative; thus $\sqrt[3]{-8} = -2$.

Generally, by $\sqrt[q]{x}$ or $x^{1/q}$, where q is a positive integer, we mean one real number. If x is positive or zero, q may be odd or even, and $\sqrt[q]{x}$ is the positive root. If x is negative, q must be odd, and $\sqrt[q]{x}$ is the negative real root. Further, $x^{p/q}$ means $(\sqrt[q]{x})^p$, with the understanding that if x is negative q must be odd.*

Before tackling the problem of the derivative of $y = x^{p/q}$, let us consider the simpler case of $y = x^{1/2} = \sqrt{x}$. To find the derivative at the value x_0, we proceed by the method of increments. We start with the values of x and y at x_0. That is,

$$y_0 = \sqrt{x_0}.$$

We now let x change to the value $x_0 + \Delta x$. Then

$$y_0 + \Delta y = \sqrt{x_0 + \Delta x}.$$

The change in y is

$$\Delta y = \sqrt{x_0 + \Delta x} - \sqrt{x_0}.$$

* It is also true, by a theorem on exponents, that

$$(\sqrt[q]{x})^p = \sqrt[q]{x^p}.$$

Then the average rate of change of y with respect to x in the interval Δx is

(17)
$$\frac{\Delta y}{\Delta x} = \frac{\sqrt{x_0 + \Delta x} - \sqrt{x_0}}{\Delta x}.$$

We seek the limit approached by $\Delta y/\Delta x$ as Δx approaches 0. However, the value of this limit is not evident from an examination of the right-hand side of (17). Nor can we divide numerator and denominator by Δx to obtain a simpler function from which the limit might be evident.

The way out of the dilemma is a trick. We multiply the numerator and denominator on the right side of (17) by $\sqrt{x_0 + \Delta x} + \sqrt{x_0}$. This does not change the value of $\Delta y/\Delta x$. Then

$$\frac{\Delta y}{\Delta x} = \frac{\sqrt{x_0 + \Delta x} - \sqrt{x_0}}{\Delta x} \times \frac{\sqrt{x_0 + \Delta x} + \sqrt{x_0}}{\sqrt{x_0 + \Delta x} + \sqrt{x_0}}.$$

By multiplying the two numerators and then the two denominators we obtain

$$\frac{\Delta y}{\Delta x} = \frac{x_0 + \Delta x - x_0}{\Delta x\{\sqrt{x_0 + \Delta x} + \sqrt{x_0}\}}.$$

The numerator reduces to Δx, and we may then cancel the Δx in the numerator and denominator. This leaves us with

(18)
$$\frac{\Delta y}{\Delta x} = \frac{1}{\sqrt{x_0 + \Delta x} + \sqrt{x_0}}.$$

The right-hand side of (18) yields exactly the same values as the right side of (17). From (18), however, we can see what the desired limit should be. When Δx approaches 0, $\sqrt{x_0 + \Delta x}$ approaches $\sqrt{x_0}$, because the square root of a number changes gradually as the number changes. However, we can also see the result geometrically. Consider the function $y = \sqrt{x}$ (Fig. 5-4; compare Fig. 4-13). The function values $\sqrt{x_0}$ and $\sqrt{x_0 + \Delta x}$, which correspond to x_0 and $x_0 + \Delta x$, respectively, are shown in the figure. When Δx approaches 0, the function value $\sqrt{x_0 + \Delta x}$ approaches $\sqrt{x_0}$. Hence we see

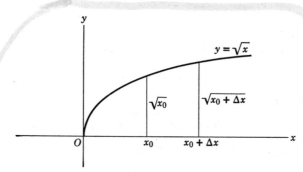

Figure 5-4

from (18) that

(19)
$$\dot{y} = \lim_{x \to 0} \frac{\Delta y}{\Delta x} = \frac{1}{2\sqrt{x_0}}.$$

We have found the derivative of $y = \sqrt{x}$ at x_0. This result can be written in terms of negative exponents. Thus

(20)
$$\dot{y} = \frac{1}{2\sqrt{x_0}} = \frac{1}{2x_0^{1/2}} = \tfrac{1}{2}x_0^{-1/2}.$$

The interesting point about the result in this form is that, because the original function is $y = x^{1/2}$, the derivative is obtained by the same process as is used for the derivative of $y = x^n$, that is, by the power rule. In the present case $n = \tfrac{1}{2}$, and the derivative is indeed of the form nx^{n-1} in accordance with (10).

Let us note next what the derived function of $y = \sqrt{x}$ is. The derived function exists wherever the derivative of $y = \sqrt{x}$ exists. The derivative at x_0 is $1/2\sqrt{x_0}$. This derivative is meaningful for any x_0 except $x_0 = 0$ and negative values of x. Hence the derived function

(21)
$$\dot{y} = \frac{1}{2\sqrt{x}}$$

exists or has a value only for positive values of x although the original function exists also at $x = 0$.

What does the nonexistence of the derived function at $x = 0$ mean geometrically? The derivative at any value of x is the slope of the tangent to the curve at that value of x. If we examine Fig. 5-4, we see that for x closer and closer to 0 the slope of the tangent increases more and more. Moreover, this slope can be one million, ten million, and in fact a number as large as one pleases if x is close enough to 0. We describe this unbounded increase in the slope by saying that the slope becomes infinite as x approaches 0. We do *not* say that there is a number infinity which is the value of the slope at $x = 0$. In fact, although there is a tangent to $y = \sqrt{x}$ at $x = 0$, this tangent, which is a vertical line, does not have a slope, that is, there is no number to represent its slope.

What we have said about slope applies to the derived function $1/2\sqrt{x}$. As x approaches 0, the derived function becomes larger and, indeed, by taking x close enough to 0, the derived function can be as large a number as one pleases. However, there is no value of the derived function for $x = 0$.

The statement that *as x approaches 0 the values of $1/2\sqrt{x}$ become larger and larger and, in fact, as large as any number one can name,* is of course very lengthy. Hence a symbolic shorthand is used, namely,

(22)
$$\lim_{x \to 0} \frac{1}{2\sqrt{x}} = \infty.$$

This shorthand is somewhat unfortunate because it suggests that ∞ is a number and that the function is approaching that number. In fact, we have often said that a limit is a number. However, the symbol ∞ in (22) does *not* represent a number, and the entire equation must be understood in the sense of the italicized statement above. The concept of a variable becoming infinite is a bit outlandish. The nineteenth-century logician and mathematician Augustus DeMorgan said to his fellow mathematician, William R. Hamilton, that the concept reminded him of the story of a man who was pulling a rope and, finding that it did not end, cried out that somebody has cut off the other end.

Let us turn now to the function $y = x^{p/q}$, where p and q are positive integers and x is limited to positive values and zero when q is even. We shall find the derivative at a definite value of x, namely x_0. Our proof will be somewhat loose but we shall see a little later that the loose arguments can be improved. We start then with

$$(23) \qquad\qquad y_0 = x_0^{p/q}$$

and let x change to $x_0 + \Delta x$. Then

$$(24) \qquad\qquad y_0 + \Delta y = (x_0 + \Delta x)^{p/q}.$$

Subtraction of (23) from (24) and division by Δx gives for the average rate of change of y with respect to x in the interval Δx

$$(25) \qquad\qquad \frac{\Delta y}{\Delta x} = \frac{(x_0 + \Delta x)^{p/q} - x_0^{p/q}}{\Delta x}.$$

Again, as in the special case (17), we cannot see readily what the limit of $\Delta y / \Delta x$ is as Δx approaches 0. It appears as though the limit should be 0/0, which is meaningless, and if we do the wrong thing of substituting 0 for Δx, we obtain the meaningless 0/0. The way out is again a trick.

First, we write (25) in the form

$$(26) \qquad\qquad \frac{\Delta y}{\Delta x} = \frac{(x_0 + \Delta x)^{p/q} - x_0^{p/q}}{x_0 + \Delta x - x_0}.$$

We now denote $x_0^{1/q}$ by s_0 and $(x_0 + \Delta x)^{1/q}$ by s. Then (26) becomes

$$(27) \qquad\qquad \frac{\Delta y}{\Delta x} = \frac{s^p - s_0^p}{s^q - s_0^q}.$$

We now use a theorem of algebra, namely, when n is a positive integer,

$$(28) \qquad a^n - b^n = (a - b)(a^{n-1} + a^{n-2}b + \cdots + ab^{n-2} + b^{n-1}).$$

The dots indicate the terms between the first and the last two, their number depending on n. The theorem is readily proved by multiplying the two factors on the right.

Both the numerator and denominator of the right side of (27) are of the form $a^n - b^n$ for positive integral n. Hence both are divisible by $s - s_0$.

The result is

(29)
$$\frac{\Delta y}{\Delta x} = \frac{s^{p-1} + s^{p-2}s_0 + \cdots + ss_0^{p-2} + s_0^{p-1}}{s^{q-1} + s^{q-2}s_0 + \cdots + ss_0^{q-2} + s_0^{q-1}}.$$

Now $s = (x_0 + \Delta x)^{1/q}$ and $s_0 = x_0^{1/q}$. If Δx approaches 0, then $(x_0 + \Delta x)^{1/q}$ approaches x_0. The reason is essentially the same as that adduced in connection with $\sqrt{x_0 + \Delta x}$. In the present case we are dealing with a qth root rather than a square root, but it is true here too that the closer one number is to another, the closer is the qth root of the first number to that of the second. We base this assertion on the somewhat loose argument that if $(x_0 + \Delta x)^{1/q}$ did not approach $x_0^{1/q}$ but some other number, say $a^{1/q}$, then $x_0 + \Delta x$ would approach a and not x_0; but $x_0 + \Delta x$ certainly approaches x_0.

Let us accept the admittedly intuitive argument that s or $(x_0 + \Delta x)^{1/q}$ approaches s_0 or $x_0^{1/q}$ and see what this implies in (29). Each term in the numerator except the last one contains s to some power. Consider, as an example, s^3. This is $s \cdot s \cdot s$. If each factor s approaches s_0, it is reasonable to expect that the product approaches $s_0 \cdot s_0 \cdot s_0$. We may see this better if we regard s as $s_0 + \Delta s$. Then

$$s^3 = (s_0 + \Delta s)^3 = s_0^3 + 3s_0^2\,\Delta s + 3s_0(\Delta s)^2 + (\Delta s)^3.$$

When Δs approaches 0, which is what happens when s approaches s_0, all the terms except the first approach 0 and s^3 approaches s_0^3. Hence each term in the numerator of (29) approaches (or already is) s_0^{p-1}. The same argument applies to the denominator. Each term there approaches or is s_0^{q-1}. Let us note also that there are p terms in the numerator and q in the denominator.

When Δx approaches 0, s approaches s_0. Hence

$$\dot{y} = \lim_{\Delta x \to 0} \frac{\Delta y}{\Delta x} = \frac{ps_0^{p-1}}{qs_0^{q-1}} = \frac{p}{q}\,s_0^{p-1-(q-1)} = \frac{p}{q}\,s_0^{p-q}.$$

Because $s_0 = x_0^{1/q}$,

(30)
$$\dot{y} = \frac{p}{q}\,(x_0^{1/q})^{p-q} = \frac{p}{q}\,x_0^{(p-q)/q} = \frac{p}{q}\,x_0^{(p/q)-1}.$$

Let us see what we have accomplished. We started with

(31)
$$y = x^{p/q}$$

and showed that at x_0

(32)
$$\dot{y} = \frac{p}{q}\,x_0^{(p/q)-1}.$$

We observe first that the derivative of (31) can be obtained by the power rule; that is, if we regard (31) as of the form $y = x^n$, the derivative is of the form nx^{n-1} where n in the present case is p/q.

What about the derived function of $y = x^{p/q}$? Let us recall that the function itself is defined for positive x and zero when q is even and for positive and negative x when q is odd. Hence the derived function is certainly limited to these values of x. In addition we run into the same point here as in the case of $y = x^{\frac{1}{2}}$. Suppose that $p/q = \frac{2}{3}$. Then $y = x^{\frac{2}{3}}$ and $\dot{y} = \frac{2}{3}x^{-\frac{1}{3}}$ or

$$\dot{y} = \frac{2}{3}\frac{1}{x^{\frac{1}{3}}} = \frac{2}{3}\frac{1}{\sqrt[3]{x}}.$$

We see that at $x = 0$ the derived function has no meaning. Of course, if $p/q = \frac{5}{3}$, for example, this exception does not arise.

We may embody these results in the following theorem:

Theorem: *Suppose that*

(33) $$y = x^{p/q},$$

where p and q are positive integers. The function is defined for positive x and zero when q is even and for positive and negative x when q is odd. Then the derived function is

(34) $$\dot{y} = \frac{p}{q}x^{(p/q)-1}$$

> what about x?

with the understanding that the derived function is subject to the same limitations on the values of x as is the original function and the additional limitation that the derived function does not exist at $x = 0$ if $(p/q) - 1$ is less than 0.

Now that we know that the derived function of (33) is (34), we may also consider the integral of (34). Because finding the integral means finding the function that has the given derived function, the integral is $y = x^{p/q} + C$. However, as in the case of $y = x^n$, we are not usually given the derived function in the form (34) but in the form

(35) $$\dot{y} = x^{p/q}.$$

We know that in finding the derived function one multiplies the function by the exponent and then reduces the exponent by 1; to find the integral we increase the exponent by 1 and divide by the new coefficient. Thus we have the following theorem:

Theorem: *If*

$$\dot{y} = x^{p/q}$$

then

(36) $$y = \frac{x^{(p/q)+1}}{\dfrac{p}{q} + 1} + C.$$

The quantity $(p/q) + 1$ must be greater than 0.

We can remember (34) and (36) separately or we can remember that the combination of the results obtained here and in Section 2 amounts to the following. If $y = x^n$, where n is a positive integer or positive fraction,

follows power rule

$\dot{y} = nx^{n-1}$; if $\dot{y} = x^n$, where n is a positive integer or fraction greater than -1,

(37)
$$y = \frac{x^{n+1}}{n+1} + C.$$

Exercises

1. Suppose that a variable (independent or dependent) takes on larger and larger values. Does it follow that the variable is becoming infinite? Can you give an example to support your answer?

2. What does the statement $\lim_{x \to 0} 1/x^2 = \infty$ mean?

3. Does the proof that when $y = x^{p/q}$, $\dot{y} = (p/q)x^{(p/q)-1}$ hold when $q = 1$? If so, do we have a second proof of the power rule when n is a positive integer?

4. Use the method of increments to find the derived function of $y = 1/x$.

5. Discuss the variation of the slope of $y = x^{1/2}$ as x increases from 0 to ∞. Base your discussion on the derived function and verify your conclusions by using the curve of the function.

6. Find the derived function for the following:

(a) $y = x^7$.　　　　Ans. $\dot{y} = 7x^6$.

(b) $y = x^{7/2}$.　　　Ans. $\dot{y} = \frac{7}{2}x^{5/2}$.

(c) $y = x^{1/3}$.　　　Ans. $\dot{y} = \frac{1}{3}x^{-2/3}$.

(d) $y = \sqrt[3]{x}$.

(e) $y = \sqrt[3]{x^2}$.　　Ans. $\dot{y} = \frac{2}{3}x^{-1/3}$.

(f) $y = \sqrt[4]{x}$.

(g) $y = x^{p/3}$.　　Ans. $\dot{y} = \frac{p}{3}x^{(p/3)-1}$.

(h) $y = x^{5/q}$.　　Ans. $\dot{y} = \frac{5}{q}x^{(5/q)-1}$.

(i) $y = t^{5/3}$.

(j) $s = t^{1/2}$.

(k) $s = \sqrt{t^3}$.　　Ans. $\dot{s} = \frac{3}{2}t^{1/2}$.

(l) $s = \sqrt[3]{t}$.

7. Find the antiderived function or integral for the following:

(a) $\dot{y} = x^{4/3}$.　Ans. $y = \frac{3}{7}x^{7/3} + C$.

(b) $\dot{y} = x^{3/2}$.　Ans. $y = \frac{2}{5}x^{5/2} + C$.

(c) $\dot{y} = \sqrt[3]{x}$.

(d) $\dot{y} = \sqrt[3]{x^2}$.　Ans. $y = \frac{3}{5}x^{5/3} + C$.

(e) $\dot{s} = t^{2/3}$.

(f) $\dot{s} = t^{-1/3}$.

(g) $\dot{y} = x^{-1/2}$.　Ans. $y = 2x^{1/2} + C$.

(h) $\dot{y} = (\sqrt[5]{x})^7$.

　　　　　　　Ans. $y = \frac{5}{12}x^{12/5} + C$.

(i) $\dot{s} = t^{3/5}$.

(j) $\dot{s} = \sqrt[4]{t^3}$.　Ans. $s = \frac{4}{7}t^{7/4} + C$.

(k) $\dot{s} = t^{1/2}$.

(l) $\dot{s} = t^{-2/3}$.

5. *The Calculation of Curvilinear Areas.*

We mentioned at the outset that one of the major problems that occupied mathematicians of the seventeenth century was the calculation of areas bounded by curves. The Greeks did have a lengthy method, known as the method of exhaustion, which served to find the areas bounded by the simplest of curves, but even in these cases the method was cumbersome. Despite the fact that our knowledge of the calculus is still restricted to just a few types of functions, we can already calculate some areas which are beyond the power of the Greek method.

Let us start a very simple example. We shall try to calculate the area *DEFG* of Fig. 5-5, where *GF* is an arc of $y = x^2$. This area is bounded only on the upper side by a curve. Before we undertake to apply the calculus, let us see why the calculus is potentially useful. We can think of a vertical line segment, *QP* in the figure, which starts at *DG* and moves to the right. The segment *QP* in any position extends from the x-axis to the curve. As *QP*

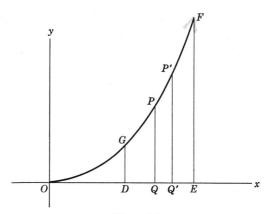

Figure 5-5

moves to the right, we can think of it as sweeping out or generating area, so that when it reaches the position shown in the figure it has generated the area *DQPG*. As *QP* moves farther to the right, the area it generates, of course, increases. Intuitively we can think of the increases in area as contributed by segments such as *QP*, *Q'P'*, and other vertical line segments. That is, intuitively we can think that as *QP* moves to the right it adds vertical segments to the area. This view of the increase in area is very crude because line segments have zero area and the addition of more and more zero areas does not increase the area already generated. Nevertheless, it is helpful to accept it for the moment, because it suggests that the area generated is a function of the position of *QP* and that the rate of increase of this area is the length of *QP*. Because *QP* changes in length as it moves, the area changes at a continually varying rate. We are then seeking a quantity, area, whose rate of change continually varies. This is precisely the type of situation in which the calculus is effective.

Although so far we have made only crude observations, let us express them in mathematical language. Suppose that we denote the position of *QP* by the abscissa or x-value of *Q* and that we denote the area *DQPG* as *A*. Then the fact that the instantaneous rate of change of area with respect to x is the length of *QP* is expressible in calculus language by the statement

(38) $$\dot{A} = y,$$

because the length of *QP* in any position is the y-value of the point *P*.

We shall now try to derive (38) more carefully to see if it is really correct. We wish to find the area *DEFG* (Fig. 5-6), and we regard this area as swept out by the line segment *QP* that starts at *DG* and moves to the right. Suppose that *QP* has reached the position shown. The position of *QP* is specified by the *x*-value of *Q*, say x_0, and the area generated for this position of *QP*, namely *DQPG*, can be denoted by A_0. Suppose that *QP* moves to *Q'P'*.

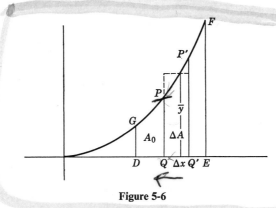

Figure 5-6

Let the distance *QQ'* be denoted by Δx. When *QP* moves to *Q'P'*, the area increases by the amount *QQ'P'P*, which we denote by ΔA. This increment in area is larger than $QP \times \Delta x$ and smaller than $Q'P' \times \Delta x$. Because the ordinates between *QP* and *Q'P'* increase continuously, there must be some ordinate between them, say, $\bar{y}$ such that

$$\Delta A = \bar{y} \times \Delta x.$$

Then

$$\frac{\Delta A}{\Delta x} = \bar{y}.$$

To obtain the instantaneous rate of change of area, that is, the rate of change of *A* with respect to *x* at the value x_0 of *x*, we must find the limit of $\Delta A/\Delta x$ as Δx approaches 0. As Δx approaches 0, *Q'* moves to *Q* and *Q'P'* moves to *QP*. For any value of Δx the ordinate $\bar{y}$ is always between *QP* and *Q'P'*. Hence $\bar{y}$ must also approach *QP*. The value of *QP* is the ordinate or *y*-value corresponding to x_0. Hence *QP* is y_0. Then

$$\dot{A} = y_0$$

or, since the equation of the curve is $y = x^2$,

$$\dot{A} = x_0{}^2.$$

Because this result is true for any value of *x* in the interval *DE*, we may as well write the derived function, namely,

$$\dot{A} = x^2.$$

To find the area A itself we apply antidifferentiation. Then

$$A = \frac{x^3}{3} + C.$$

The problem of determining C arises again. Here when QP is at DG, the value of A is 0. To be more specific, suppose that the x-value of D is 3. Then we know that when $x = 3$, $A = 0$. If we substitute these values in our equation, we obtain

$$0 = \frac{3^3}{3} + C$$

or

$$C = -9.$$

Then

$$A = \frac{x^3}{3} - 9$$

is the function which expresses the area from DG to any position of QP, the abscissa of Q being x.

To find the area $DEFG$, which we originally set out to do, we have but to note that this area is attained when QP reaches EF. Suppose that the abscissa of E is 6. Then we merely substitute 6 for x in the expression for A and obtain

$$A = \frac{6^3}{3} - 9 = 72 - 9 = 63.$$

Thus we have found the area bounded at least in part by a curve through the process of antidifferentiation or integration. To apply this process, we must of course know the equation of the curve.

We see, then, that to find the area bounded by an arc of a curve (whose equation we must know), two ordinates, and the x-axis, the procedure is simple. Suppose that $y = x^3$ is the equation of the curve and the ordinates are at, say, $x = 3$ and $x = 7$. By (38)

$$A = x^3.$$

We integrate this function to obtain

$$A = \frac{x^4}{4} + C.$$

In practice we need not write the constant of integration because, as we have seen, it turns out to be the negative of the value of A when $x = 3$. We merely substitute 7 for x, then 3 for x, and then subtract the second result from the first. That is,

$$A = \frac{7^4}{4} - \frac{3^4}{4}.$$

The areas we have found so far, such as *DEFG* in Fig. 5-5, are bounded on only one side by a curve. It might seem, therefore, that the calculus method of finding areas bounded by curved figures is rather limited. We shall see later, when more technique is at our disposal, that the method is really very powerful. However, even the areas that we can now compute include ones that the Greeks could not compute at all, and the areas that they could find can be computed more easily by our method.

Exercises

1. Find the area bounded by the curve $y = x^2$, the x-axis, and the following:

   (*a*) The ordinates at $x = 2$ and $x = 6$.   (*b*) The ordinates at $x = 4$ and $x = 8$.

   Ans. $69\frac{1}{3}$.

2. By the method of the calculus find the area bounded by the straight line $y = x$, the x-axis, and the ordinates at $x = 4$ and $x = 6$. Check your result by using plane geometry.   *Ans.* 10.

3. Find the area bounded by the curve $y = x + 9$, the x-axis, and the ordinates at $x = 3$ and $x = 6$.

4. Find the area bounded by the curve $y = x^{1/3}$, the x-axis, and the ordinates at $x = 2$ and $x = 8$.   *Ans.* $12 - \frac{3}{2}\sqrt[3]{2}$.

5. Find the area bounded by the curve $y = x^2$, the x-axis, and the ordinate at $x = 5$.

$$y = x + 9$$

$$A = y$$

$$A = \frac{x^2}{2} + 9x$$

$$A = 0 \text{ at } x = ?$$

$$0 = \frac{x^2}{2} + 27)^6$$

$$-31\frac{1}{2} = 6$$

$$A = \frac{36}{2} + 54 - 31\frac{1}{2}$$

$$A = 18 + 3^4 \quad -31\frac{1}{2}$$

$$A = 40\frac{1}{2}$$

Some Theorems on Differentiation and Antidifferentiation

1. Introduction. Thus far we have learned how to differentiate and anti-differentiate only the simplest functions. Fortunately, or unfortunately, the uses of the calculus call for a great variety of functions. To encompass them we must extend our knowledge of the basic processes of differentiation and antidifferentiation. For example, suppose that we have to differentiate

$$(1) \qquad\qquad y = x^7 + x^5.$$

We might guess that the derivative, $\dot{y}$, is the sum of the derivatives of x^7 and x^5. Indeed, in some very simple cases treated earlier we saw that the derivative of a sum of two functions is the sum of the derivatives, but there we showed this to be true by applying the method of increments to the entire function. We certainly do not wish to go through the method of increments, which is lengthy, if we can establish a general result once for all. We know that the derived function of x^7 is $7x^6$ and that of x^5 is $5x^4$. If we knew generally that the derivative of a sum of two functions is the sum of the derivatives, we could write down the derivative of the function in (1) immediately.

What we have said about the sum of two functions applies also to the difference, the product, and the quotient of two functions, and to the product of a constant and a function. The results in each case may seem obvious, but there are some surprises in store for us.

2. Some Remarks About Functions. While working with a specific function, we can examine the function itself to see if it possesses some requisite property. For example, if we are interested in the derivative of $y = x^2$, we can go through the method of increments to see if the limit of $\Delta y / \Delta x$ exists as Δx approaches 0 and to find the limit if it does exist.

However, we now wish to prove theorems about functions in general and therefore cannot examine individual functions to see, for example, that $\Delta y / \Delta x$ approaches a limit. We can, however, specify that we shall restrict the functions studied to those that have the requisite properties, which is what we actually do. One of these properties is that Δy must approach 0 as Δx does. This is known as the property of continuity. The property is so important that we shall consider it at some length.

We can best understand what continuity means if we consider the graphs of functions. In graphical terms a function is continuous if the curve can be drawn with one uninterrupted motion of a pencil. Thus $y = x^2$ is continuous because the curve (Fig. 6-1) can be drawn with one uninterrupted motion of the pencil. In drawing this curve we can start as far to the left and go as far to the right as we wish without lift-ing the pencil from the paper.

The function $y = x^2$ is especially simple. To pursue the notion of con-tinuity a little further, let us consider the function

(2) $$y = \frac{1}{x - 2}.$$

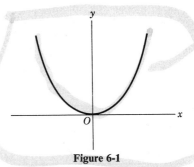

Figure 6-1

The graph of this function (Fig. 6-2) consists of two parts. We can draw the first part but cannot without lifting the pencil from the paper proceed to draw the second part. The trouble, of course, arises from the fact that the function has no value at $x = 2$. Moreover, as x approaches 2 through larger values, the corresponding y-values become larger and larger without bound, and as x approaches 2 through values smaller than 2, the y-values become smaller and smaller without bound. Hence no matter how much we draw of the curve for values of x less than 2, we must skip from these values of x to values of x greater than 2 to draw the right-hand portion of the curve. We can say that the function (2) is continuous for $x > 2$ and continuous for $x < 2$ but it is discontinuous for $x = 2$. This function illustrates the fact that a function may be continuous for some values of x and discontinuous for others. The fact that the function is discontinuous at $x = 2$ does not detract from its usefulness. We may be interested in using the function

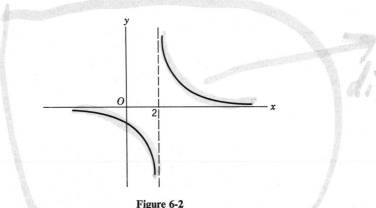

Figure 6-2

to describe some physical phenomenon in which x represents values greater than 2. For such an application we do not care how the function behaves when $x = 2$ or when x is less than 2.

Let us consider the matter of continuity in connection with another function. In trigonometry we study the function

(3) $y = \tan x.$

The graph of this function is shown in Fig. 6-3. We see from the graph that from values of x arbitrarily close to $-90°$ or $-\pi/2$ radians to values arbitrarily

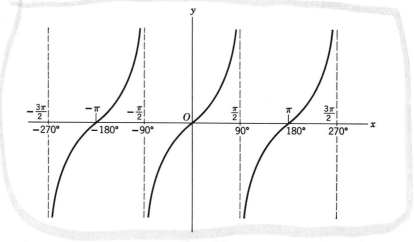

Figure 6-3

close to $x = 90°$ or $\pi/2$ radians the graph is one uninterrupted curve and is therefore continuous in this interval of x-values. However, at $x = 90°$ the function has about the same behavior as the function in (2) at $x = 2$. That is, the function values jump from larger and larger positive values as x approaches 90° from the left to values that become smaller and smaller as x approaches 90° from the right. At $x = 90°$ the function has no value. We can draw the portion of the curve that belongs to x-values less than but as close to 90° as we wish, but to draw the portion that corresponds to x-values larger than 90° we must lift the pencil from the paper and then start afresh. This function is then discontinuous at $x = 90°$, and for that matter it is discontinuous at $x = 270°$, 450°, and at every value of x that results from adding multiples of 180° to 90°; the function is also discontinuous at $x = -90°$ and at every value of x that results from subtracting multiples of 180° from $-90°$.

The discontinuities in (2) and (3) are a common type. The function is not defined at one or more specific values of x, and in addition the function values become larger and larger without bound or smaller and smaller without bound as the values of x approach these specific values.

A function can fail to be continuous, that is, it can be discontinuous, for another reason. Suppose that the graph of a function is that shown in Fig. 6-4. It is understood there that the value of the function at x_0 is the y_0 indicated. If we attempt to draw this curve by starting at Q, we can carry out an uninterrupted motion until the vertical line at x_0 is reached. But then to draw the portion at x_0 and to the right of x_0, we must move up suddenly at x_0 to the level of P_0. We say that the function values jump at x_0 and the function is discontinuous at $x = x_0$. The behavior of this function might seem outlandish and we might think that no self-respecting function would behave in this way. We may stand fast in this moral judgment for the present because we intend to ignore such functions; all we are trying to do here is to learn what to avoid.

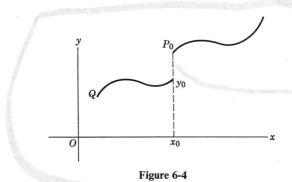

Figure 6-4

The derivative is calculated at a value of x, say x_0. When differentiating a function, we expect Δy to approach 0 as Δx approaches 0, because if Δy should approach some non-zero number or become infinite, the quotient $\Delta y / \Delta x$ would not approach a definite number. Now let us see that continuity is what we really use when we consider derivatives. Suppose that the curve in Fig. 6-5 is the graph of some continuous function and that we are considering the derivative at P_0 which has the coordinates (x_0, y_0). The fact that the curve is drawn with an uninterrupted motion of the pencil means that, as we draw

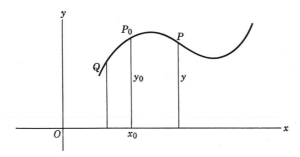

Figure 6-5

the portion from a nearby point P to P_0 or from a nearby point Q on the left to P_0, the y-values change gradually and approach y_0, the y-value at P_0. To say that P and Q approach P_0, is, of course, to say that the x-values of P and Q approach x_0. If, as P (or Q) moved along the curve so that its x-values approached x_0, the y-values became larger and larger without bound or approached some y-value other than y_0, the pencil would have to be shifted abruptly when x_0 is reached and the curve would not be continuous. In other words, for the curve to be continuous at x_0, if we take an x-value that differs just a little from x_0, the corresponding y-value must differ very little from y_0. And the closer x comes to x_0, the closer y must come to y_0. The difference between x_0 and x is what we have denoted by Δx and the difference between y_0 and y is denoted by Δy. We see then that continuity at (x_0, y_0) means that, as Δx approaches 0, Δy approaches 0.

We can of course require our mathematical functions to be continuous at those values of x at which the derivative is to be calculated, but are such functions useful? Fortunately, physical phenomena are usually continuous. As a ball falls, the distance it travels changes continuously with the time of travel. The distance does not jump abruptly from one value to another or become infinite as the time increases. We shall see as we take up many other physical applications that the functions representing them are continuous at least in the intervals of x-values that matter for the applications. Hence requiring continuity of our mathematical functions does not detract from their usefulness.

In calculating the derivative of a function at a value x_0 of x, more is involved than continuity. The continuity of a function at x_0, for example, guarantees that Δy approaches 0 as Δx does. We are, however, interested in

(4)
$$\lim_{\Delta x \to 0} \frac{\Delta y}{\Delta x}.$$

Despite the fact that Δy and Δx both approach zero, it is conceivable that the ratio $\Delta y/\Delta x$ may not approach a definite number. For example, the function whose graph is shown in Fig. 6-6 is continuous at all values of x but it does not have a derivative at x_0 because there is no unique tangent at x_0 (review the discussion in Chapter 4, Section 5). The curve shown in

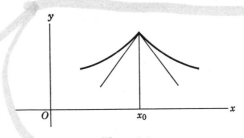

Figure 6-6

Fig. 6-6 changes direction abruptly at x_0 and is said to have a corner or cusp there. Because we wish to consider functions that do have derivatives at least in the domain of x-values in which we shall be interested we shall limit ourselves to those for which the limit (4) does exist at each x-value in the domain. Such functions are said to be differentiable at the x-values in question. If a function is continuous and differentiable in a domain or an interval of x-values, its graph is smooth, that is, without corners, and the function is often described as smooth.*

Thus we impose two restrictions on the general functions that we shall treat. The *first is that they must be continuous, at least in the intervals in which we shall use them, and the second is that they must be differentiable.* We shall not bother to state these hypotheses in our theorems because to do so would mean enormous repetition. Where we depart from these conditions, we shall discuss the situation.

1. Must be continuous

2. Must be differentiable

Exercises

1. Sketch the following functions and determine from the graphs the values of x for which they are continuous and those for which they are discontinuous:

(*a*) $y = 3x$.

(*b*) $y = \sin x$.

(*c*) $y = \sqrt{1 - x}$.

(*d*) $y = \dfrac{1}{x^2}$.

(*e*) $y = \dfrac{x^2 - 9}{x - 3}$.

  Suggestion: see Chapter 2, Section 2.

(*f*) $y = \dfrac{x^3 - 1}{x - 1}$.

2. Associated with each point P of a curve (Fig. 6-7) is its abscissa x and the angle of inclination A of the tangent at P. Corresponding to each value of x in the interval OC there is a unique value of A. Hence A is a function of x. Determine whether A is a continuous function of x in the interval OC.   *Ans.* No.

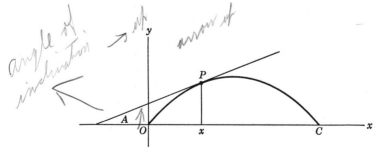

Figure 6-7

* Some authors use the word smooth to include the additional condition that the derived function also be continuous in the interval.

3. The slope of the curve in Fig. 6-7 at any point P is, by definition, the slope of the tangent at P. The slope is tan A, which we now denote by z. This z also varies with x. Determine whether z is a continuous function of x in the interval OC.

Ans. Yes.

4. The statement that y approaches ∞ describes (*a*) the number that y approaches, (*b*) a state of mind, (*c*) the fact that the values of y include any number however large, and (*d*) the fact that y takes on the value 10^{12}. Which alternative is most appropriate?

Ans. (*c*).

There is one more preliminary to be disposed of and that is the matter of notation. We wish to talk about any function that is continuous in some interval and is differentiable. How should we refer to such functions? We could say, let "y be any function of x." This is a bit lengthy. It is customary to shorten it and to write $y = f(x)$. This is read "y is f of x." The notation implies that x is the independent variable, that y is the dependent variable, and that y is a function of x. We could use the notation $y = fx$; it has been used in the past. But $f(x)$ is now standard. We must remember to treat the symbols $f(x)$ as an entity and *not* as a product of f and x.

We might and, in fact, shall face the situation wherein we wish to discuss two arbitrary functions at the same time. It would be confusing to use $y = f(x)$ for both. The situation is handled by using $y = f(x)$ for one function and, say, $y = g(x)$ for the other. Even this device may not suffice for some purposes, because the same letters are used for the independent and dependent variables in both functions. If necessary, we shall use $u = f(x)$ and $v = g(x)$ to distinguish the dependent variables or even $u = f(x)$ and $v = g(t)$ to distinguish both independent and dependent variables.

The notation $y = f(x)$ has another advantage. We might wish to speak of the value of y when x is given the value 2. In this special function notation the value of y when $x = 2$ is indicated by $y = f(2)$ or simply by $f(2)$. Moreover, suppose that we are dealing with a *particular* function, say,

$$y = x^2 - 3x + 7.$$

We might wish to refer to this function many times, and instead of repeating the whole function we might let

(5) $$f(x) = x^2 - 3x + 7.$$

Here $f(x)$ stands for just the one function. To indicate the value of this function when $x = 2$, we might again use $f(2)$. To find out what the number $f(2)$ is, we must substitute 2 for x on the right side of (5). The answer is 5. Again, suppose that $f(x)$ stands for the particular function

$$f(x) = -x^2 + 3x + 7.$$

What is $f(-2)$? We must remember that -2 is to be substituted for x itself, so that we obtain

$$f(-2) = -(-2)^2 + 3(-2) + 7 = -3.$$

The function notation lends itself to a legitimate distinction that is most often honored in the breach. Strictly speaking, a function is a relation between two variables, x and y say. The relation might be that y is the square of x. Then the relation is neither x nor y but something connecting the two. Thus when one says that John is the father of William, the relationship is fatherhood, and this relation is neither John nor William but a connection between them. Yet in speaking about these people one might use the word father to mean John, whereas the word strictly refers to the relationship. Likewise in dealing with functions we should distinguish between the relation and y itself. We could use f to denote the relation between y and x and use $f(x)$ to mean y. However, we often use y or $f(x)$ to mean the relation. Fortunately, this use of y or $f(x)$ in the double sense causes no confusion and avoids a lot of unnecessary words.

When a relation between x and y is denoted by $y = f(x)$, it is customary to denote the derived function by $f'(x)$ and the second derived function by $f''(x)$. It is also common to use y' in place of $\dot{y}$ and y'' in place of $\ddot{y}$.

Exercises

1. If $f(x) = x^2 - 9x$, calculate $f(0), f(2), f(-1)$, and $f(9)$.   *Ans.* 0, −14, 10, 0.
2. If $f(x) = -x^2 - 9x$, calculate $f(0), f(2), f(-2), f(9)$, and $f(-9)$.
3. For the functions in Exercises 1 and 2, calculate $f(a)$ and $f(x_0)$.

$$\textit{Ans. } a^2 - 9a; \quad -a^2 - 9a.$$

4. If $y = f(x)$, what does $f(x) - f(x_0)$ denote in more familiar notation?

$$\textit{Ans. } \Delta y.$$

5. If $y = f(x)$, what does $\dfrac{f(x) - f(x_0)}{x - x_0}$ denote in more familiar notation?

6. If $y = f(x)$, what does $\lim\limits_{x \to x_0} \dfrac{f(x) - f(x_0)}{x - x_0}$ denote in more familiar notation?

7. If $y = f(x)$, what does $f'(x_0)$ denote?   *Ans.* $\dot{y}$ at x_0 or dy/dx at x_0.

8. If $f(x) = \dfrac{x^2 - 9}{-x^2 + 7}$, find $f(0), f(2), f(-2)$, and $f(\sqrt{7})$.

9. If $f(x) = \tan x$, find $f(0), f(\pi/4)$, and $f(-\pi/4)$.   *Ans.* 0, 1, −1.
10. If $f(x) = x^2 - 9$, find $f'(2), f'(-2)$.

11. Interpret geometrically $\dfrac{f(x_0 + \Delta x) - f(x_0 - \Delta x)}{2\Delta x}$.

12. Prove that

$$\lim_{\Delta x \to 0} \frac{f(x_0 + \Delta x) - f(x_0 - \Delta x)}{2\,\Delta x} = f'(x_0).$$

Suggestion: add and subtract $f(x_0)$ in the numerator.

13. If $f(x) = x - \dfrac{1}{x}$, show that

(a) $f(-x) = -f(x)$,

(b) $f\left(\dfrac{1}{x}\right) = -f(x)$.

3. *The Differentiation of Sums and Differences of Functions.* Let us now turn to the problem mentioned in Section 1, and let us start with the case of a function that is a constant times another function. When we differentiated $y = 16x^2$, we found the result to be $\dot{y} = 32x$. We can obtain the same result by keeping the constant separate; we can differentiate x^2 to obtain $2x$ and then multiply 16 by $2x$. What we are really saying then is that the derivative of a constant times a function, that is $16 \cdot x^2$, is the constant times the derivative, that is $16 \cdot 2x$. Hence we have reason to believe that the derivative of a constant times a function is the constant times the derivative of the function. Let us express this statement symbolically. Suppose that u is a function of x and

(6)
$$y = cu.$$

Then what we believe is that

(7)
$$\dot{y} = c\dot{u}.$$

Let us see if we can prove (7). To prove basic facts about differentiation we go back to the method of increments. Suppose that x_0 is the value of x at which we wish to calculate $\dot{y}$. At x_0, the value of u is, say, u_0 and the value of y is y_0. Then

(8)
$$y_0 = cu_0.$$

We change x to the value $x_0 + \Delta x$. Consequently, y and u both change, and we denote the changes by Δy and Δu, respectively. Then

(9)
$$y_0 + \Delta y = c(u_0 + \Delta u) = cu_0 + c\Delta u.$$

We subtract (8) from (9), so that

(10)
$$\Delta y = c\Delta u.$$

In accordance with the method of increments we divide both sides of (10) by Δx. To divide the product $c\Delta u$ by Δx, it is correct to divide only one of the factors. Then

(11)
$$\frac{\Delta y}{\Delta x} = c\frac{\Delta u}{\Delta x}.$$

We now wish to determine the limit of $\Delta y/\Delta x$ as Δx approaches 0. On the right side we have a product. Because u is a function of x, the quantity $\Delta u/\Delta x$ approaches the limit $\dot{u}$. But what about the product? As $\Delta u/\Delta x$ gets closer and closer to its limit $\dot{u}$, the product should get closer and closer to $c\dot{u}$. Thus, as x approaches 2, x^2 approaches 4, and therefore $3x^2$ approaches 12. Of course, this argument by example is not a mathematical proof. What we need to know is that if any function, which in our case is $\Delta u/\Delta x$ as a function of Δx, approaches a certain limit, a constant times that function approaches the constant times the limit. At the present time we shall rely on what intuitively seems to be a very reasonable fact and conclude that $\dot{y} = c\dot{u}$. Although our proof is incomplete, we affirm our result as a theorem.*

Theorem 1: *If y and u are functions of x and y = cu, then*

$$\dot{y} = c\dot{u}. \tag{12}$$

That is, the derivative (and derived function) of a constant times a function is the constant times the derivative (derived function) of that function.

Let us consider next the problem of how to differentiate the sum of two functions. Suppose that u and v are functions of x and $y = u + v$. Thus u could be x^2 and v, $7x^3$; then y would be $x^2 + 7x^3$. Is it true that $\dot{y} = \dot{u} + \dot{v}$? We shall resort to the method of increments. Let x_0 be the value of x at which we calculate the derivatives. Then, with the usual meanings,

$$y_0 = u_0 + v_0. \tag{13}$$

We change x to $x_0 + \Delta x$. Let Δy, Δu, and Δv denote the changes in the respective functions. Then

$$y_0 + \Delta y = u_0 + \Delta u + v_0 + \Delta v. \tag{14}$$

Subtraction of (13) from (14) yields

$$\Delta y = \Delta u + \Delta v.$$

The average rate of change of y with respect to x in the interval Δx is

$$\frac{\Delta y}{\Delta x} = \frac{\Delta u}{\Delta x} + \frac{\Delta v}{\Delta x}.$$

We now wish to determine the limit of $\Delta y / \Delta x$ as Δx approaches 0, and we face a problem analogous to that encountered above. We want the limit of the entire right-hand side of (15), that is,

$$\lim_{\Delta x \to 0} \left(\frac{\Delta u}{\Delta x} + \frac{\Delta v}{\Delta x} \right).$$

May we conclude that this limit is the same as

$$\lim_{\Delta x \to 0} \frac{\Delta u}{\Delta x} + \lim_{\Delta x \to 0} \frac{\Delta v}{\Delta x} ?$$

That is, may we conclude that the limit of a sum of two functions is the sum of the limits of the summands? The answer would seem to be affirmative. For example, we know that as x approaches 1, $5x^2$ approaches 5 and $3x$ approaches 3. Then as x approaches 1, $5x^2 + 3x$ certainly approaches 8. Again we must point out that this example does not constitute a proof of the

---

* The reader who wishes to delve further into the proofs of this and the next few theorems at this time should consult Chapter 24.

theorem on limits, but we rest on this limited evidence for the present and assert the following theorem:

Theorem 2:   If u and v are functions of x and y = u + v, then

(16) $$\dot{y} = \dot{u} + \dot{v}.$$

That is, the derivative (and derived function) of a sum of two functions is the sum of the derivatives (derived functions).

What holds for a sum of *two* functions, holds for a sum of three and more functions. Thus suppose that $y = u + v + w$, where u, v, and w are functions of x. We may regard y as

(17) $$y = (u + v) + w.$$

Certainly, $u + v$ can be regarded as a single function of x because to each value of x in some domain, $u + v$ has a value, namely, the sum of the values of u and v. Then, as expressed in (17), y is the sum of two functions, $u + v$ and w. Hence by Theorem 2

$$\dot{y} = \overline{u + v} + \dot{w}.$$

Here $\overline{u + v}$ means the derivative of the entire function $u + v$. However, by Theorem 2 again, $\overline{u + v} = \dot{u} + \dot{v}$. Hence

(18) $$\dot{y} = \dot{u} + \dot{v} + \dot{w}.$$

This argument can be extended to a sum of four or more functions by repeated application of Theorem 2. Hence we have the following theorem:

Theorem 3:   If y is the sum of any fixed finite number of functions, that is, if $y = u_1 + u_2 + \cdots + u_n$, then

(19) $$\dot{y} = \dot{u}_1 + \dot{u}_2 + \cdots + \dot{u}_n.$$

That is, the derivative (and derived function) of a sum of a finite number of functions is the sum of the derivatives (derived functions).

Finding the derivative of a difference of two functions, that is, the derivative of $y = u - v$ where u and v are functions of x, could be considered as a separate problem. However, we can write $y = u + (-v)$ and regard y as the sum of u and $-v$. Then, by Theorem 2, the derivative of y is the sum of the derivatives of u and $-v$. The derivative of $-v$ is the derivative of $-1 \cdot v$ and, by Theorem 1, this derivative is $-\dot{v}$. Hence $\dot{y} = \dot{u} - \dot{v}$. Thus we have the following theorem:

Theorem 4:   If u and v are functions of x and if y = u − v, then

(20) $$\dot{y} = \dot{u} - \dot{v}.$$

That is, the derivative (and derived function) of a difference of two functions is the difference of the derivatives (derived functions) of the separate functions.

Before considering additional theorems on differentiation, let us see how those already given are used in actual problems of differentiation. Suppose that we must find $\dot{y}$ when

$$y = 10x^7 + 6x^3.$$

We see, first, that y is the sum of two functions. Hence, by Theorem 2, we may differentiate each separately. We consider then the function $10x^7$. According to Theorem 1, the derived function of this function is the constant 10 times the derived function of x^7. In the Chapter 5 we learned that the derived function of x^7 is $7x^6$. Hence the derived function of $10x^7$ is $70x^6$. Likewise the derived function of $6x^3$ is $6 \cdot 3x^2$ or $18x^2$. Hence

$$\dot{y} = 70x^6 + 18x^2.$$

Exercises

1. Find the derived functions of the following functions:

(a) $y = 10x^6$.   *Ans.* $\dot{y} = 60x^5$.

(b) $y = 10x^{2/3}$.

(c) $y = x^3 + 7x^5$.

   Ans. $\dot{y} = 3x^2 + 35x^4$.

(d) $y = 5x^4 + 7x^{1/3}$.

(e) $y = x^3 - 7x^2$.

   Ans. $\dot{y} = 3x^2 - 14x$.

(f) $y = (x^2 + x)7x$.

(g) $y = x^{5/2}(x^2 + 3x)$.

   Ans. $\dot{y} = \frac{9}{2}x^{7/2} + \frac{21}{2}x^{5/2}$.

(h) $y = (x^2 + x)(x - 3)$.

(i) $y = 8\sqrt{x}$.   *Ans.* $\dot{y} = 4x^{-1/2}$.

(j) $y = 4\sqrt{x} + 6\sqrt[3]{x}$.

(k) $y = \sqrt{8x}$.   *Ans.* $\dot{y} = \sqrt{\dfrac{2}{x}}$.

(l) $y = \sqrt{4x} + \sqrt[3]{6x}$.

2. If $y = f(x) + g(x)$, what is $\dot{y}$?   *Ans.* $\dot{y} = f'(x) + g'(x)$.

3. If $y = f(x) - g(x)$, what is $\dot{y}$?

4. If $y = cf(x)$, what is $\dot{y}$?   *Ans.* $\dot{y} = cf'(x)$.

5. An airplane reaches an altitude of $15x^2 - x^3$ feet after having traveled x miles (horizontally).

(a) Find the rate of increase of altitude with respect to horizontal distance traveled when the airplane has traveled 2 miles.   *Ans.* 48 ft/mi.

(b) Graph the function $y = 15x^2 - x^3$ from $x = 0$ to $x = 10$.

(c) Find the slope of the graph at $x = 2$, $x = 5$, $x = 7$, and $x = 10$.

   Ans. 48, 75, 63, 0.

(d) Taking into account any change of scale you may have used for the y-axis, would you say that the graph could be an actual picture of the airplane's flight path?

6. The rate of change of the area of a circle with respect to the radius is geometrically the circumference of the circle. [See Chapter 2, (28)]. Generalize this result for circles to spheres and prove that your generalization is correct.

4. The Differentiation of Products and Quotients of Functions.   Let us consider now the problem of how to differentiate the product of two functions.

For example, we might have to differentiate the function

(21) $$y = (x^2 + 3)x^3.$$

It is true in this case, although it will not be true of problems we shall encounter later, that we can avoid the product form by multiplying x^3 into each term in the parentheses. However, just to be perverse let us insist on trying to differentiate this product.

To obtain $\dot{y}$ we might apply the reasonable conjecture that the derived function of a product of two functions is the product of the derived functions. Accordingly,

(22) $$\dot{y} = 2x \cdot 3x^2 = 6x^3.$$

To check our conjecture let us multiply out, that is, let us apply the distributive axiom in (21). Then

$$y = x^5 + 3x^2.$$

If we differentiate this function, we obtain

(23) $$\dot{y} = 5x^4 + 6x.$$

Now (22) and (23) do not agree. Hence our conjecture must be wrong. Let us not be too dejected, however, because Leibniz made the same conjecture and it took him quite a while to see what was wrong with it.

Let us resort to the method of increments. Suppose that

(24) $$y = uv$$

where u and v are functions of x. At $x = x_0$, u, v, and y have values that we denote by u_0, y_0, and y_0. Then

(25) $$y_0 = u_0 v_0.$$

We let x change to the value $x_0 + \Delta x$. Then

$$y_0 + \Delta y = (u_0 + \Delta u)(v_0 + \Delta v)$$

or

(26) $$y_0 + \Delta y = u_0 v_0 + u_0 \Delta v + v_0 \Delta u + \Delta u \Delta v.$$

We subtract (25) from (26) to obtain

$$\Delta y = u_0 \Delta v + v_0 \Delta u + \Delta u \Delta v.$$

The average rate of change of y with respect to x in the interval Δx is obtained by dividing by Δx. Of course, to divide a product by Δx it is correct to divide either factor by Δx. Hence

(27) $$\frac{\Delta y}{\Delta x} = u_0 \frac{\Delta v}{\Delta x} + v_0 \frac{\Delta u}{\Delta x} + \Delta u \frac{\Delta v}{\Delta x}.$$

To obtain the limit of $\Delta y / \Delta x$ as Δx approaches 0, we note first of all that the right-hand side of (27) consists of three terms, whereas we want the limit of the entire sum. However, we have already had occasion to point out in connection with Theorem 2 that intuitively it is reasonable that the limit of a sum of functions should be the sum of the limits of the summands. Hence we take the limit of each term separately. The first two terms are alike in that each contains a constant, u_0 in the first term and v_0 in the second, multiplied into a function of Δx. To find

$$\lim_{\Delta x \to 0} u_0 \frac{\Delta v}{\Delta x}$$

we recall the proof of Theorem 1. We found it reasonable to conclude there that the limit of a constant times a function is the constant times the limit of the function. Hence

(28)
$$\lim_{\Delta x \to 0} u_0 \frac{\Delta v}{\Delta x} = u_0 \dot{v}.$$

Likewise

(29)
$$\lim_{\Delta x \to 0} v_0 \frac{\Delta u}{\Delta x} = v_0 \dot{u}.$$

The third term on the right side of (27) presents a new problem. Here we have a product of two functions of Δx, namely, Δu and $\Delta v/\Delta x$. Both functions vary as Δx approaches 0. The function Δu approaches 0 as Δx approaches 0 because the smaller the increment in x, the smaller is the increment in the function u. The function $\Delta v/\Delta x$ approaches some number $\dot{v}$ as Δx approaches 0. What does the product of Δu and $\Delta v/\Delta x$ approach?

Let us consider the two functions $2x^2$ and $3x$. As x approaches 1, $2x^2$ approaches 2 and $3x$ approaches 3. What does the product $6x^3$ approach? Certainly, as x approaches 1, $6x^3$ approaches 6. Judging from this example, then, the limit of a product of two functions is the product of the limits. This example is not a proof, but it gives some ground for believing that the conclusion is correct.

We shall rest on this incomplete argument for the present and assert that the limit of the product

$$\Delta u \cdot \frac{\Delta v}{\Delta x}$$

is the product of the limits. We have already noted that the separate limits are 0 and $\dot{v}$. Hence

(30)
$$\lim_{\Delta x \to 0} \Delta u \cdot \frac{\Delta v}{\Delta x} = 0.$$

If we now use (28), (29), and (30), we see from (27) that

$$\lim_{\Delta x \to 0} \frac{\Delta y}{\Delta x} = u_0 \dot{v} + v_0 \dot{u} + 0$$

or that the derived function $\dot{y}$ is given by

$$\dot{y} = u\dot{v} + v\dot{u}.$$

Hence we have "proved" the following Theorem:

    Theorem 5:   If $y = uv$ where u and v are functions of x,

(31) $\dot{y} = u\dot{v} + v\dot{u}.$

That is, the derivative (and derived function) of a product of two functions is the first factor times the derivative (derived function) of the second plus the second times the derivative (derived function) of the first.

    We see from Theorem 5 that the procedure for differentiating the product of two functions is not what we guessed at the outset but is slightly more complicated.

    The type of argument that we used to derive Theorem 3 from Theorem 2 can now be applied to derive the following theorem:

    Theorem 6:   If $y = uvw$, where u, v, and w are functions of x,

(32) $\dot{y} = uv\dot{w} + uw\dot{v} + vw\dot{u}.$

    We consider next the procedure for differentiating the quotient of two functions. Thus

$$y = \frac{x^2 + 1}{x + 7}$$

is a quotient of the functions in the numerator and denominator. We might conjecture that $\dot{y}$ is the quotient of the derivative of the numerator and the derivative of the denominator. However, our experience with the procedure for obtaining the derivative of a product of two functions might forewarn us that this conjecture is in error, and in fact it is. To see that it is we can differentiate $y = x^3/x^2$ by forming the quotient of the derivative of the numerator and the derivative of the denominator and comparing with the derivative of $y = x$. To obtain the correct procedure we use the method of increments.

    Let u and v each be a function of x and let

(33) $y = \dfrac{u}{v}.$

To obtain $\dot{y}$ at the value of x_0 of x, we first substitute x_0 for x in the functions u, v, and y. If, as usual, we denote the function values by u_0, v_0, and y_0, then

(34) $y_0 = \dfrac{u_0}{v_0}.$

We now replace x by $x_0 + \Delta x$ in (33) and denote the new values of u, v, and y by $u_0 + \Delta u$, $v_0 + \Delta v$, and $y_0 + \Delta y$. Then

(35) $y_0 + \Delta y = \dfrac{u_0 + \Delta u}{v_0 + \Delta v}.$

In accordance with the method of increments we subtract (34) from (35) and obtain

(36)
$$\Delta y = \frac{u_0 + \Delta u}{v_0 + \Delta v} - \frac{u_0}{v_0}.$$

We now divide both sides by Δx. The division is indicated by

(37)
$$\frac{\Delta y}{\Delta x} = \frac{u_0 + \Delta u}{(v_0 + \Delta v)\Delta x} - \frac{u_0}{v_0 \Delta x}.$$

We are, of course, interested in the limit of the right side of (37) as Δx approaches 0. If we try to determine the limit of the separate fractions, we run into trouble because both terms become infinite. One possible move that avoids this difficulty is to carry out the subtraction of the two fractions before determining the limit. However, we obtain the same result more easily if we first perform the subtraction called for in (36). The lowest common denominator is $(v_0 + \Delta v)v_0$, and therefore we obtain

$$\Delta y = \frac{v_0(u_0 + \Delta u) - u_0(v_0 + \Delta v)}{(v_0 + \Delta v)v_0}.$$

The numerator can be simplified to yield

$$\Delta y = \frac{v_0 \Delta u - u_0 \Delta v}{(v_0 + \Delta v)v_0}.$$

Now we divide both sides by Δx. To divide the right side by Δx, it is correct algebra to divide the numerator by Δx. Moreover, in dividing each of the products in the numerator, we must divide one factor only. Hence

(38)
$$\frac{\Delta y}{\Delta x} = \frac{v_0 \dfrac{\Delta u}{\Delta x} - u_0 \dfrac{\Delta v}{\Delta x}}{(v_0 + \Delta v)v_0}.$$

To determine the limit of $\Delta y/\Delta x$ we face a new difficulty. The right-hand side of (38) is a quotient, and both the numerator and the denominator vary as Δx approaches 0. May we determine the limit of the quotient by determining the limits of the numerator and denominator separately? Suppose, for example, that we are faced with the quotient

$$\frac{x^2 + 3x + 2}{x + 1}$$

and that we must find the limit approached by the quotient as x approaches 0. The numerator certainly approaches 2 as x approaches 0, because x^2 and $3x$ become smaller and smaller and approach 0. The denominator approaches. Hence the quotient of the limits is 2/1 or 2. It so happens that the numerator can be factored into $(x + 2)(x + 1)$ and the value of the fraction is $x + 2$; thus we see that this fraction approaches 2 as x approaches 0.

Hence it does seem as though the limit of a quotient can be obtained by taking the quotient of the limit of the numerator and the limit of the denominator (provided that the limit of the denominator is not zero).

For the present we shall accept the evidence of this example and proceed to evaluate the limit in (38) by calculating the limit of the numerator and the limit of the denominator. The limit of the numerator is evaluated by practically the same argument that enabled us to proceed from (27) to (31). The limit of the difference of the two terms in the numerator is the difference of the limits. The limit of $v_0 \Delta u / \Delta x$, as in (28), is $v_0 \dot{u}$ and the limit of $u_0 \Delta v / \Delta x$, as in (29), is $u_0 \dot{v}$. Hence the limit of the numerator is

$$v_0 \dot{u} - u_0 \dot{v}.$$

The limit of the denominator in (38) is readily determined. As Δx approaches 0, Δv approaches 0. Hence $v_0 + \Delta v$ approaches v_0. The other factor v_0 is constant as Δx varies. Because the limit of a constant times a function is the constant times the limit of the function, the limit of the product $(v_0 + \Delta v)v_0$ is v_0^2.

Then the derivative of y with respect to x at $x = x_0$ is

$$(39) \qquad \dot{y} = \lim_{\Delta x \to 0} \frac{\Delta y}{\Delta x} = \frac{v_0 \dot{u} - u_0 \dot{v}}{v_0^2}.$$

The derived function exists for all x_0 for which the derivative $\dot{y}$ exists. We see from (39) that the derivative exists for all x_0 for which v_0 does not equal zero. Of course, if v_0 is 0, the original function also has no meaning at x_0. We then have the following theorem:

Theorem 7:   If $y = u/v$, where u and v are functions of x, then

$$(40) \qquad \dot{y} = \frac{v\dot{u} - u\dot{v}}{v^2}.$$

That is, the derivative (and derived function) of a quotient of two functions is the denominator multiplied into the derivative (derived function) of the numerator minus the numerator multiplied into the derivative (derived function) of the denominator, all divided by the square of the denominator. The derivative (derived function) exists where v does not equal 0.

The use of the theorems on the derivative of a product and quotient of functions is somewhat novel, and we might therefore consider one or two examples. Suppose that we must find the derived function of

$$y = (x^2 - 1)(x^2 + 6x + 5).$$

We could, of course, multiply the two polynomials and obtain a single polynomial. We could then apply the theorem on the derived function of a sum of functions and obtain the required result. However, it is easier to apply Theorem 5 on the derived function of a product of two functions. We think of $x^2 - 1$ as a function u of x and of $x^2 + 6x + 5$ as a function v of x. Then

$$\dot{y} = u\dot{v} + v\dot{u} = (x^2 - 1)(2x + 6) + (x^2 + 6x + 5)(2x).$$

We can, of course, simplify the result by purely algebraic processes. Whether or not we should do so depends on what we plan to do with the derived function.

Let us consider next an example of the use of the theorem on the derived function of a quotient. Suppose that

$$y = \frac{x^2 + 3}{2x - 1}.$$

Such a function, that is, a quotient of two polynomials, is called a *rational function*. To obtain the derived function we apply the theorem on quotients. We think of $x^2 + 3$ as a function u of x and of $2x - 1$ as a function v of x. Then

(41) $$\dot{y} = \frac{v\dot{u} - u\dot{v}}{v^2} = \frac{(2x - 1)(2x) - (x^2 + 3)(2)}{(2x - 1)^2}.$$

Again, we can simplify the result if the use to be made of it warrants doing so.

Exercises

1. Find the derived function of each of the following functions:

(a) $y = (x^2 - 1)(x + 2)$.
  Ans. $\dot{y} = 3x^2 + 4x - 1$.

(b) $y = x(x^2 - 1)(x + 2)$.

(c) $y = \dfrac{x}{x - 1}$.
  Ans. $\dot{y} = \dfrac{-1}{(x - 1)^2}$.

(d) $y = \dfrac{x^2 - 1}{x + 3}$.

(e) $y = \dfrac{x^2 - 1}{x^2 + 3}$.
  Ans. $\dot{y} = \dfrac{8x}{(x^2 + 3)^2}$.

(f) $y = \dfrac{x(x^2 - 1)}{x + 3}$.

(g) $y = \dfrac{x^3 + 3x^2 + 7}{x - 1}$.
  Ans. $\dot{y} = \dfrac{2x^3 - 6x - 7}{(x - 1)^2}$.

(h) $y = 7x^2 + \dfrac{3}{x - 1}$.

2. If in step (27) of the proof of Theorem 5 we had written $(\Delta u/\Delta x)\,\Delta v$, would it have been correct and would the proof still go through? *Ans. Yes.*

3. Had we established earlier in the logical development of the calculus the theorem on the derived function of a product of two functions, we could have given another proof of the power rule for positive integral n; that is, if $y = x^n$, then $\dot{y} = nx^{n-1}$. The alternative proof uses mathematical induction, the idea of which

is the following. We know by application of the method of increments that when $n = 1$, $\dot{y} = 1x^{\circ}$. Now assume, in accordance with the method of mathematical induction, that for $n = k - 1$, $\dot{y} = (k - 1)x^{k-2}$, and let us prove that for $n = k$, $\dot{y} = kx^{k-1}$. Hence consider $y = x^{k} = x \cdot x^{k-1}$. Complete the proof.

4. If $y = f(x) \cdot g(x)$, what is y'?   *Ans.* $y' = f(x)g'(x) + f'(x)g(x)$.

5. If $y = f(x)/g(x)$, what is y'?   *Ans.* $y' = \dfrac{g(x)f'(x) - f(x)g'(x)}{[g(x)]^{2}}$.

5. *The Integration of Combinations of Functions.* Whenever a theorem on differentiation is established it is helpful to think immediately of the inverse process of antidifferentiation, because the inverse process is equally important. Theorem 1 tells us that if $y = cu$, then $\dot{y} = c\dot{u}$. It tells us that the constant factor c can, so to speak, be ignored for the moment while we differentiate the function u and that we then multiply the result of the differentiation by c. The very meaning of antidifferentiation, that is, finding the function that has a given derived function, enables us to state the following theorem:

   Theorem 8:   *If* $\dot{y} = c\dot{u}$, *then* $y = cu + C$.

In practice this means that in antidifferentiation or integration we may ignore the constant factor for a moment, integrate the function, and then multiply the antiderivative or integral by the constant. Of course, the constant of integration C must be added on.

Just as Theorem 8 follows from Theorem 1, so a consequence of Theorem 2 on the differentiation of a sum of functions is the following theorem:

   Theorem 9:   *If* $\dot{y} = \dot{u} + \dot{v}$, *then* $y = u + v + C$. *That is, the integral of a sum of functions is the sum of the integrals plus the constant of integration.*

In view of Theorem 3, we could of course extend Theorem 9 to a sum of n functions. There is no need to state a separate theorem.

We might ask next, what theorems on antidifferentiation correspond to Theorems 5 and 7 on the differentiation of products and quotients? There is a very useful inverse to Theorem 5, called *integration by parts.* However, we shall delay studying it until we can make significant use of it. (See Chapter 13, Section 2.) As for Theorem 7, we can indeed state that if

(42) $$\dot{y} = \frac{v\dot{u} - u\dot{v}}{v^{2}},$$

then

$$y = \frac{u}{v} + C.$$

However, this result is rarely useful. The reason is that a derived function is seldom presented to us in the explicit form (42). A derived function may indeed have resulted from the application of the theorem on quotients, as was the case in (41), but when the result is simplified algebraically, it is no longer possible to recognize what the original u and v were. Hence the antidifferentiation is performed in accordance with some other theorem.

Exercises

1. Find the integrals of the following derived functions:

(a) $\dot{y} = 8x^2$.   Ans. $y = \frac{8}{3}x^3 + C$.

(b) $\dot{y} = 7x^{\frac{2}{3}}$.

(c) $\dot{y} = \sqrt{8x}$.

Ans. $y = \dfrac{4\sqrt{2}}{3} x^{\frac{3}{2}} + C$.

(d) $\dot{y} = 7x^{\frac{2}{3}} + \sqrt{8x}$.

Ans. $y = \frac{21}{5}x^{\frac{5}{3}} + \dfrac{4\sqrt{2}}{3} x^{\frac{3}{2}} + C$.

(e) $\dot{y} = 7x^2 + 6x - 3$.

Ans. $y = \frac{7}{3}x^3 + 3x^2 - 3x + C$.

(f) $\dot{y} = \sqrt{4x}$.

(g) $\dot{y} = -7x^2 - 6x + 3$.

(h) $\dot{y} = \dfrac{x^4 + 3x^2}{x^2}$.

Ans. $y = \dfrac{x^3}{3} + 3x + C$.

(i) $\dot{y} = \dfrac{x^4 + 3x^2}{\sqrt{x}}$.

(j) $\dot{y} = ax^2 + bx + c$.

Ans. $y = \dfrac{a}{3} x^3 + \dfrac{b}{2} x^2 + cx + C$.

(k) $\dot{y} = 3x^4 - 7x^2 + 5x - 6$.

6. All Integrals Differ by a Constant. The theorems on the differentiation of combinations of functions, in conjunction with what we have already learned about the geometrical interpretation of the derived function as the slope of a curve, permit us to give a rather convincing geometrical argument in support of a fact that we have been using right along. We have said, for example, that if

(43) $$\dot{y} = 4x$$

then

(44) $$y = 2x^2 + C;$$

that is, *all* integrals of (43) are comprised in (44). In other words, all integrals of a given derived function are obtained by finding one integral and adding a constant. Let us prove this geometrically.

It is more convenient here to use the function notation. Suppose that

(45) $$\dot{y} = f'(x).$$

Then certainly

$$y = f(x)$$

is one integral of (45). Now let $g(x)$ be any other integral of (45); that is, $g'(x) = f'(x)$. We should like to show that $g(x)$ can differ from $f(x)$ by at most a constant. Then let

(46) $$w = f(x) - g(x).$$

By the theorem on the differentiation of the difference of two functions,

$$\dot{w} = f'(x) - g'(x) = 0.$$

We now ask, what function has the derived function that is 0 over some interval of x-values? Geometrically it seems clear that if the slope of some curve is always 0, this curve must be a straight line parallel to the x-axis. Then the equation of w as a function of x must be $w = $ constant. Hence we see from (46) that $g(x) = f(x) + $ constant. Because $g(x)$ is *any* integral of (45) other than $f(x)$, we see that all integrals of (45) are given by

$$(47) \qquad\qquad y = f(x) + C.$$

7. The Power Rule for Negative Exponents. The general theorems on differentiation that we proved in Section 4 enable us to extend at once the range of the power rule. We have already proved that when n is a positive integer or a positive fraction, the derived function of $y = x^n$ is $\dot{y} = nx^{n-1}$. We now prove that the power rule holds when n is a negative integer or negative fraction. The proof is simple. We start with

$$(48) \qquad\qquad y = x^n$$

where n is a negative integer or a negative fraction. By the very meaning of a negative exponent we have

$$(49) \qquad\qquad y = \frac{1}{x^{-n}}$$

where, of course, $-n$ is positive. We can regard (49) as a quotient of two functions, namely, 1 and x^{-n}. We know how to differentiate a quotient and we know how to differentiate x^{-n} because the exponent is positive. We apply (40). Then

$$\dot{y} = \frac{x^{-n}(0) - 1(-nx^{-n-1})}{(x^{-n})^2}$$

or

$$\dot{y} = \frac{nx^{-n-1}}{x^{-2n}} = nx^{-n-1-(-2n)}$$

or

$$(50) \qquad\qquad \dot{y} = nx^{n-1}.$$

If we compare (48) and (50), we see that $\dot{y}$ is obtained from y by a straightforward application of the power rule, even though n is a negative whole number or a negative fraction. Hence the power rule holds when n is a positive or negative whole number or fraction. We should note that for negative n, for example x^{-3}, the function is not defined at $x = 0$, and therefore neither the derivative nor the derived function has any meaning at $x = 0$.

If we combine what we proved in Chapter 5, Section 4, with what we just proved, we have the following theorem:

Theorem 10:   *If $y = x^n$, where n is a positive or a negative whole number or fraction or zero, then*

$$(51) \qquad \qquad \dot{y} = nx^{n-1}.$$

Corresponding to the theorem on differentiation is a theorem on anti-differentiation. We could state the new theorem thus: if $\dot{y} = nx^{n-1}$, where n is a positive or negative integer or fraction or zero, then $y = x^n + C$. However, in practice we generally encounter $\dot{y}$ in the form $\dot{y} = x^n$. To obtain the integral we reverse what is done when differentiating a power of x, that is, we increase the exponent by 1 and divide by the new exponent. The result is

$$y = \frac{x^{n+1}}{n+1} + C.$$

We notice now that the result is meaningless when $n = -1$. In other words, the derived function $\dot{y} = 1/x$ cannot be integrated, at least not by the power rule. Our result then is the power rule for integration:

Theorem 11:   *If $\dot{y} = x^n$ where n is any positive or negative whole number or fraction or zero except -1, then*

$$(52) \qquad \qquad y = \frac{x^{n+1}}{n+1} + C.$$

Exercises

1. Find the derived functions of the following functions:

(a) $y = x^{-7}$.   *Ans.* $\dot{y} = -7x^{-8}$.

(b) $y = x^{-3/2}$.

(e) $y = \dfrac{1}{\sqrt{3x}}$.

(c) $y = \dfrac{2}{x}$.   *Ans.* $\dot{y} = -2x^{-2}$.

   Ans. $\dot{y} = -\dfrac{1}{2\sqrt{3}} x^{-3/2}$.

(d) $y = \dfrac{1}{\sqrt{x}}$.

(f) $y = \dfrac{x^2 + 7x}{x^3}$.

2. Find the integrals of the following derived functions:

(a) $\dot{y} = x^{-7}$.   *Ans.* $y = -\dfrac{x^{-6}}{6} + C$.

(e) $\dot{y} = \dfrac{1}{\sqrt{8x}}$.

(b) $\dot{y} = x^{-1/2}$.

   Ans. $y = \dfrac{1}{\sqrt{2}} x^{1/2} + C$.

(c) $\dot{y} = \dfrac{1}{\sqrt{x}}$.   *Ans.* $y = 2x^{1/2} + C$.

(d) $\dot{y} = \dfrac{1}{8x^2}$.

3. Show that the segment of the tangent at any point (Fig. 6-8) of the curve $y = 1/x$ (the curve is called a hyperbola) that is cut off by the axes is bisected at the point of contact.

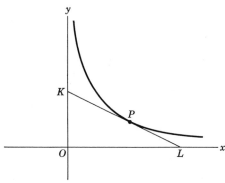

Figure 6-8

4. Show that the tangent at any point of the curve $y = 1/x$ (Fig. 6-8) cuts off from the axes a triangle which always has the same area.

5. When light is given off by a source, which is often idealized as a point, it spreads out in all directions. At some subsequent time it illuminates a spherical area of radius $\dot{r}$ feet or an area of $4\pi r^2$ square feet. If the intensity given off by the source is A units (lumens is the technical name for the unit), the intensity per square unit of area illuminated is $I = A/4\pi r^2$. Find the rate of change of the intensity with distance when $r = 20$ feet and when $r = 200$ feet. How would you explain physically that the numerical value or absolute value of the rate of change is much less when $r = 200$ feet than when $r = 20$ feet?

   Ans. At $r = 20$, $dI/dr = -A/1600\pi$; at $r = 200$, $dI/dr = -A/16{,}000{,}000\pi$.

8. *Extension of the Method of Calculating Areas.* In Chapter 5 we found that we could calculate certain curvilinear areas, that is, areas bounded in part by arcs of curves. The method we employed was limited to areas such as *DEFG* (Fig. 6-9) which is bounded on only one side by a curve. It may

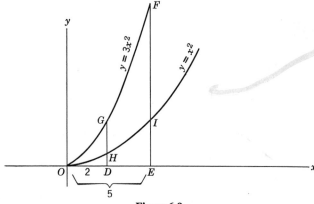

Figure 6-9

seem, therefore, that our calculus method of finding areas bounded by curved figures is limited to very special curvilinear areas. However, the method is more powerful than our previous experience would lead us to believe.

Let us try to find the area *GHIF* (Fig. 6-9) bounded by the arc *HI* of the curve $y = x^2$, the arc *GF* of the curve $y = 3x^2$, the portion *HG* of the vertical line at $x = 2$, and the portion *IF* of the vertical line at $x = 5$. Here we have an area bounded on two sides by arcs. This shape is presumably not encompassed by the method we previously examined. However, we can find the area *GDEF* by the earlier method, for this area is bounded only above by an arc of a curve. Likewise we can find the area *HDEI*. The difference of these two areas is the area we seek.

To find the area *GDEF* we introduce the derived function

(53) $$\dot{A} = y,$$

where y is the ordinate of the curve $y = 3x^2$. Then

$$\dot{A} = 3x^2.$$

By antidifferentiation we find that

(54) $$A = x^3.$$

We recall from Chapter 5, Section 5 that we need not introduce the constant of integration. We have but to substitute 5 for x in (54) and then 2 for x, and subtract the second result from the first. Thus

$$GDEF = 125 - 8 = 117.$$

To find the area *HDEI* we repeat the procedure, except that this time the y in (53) refers to the curve $y = x^2$. Then

$$\dot{A} = x^2,$$

and by antidifferentiation

$$A = \frac{x^3}{3}.$$

Again, we substitute 5 for x and then 2 for x, and subtract the second result from the first. Then

$$HDEI = \tfrac{125}{3} - \tfrac{8}{3} = \tfrac{117}{3}.$$

In accordance with our plan,

$$GHIF = GDEF - HDEI = 117 - \tfrac{117}{3} = \tfrac{234}{3} = 78.$$

The method of subtracting one area from another enables us to find other kinds of curvilinear areas. Let us try to find the area between the two curves $y = x^2$ and $y = \sqrt{8x}$. To visualize this area, we graph the two functions

(Fig. 6-10). Both curves, incidentally, are parabolas; the curve $y = x^2$ has a vertical axis of symmetry which is the positive half of the y-axis, and the curve $y = \sqrt{8x}$ has a horizontal axis of symmetry which is the positive half of the x-axis. The graph shows that the area we seek is bounded by the arcs OPQ and ORQ.

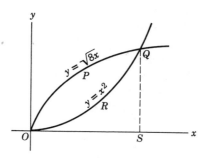

Figure 6-10

This area is not quite of the type that we learned to find in the preceding example. However, we can find the area bounded by OPQ, the ordinate QS, and the segment OS of the x-axis. We can also find the area bounded by ORQ, the ordinate QS, and the segment OS. The difference of the two areas is the area we want. Hence we can find the area $OPQRO$.

We proceed with the plan just described. To do so we need the x-value of the point S. This x-value is the abscissa of Q. But the coordinates of Q are readily found by solving simultaneously the equations

$$y = x^2$$

and

$$y = \sqrt{8x}.$$

At the point Q both y-values are the same. Hence at Q

$$x^2 = \sqrt{8x}.$$

By squaring both sides and by factoring we find that the real solutions are $x = 0$ and $x = 2$. The value $x = 0$ is the abscissa at the origin 0, and the value $x = 2$ must then be the abscissa of Q.

We can then proceed with the determination of the area $ORQSO$. Here $y = x^2$, so that

$$A = x^2.$$

Then

$$A = \frac{x^3}{3}.$$

We substitute 2 for x and then 0 for x, and subtract the second result from the first. Then

$$\text{area } ORQSO = \tfrac{8}{3} - 0 = \tfrac{8}{3}.$$

To find the area *OPQSO* we start with

$$\dot{A} = \sqrt{8x} = 8^{\frac{1}{2}}x^{\frac{1}{2}}.$$

Then by antidifferentiation

$$A = 8^{\frac{1}{2}}\frac{x^{\frac{3}{2}}}{\frac{3}{2}} = \tfrac{2}{3}8^{\frac{1}{2}}x^{\frac{3}{2}}.$$

We now substitute 2 for *x*. Then

$$\tfrac{2}{3}8^{\frac{1}{2}}2^{\frac{3}{2}} = \tfrac{2}{3}8^{\frac{1}{2}}\cdot 8^{\frac{1}{2}} = \tfrac{2}{3}\cdot 8 = \tfrac{16}{3}.$$

The substitution of 0 for *x* of course yields 0. Then

$$\text{area } OPQSO = \tfrac{16}{3} - 0 = \tfrac{16}{3}.$$

Finally,

$$\text{area } OPQRO = \text{area } OPQSO - \text{area } ORQSO = \tfrac{16}{3} - \tfrac{8}{3} = \tfrac{8}{3}.$$

Thus we have found an area bounded entirely by arcs of curves.

Exercises

In the following problems draw a figure to show the area sought.

1. Find the area between the curves $y = 3x^2$ and $y = 5x^2$ and between the ordinates at $x = 2$ and $x = 4$.   *Ans.* $37\frac{1}{3}$.
2. Find the area between the curve $y = 1/x^2$ and the *x*-axis and between $x = 1$ and $x = 3$.
3. Find the area between the curve $y = x^2$ and the line $y = 2x$.   *Ans.* $\frac{4}{3}$.
4. Find the area between the curves $y = x^2$ and $y = \sqrt{5x}$.
5. Find the area between the curves $y = 9 - x^2$ and $y = x^2$.   *Ans.* $18\sqrt{2}$.
6. Find the area between the curve $y = x^2$ and the straight line $y = 8x - 4$.
7. Find the area between the parabolas $y = 2x^2 + 1$ and $y = x^2 + 5$.   *Ans.* $10\frac{2}{3}$.
8. Find the area between $y^2 = 16x$ and $y^2 = x^3$.   *Ans.* $8\frac{8}{15}$.

9. Areas Lying Below the X-axis. Let us use our method of finding curvilinear areas to calculate the area bounded by the curve $y = x^2 - 9$, the *x*-axis, and the vertical lines $x = 1$ and $x = 4$. The area is the shaded region shown in Fig. 6-11.

In accordance with our method we write

(55) $$\dot{A} = x^2 - 9.$$

Hence

(56) $$A = \frac{x^3}{3} - 9x.$$

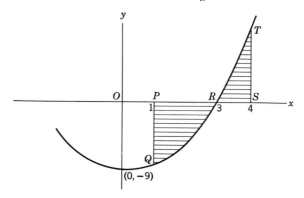

Figure 6-11

We now substitute 4 for x, then 1 for x, and subtract the second result from the first. Thus

$$\text{area } PQRST = \tfrac{64}{3} - 36 - (\tfrac{1}{3} - 9) = -6.$$

We obtain a negative area, a rather surprising result.

One might suspect at once that the negative result is due to the fact that part of the area lies below the x-axis, for this is the essential difference between what we have here and what we had in earlier calculations of area. Let us see if this fact is the source of the trouble. When we developed the method of finding areas, we started by thinking of a vertical line which is initially at the left-hand boundary, at PQ in our present example, and which sweeps out area as it moves to the right. We found, further, that $\dot{A}$ is given by the y-value of the curve or in the present case by (55). Then the function A is given by

$$A = \frac{x^3}{3} - 9x + C,$$

and we determined C so that $A = 0$ when $x = 1$. Thus

(57) $$A = \frac{x^3}{3} - 9x + \frac{26}{3}$$

Now we can see from (55) that for any value of x between $x = 1$ and $x = 3$ the value of $\dot{A}$ is negative. That is, the rate of change of area with respect to x at any value of x between 1 and 3 is negative. When the rate of change of a function is negative, the function must be decreasing. We have but to recall the work·with velocity to recognize this fact. If the positive direction for height above the ground is upward, a negative velocity means that the height is decreasing. Likewise A here is decreasing and, because it starts from the value 0 at $x = 1$, the value of A at any value of x between 1 and 3 is *negative*. In fact, we see from (57) that at $x = 3$, $A = -28/3$. When we arrive at values of x between 3 and 4, $\dot{A}$ is positive, which means that the area is increasing. However, the value of A at $x = 3$ is already negative, and therefore its increase after $x = 3$ means that it increases from $-28/3$ to some larger value, negative or positive, depending on how far the area extends to the right of $x = 3$.

This analysis thus shows us that when an area or part of an area that we seek lies below the x-axis, this area (or part) is negative. Of course, physically the area PQR is as positive as the area RST, and its negative value is due only to the mathematical representation. Therefore, if we want to obtain the physical size of the area $PQRST$, we must first find the negative part, ignore the negative sign, and add it to the positive area. In the present case we have from (56)

$$\text{area } PQR = \left(\frac{3^3}{3} - 9 \cdot 3\right) - \left(\frac{1^3}{3} - 9 \cdot 1\right) = -\frac{28}{3},$$

$$\text{area } RST = \left(\frac{4^3}{3} - 9 \cdot 4\right) - \left(\frac{3^3}{3} - 9 \cdot 3\right) = \frac{10}{3}.$$

The actual area $PQRST$ is

$$\frac{28}{3} + \frac{10}{3} = \frac{38}{3}.$$

Exercises

1. Calculate the physical area in the region bounded by the curve $y = x^3 - 8$, the x-axis, and the vertical lines $x = 1$ and $x = 3$.   *Ans.* $12\frac{1}{2}$.

10. *The Concept of Work and an Application.* An important concept for scientific and engineering purposes is work. As used in these fields the word has a technical meaning, but for the moment let us rely upon our intuitive understanding and consider why one should be interested in it. A train or an airplane which pulls a load over some distance, a crane which lifts a steel girder from the ground to some height, and a rocket which shoots up into the air all do work. Of course, the work that these mechanisms do is powered by engines and fuel. To design the engines and to choose the suitable kind and amount of fuel one must know how much work is to be done. Thus a quantitative measure of the work is called for.

The performance of work involves the application of a force. Pushing or pulling an object along the ground is a force which is needed to overcome the force of friction between the object and the ground. Raising an object calls for the exertion of a force by a person or an engine to overcome the force of gravity. In the technical use of the concept of work the force applied must cause motion. If one holds an object in his hands, one is exerting a force, namely, the force that counters gravity, but in the technical sense one does no work. Loosely speaking, work is force multiplied by the distance through which the force acts.

The unit of force in the British system is the poundal or the pound which is 32 poundals (in the metric system it is the dyne). Because work is force times distance and distance is measured in feet, the unit of work is the foot-poundal (in the metric system the unit of work is the erg or the dyne-centimeter). Thus if a force of 50 poundals pushes an object for 10 feet, the work done is 500 foot-poundals (ft-pdl) or 500/32 foot-pounds (ft-lb).

The examples of work that we shall consider here involve the action of gravity, that is, the gravitational attraction which the earth exerts on objects. When gravity acts on an object and, for example, causes it to fall, we say that gravity does work on the object. If we raise an object, we say that we have done work against gravity. The same amount of force is involved in both cases and, if the object moves the same distance, the work done is the same.

Let us consider the force of gravity. As we have already had occasion to note in Chapter 3, Section 4, the force which the earth's gravity exerts on an object is called the *weight* of the object. This concept of weight involves more than is commonly supposed; in particular, it involves the notion of *mass*. Every piece of matter has mass, which is a property quite different from weight. Technically the mass of an object is the resistance it offers to any change in its velocity. However, for our purposes it is adequate to think of the mass of an object as the quantity of matter in it. It is intuitively clear that a cubic foot of lead has more mass than a cubic foot of wood, which in turn has more mass than a cubic foot of sponge. The matter in lead, that is, the atoms and molecules, are more tightly packed which accounts for the greater mass.

Near the surface of the earth the *weight* of an object is always 32 times the amount of *mass*; in symbols,

$$(58) \qquad\qquad w = 32m.$$

This fact is established by direct measurement of mass and weight. The unit of mass is pounds and the unit of weight, because it is a force, is poundals. Unfortunately, the use of the pound for 32 poundals of force causes some confusion, but is also convenient because 1 pound of mass weighs 1 pound.

If an object is near the surface of the earth, its weight does not change appreciably. Hence if gravity pulls an object weighing 100 poundals down a distance of 25 feet, the work which gravity does is 2500 ft-pdl. Certainly, we do not need the calculus to calculate this work.

If an object is at a great distance from the surface of the earth, its weight or the gravitational force exerted on it by the earth is no longer the weight near the surface and, in fact, the weight varies with the distance from the earth. The force which the earth exerts on any object at any distance from the earth's center is given by the famous axiom of physics known as Newton's law of gravitation. This law states that *any* two objects in the universe attract each other, and the force with which each attracts the other is given quantitatively by the formula

(59)
$$F = \frac{GmM}{r^2}.$$

→ *Newton's law or gravitation*

In this formula G is a constant; it is the same number no matter what the masses involved and no matter what the distance between them. The quantities m and M are the *masses* of the two objects measured in pounds. The quantity r is the distance between the two objects. We shall say more about r later.

Because the quantity G is constant, we can take two known masses, measure the distance between them, measure the force with which they attract each other, and then calculate G, the only unknown in (59). This has been done many times, and the value of G turns out to be, in the foot-poundal-second system, $1.07 \cdot 10^{-9}$ (in the metric system G is $6.67 \cdot 10^{-8}$).

Let us now suppose that m is the mass of some object above the surface of the earth and M is the mass of the earth itself. We intend to apply Newton's law to the action of M on m. There is a difficulty here. Strictly speaking, Newton's law applies to particles, that is, to objects which, in the situation being studied, can be idealized as concentrated at one point. An object which is treated as a particle is not necessarily small. Thus in treating some aspects of the motion of the earth around the sun it may be adequate to regard the earth and sun as particles or point-masses. It is likewise often possible to treat an object which falls to earth as a particle, and we shall do so in the present section. However, the earth is vast compared to the object, and the various portions of the earth pull the object in different directions and with different strengths because their distances from the falling object vary considerably. Hence it does not seem possible to treat the earth as a particle. There is, however, a remarkable theorem, which we shall prove much later and which states that the earth, if regarded as a sphere, attracts particles *as though* the earth's mass were concentrated at its center. Hence we can take the distance between the earth and the object, the quantity r in (59), to be the distance from the *center* of the earth to the object and M in (59) stands for the mass of the earth. With these understandings about m, M, and r, the force F given by (59) is the weight of the object. We see that the weight of an object does vary with its distance from the center of the earth; in fact, the weight decreases as the distance increases.

How does this formula for weight compare with formula (58), namely, $w = 32m$? When the value of G is substituted in (59), when M is replaced by the mass of the earth, and when r is taken to be $4000 \cdot 5280$, that is, when the object is at or practically at the surface of the earth, the quantity GM/r^2 reduces to 32, so that GMm/r^2 becomes $32m$ and w is then only a special designation of F. In other words, for the values of G and M just mentioned and for the value of r just specified

(60) $$\frac{GM}{(4000 \cdot 5280)^2} = 32.$$

In practice we often use this equation to find the product GM.

To calculate the work done by gravity in pulling an object some distance straight down, we cannot multiply the force by the distance because the force varies from point to point along the path. We must use the calculus. Let us actually compute the work done by gravity in pulling an object some distance downward.

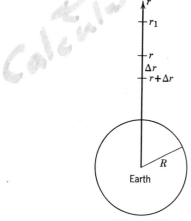

Let us choose the direction from the center of the earth upward as the positive direction for r (Fig. 6-12). Because the force of gravitation acts toward the center, we write

(61) $$F = -\frac{GmM}{r^2}$$

where M is the mass of the earth and m is the mass of the object. Suppose that the object is at some distance r from the center of the earth and gravity pulls the object downward a small distance Δr. Even over this small distance Δr the force of gravity is not constant, and therefore strictly we cannot say that the force is given by (61). However, it is reasonable to suppose that there is some value $\bar{r}$ in the interval Δr at which the force

Figure 6-12

$$\bar{F} = -\frac{GMm}{\bar{r}^2}$$

has an average value for the interval Δr. Geometrically, this assertion is evident. Suppose that we graph F as a function of r (Fig. 6-13). If we used the value of F at r and $F \cdot \Delta r$ as the work done in the interval Δr, the work

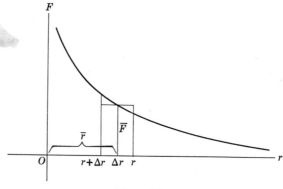

Figure 6-13

would be too small. If we used the value of F at $r + \Delta r$, the quantity $F\Delta r$ would be too large. There is some value $\bar{r}$ and a corresponding $\bar{F}$ such that $\bar{F}\Delta r$ is precisely the work done in the interval Δr. (This quantity $\bar{F}$ is entirely analogous to the quantity $\bar{y}$ used in Fig. 5-6 for our derivation of the formula for area.) Let us denote the work done by gravity in moving the object over the interval Δr by ΔW. Then

$$\Delta W = \bar{F}\Delta r.$$

By division

$$\frac{\Delta W}{\Delta r} = \bar{F}.$$

We now determine the limit of $\Delta W / \Delta r$ as Δr approaches 0. As Δr approaches 0, $\bar{r}$ must come closer and closer to r because $\bar{r}$ is between r and $r + \Delta r$. Then $\bar{F}$ must come closer and closer to the value of F at r. That is,

$$\dot{W} = \lim_{\Delta r \to 0} \frac{\Delta W}{\Delta r} = F$$

or, in view of (61),

$$\dot{W} = -\frac{GmM}{r^2}.$$

We may now apply formula (52), the inverse of the power law, to assert that

(62)
$$W = \frac{GmM}{r} + C.$$

To determine the constant of integration we suppose that the object is to start at the distance r_1 from the center of the earth and that no work has been done as yet by gravity. This means that when $r = r_1$, $W = 0$. Then $C = -GmM/r_1$ and

(63)
$$W = \frac{GmM}{r} - \frac{GmM}{r_1}.$$

This is the formula for the work done by gravity in pulling an object of mass m down from a point r_1 feet from the center of the earth to a point r feet from the center.

To use formula (63) we must know the value of the product GM. It is given by (60), which shows that

(64)
$$GM = 32(4000 \cdot 5280)^2.$$

If we should happen to need the values of G and M separately, we could use the measured value of G, which is

$$G = 1.07 \cdot 10^{-9},$$

and calculate M, which proves to be

$$M = 13.1 \cdot 10^{24} \text{ pounds.}$$

We also note that for the purpose of simple algebraic transformations it is convenient to let R denote the radius of the earth, that is,

$$R = 4000 \cdot 5280;$$

then (64) reads

(65) $GM = 32R^2.$

Exercises

1. Show that the work done by gravity in pulling an object of mass m straight down from a distance r_1 from the center of the earth to the surface of the earth is $W = 32mR[1 - (R/r_1)]$.

2. Calculate the work that gravity does in pulling a mass of 100 pounds from a height of 500 miles above the earth to the surface of the earth.

$$\textit{Ans.} \quad \frac{22{,}528 \cdot 10^6}{3} \text{ ft-pdl.}$$

3. Suppose that we use $32m$ as the constant force of gravity and calculate the work done by gravity in pulling an object over the same path as in Exercise 2. Before calculating, determine whether the answer will be greater or smaller than the answer in Exercise 2 and then carry out the calculation.

$$\textit{Ans.} \ 8{,}448 \cdot 10^6 \text{ ft-pdl.}$$

4. How much work is done in raising a satellite with a mass of 1000 pounds from the surface of the earth to a height of 1500 miles?

5. Formula (63) gives the work done by gravity in pulling an object down when the work is 0 at the height r_1. Suppose that we want to measure work so that it is 0 when the object is at the surface of the earth, that is, when $r = R$. Obtain the appropriate formula for the work done in moving the object from the distance r to the surface.

$$\textit{Ans.} \ W = 32mR \left(\frac{R}{r} - 1 \right).$$

6. A cable weighing 2 pounds per foot of length (and so having a mass of 2 pounds per foot) is suspended from the top of a well 200 feet deep and extends to the bottom. Find the work done in raising the cable to the surface. Over the distance of 200 feet you may use $32m$ as the constant weight of a mass m.

7. Suppose that the cable described in Exercise 6 has a tool weighing 300 pounds attached to the lower end. Calculate the work done in raising the tool to the surface.   *Ans.* 3,200,000 ft-pdl.

8. The law of gravitation applies of course also to the moon and to any object which the moon attracts. The mass of an object is the same everywhere, so that an object with mass m on the earth has mass m on or near the moon. However, the weight of an object of mass m is $5.3m$ on the surface of the moon. The moon's radius is about 1100 miles so that [cf. (60)] is M if the mass of the moon

$$\frac{GM}{(5280 \cdot 1100)^2} = 5.3.$$

(*a*) Determine first whether formula (63) applies to work done by the moon's
gravity.   *Ans.* Yes.

(*b*) Derive the formula analogous to that given in Exercise 1, that is, the formula
for the work done by the moon's gravity in moving an object of mass *m*
from a distance of r_1 from the center to the surface of the moon.

Ans. $W = 5.3mR[1 - (R/r_1)]$;   *R* is the radius of the moon.

9. Using the data of Exercise 8, calculate the work which the moon's gravity does
in pulling a mass of 100 pounds from a height of 500 miles above the surface
to the surface (cf. Exercise 2).

10. How much work must be done to raise a satellite with a mass of 1000 pounds
from the surface of the moon to a height of 1500 miles (cf. Exercise 4).

$$\textit{Ans.} \quad \frac{230{,}868 \cdot 10^6}{13} \text{ ft-pdl.}$$

11. (*a*) To push an object up a smooth inclined plane, one must overcome the
force of gravity which causes the object to slide down the plane. Hence
according to formula (32) of Chapter 3 the force which must be applied is
w sin *A* where *w* is the weight of the object and *A* is the angle of inclination
of the plane. Suppose that you push the object from the ground level to a
point *h* feet above the ground. How much work is done?   *Ans. wh.*

(*b*) Is the result remarkable in any respect?

CHAPTER SEVEN

The Chain Rule

1. Introduction. The problems that we have considered so far have called for straightforward differentiation and integration. That is, given y as a function of x we found the derived function $\dot{y}$, or given $\dot{y}$ as a function of x we found y as a function of x. These processes suffice to handle a number of physical problems; some have already appeared and others will be encountered later. However, the physical information that some problems offer leads to a somewhat more involved mathematical problem. As we shall see later in this chapter, we may have to start our mathematical work with the information that the acceleration is a given function of the distance traveled. For example, we might have that

$$a = s^2.$$

Because a is $\dot{v}$ or dv/dt, we have

(1) $$\frac{dv}{dt} = s^2.$$

We have deliberately used the Leibnizian notation dv/dt rather than $\dot{v}$ in (1) because we wish to be very explicit about the variables involved.

Suppose now that we wish to find the velocity as a function of the time or the velocity as a function of the distance. How should we proceed? We cannot integrate with respect to t because the right-hand side of (1) is not explicitly a function of t; nor can we treat s as a constant. It is equally incorrect to integrate with respect to s because the given derivative is with respect to t.

We face in (1) a situation involving three variables: s, v and t. Physically it is clear that s, the distance traveled, is a function of the velocity v and v is a function of t. Of course, s is also a function of t. If we could replace dv/dt in (1) by ds/dt or ds/dv, we might be able to proceed because then only two variables would enter into the entire equation. The possible derivatives involved are

$$\frac{ds}{dt}, \quad \frac{ds}{dv} \quad \text{and} \quad \frac{dv}{dt}.$$

Let us see if we can build up some connection among these three derivatives.

2. *The Chain Rule*. Instead of using s, v, and t, which usually refer to motion problems, let us use the standard letters y, u, and x. Then the situation we wish to consider is that we have y as a function of u and u as a function of x. Thus we might have

(2) $$y = 3u^2 \quad \text{and} \quad u = 7x^3 - 6x^2 - 9.$$

This situation is often described by saying that y is a function of a function or that y is a composite function of x.

We can, of course, find dy/du and du/dx. Can we find dy/dx from these two quantities, that is, without resorting to substituting the value of u in (2) into the function of u? We have used the Leibnizian notation for the derivatives because several variables are involved and we have to be clear about the independent and dependent variables in each derivative. This notation suggests that

(3) $$\frac{dy}{dx} = \frac{dy}{du} \cdot \frac{du}{dx}.$$

The Leibnizian notation is very helpful in specifying the variables, but here it may lead to some wrong inferences. We might conclude in looking at (3) that all we must do to prove the equality is to cancel the du's. We recall, however, that the symbolism dy/du, for example, does not mean a quotient. The entire symbol stands for a limit, which is not a quotient but a number approached by the entire fraction $\Delta y/\Delta u$ as Δu approaches 0.

However, (3) is correct, and the method of increments yields the desired proof. Before using it, let us remind ourselves that (3) is a meaningful statement, first of all, at a point. That is, if x_0 is some value of x, u_0 the corresponding value of u, and y_0 the corresponding value of y, then dy/dx at $x = x_0$ is the product of dy/du at u_0 and du/dx at x_0, if du/dx exists at x_0 and if dy/du exists at u_0. Secondly, (3) is also a statement about the derived *functions* dy/dx, dy/du, and du/dx for those x_0's and u_0's for which the equality holds among the derivatives.

We now apply the method of increments. We note that if we change x_0, the value of x at which we seek the derivative, by an amount Δx, then u changes by some amount Δu because u is a function of x. However, if u changes by an amount Δu, then y changes by an amount Δy. We can write the purely algebraic relation

(4) $$\frac{\Delta y}{\Delta x} = \frac{\Delta y}{\Delta u} \cdot \frac{\Delta u}{\Delta x}.$$

Each of these fractions is a true quotient, and therefore this equation is justified merely because we can cancel Δu's on the right side. We intend to apply a limit process, but before doing so we note that when Δx approaches 0, Δu approaches 0. This is true when du/dx exists, for if Δu did not approach 0 when Δx does, the limit du/dx could not exist—it would be infinite. Hence, to require that Δx approach 0 is to require that Δu approach 0. Likewise when Δu approaches 0, Δy approaches 0. If we take the limit as Δx approaches 0 in (4), the limit on the right side, which is a product, can be calculated as the product of the limits. The limit of $\Delta u/\Delta x$ is of course du/dx; the limit of $\Delta y/\Delta u$ is dy/du. Then*

$$(5) \qquad\qquad \frac{dy}{dx} = \frac{dy}{du} \cdot \frac{du}{dx}.$$

Thus we have proved the following theorem:

Theorem 1: *If y is a function of u and u is a function of x, then*

$$(6) \qquad\qquad \frac{dy}{dx} = \frac{dy}{du} \cdot \frac{du}{dx}.$$

This theorem is called the chain rule because it deals with a "chain" of functions.

3. Application of the Chain Rule to Differentiation.   We shall make extensive use of the chain rule. The first advantage we derive from it is to enlarge considerably the class of functions we can differentiate and integrate. At present we consider differentiation.

Let us consider the function

$$(7) \qquad\qquad y = \sqrt{x^2 + 1}.$$

No one of the theorems that we have encountered so far for differentiating a function applies to (7). However, with the chain rule at hand we can proceed as follows. We know that we can differentiate $y = \sqrt{u}$ with respect to u, and therefore we let

$$(8) \qquad\qquad u = x^2 + 1.$$

Then in place of (7) we have

$$y = \sqrt{u} \quad \text{and} \quad u = x^2 + 1.$$

Now we see that

$$\frac{dy}{du} = \tfrac{1}{2}u^{-\frac{1}{2}} \quad \text{and} \quad \frac{du}{dx} = 2x.$$

Then by the chain rule

$$\frac{dy}{dx} = \frac{dy}{du} \cdot \frac{du}{dx} = \tfrac{1}{2}u^{-\frac{1}{2}} \cdot 2x.$$

* This proof of (5) is not quite complete. It is possible for Δu to be 0 when Δx is not 0. Then the algebraic equation (4) is not justified. Actually if Δu is not 0 for any small interval about u_0, the proof is right, for we need to consider only small Δx to obtain the limit as Δx approaches 0. However, Δu may be 0 at values of x arbitrarily close to x_0. Nevertheless, (5) can be shown to be true in this case also.

In view of the value of u in (8),

(9)
$$\frac{dy}{dx} = \frac{x}{\sqrt{x^2 + 1}}.$$

The chain rule can also be used to expedite differentiations that could be performed without it but are more readily done with it. Thus suppose that

(10)
$$y = (x^2 + 1)^5.$$

We could, of course, expand the binomial and obtain a polynomial and then differentiate the polynomial by using earlier theorems. However, it is easier to proceed as follows. Let

$$u = x^2 + 1.$$

Then

$$y = u^5 \quad \text{and} \quad u = x^2 + 1.$$

Furthermore,

$$\frac{dy}{du} = 5u^4 \quad \text{and} \quad \frac{du}{dx} = 2x.$$

Then by the chain rule

$$\frac{dy}{dx} = \frac{dy}{du} \cdot \frac{du}{dx} = 5u^4 \cdot 2x = 5(x^2 + 1)^4 \cdot 2x.$$

Thus by the application of the chain rule we have obtained dy/dx rapidly, and we have the answer in a compact form. Let us pay particular attention to the appearance of the factor $2x$ in the answer. It enters the answer because of the factor du/dx in the chain rule.

This example suggests that we can profitably generalize Theorem 10 of Chapter 6. There we learned that if

$$y = x^n$$

where n is a positive or negative integer or fraction or zero, then

(11)
$$\dot{y} = nx^{n-1}.$$

Now suppose that we have $y = u^n$ where u is a function of x. Then the chain rule tells us that

$$\frac{dy}{dx} = \frac{dy}{du} \cdot \frac{du}{dx}.$$

To find dy/du we can apply (11) because u is as much a variable as x is. Then

$$\frac{dy}{dx} = nu^{n-1} \frac{du}{dx}.$$

This result, which is basic in differentiation, should be stated as a theorem:

Theorem 2:   If $y = u^n$ where u is a function of x and n is a positive or negative integer or fraction or zero, then

(12) $$\frac{dy}{dx} = nu^{n-1}\frac{du}{dx}.$$

We call this result the generalized power rule for differentiation.

Exercises

1. Differentiate the following functions:

(a) $y = (x^3 + 1)^4$.
    Ans. $\dot{y} = 12(x^3 + 1)^3 x^2$.

(b) $y = (x^2 - 7x + 6)^4$.

(c) $y = \sqrt[3]{x^2 + 1}$.
    Ans. $\dot{y} = \frac{2}{3}(x^2 + 1)^{-\frac{2}{3}}x$.

(d) $y = \left(\frac{x}{x+1}\right)^4$.

(e) $y = \sqrt{x^2 - x}$.
    Ans. $\dot{y} = \frac{1}{2}(x^2 - x)^{-\frac{1}{2}}(2x - 1)$.

(f) $y = \sqrt{x^2 - x}\,(x^2 + 1)$.

(g) $y = \sqrt{\dfrac{x}{1 + x}}$.
    Ans. $\dot{y} = \dfrac{1}{2\sqrt{x}(1 + x)^{\frac{3}{2}}}$.

(h) $y = \sqrt{1 + x}\sqrt{1 - x}$.

(i) $y = (\dot{y})^2$.   Ans. $\dot{y} = 2\dot{y}\ddot{y}$.

2. As an object increases its height x above the surface of the earth, its weight w decreases because the pull of gravity on the object decreases. Suppose that a rocket weighs $80/(x + 4000)^2$ million pounds at an altitude of x miles and is rising at the constant rate of 100 mi/min. Find the rate of change of weight with respect to time at any instant.   Ans. $dw/dt = -16,000/(x + 4000)^3$.

4. The Differentiation of Implicit Functions.   A function is a relation between two variables such that given a value of one in some domain a unique value of the second is determined. Thus $y = x^3 - 7x^2$ is a typical function. Functions often occur in less convenient form. Thus the relation between abscissa and ordinate of a circle (Fig. 7-1) of radius 5 is, by the Pythagorean theorem,

(13) $$x^2 + y^2 = 25.$$

Here y is not expressed in terms of x. We can, of course, solve for y and obtain

$$y = \pm\sqrt{25 - x^2}.$$

We should note that (13) gives rise to *two* functions:

(14) $$y = \sqrt{25 - x^2} \quad \text{and} \quad y = -\sqrt{25 - x^2}.$$

The first function represents the positive y-values as x ranges from -5 to 5 and the second the negative y-values for the same domain of x-values. Thus in our sense of the term two (single-valued) functions are needed to represent the circle. We say that (13) represents each of these functions *implicitly*, whereas (14) gives each one explicitly.

Figure 7-1

We might be interested in either of these functions. Let us say that we are interested in

(15) $$y = \sqrt{25 - x^2},$$

and that we wish to calculate the derived function, $\dot{y}$, but are given (13) instead of (15). How then do we find $\dot{y}$? One procedure that can often be followed is to solve (13) for y, as in (15), and then differentiate by using the chain rule. However, for many purposes it would be easier to work with the implicit function (13) if we could find some method of differentiating it as it stands.

There is at least one other reason for trying to work with implicit functions. Consider the equation

(16) $$y^3 + xy^2 + x^2 = 0.$$

As far as y is concerned, this is a cubic equation and can be solved for y in terms of x and the constants. In fact, there are (usually) three distinct solutions; that is, the equation (16) represents implicitly three distinct functions. If we wanted to work with any one of these functions, we could solve for y, but the expression that results is quite complicated. It would be simpler to work with (16) as it stands. Furthermore, suppose that we have the equation

(17) $$y^5 + 4y^3 - 3xy^2 + xy + 7 = 0.$$

Here we have a fifth degree equation in y, and only exceptional fifth degree equations can be solved algebraically. Hence even if we were willing to work with a complicated expression for y, we could not obtain it. If we have to work with any one of the five functions represented implicitly by (17), we must learn how to work with the implicit representation.

Let us consider the problem of differentiating a function which is given implicitly and let us start with the simple case of (13). We know that y in (13) represents some function of x, but we do not care to know or utilize the precise form of this function. If we recognize that the left side of (13) is then only a set of terms in x, we may be able to differentiate it. The derivative of x^2 is $2x$. The real problem is, what is the derivative of y^2 with respect to x? Here we have a function of y, namely y^2, and y itself is a function of x. Finding the derivative of y^2 with respect to x should remind us of the chain rule. This rule tells us (y plays the role of u in the chain rule) that we must differentiate with respect to y and then multiply by dy/dx; that is,

$$\frac{d(y^2)}{dx} = 2y\frac{dy}{dx}.$$

We have then the derivative of the left side of (13). The right side is a constant and its derivative is 0. Hence we obtain

(18)
$$2x + 2y\frac{dy}{dx} = 0.$$

From this we have

(19)
$$\frac{dy}{dx} = \dot{y} = -\frac{x}{y}.$$

It is true that the derivative involves y as well as x. Sometimes the derivative can be used in exactly this form. For example, to calculate the slope of the circle at (3, 4), we can substitute directly in (19). Alternatively, if we can find y explicitly, and we can in this case, we can substitute the value of y in (19) and obtain $\dot{y}$ as a function of x. We must be careful, however, to keep in mind which function is involved. If we are interested in the upper half of the circle, we must use $y = \sqrt{25 - x^2}$, and if in the lower half of the circle, then $y = -\sqrt{25 - x^2}$.

The differentiation of an equation such as (16) involves another, minor consideration. We have

(20)
$$y^3 + xy^2 + x^2 = 0.$$

Again we argue that because this equation defines y as a function of x, the left side is a function of x. To differentiate y^3 we again use the chain rule and obtain

$$\frac{d(y^3)}{dx} = 3y^2\frac{dy}{dx}.$$

To differentiate the term xy^2 we must first take into account the fact that we have a product of two functions of x. Then

$$\frac{d}{dx}(xy^2) = \frac{d(x)}{dx}y^2 + x\frac{d(y^2)}{dx} = y^2 + x \cdot 2y\frac{dy}{dx}.$$

The derivative of the third term in (20), namely x^2, is of course $2x$. Because the right side of (20) is 0, its derivative is 0. We now put together the result of differentiating the several terms in (20) and obtain

$$3y^2 \frac{dy}{dx} + y^2 + 2xy \frac{dy}{dx} + 2x = 0.$$

To obtain dy/dx or $\dot{y}$ we must solve this equation for $\dot{y}$. This process gives

$$\dot{y} = \frac{-y^2 - 2x}{3y^2 + 2xy}.$$

In this case it is almost necessary to leave the result in terms of x and y because the explicit expression for any one of the functions y would be cumbersome.

Now that we know how to differentiate functions defined implicitly we can obtain a simpler proof of the power law for positive fractional n than the one in Section 4 of Chapter 5. The problem is to obtain the derivative of

(21) $$y = x^{p/q},$$

where p and q are positive integers and x may be positive, zero, or negative if q is odd but only 0 or positive if q is even. By raising both sides of this equation to the qth power, we have

(22) $$y^q = x^p.$$

Now let us differentiate this equation. By the chain rule

$$\frac{d(y^q)}{dx} = qy^{q-1} \frac{dy}{dx}.$$

The derivative of x^p is px^{p-1}. Then

$$qy^{q-1} \frac{dy}{dx} = px^{p-1}.$$

By solving for dy/dx we obtain

$$\frac{dy}{dx} = \frac{p}{q} \frac{x^{p-1}}{y^{q-1}} = \frac{p}{q} \frac{x^{p-1}y}{y^q}.$$

We have the values of y and y^q in (21) and (22). If we use these, we obtain

$$\frac{dy}{dx} = \frac{p}{q} \frac{x^{p-1}x^{p/q}}{x^p} = \frac{p}{q} x^{-1}x^{p/q} = \frac{p}{q} x^{(p/q)-1}.$$

Thus we see again that the power rule is correct for positive fractional exponents. The extension to negative fractional and negative integral exponents can now be made as in Chapter 6, Section 7.

Exercises

1. Find dy/dx for the functions defined implicitly by the following equations:

(a) $xy = 1$.   *Ans.* $\dfrac{dy}{dx} = -\dfrac{y}{x}$.   (d) $x^2 + xy + y^2 + 7 = 0$.

(b) $x^2 + y^2 - 5 = 0$.   (e) $y^3 + xy^2 + y + 2x = 0$.

(c) $3x^2 + 2y^2 - 5 = 0$.

Ans. $\dfrac{dy}{dx} = -\dfrac{y^2 + 2}{3y^2 + 2xy + 1}$.

Ans. $\dfrac{dy}{dx} = -\dfrac{3x}{2y}$.   (f) $y^2 = 4x$.

2. Find the expression for the slope at points on the lower half of the circle
$x^2 + y^2 = 25$.   *Ans.* $\dot{y} = x(25 - x^2)^{-\frac{1}{2}}$.

3. Find the slope at the point P (Fig. 7-2) whose abscissa is 2 of the parabola
$y^2 = 8x$.

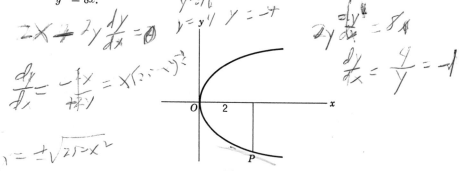

Figure 7-2

4. Given that $\dot{y} = -x/y$, find $\ddot{y}$ in terms of x and y.   *Ans.* $\ddot{y} = -(y^2 + x^2)/y^3$.

5. Show that the equation of the tangent to the parabola $y^2 = 4px$ at the point
(x_0, y_0) is $y - y_0 = \dfrac{2p}{y_0}(x - x_0)$.

6. Show that the x-intercept of the tangent to the parabola $y^2 = 4px$ at the point
(x_0, y_0) is $-x_0$.

7. Show that the x-intercept of the normal to the parabola (the line perpendicular
to the tangent) $y^2 = 4px$ at the point (y_0, y_0) is $x_0 + 2p$.

5. Equations of the Ellipse and Hyperbola.

The method of differentiating implicitly functions is especially useful when applied to the functions representing the conic sections, that is, the parabola, circle, ellipse, and hyperbola. Let us consider first the equations of the ellipse and hyperbola.

The ellipse is usually defined in the following way. We start with two points, F and F' of Fig. 7-3, which are called the foci.

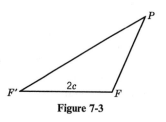

Figure 7-3

The two points are a given fixed distance apart, denoted by $2c$. (We could say c but the ensuing algebra is simpler if we use $2c$.) We choose a number $2a > 2c$ and consider all points (in one plane) whose distances from F and F' add up to $2a$. This set of points constitutes an ellipse. Thus if P is a point on the ellipse, then

$$(23) \qquad\qquad PF + PF' = 2a.$$

We note, incidentally, that $2a$ must be greater than $2c$ because the sum of two sides of a triangle is greater than the third side.

To find the equation of the ellipse, we locate the coordinate axes in a way that experience shows, gives the simplest equation (Fig. 7-4). That is, we let

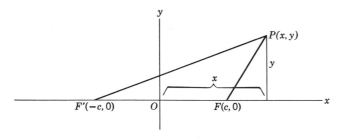

Figure 7-4

the x-axis be the line joining the two foci and we let the y-axis be the line perpendicular to the x-axis and halfway between F' and F. Then the coordinates of F are $(c, 0)$ and the coordinates of F' are $(-c, 0)$. Let the coordinates of any point P on the ellipse be (x, y). Because PFQ is a right triangle, we see that

$$PF = \sqrt{(x - c)^2 + y^2},$$

and because $PF'Q$ is a right triangle and the (geometric) distance $F'Q$ is $x + c$, we see that

$$PF' = \sqrt{(x + c)^2 + y^2}.$$

Then the algebraic equivalent of (23) is

$$(24) \qquad\qquad \sqrt{(x - c)^2 + y^2} + \sqrt{(x + c)^2 + y^2} = 2a.$$

We could maintain that this result is the algebraic equation of the ellipse because it expresses the condition which the coordinates (x, y) of any point on the ellipse must satisfy. However, we can simplify this equation.

The easiest way to simplify it is to first rewrite (24) as

$$\sqrt{(x - c)^2 + y^2} = 2a - \sqrt{(x + c)^2 + y^2}.$$

Now let us square both sides. This step gives

$$(x - c)^2 + y^2 = 4a^2 - 4a\sqrt{(x + c)^2 + y^2} + (x + c)^2 + y^2.$$

If we expand $(x - c)^2$ on the left side and $(x + c)^2$ on the right, subtract equal terms from both sides, and put all terms except the radical on one side, we obtain

$$-4cx - 4a^2 = -4a\sqrt{(x + c)^2 + y^2}.$$

Dividing both sides by -4 yields

$$+cx + a^2 = a\sqrt{(x + c)^2 + y^2}.$$

We square both sides again and obtain

$$c^2x^2 + 2a^2cx + a^4 = a^2[(x + c)^2 + y^2].$$

Expanding $(x + c)^2$ and multiplying the terms in the brackets by a^2 gives

$$c^2x^2 + 2a^2cx + a^4 = a^2x^2 + 2a^2cx + a^2c^2 + a^2y^2.$$

If we subtract $2a^2cx$ from both sides and rearrange terms, we obtain

$$a^2x^2 - c^2x^2 + a^2y^2 = a^4 - a^2c^2$$

or

$$x^2(a^2 - c^2) + a^2y^2 = a^2(a^2 - c^2).$$

The combination $a^2 - c^2$ occurs twice. Because $a > c$, $a^2 - c^2$ is a positive quantity and we can let

(25) $$a^2 - c^2 = b^2.$$

Then

(26) $$b^2x^2 + a^2y^2 = a^2b^2.$$

This form of the equation of the ellipse is simple. We can also divide the equation by a^2b^2 and write*

(27) $$\frac{x^2}{a^2} + \frac{y^2}{b^2} = 1.$$

* Because we squared an equation twice to derive (27) from (24), there is the possibility that we introduced values of x and y which satisfy (27) but not (24). That squaring can introduce new solutions is obvious from the example $x = y$. Squaring produces $x^2 = y^2$, and there are many x and y satisfying the latter equation which do not satisfy the former. To show that (27) has exactly the same solutions (x, y) as (24), let us suppose that (x_1, y_1) satisfies (27) but not (24). (x_1, y_1) are the coordinates of some point. The sum of the distances of this point from the foci is then not $2a$ but, say, $2k$. Moreover $2k > 2c$ because if we take any point Q [other than those on the segment FF' which points can be ruled out at once as not satisfying (27)], $QF + QF' > 2c$. By starting with an equation which is (24) except that $2a$ is replaced by $2k$ and by going through steps (24) to (27) we obtain the result

$$\frac{x_1^2}{k^2} + \frac{y_1^2}{k^2 - c^2} = 1.$$

Suppose that $k < a$. Then $x_1^2/k^2 > x_1^2/a^2$ and because $k^2 - c^2 < a^2 - c^2$, $y_1^2/(k^2 - c^2) > y_1^2/b^2$. Then (x_1, y_1) cannot satisfy (27). If we suppose that $k > a$, we can obtain a similar contradiction.

It is helpful to know the shape and size of the ellipse in terms of the quantities a, b, and c. We see from (26) that when $y = 0$, $x = \pm a$. The two points $(a, 0)$ and $(-a, 0)$ are the points at which the ellipse cuts the x-axis (Fig. 7-5). Likewise when $x = 0$, we see from (26) that $y = \pm b$. These two points $(0, b)$ and $(0, -b)$ are the points at which the ellipse cuts the y-axis.

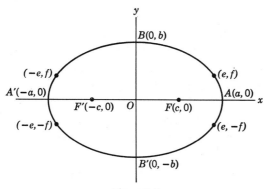

Figure 7-5

To obtain some idea of how the curve behaves, we note first that if (e, f) are the coordinates of a point that satisfy equation (26) or (27), then $(-e, f)$ also satisfy the equation. This means geometrically that the curve is symmetric with respect to the y-axis, because $(-e, f)$ is, so to speak, the mirror image of (e, f) in the y-axis. We also observe from (26) or (27) that if (e, f) are the coordinates of a point on the curve, then $(e, -f)$ are the coordinates of another point on the curve because if (e, f) satisfy (26) then so do $(e, -f)$. Geometrically this means that the curve is symmetric with respect to the x-axis because $(e, -f)$ is the mirror image of (e, f) in the x-axis.

The significance of knowing that a curve is symmetric with respect to the x-axis, or the y-axis, or both is that if we know what the curve looks like in the first quadrant, that is, where x and y are both positive, we also know how it looks in one or more of the other quadrants. In the case of the ellipse, if we could find out what the curve looks like in the first quadrant, then, because it is symmetric with respect to the x-axis, we also know how it looks in the fourth quadrant. Also, because the curve is symmetric with respect to the y-axis, we know how it looks in the second and third quadrants. Hence, as far as the ellipse is concerned, determining the shape of the curve reduces to determining what the curve looks like in the first quadrant.

We could use the geometrical definition of the ellipse to determine the shape in the first quadrant. Thus, to be concrete, choose a number for $2c$, say 8, and a number for $2a$, say 12. We could then place two points 8 units apart, which would be the foci. A point on the ellipse must have the sum of its distances from these two points equal to 12. We pick any two numbers whose sum is 12, say 9 and 3. Then we draw a circle with F' as center and

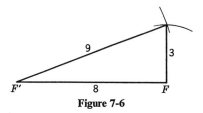

Figure 7-6

radius 9 and another circle with F as center and radius 3 (Fig. 7-6). Where these two circles intersect, we have a point on the ellipse. In this way we can locate a number of points and then join them by a smooth curve.

There is also a simple string construction for the ellipse. Let us use the same values of $2c$ and $2a$ for purposes of illustration. Place two tacks in a drawing board 8 units apart. The locations of these tacks are the locations of the foci. Now choose a piece of string which is $8 + 12$ or 20 units long and let the string go around the tacks as shown in Fig. 7-7. A pencil is placed inside the loop $F'PF$ and the pencil is pulled back enough to keep the loop taut. As the pencil moves around while keeping the loop taut, it traces out the ellipse.

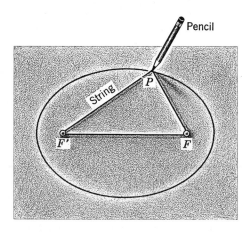

Figure 7-7

We can also use the equation of the ellipse to determine the shape in the first quadrant. We see from (26) that

$$a^2y^2 = a^2b^2 - b^2x^2$$

or that

(28) $$y = \pm \frac{b}{a}\sqrt{a^2 - x^2}.$$

If we wish to locate points in the first quadrant, we use the function

$$y = \frac{b}{a}\sqrt{a^2 - x^2}.$$

For a given ellipse, that is, for a definite choice of $2a$ and $2c$, say 12 and 8 again, we can calculate b by (25). In this case $b = \sqrt{20}$ and a of course equals

6. Then our function becomes

$$y = \sqrt{20}\,\sqrt{36 - x^2}.$$

Next we can choose a few values of x, calculate the corresponding values of y, and plot the points corresponding to each pair of x- and y-values. The shape of the curve in the first quadrant and consequently in all four quadrants is shown in Fig. 7-5. We shall see in the next section how we can learn more about the curve.

The shape of the ellipse is, of course, the same no matter where we choose the axes. Hence we see that an ellipse is symmetrical about two lines which are mutually perpendicular. The intersection of these two lines, the point O in Fig. 7-5, is called the *center* of the ellipse. (This center is also the mid-point of FF'.) The longest chord through O, the segment AA' in Fig. 7-5, is called the *major axis* and its length is $2a$. The shortest chord through O is the segment BB' and it is called the *minor axis*. Its length is $2b$.

For each choice of a and c with $a > c$ there is an ellipse. Hence there is not one ellipse but an infinity of ellipses. How do they differ from each other? If a and c are altered but the ratio is kept the same, we obtain an ellipse of the same shape but of different size. We can prove this readily. Because

$$b^2 = a^2 - c^2,$$

if we replace a by ra and c by rc, the new b value is r times the old b value. Furthermore, if we denote by primes the coordinates of the ellipse determined by ra and rc, we have from (27)

(29)
$$\frac{x'^2}{r^2 a^2} + \frac{y'^2}{r^2 b^2} = 1.$$

If we set

$$x' = rx, \qquad y' = ry,$$

(29) reduces to (27). That is, to each x and y of the ellipse determined by a and c, there is an x' and y' of the ellipse determined by ra and rc which are r times x and y, respectively. This new ellipse has the same shape as the original one.

To distinguish ellipses by shapes we must change the ratio of a to c. We define a new quantity called the *eccentricity*, which is denoted by e, namely,

$$e = \frac{c}{a}.$$

When the eccentricity changes, the shape of the ellipse changes. Since only the ratio e counts as far as shape is concerned, we may keep a fixed and vary c. Because $2c$ is the distance between the foci, c can be 0 or positive. When c is 0, the two foci coincide and, since $b^2 = a^2 - c^2$, $a = b$. We see then from (26) that when $e = 0$, the ellipse becomes a circle. As c increases, while a

remains fixed, (25) tells us that the ellipse becomes flatter. Because c must be less than a, e is always less than 1.

The mathematics of the hyperbola is in many respects similar to that of the ellipse. Geometrically the curve is defined as follows. We start with two fixed points, F and F' in Fig. 7-8, which are called the foci. The two points are a given fixed distance apart denoted by $2c$. Now we consider all points (in one plane) whose distances from F and F' differ by the same constant which we denote by $2a$. The set of all points which satisfy this condition is called a hyperbola. That is, the hyperbola consists of all points P for which

$$PF - PF' = 2a \quad \text{or} \quad PF' - PF = 2a.$$

We note that the $2a$ must be less than $2c$ because if P is a point on the hyperbola, then $|PF' - PF|$ must be less than $F'F$, for the difference of any two sides of a triangle must be less than the third side.

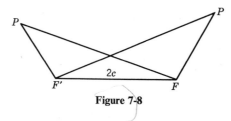

Figure 7-8

To visualize what the hyperbola looks like we may employ a string construction similar to that described for the ellipse. We fasten two tacks into a board at the positions of the foci. We take a piece of string and lay it out so that it passes around F and both ends pass over F' (Fig. 7-9). A pencil is tied to the string at P which is chosen so that the length PF' minus the length PF is $2a$. Now as P moves while both ends of the string are kept together and the string is allowed to slide over F', the quantity $PF' - PF$ is constant so that P describes the right-hand curve of the figure. By reversing the looping of the string at F and F' and choosing P on the string so that $PF - PF' = 2a$, we can make the point P describe the left-hand curve of the figure. These two curves constitute the hyperbola. The separate curves are called the branches of the hyperbola.

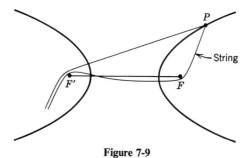

Figure 7-9

Let us find the equation of the hyperbola. The geometrical definition requires that for any point P on the hyperbola either

$$PF - PF' = 2a \quad \text{or} \quad PF' - PF = 2a.$$

We locate the coordinate axes in a way that, experience shows, gives the simplest equation. That is, we let the x-axis (Fig. 7-10) be the line through F and F' and we let the y-axis be the line perpendicular to the x-axis and

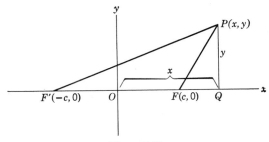

Figure 7-10

halfway between F and F'. Because the distance FF' is $2c$, the coordinates of F are $(c, 0)$ and the coordinates of F' are $(-c, 0)$. If we denote the co-ordinates of any point P by (x, y), then as in the case of the ellipse

$$PF = \sqrt{(x - c)^2 + y^2},$$

$$PF' = \sqrt{(x + c)^2 + y^2}.$$

The definition of the hyperbola then states that the curve consists of all (x, y) for which

(30) $$\sqrt{(x - c)^2 + y^2} - \sqrt{(x + c)^2 + y^2} = 2a$$

or

(31) $$\sqrt{(x + c)^2 + y^2} - \sqrt{(x - c)^2 + y^2} = 2a.$$

Let us consider the first of these equations and simplify it. The easiest way to begin the simplification is to rewrite (30) as

(32) $$\sqrt{(x - c)^2 + y^2} = 2a + \sqrt{(x + c)^2 + y^2}.$$

We now repeat the processes we used to simplify the analogous case—equation (24) for the ellipse; that is, we square both sides of (32), eliminate equal terms on both sides, and rearrange the terms. We obtain

(33) $$-cx - a^2 = a\sqrt{(x + c)^2 + y^2}.$$

We again square both sides, subtract equal terms, and simplify precisely as in the corresponding steps for the ellipse to obtain

(34) $$x^2(a^2 - c^2) + a^2 y^2 = a^2(a^2 - c^2).$$

Before we proceed, we might go back and look at (31). We know that (30) leads to (34), but presumably the points (x, y) satisfying (31) would satisfy some other equation than (34). However, if we write (31) as

$$-\sqrt{(x - c)^2 + y^2} = 2a - \sqrt{(x + c)^2 + y^2}$$

and perform the steps leading to (33), the only difference is that we obtain

(35) $$-cx - a^2 = -a\sqrt{(x + c)^2 + y^2}.$$

If we now square again, as we did in going from (33) to (34), we obtain (34). In other words, the second squaring operation, which we performed to obtain (34), introduces automatically the points satisfying the condition (31), and (34) represents *both* (30) and (31).

We may then confine ourselves to (34) and because, in the case of a hyperbola $2a < 2c$, we set

$$c^2 - a^2 = b^2,$$

and (34) becomes

(36) $$b^2x^2 - a^2y^2 = a^2b^2$$

or, by dividing each term by a^2b^2,

(37) $$\frac{x^2}{a^2} - \frac{y^2}{b^2} = 1.$$

Either equation, (36) or (37), represents all points on the hyperbola.

To use either equation effectively, it is desirable to know not only the shape of the hyperbola but what the quantities a, b, and c mean geometrically. We can use either equation to obtain this information. We note from equation (36) that when $y = 0$, $x = \pm a$. The points $(a, 0)$ and $(-a, 0)$ are then the x-intercepts, that is, the points at which the curve cuts the x-axis (Fig. 7-11). However, when we set $x = 0$, we see that there are no real values for y. This means that the curve does not cut the y-axis.

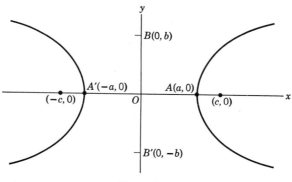

Figure 7-11

The argument we gave for the ellipse showing that that curve is symmetric with respect to the x- and y-axes, applies equally well to the hyperbola. Hence, as in the case of the ellipse, the problem of determining the shape of the curve reduces to determining the shape in the first quadrant. However, we see from (36) that

$$a^2y^2 = b^2x^2 - a^2b^2$$

or that

$$y = \pm \frac{b}{a} \sqrt{x^2 - a^2}.$$

To discuss the curve in the first quadrant, we need to consider only

$$y = \frac{b}{a} \sqrt{x^2 - a^2}.$$

We see first of all that if $x < a$, then y is complex. Hence there are no points on the curve with abscissas less than a. We see also that as x increases, y increases; moreover x can become infinite and, as it does so, y also becomes infinite. Of course, so far we do not know the precise shape of the curve in the first quadrant. We can obtain this from our string construction (Fig. 7-9) or we can choose specific values of a and c, and therefore of b, and calculate the y-values for a few x-values. The shape is shown in Fig. 7-11. Now by using the symmetry of the curve we obtain the entire figure. We see that the full curve consists of two separate or disjoined branches. The two branches make up the hyperbola.

The hyperbola is symmetric with respect to two lines which are perpendicular to each other. With the choice of coordinate axes that we made, the two lines are of course the x- and y-axes. The intersection of the two lines, the origin in the case of Fig. 7-11, is called the *center*. The segment AA' is called the *major* or *transverse* axis. Its length, as we know, is $2a$. Although the curve does not cut the y-axis, it is helpful to mark off the segment BB' (Fig. 7-11) of length $2b$, which is called the *minor* or *conjugate* axis. The usefulness of this length will be apparent shortly.

We have seen that the equation of a hyperbola is

$$b^2x^2 - a^2y^2 = a^2b^2.$$

Associated with the hyperbola is a pair of lines, called the *asymptotes*, whose equation is

$$b^2x^2 - a^2y^2 = 0.$$

To see that this equation represents a pair of lines, we have but to factor it and write it as

(38) $$(bx - ay)(bx + ay) = 0.$$

The curve corresponding to (38) consists of all points which satisfy

(39) $$bx - ay = 0 \quad \text{or} \quad bx + ay = 0.$$

The reason is that if the coordinates of some point (x_1, y_1) satisfy $bx - ay = 0$, the left factor in (38) is 0 whether or not the right factor is. Likewise if (x_1, y_1) are coordinates which satisfy $bx + ay = 0$, the right factor in (38) is 0 whether or not the left factor is. Then the curve belonging to (38) is the curve of the first equation in (39) *and* the curve of the second equation in (39).

Now the equations in (39) can be written as

(40) $$y = \frac{b}{a} x \quad \text{and} \quad y = -\frac{b}{a} x.$$

We see, then, that each is a straight line (Fig. 7-12), the first having the slope $\frac{b}{a}$ and the second, the slope $-\frac{b}{a}$.

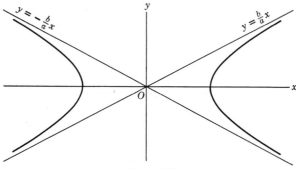

Figure 7-12

The importance of these lines, the asymptotes, is that the branches of the hyperbola lie between them as shown in Fig. 7-12. As the figure suggests, the points farther and farther out along the curve in the first quadrant come closer and closer to the asymptote, but the curve does not ever touch or cut the asymptote. The same is true in each of the other quadrants. We shall not prove this assertion. (See Exercise 17.)

For each value of a and c, with $c > a$, a hyperbola is determined. Hence there is not one hyperbola but an infinite number of them. We can distinguish them by specifying the values of a and c. However, as in the case of the ellipse, the shape of the hyperbola is determined not by the individual values of a and c but by the ratio c/a. We call this ratio the *eccentricity* and denote it by e; that is,

$$e = \frac{c}{a}.$$

Since $c > 1$, e is always greater than 1. To see how e measures the shape, let us note that

$$b^2 = c^2 - a^2 = a^2\left(\frac{c^2}{a^2} - 1\right) = a^2(e^2 - 1).$$

If a is kept fixed and e varies, we see that b varies. We now recall that the equations of the asymptotes are $y = bx/a$ and $y = -bx/a$. Hence the asymptotes lie close to the x-axis when b is small and farther away when b is large. Because the hyperbola always lies between the asymptotes, as shown in Fig. 7-12, the curve is narrower or wider depending on the value of b or the related value of e.

Exercises

1. Given the equation $(x^2/16) + (y^2/9) = 1$ for an ellipse, how much are a, b, c, and e?   *Ans.* $a = 4$, $b = 3$, $c = \sqrt{7}$, $e = \sqrt{7}/4$.
2. Given the equation $8x^2 + 10y^2 = 80$ for an ellipse, how much are a, b, c, and e?
3. How long are the major and minor axes of the ellipse $(x^2/36) + (y^2/10) = 1$?

   Ans. 12, $2\sqrt{10}$.

4. Write the equation of the ellipse for the following cases:
   (*a*) $a = 8$, $b = 2$.   *Ans.* $(x^2/64) + (y^2/4) = 1$.
   (*b*) $a = 8$ and the distance between the foci is 4.
   (*c*) $a = 5b$ and passing through the point $(7, 2)$.
   (*d*) The major axis is 12 and the minor axis is 8.   *Ans.* $(x^2/36) + (y^2/16) = 1$.
5. The width of an ellipse is often specified by giving the length of the chord passing through a focus and perpendicular to the x-axis. Show that this length, which is called the *latus rectum*, is $2b^2/a$.
6. Suppose that the foci of an ellipse which are $2c$ units apart lie on the y-axis (Fig. 7-13) and the x-axis is halfway between them and, of course, perpendicular to the y-axis. If we continue to use $2a$ for the sum of the distances of any point on the ellipse from the two foci, show that the equation of the ellipse is $(x^2/b^2) + (y^2/a^2) = 1$.

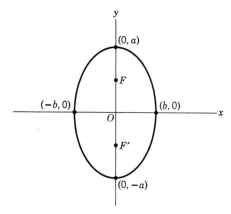

Figure 7-13

7. An arch in the shape of the upper half of an ellipse is to support a bridge over a roadway 50 feet wide. The center of the arch is to be 25 feet above the center of the roadway. Write the equation of the ellipse.

   Ans. $(x^2/625) + (y^2/625) = 1$.

8. The orbit of the earth about the sun is practically an ellipse with the sun at one focus. The ratio of the earth's least distance from the sun (which occurs when the earth is at one end of the major axis) to the greatest distance (which occurs at the other end of the major axis) is 29/30. Find the eccentricity of the ellipse.

Ans. 1/59.

9. Given the equation $(x^2/16) - (y^2/9) = 1$ for a hyperbola, how much are a, b, c, and e?   *Ans.* $a = 4$, $b = 3$, $c = 5$, $e = \frac{5}{4}$.

10. Given the equation $8x^2 - 10y^2 = 80$ for a hyperbola, how much are a, b, c, and e?

11. How long are the transverse and conjugate axes of the hyperbola $(x^2/36) - (y^2/9) = 1$?   *Ans.* 12, 6.

12. Write the equation of the hyperbola for the following cases:
   (a) $a = 8$, $b = 2$.   *Ans.* $(x^2/64) - (y^2/4) = 1$.
   (b) $a = 8$ and the distance between the foci is 20.
   (c) $a = 8$ and $b = 10$.   *Ans.* $(x^2/64) - (y^2/100) = 1$.
   (d) The transverse axis is 12 and the conjugate axis is 8.

13. In the case of an ellipse a is always greater than (or at least equal to) b. What is the corresponding relation of a to b for the hyperbola?

14. The width of a hyperbola is often specified by giving the length of the chord passing through a focus and perpendicular to the x-axis. Show that this length, which is called the latus rectum, is $2b^2/a$.

15. Suppose that the foci, which are $2c$ units apart, of a hyperbola lie on the y-axis (Fig. 7-14) and the x-axis lies halfway between them and perpendicular to the y-axis. If we continue to use $2a$ for the difference of the distances of any point on the hyperbola from the foci, show that the equation of the hyperbola is $(x^2/b^2) - (y^2/a^2) = -1$.

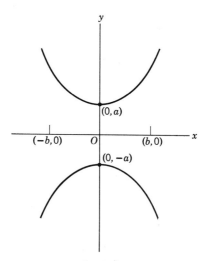

Figure 7-14

16. If we multiply the equations of the two lines $5x + 2y = 25$ and $5x - 2y = 16$, we obtain $25x^2 - 4y^2 = 400$. According to the argument given in connection

with (38), the equation of the product should still represent the two lines. However, the points (4, 0) and (−4, 0) satisfy the product but do not satisfy either of the linear equations. What is amiss?

17. Given the hyperbola $(x^2/a^2) - (y^2/b^2) = 1$, so that $y = \pm(b/a)\sqrt{x^2 - a^2}$, let $y_1 = (b/a)\sqrt{x^2 - a^2}$ and let $Y_1 = bx/a$. Show that $Y_1 - y_1$ approaches 0 as x becomes arbitrarily large (approaches infinity). *Suggestion:* $Y_1 - y_1 = (b/a)(x - \sqrt{x^2 - a^2})$. Now multiply by $(x + \sqrt{x^2 - a^2})/(x + \sqrt{x^2 - a^2})$.

6. Differentiation of the Equations of Ellipse and Hyperbola. Our chief concern in this chapter has been the chain rule, and we have seen so far that it enables us to differentiate many functions that we could not handle previously, including implicit functions. Let us apply the chain rule to the particular implicit functions which represent the equations of the ellipse and hyperbola.

We found that the equation of the ellipse is of the form

$$(41) \qquad b^2x^2 + a^2y^2 = a^2b^2$$

when the coordinate axes are chosen as in Fig. 7-4. In trying to determine the curve which belongs to this equation, we found that, by reason of symmetry with respect to the x- and y-axes, all we had to do was to determine the shape in the first quadrant. At that point the best suggestion we could make was to solve (41) for y, obtaining for the first quadrant

$$(42) \qquad y = \frac{b}{a}\sqrt{a^2 - x^2},$$

and then calculate a few pairs of x- and y-values. With the calculus we can do a little more to determine the shape of the curve.

The derivative of a function representing a curve tells us the slope of the curve. Let us find the slope at any point of the ellipse. We could differentiate the function in (42), but it is easier to work with the implicit equation (41). If we differentiate it with respect to x, we obtain

$$2b^2x + 2a^2y\dot{y} = 0$$

or

$$(43) \qquad \dot{y} = -\frac{b^2x}{a^2y}.$$

We see at once that, because x and y are positive in the first quadrant, $\dot{y}$ is always negative (except at $y = 0$). Moreover, as x increases from 0 to a, we see from (42) that y decreases from b to 0. Hence as x increases from 0 to a, the slope becomes more and more negative, starting at $x = 0$ with 0 slope. We know then that the slopes of the tangents to the curve must behave as shown in Fig. 7-15. Then the curve itself must have the shape shown in that figure. Thus we obtain a somewhat better picture of the graph than if we had plotted a few points and had connected them with a smooth curve.

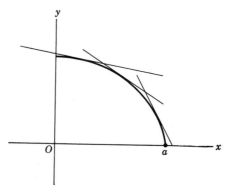

Figure 7-15

We can also find the equation of the tangent to the ellipse at any point. Let (x_1, y_1) be a point on the curve. By (43) we know that the slope of the curve, which is the slope of the tangent, must be

$$\dot{y} = -\frac{b^2 x_1}{a^2 y_1}$$

We now use the fact (Chapter 3, Section A7) that the equation of a line passing through the point (x_1, y_1) and having slope m is given by

$$y - y_1 = m(x - x_1).$$

In our case we have

(44)
$$y - y_1 = -\frac{b^2 x_1}{a^2 y_1}(x - x_1).$$

We must, of course, be careful about what value we use for y_1. If we are dealing with a point that lies on the upper half of the ellipse, then for a given x_1, y_1 is given by

$$y_1 = \frac{b}{a}\sqrt{a^2 - x_1^2}.$$

If we are dealing with a point that lies on the lower half of the ellipse, then for a given x_1, y_1 is given by

$$y_1 = -\frac{b}{a}\sqrt{a^2 - x_1^2}.$$

Let us note that we can do the same for the hyperbola. The equation of the hyperbola is

(45)
$$b^2 x^2 - a^2 y^2 = a^2 b^2.$$

Then the slope of the hyperbola is given by $\dot{y}$, which we calculate from (45) by differentiating the implicit equation. We find first that

$$2b^2x - 2a^2y\dot{y} = 0$$

and therefore

(46)
$$\dot{y} = \frac{b^2x}{a^2y}.$$

Thus in the first quadrant the slope is always positive.

Exercises

1. Determine the shape of the hyperbola in the first quadrant by analyzing the formula for the slope.
2. Find the equation of the tangent to the ellipse $4x^2 + 5y^2 = 40$ at $x = 1$. There are two points on the ellipse at which $x = 1$; hence there should be two answers.   *Ans.* $y \pm \dfrac{6}{\sqrt{5}} = (x - 1)\left(\pm \dfrac{2\sqrt{5}}{15}\right).$
3. Find the equation of the tangent to the ellipse in Exercise 2 at $x = -1$. Again there should be two answers.
4. Find the equation of the tangent to the ellipse $(x^2/16) + (y^2/9) = 1$ at $x = \sqrt{7}$.

   There are two answers.   *Ans.* $y \pm \frac{9}{4} = (x - \sqrt{7})\left(\pm \dfrac{\sqrt{7}}{4}\right).$
5. Find the equation of the tangent to the hyperbola $4x^2 - 5y^2 = 40$ at $x = 5$. There are two answers.
6. Find the equation of the tangent to the hyperbola $(x^2/9) - (y^2/16) = 1$ at $x = -5$. There are two answers.   *Ans.* $y \pm \frac{16}{3} = (x + 5)(\pm \frac{5}{3}).$
7. (a) Show that the lines FP and $F'P$ from the foci to any point P on the ellipse (Fig. 7-16) make equal angles with the tangent at P.

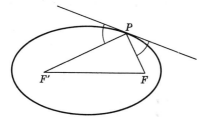

Figure 7-16

(b) Suppose that a light ray issues from F' and strikes an elliptical mirror at P. What direction does the reflected ray take?   *Ans.* Toward F.
8. Consider the equation $\dfrac{x^2}{a^2 - k} + \dfrac{y^2}{b^2 - k} = 1.$

(*a*) Discuss the loci represented by this equation for fixed *a* and *b* but as *k* varies. *Suggestion:* First let *k* vary from 0 to b^2; then let *k* vary from b^2 to a^2; and finally let *k* vary from a^2 upward.   *Ans.* Ellipse for $0 \le k < b^2$; hyperbola for $b^2 < k < a^2$; no locus for $k > a^2$.

(*b*) Calculate the foci of the various conics represented by the equation.

9. Show that an ellipse and any confocal hyperbola, that is, any hyperbola which has the same foci as the ellipse, intersect at right angles. *Suggestion:* Use the representation given in Exercise 8.

10. Show that the product of the distances from the foci to any tangent of an ellipse is b^2 where *b* is the semi-minor axis.

11. Show that the tangent at any point *P* of a hyperbola (Fig. 7-17) bisects the angle *F'PF*, where *F* and *F'* are the foci.

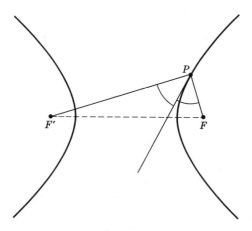

Figure 7-17

12. Show that the segment of a tangent to a hyperbola which lies between the asymptotes is bisected at the point of tangency.

13. Show that the tangent at any point *P* of the parabola $y^2 = 4px$ cuts the *x*-axis at a point *T* (Fig. 7-18) whose abscissa is the negative of the abscissa of *P*.

Figure 7-18

14. Show that if PG is the normal (Fig. 7-19) to the ellipse $(x^2/a^2) + (y^2/b^2) = 1$ at the point P then $OG = e^2 \cdot ON$ where e is the eccentricity of the ellipse. ON is the abscissa of P.

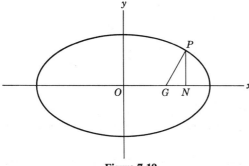

Figure 7-19

15. Show that if TPt (Fig. 7-20) is the tangent to the ellipse $(x^2/a^2) + (y^2/b^2) = 1$ at the point P, then $ON \cdot OT = a^2$ and $OM \cdot Ot = b^2$. ON is the abscissa of P and OM is the ordinate.

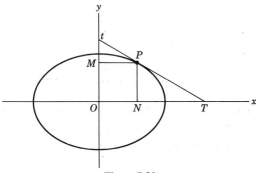

Figure 7-20

16. Show that the condition that the two ellipses $(x^2/a^2) + (y^2/b^2) = 1$ and $(x^2/A^2) + (y^2/B^2) = 1$ meet at right angles is that $a^2 - b^2 = A^2 - B^2$.

7. Integration Employing the Chain Rule. The increased power to differentiate functions means, of course, increased power to integrate because the latter process is merely the inverse of the former. In Theorem 2 of this chapter we learned that if $y = u^n$, where u is a function of x, then $dy/dx = nu^{n-1} \, du/dx$. Given dy/dx in this form, we can state at once that $y = u^n + C$. However, as in the case of the simpler formula $dy/dx = nx^{n-1}$, the derived function is generally not given us in precisely the form $nu^{n-1} \, du/dx$. Rather, we are given

$$\frac{dy}{dx} = u^n \frac{du}{dx}$$

and are required to find y. However, we know that in differentiating $y = u^n$ the exponent becomes a coefficient and the new exponent is one less. Hence we reverse this process. The result is the single most important formula for integration:

Theorem 3: If

$$\frac{dy}{dx} = u^n \frac{du}{dx} \tag{47}$$

where u is a function of x and $n \neq -1$, then

$$y = \frac{u^{n+1}}{n+1} + C. \tag{48}$$

This theorem generalizes Theorem 2 of Chapter 6, and therefore we refer to it as the generalized power rule for integration or the inverse of the generalized power rule.

Let us see how useful Theorem 3 can be. Suppose that we are given

$$\frac{dy}{dx} = 5(x^2 + 1)^4 \cdot 2x \tag{49}$$

and are obliged to find y as a function of x. Knowing Theorem 3, we try to think of the right side of (49) as a function of u times du/dx. The obvious candidate for u is $x^2 + 1$ because then the $2x$ is du/dx. Hence we let

$$u = x^2 + 1$$

and write (49) as

$$\frac{dy}{dx} = 5u^4 \frac{du}{dx}. \tag{50}$$

We now compare (50) with (47). Apart from the factor 5, (50) is in the form (47). However, a constant factor can be ignored during integration and then multiplied into the integral. By (48) we obtain

$$y = 5\frac{u^5}{5} + C = u^5 + C.$$

In view of the value of u

$$y = (x^2 + 1)^5 + C. \tag{51}$$

The result in (51) appears peculiar at first sight. Corresponding to the factor $5(x^2 + 1)^4$ in (49), we do have $(x^2 + 1)^5$ in (51), but nothing in (51) corresponds to the factor $2x$ in (49). This is as it should be. In differentiating (51) by the chain rule, we would let $u = x^2 + 1$. Then the chain rule calls for

$$\frac{dy}{dx} = \frac{dy}{du} \cdot \frac{du}{dx}.$$

The factor du/dx is, in the present example, $2x$ and this appears in the derivative in addition to whatever dy/du calls for. We must expect then that in reversing the chain rule the quantity du/dx will "disappear."

Let us consider another example. Given

$$\frac{dy}{dx} = \frac{x}{\sqrt{x^2 + 1}},$$

we shall try to find y as a function of x. We can, of course, write this derived function as the product

(52) $$\frac{dy}{dx} = \frac{1}{\sqrt{x^2 + 1}} \cdot x.$$

A likely candidate for the function u is $x^2 + 1$, but then du/dx is $2x$, whereas we have only the factor x in (52). However, it is algebraically correct to write (52) as

$$\frac{dy}{dx} = \frac{1}{2}\frac{1}{\sqrt{x^2 + 1}} \cdot 2x.$$

If we now let u be $x^2 + 1$, we have

$$\frac{dy}{dx} = \frac{1}{2}\frac{1}{\sqrt{u}}\frac{du}{dx} = \tfrac{1}{2}u^{-\frac{1}{2}}\frac{du}{dx}.$$

Apart from the constant factor $\frac{1}{2}$, this derivative is in the form (47). Then by (48)

(53) $$y = \frac{1}{2}\frac{u^{\frac{1}{2}}}{\frac{1}{2}} + C = u^{\frac{1}{2}} + C = \sqrt{x^2 + 1} + C.$$

In using (48) in the examples, we replaced a function of x in the integrand by u. This device, which will be often employed later, is called *integration by substitution* of a new variable.

Exercises

1. Integrate the following functions:

(a) $\dot{y} = 4(x^2 + 1)^3 2x$.

    Ans. $y = (x^2 + 1)^4 + C.$

(b) $\dot{y} = (x^2 + 1)^3 \cdot 2x.$

(c) $\dot{y} = (x^2 + 1)^3 \cdot x.$

    Ans. $y = \dfrac{(x^2 + 1)^4}{8} + C.$

(d) $\dot{y} = 4(x^2 + 7x)^3(2x + 7).$

(e) $\dot{y} = (x^2 + 7x)^3(2x + 7).$

    Ans. $y = \dfrac{(x^2 + 7x)^4}{4} + C.$

(f) $\dot{y} = (x^2 + 6x)^4(x + 3).$

(g) $\dot{y} = \dfrac{2x}{(x^2 + 6)^5}.$

    Ans. $y = -\dfrac{1}{4(x^2 + 6)^4} + C.$

(h) $\dot{y} = (1 + 5x)^5.$

(i) $\dot{y} = \sqrt{1 + 5x}.$

    Ans. $y = \dfrac{2(1 + 5x)^{\frac{3}{2}}}{15} + C.$

(j) $\dot{y} = \dfrac{1}{\sqrt{2 - 3x}}.$

(k) $\dot{y} = \dfrac{x}{(x^2 + 4)^{\frac{3}{2}}}.$

    Ans. $y = -(x^2 + 4)^{-\frac{1}{2}} + C.$

(l) $\dot{y} = \left(1 + \dfrac{x}{2}\right)^3.$

(m) $\dot{y} = x\sqrt{4 + 5x}.$ *Suggestion:* let $u = 4 + 5x$ and replace x by its value in terms of u.

    Ans. $y = \dfrac{2(4 + 5x)^{\frac{5}{2}}}{125}$

    $\quad - \dfrac{8(4 + 5x)^{\frac{3}{2}}}{75} + C.$

2. Find the area between the curve $y = \sqrt{x+1}$ and the x-axis and between the ordinates at $x = 1$ and $x = 5$.   *Ans.* $\frac{2}{3}(6^{3/2} - 2^{3/2})$.

3. Find the area between the curve $y = -\sqrt{2x+1}$ and the x-axis and between the ordinates at $x = 1$ and $x = 5$.

4. A particle moving along AM (Fig. 7-21) is attracted to a fixed point O with a force which varies inversely as the square of the distance from O. Find the work done on the particle as it moves the distance l from A to B. *Suggestion:* Let x be the distance from A to any point P on AB and let r be the variable distance from P to O. The force F attracting P to O is k/r^2. But only the component of this force along AB serves to move the particle along AB. This component is $(k/r^2) \cos OPM = (k/r^2)(c-x)/r$. Then $\dot{W}$ or $dW/dx = k(c-x)/r^3$ and $r = \sqrt{p^2 + (c-x)^2}$.   *Ans.* $\dfrac{k}{b} - \dfrac{k}{a}$.

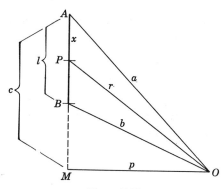

Figure 7-21

5. The integral of $(2x-1)^3$ obtained by replacing $2x-1$ by u and applying the chain rule is $(2x-1)^4/8 + C$. On the other hand, we can expand $(2x-1)^3$ by the binomial theorem and integrate without using the chain rule. The result is $2x^4 - 4x^3 + 3x^2 - x + C$. Do these two integrals agree?   *Ans.* Yes.

6. If $y' = f(x)g(x)$ and if $g'(x) = f(x)$, find y.   *Ans.* $y = \dfrac{[g(x)]^2}{2} + C.$

8. *The Problem of Escape Velocity.* The problem of calculating the velocity with which an object must be shot straight up into the air in order to have it reach a given altitude is important for scientific and practical purposes. For example, an antiaircraft gun that seeks to hit an airplane flying directly overhead must be able to fire the shells with sufficient initial velocity to have them reach the plane. The launching of satellites requires sending them up to a given height before they are directed around the earth, and the launching of rockets and spaceships involves similar problems.

The velocity with which an object is to be shot up to reach a given height must be such that though the object loses velocity as it rises, it will have enough velocity to keep going until it reaches the desired height. To send an object to a point not too high above the surface of the earth, we can apply the fact that gravity causes a downward acceleration of 32 ft/sec². Then the problem of calculating the initial velocity is rather easy (see Chapter 3, Section 3, Exercise 12). However, if an object is to be sent to a great height, the acceleration of 32 ft/sec² is no longer a reliable figure. What then is the proper acceleration?

The acceleration toward the earth that any object experiences is due to the earth's gravitational attraction. This force, as we already know, is given by the formula

$$(54) \qquad\qquad F = G\frac{mM}{r^2},$$

where M is the mass of the earth, m is the mass of the object, and r is the distance of the object from the center of the earth. Thus we know the force that the earth exerts on the object but not the acceleration.

To determine the acceleration we must have recourse to a basic law of physics. Newton's first law of motion states that if no force acts on an object and the object is at rest, the object remains at rest, and if the object is in motion, it continues to move at a constant speed in a straight line. However, suppose that a force does act. What does the force do? Newton's second law of motion states that the force changes the speed or the direction of motion or both. This second law of motion is a physical principle established on the basis of observations and measurements. Forces are vector quantities; that is, they have magnitude and direction. So are velocities. If a force changes the speed or the direction of motion or both, it causes a change in the velocity regarded as a vector, and this change in the velocity vector is an acceleration. The present use of the term acceleration includes the change in both the magnitude and direction of the velocity, and so the acceleration is also a vector.

To indicate a vector quantity, it is customary to use boldface type. Thus a vector force is printed as **F** and its magnitude is denoted by |**F**|; a vector velocity with magnitude |**v**| is printed as **v**.* To pursue further the notion of acceleration as a vector, suppose that an object is moving in the direction of the velocity $\mathbf{v}_1$ shown in Fig. 7-22 and a force acts to cause the object to move in the direction of the velocity $\mathbf{v}_2$. The force produces the vector acceleration **a**. Let us note that $\mathbf{v}_2$ is the sum of $\mathbf{v}_1$ and **a** because $\mathbf{v}_1$ and **a** are the sides of a parallelogram and $\mathbf{v}_2$ is the diagonal that gives the sum in the sense already discussed in connection with forces in Chapter 3, Section 4.

Newton's second law of motion is a statement about vectors and quantitatively it says that

$$(55) \qquad\qquad \mathbf{F} = m\mathbf{a};$$

---

* In handwriting vectors are commonly denoted by putting an arrow over the letter representing the magnitude; thus $\vec{v}$ is a vector velocity with magnitude $|\vec{v}|$.

that is, the vector force imparts to a mass m a vector acceleration **a**. The force and the acceleration have the same direction (Fig. 7-23), but the magnitude of the force is m times the magnitude of the acceleration. The unit of magnitude for **F** is poundal, for m it is pounds, and for **a** it is ft/sec².

Figure 7-22   Figure 7-23

We shall have occasion to work with the magnitudes of **F** and **a** multiplied however by a plus or a minus sign. For these quantities we shall use F and a. Equation (55) tells us that

$$(56) \qquad\qquad\qquad F = ma.$$

It is important to know that Newton's second law is a vector law, and we shall make several important uses of this fact. However, in our present problem of the motion of an object straight up or straight down, the vector nature of the law plays a minor role because only two directions are involved.

We entered into the discussion of Newton's second law because, given the force of gravitation (54) acting on a mass m, we wished to know the acceleration that this force imparts to m. Formula (56) answers this question. If we write (54) as

$$F = m\,\frac{GM}{r^2}$$

and compare it with (56) which holds for *any* force, we see that the acceleration that the force of gravity gives to the object of mass m is

$$(57) \qquad\qquad\qquad a = \frac{GM}{r^2}\,.$$

We pointed out in Chapter 6, Section 10 [see formula (60) there] that when r is the radius R of the earth, that is, $4000 \cdot 5280$ feet, then

$$(58) \qquad\qquad 32 = \frac{GM}{(4000 \cdot 5280)^2} = \frac{GM}{R^2}\,.$$

If we compare (57) and (58), we see that the acceleration due to gravity of an object at or practically at the surface of the earth is 32 ft/sec², a fact we already know but which we now see is a special case of the general formula for the acceleration of gravity.*

---

* We have been using 32 ft/sec² as the acceleration due to gravity at the surface of the earth. Actually, the acceleration is not exactly the same at all points on the surface even at sea level. It is common practice to use g in place of 32 as the value of GM/R^2, and then one can take g to be the correct value for any given location. We shall, however, use the value 32 most of the time.

Let us now undertake to calculate the velocity with which an object must be shot up to reach a given height. We seek, of course, the minimum velocity needed to do the job. If the velocity is greater than this minimum, the object will go even higher. Let us suppose then that the object is shot up with the proper initial velocity and is r feet from the center of the earth.

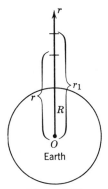

Figure 7-24.

We have the acceleration to which an object r feet from the center of the earth (and above the earth) is subject. If we take r to be positive in the upward direction (Fig. 7-24), then, because the acceleration causes a downward motion and therefore a downward velocity and so a decrease in r, we must write

$$a = -\frac{GM}{r^2}.$$

Moreover, a is the second derivative of r with respect to t. To remind ourselves of the variables involved, we use the Leibnizian notation and write

(59)
$$\frac{d^2r}{dt^2} = -\frac{GM}{r^2}.$$

We know that the acceleration is the derivative of the velocity. Hence by integrating (59) with respect to t we should obtain the velocity of an object that moves under the attraction of gravity. However, here we face a difficulty. If the right side of (59) were a function of t, we could integrate that function and state that it is the velocity, that is, dr/dt. However, the right side is a function of r.

The chain rule resolves our difficulty. Let us denote the velocity by v. Then

(60)
$$\frac{d^2r}{dt^2} = \frac{dv}{dt}.$$

Now v is a function of r because the velocity varies with distance from the center of the earth, and r is a function of t because the distance from the center of the earth varies with the time. Hence the chain rule says that

(61)
$$\frac{dv}{dt} = \frac{dv}{dr} \cdot \frac{dr}{dt} = \frac{dv}{dr} \cdot v.$$

Thus we may write (59) as

(62)
$$v\frac{dv}{dr} = -\frac{GM}{r^2}.$$

The new equation (62) does not seem to be more tractable than (59) because the factor v on the left side seems to bar what would otherwise be a straightforward integration. However, the chain rule helps us again. If the left side of (62) were merely dv/dr, we would say that the integral is v. What we do have on the left side is v multiplied by dv/dr. This is precisely the situation that can be handled by reversing the chain rule. According to the theorem of Section 7, if we have $dy/dr = v\, dv/dr$, the integral is $v^2/2$. This is the integral of the left side of (62).

As for the right side of (62), the integral with respect to r, by the inverse of the power rule, is GM/r. Hence

$$(63) \qquad \frac{v^2}{2} = \frac{GM}{r} + C.$$

To see more clearly what we have done in the integration process we should now differentiate (63) by regarding it as defining v implicitly as a function of r.

To fit the formula for velocity to the problem in hand, we must determine C. Because we wish to treat the situation in which the velocity is to be 0 at some distance r_1 from the center of the earth, we can require that v be 0 at $r = r_1$. Then

$$0 = \frac{GM}{r_1} + C$$

or

$$C = -\frac{GM}{r_1}.$$

Then from (63)

$$(64) \qquad \frac{v^2}{2} = \frac{GM}{r} - \frac{GM}{r_1}.$$

This formula gives the velocity acquired under the action of gravity by an object that starts with 0 velocity at the distance r_1 from the center of the earth and falls to a distance r from the center of the earth but external to the earth. If we wish to find the velocity v_0 at the surface of the earth, we have but to let $r = 4000 \cdot 5280$. As before, we denote the radius of the earth by R. Hence the velocity at the surface of the earth is given by

$$(65) \qquad \frac{v_0^2}{2} = \frac{GM}{R} - \frac{GM}{r_1}.$$

We can interpret this result in two ways. Because we took the velocity to be 0 at $r = r_1$, we can say that (65) gives the velocity acquired by the object when it reaches the surface of the earth. Alternatively, because an object rising from the earth with an initial velocity v_0 loses velocity in exactly the reverse order of that in which it gains velocity in falling, we can say that (65) gives the initial velocity that must be imparted to an object at the surface of the earth in order that it reach a height r_1 and have velocity 0 there. In applying (65) we can use the fact that $GM = 32(4000 \cdot 5280)^2 = 32R^2$.

A very interesting deduction from (65) is the quantity known as the escape velocity. This is the least velocity that one must give to an object so that it never falls back to earth, that is, so that it escapes. By contrast, (65) gives the initial velocity that enables the object to reach the distance r_1 but when it reaches this point, its velocity is 0 and gravity pulls it back to the earth. For the object to escape it must be able to travel up indefinitely. That is, no matter how far up it goes, it must continue to have some velocity to enable it to keep going. The mathematical formulation of this physical requirement is that as r_1 becomes infinite, the velocity should approach 0. The phrase, r_1 becomes infinite, does not mean that the distance r_1 is approaching a definite value but merely that r_1 is getting larger and larger and its values exceed any number, no matter how large, that anyone may name.

Now (65) does give the (least) initial velocity v_0 required to send an object to a height r_1. Hence we have but to see what happens to (65) as r_1 becomes infinite. In mathematical notation we seek

$$(66) \qquad\qquad \lim_{r_1 \to \infty} \frac{GM}{r_1}.$$

We should note that we do not substitute ∞ for r_1. As we have previously noted, ∞ is not a number.

As r_1 becomes larger and larger, the fraction in (66) must become smaller because the numerator is a constant. Moreover, because r_1 takes on values such as 10^6, 10^{12}, ..., the fraction becomes as small and smaller than any small quantity one may name. That is, the fraction must come closer and closer to 0 in value as r_1 becomes infinite. Then

$$\lim_{r_1 \to \infty} \frac{GM}{r_1} = 0.$$

Now we see from (65) that the escape velocity v_0 is given by

$$(67) \qquad\qquad v_0 = \sqrt{\frac{2GM}{R}}.$$

To simplify calculation, we can use the fact that $GM = 32R^2$ and therefore

$$(68) \qquad\qquad v_0 = \sqrt{64R} = 8\sqrt{R}.$$

Because R is $4000 \cdot 5280$,

$$v_0 = 36{,}800 \text{ ft/sec} = 7 \text{ mi/sec approximately.}$$

If we use 3960 miles for R, we find that v_0 is 6.93 mi/sec.

Before leaving the subject of escape velocity, let us note that in our method of integrating (59) we used a special transformation, namely (61). This transformation is important, but there is another device that is also very useful. We start again with (59), namely,

$$(69) \qquad\qquad \frac{d^2r}{dt^2} = -\frac{GM}{r^2}.$$

Now we multiply both sides of (69) by dr/dt. This gives

$$(70) \qquad\qquad \frac{dr}{dt} \cdot \frac{d^2r}{dt^2} = -\frac{GM}{r^2} \cdot \frac{dr}{dt}.$$

On the left side of (70) we can regard dr/dt as some function u. Then d^2r/dt^2 is the derivative of u. Thus the form of the left side is

$$u\,\frac{du}{dt}.$$

This form is precisely the one that permits us to integrate by reversing the chain rule. Then the integral with respect to t of the left side is $u^2/2$. Because our u is dr/dt or the velocity v, the integral of the left side of (70) is $v^2/2$. The right side of (70) is also in the form that permits reversing the chain rule. It contains a function of r multiplied by dr/dt. Hence the integral with respect to t is GM/r. Thus we obtain from (70)

$$\frac{v^2}{2} = \frac{GM}{r} + C.$$

This is exactly what we obtained in (63); therefore from here on the work is the same.

Exercises

1. Calculate the velocity that an object acquires in falling from a height of 1000 miles to the surface of the earth.   *Ans.* $640\sqrt{660}$ ft/sec.

2. Calculate the least velocity required to send an object up to a height of 4000 miles.

3. Assume that the acceleration of gravity is 32 ft/sec² at any height and calculate the least velocity required to send an object up to a height of 4000 miles. Would you expect this velocity to be greater or less than that called for in Exercise 2? Give the physical justification for your expectation.   *Ans.* $6400\sqrt{33}$ ft/sec.

4. A particle falls from rest at a point A whose height above the surface of the earth equals the radius of the earth. Show that the velocity on reaching the surface of the earth is equal to that acquired by a particle falling from rest through half the distance under the constant acceleration of 32 ft/sec².

5. Show that the velocity of escape from the earth is equal to the velocity required to send up an object to the height equal to the radius of the earth if the acceleration due to gravity were 32 ft/sec² at all heights.

6. Obtain a formula for the velocity attained by a body falling under the force of gravity if the initial velocity at height r_1 is not 0 but V. What velocity does the body acquire when it reaches the earth's surface?

$$Ans.\ V + \sqrt{2GM\left(\frac{1}{R} - \frac{1}{r_1}\right)}.$$

7. Find the velocity with which an object should be sent straight up so that it has a velocity of 1000 ft/sec when it reaches a height of 4000 miles above the earth's surface.

8. If an object falls from rest and reaches the earth's surface with a velocity of 10,000 ft/sec, from what height did it fall?

9. An object is projected upward with a velocity of 1 mi/sec. Find the maximum height it will reach.   *Ans.* 84 mi approx.

10. What can you say about the motion of an object that is shot up from the earth with a velocity greater than the escape velocity?

11. How would you modify the theory of escape velocity if the object were shot up from the moon instead of the earth?

12. If the radius of the moon is 4/15 of the earth's radius and the mass of the moon is 1/81 of the earth's mass, find the least velocity with which an object must be projected upward from the moon to escape from the moon. *Ans.* 1.50 mi/sec.

13. With what velocity must an object be projected upward from the earth's surface to reach the moon 240,000 miles away. The moon's gravitational attraction is not to be considered.   *Ans.* 6.88 mi/sec.

14. With what velocity must a body be projected from the moon to reach the earth? Neglect the attraction of the earth. Use the data of Exercises 12 and 13.
                                               Ans. 1.49 mi/sec.

15. Suppose that we determine the constant of integration in (63) so that $v = v_0$ when the object is at the surface of the earth. What is the formula for the velocity at the distance r from the center of the earth?

$$Ans.\ \frac{v^2}{2} = \frac{v_0{}^2}{2} + \frac{GM}{r} - \frac{GM}{R}.$$

16. (*a*) Calculate the velocity with which an object must be shot up from the earth (away from the sun) to just reach a given height r_1 from the center of the earth, but this time take into account the sun's gravitational attraction as well as the earth's. Suppose that the sun and earth are at rest (Fig. 7-25) and the object is shot out in the direction of the line joining the sun to the earth (which means perpendicularly to the earth's path around the sun). *Suggestion:* Let d be the distance from the center of the sun to the center of the earth. Let S be the mass of the sun. Then the *differential equation* is

$$\frac{d^2r}{dt^2} = -\frac{GM}{r^2} - \frac{GS}{(r + d)^2}.$$

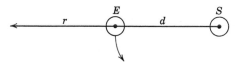

Figure 7-25

(*b*) Using the result of part (*a*) calculate the escape velocity. Use the following data. The mass S of the sun is 330,000 times the mass of the earth; the distance *d* between the earth and sun is 93,000,000 miles. To save calculation use the result from the text that $\sqrt{2GM/R} = 7$ mi/sec approximately.

Ans. 27 mi/sec approx.

17. In Exercise 13 we calculated the velocity required to send an object from the earth to the moon on the assumption that the moon's attraction was to be neglected. Because the moon attracts the object, this attraction should help the object to reach it. To obtain some estimate of the help that the moon's attraction furnishes, let us reason as follows. We assume that the earth and the moon are at rest. At some point on the line joining the earth to the moon (Fig. 7-26) the moon's gravitational attraction just offsets the earth's attraction for the object, and from that point on, which we call the stagnation point, the moon's attraction pulls the object to the surface of the moon. Hence it is necessary only to shoot the object up to reach the stagnation point. To calculate the location of the stagnation point let us use the fact that the moon's mass is 1/81 of the earth's mass. Also, the distance between the centers of the earth and moon is $60R$, where R is the earth's radius. Then if m is the mass of the object sent up and r_s denotes the distance out from the earth's center to the stagnation point,

$$\frac{GMm}{r_s{}^2} = \frac{GMm}{81(60R - r_s)^2}$$

If we solve this equation for r_s, we find that $r_s = 54R$. Now calculate the velocity required to send an object up from the earth's surface to just reach the stagnation point, assuming that during this motion the moon exerts no attraction. *Ans.* 6.86 mi/sec.

Figure 7-26

18. Using the approach discussed in the preceding exercise, calculate the velocity required to send an object from the surface of the moon to the surface of the earth by projecting the object upward with just enough velocity to reach the stagnation point. The moon's radius is 4/15 of the earth's radius.

Ans. 1.48 mi/sec.

19. (*a*) The calculation of the velocity required to send an object up from the surface of the earth to the moon by sending it to the stagnation point (Fig. 7-26) is only an approximate answer, because it neglects the fact that the moon attracts the object while it is traveling to the stagnation point and then gives it an acceleration so that it reaches the surface of the moon with more than 0 velocity. Moreover the earth's attraction continues to be effective even after the object passes the stagnation point. To take into account the continuing action of the earth's and the moon's gravitational

attraction, show that the correct differential equation is

$$\frac{d^2r}{dt^2} = -\frac{GM}{r^2} + \frac{G(M/81)}{(60R - r)^2}.$$

(b) Using the differential equation, calculate the velocity required to send an object up from the earth's surface so that it just reaches the surface of the moon with 0 velocity. Because the moon's radius is 4/15 of the earth's radius, we want the velocity to be 0 when $r = 60R - 4R/15$.

Ans. 6.6 mi/sec.

9. *Related Rates*. The chain rule permits us to answer a number of questions concerning the rate at which some variable is changing with respect to time. Suppose that a box-shaped tank with square base (Fig. 7-27) of dimensions 5 by 5 ft is being filled with water at the constant rate at 50 cu ft of water per minute. We might be interested in the rate at which the height x of the water is rising at any instant of time. In the present example, because water is being poured in at the constant rate of 50 cu ft min and the area of the base is 25 sq ft, the height of the water rises 2 ft/min. Moreover, because the water is being poured in at a constant rate and the cross section of the tank is uniform, the height of the water increases at the same rate at any instant of time, the rate of 2 ft/min. In calculus symbols, $dx/dt = 2$.

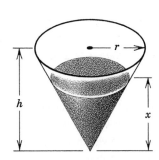

Figure 7-27   **Figure 7-28**

However, suppose that the water is poured at the same rate of 50 cu ft/min into a conical tank (Fig. 7-28). At what rate is the water level x rising? In this situation it is not possible to state at once what dx/dt is, because a fixed volume of water per minute does not increase the height of the water as much when x is large as when x is small. Let us see what we can do about calculating dx/dt.

We know that the volume of a cube of height h and radius r is

$$V = \tfrac{1}{3}\pi r^2 h.$$

To be concrete, suppose that $r = h/2$ in our case, so that

$$V = \tfrac{1}{12}\pi h^3.$$

When the height h is the variable amount x,

(71) $$V = \tfrac{1}{12}\pi x^3.$$

Now we know dV/dt; this is 50 cu ft/min at any time t, and we would like to know dx/dt. This statement suggests the chain rule, because

$$\frac{dV}{dt} = \frac{dV}{dx} \cdot \frac{dx}{dt}.$$

Application of the chain rule to (71) yields

$$\frac{dV}{dt} = \tfrac{1}{4}\pi x^2 \frac{dx}{dt}.$$

By solving for dx/dt, we obtain

(72) $$\frac{dx}{dt} = \frac{4(dV/dt)}{\pi x^2}.$$

We see that the rate at which the water level is rising depends not only on dV/dt but, as we expected, on the value of x itself. If this value is specified, we can compute dx/dt.

A very important rate that occurs in physical problems is power. Power is defined as the rate of change of work with respect to time. To put the matter loosely for the moment, if we intend to do a certain amount of work, say raise an object from a height R to a height r from the center of the earth, we can do it either slowly or rapidly. To do it rapidly requires more power during the time it is applied. An engine pulling a load uphill does work to pull the load from one place to another. The power it delivers determines the rate at which it pulls the load or does the work. This concept of power is the same as that used in electricity. An electric light operates at a certain power (measured in watts), which determines the brightness of the light.

The rate at which work is to be done is not always a matter of choice. A generator supplying electricity to a community must be prepared to supply power at the rate called for by the demand on the electricity. Hence the operating company must know whether its generators are adequate.

If the work done in any given operation is W, the definition of the power is dW/dt. Thus if an object of mass m is lifted straight up and if we assume that the distance is small so that we may use $32m$ for the weight, the work done is

$$W = 32mh$$

where h is the height to which the object is lifted, measured, say, from the surface of the earth. Then the power

$$\frac{dW}{dt} = 32m\frac{dh}{dt}.$$

We see then that the power varies with dh/dt or with the velocity with which the object is raised.

The unit of power, because it is the product of force ($32m$ in the example) and velocity, is foot-poundals per second or, because it is also possible to use pounds of force, foot-pounds per second. In engineering practice the unit of horsepower is used, 1 horsepower being 550 ft-lb/sec; that is, 1 horsepower means that 550 pounds of force are applied at the rate of 1 ft/sec or 225 pounds of force are applied at the rate of 2 ft/sec and so on. (In the centimeter-gram-second system, 1 horsepower equals 745.7 watts.)

If an object is raised to a great height so that we must take into account the varying force of gravity, we know from Section 10, formula (63), of Chapter 6 that the work done by gravity in pulling an object down from a distance r_1 from the center of the earth to a distance r is

$$W = \frac{GmM}{r} - \frac{GmM}{r_1}.$$

By the chain rule we have

$$\frac{dW}{dt} = - \frac{GmM}{r^2} \frac{dr}{dt}.$$

Again we see that the power is the force applied, namely, GmM/r^2 times the velocity dr/dt with which the power is applied.

Exercises

1. The edge e of a metal cube is expanding at the rate of 0.05 in./hr. At what rate is the volume V increasing? *Ans.* $dV/dt = 3e^2/20$ cu in./hr.

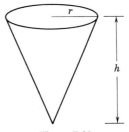

2. Suppose that fluid flows out of the bottom of a cone-shaped vessel at the rate of 3 cu ft/min. If the height of the cone is three times the radius (Fig. 7-29), how fast is the height of the fluid decreasing when the fluid is 6 inches deep in the middle?

Figure 7-29

3. A mothball of radius $\frac{1}{2}$ inch evaporates to leave a mothball of radius $\frac{1}{4}$ inch at the end of 6 months. Express the radius of the ball as a function of time. *Suggestion:* Make the physical assumption that the rate of change of volume with respect to time is proportional to the surface area. *Ans.* $r = \dfrac{1}{2} - \dfrac{t}{24}.$

4. If a mass of 10 pounds is raised from the surface of the earth to a height of several hundred miles at the rate of 25,000 ft/sec, what power must be applied at the surface of the earth and at a height of 100 miles.

Ans. $8 \cdot 10^6$ ft-pdl/sec; $8 \cdot 10^6 (40/41)^2$ ft-pdl/sec.

5. (*a*) Find the rate at which the area of a circle changes with respect to time in terms of the time rate of change of the radius.   *Ans.* $dA/dt = 2\pi r \, dr/dt$.

   (*b*) If, when the radius of a circle is 5 units, it is increasing at the rate of $\frac{1}{2}$ ft/sec, at what rate is the area changing?   *Ans.* 5π sq ft/sec.

   (*c*) Since when the radius is 5, it is changing at the rate of $\frac{1}{2}$ ft/sec, and the area is then changing at the rate of 5π sq ft/sec, does the area increase by 5π sq ft in the next second?

   (*d*) Suppose that the radius' rate of increase of $\frac{1}{2}$ ft/sec is *constant*, that is, the same at all values of r. Does the area increase by 5π sq ft in the next second after the radius is 5 ft?   *Ans.* No.

6. Find the rate of change of the area of a square when the sides are increasing at the rate of 1 ft/min and are 5 feet long.

7. Two ships start at the same point, but the first ship leaves at noon and sails east at the rate of 20 mi/hr and the second leaves at 1 P.M. and sails south at 25 mi/hr. How fast is the distance between them changing at 2 P.M.?

8. A conical tank is 14 ft across the top and 12 ft deep. Water is flowing in at the rate of 30 cu ft/min and flowing out at the rate of 20 cu ft/min. How fast is the surface of the water rising when it is 6 ft high?

9. If $y^2 = 2x$ and x is increasing at the rate of $\frac{1}{2}$ unit per minute, how fast is the slope of the graph changing when $x = 32$?

Ans. Decreasing at the rate of 1/1024 unit per minute.

10. (*a*) A train leaves a station which we take to be the origin of our coordinate system and travels along the upper half of the parabola $y^2 = 4x$. At what rate is the distance of the train from the station changing when the train is at the point $(9, 6)$ on the curve and the x-value of the train's position is increasing at the rate of 2 units per minute.   *Ans.* $22/\sqrt{117}$ units per min.

   (*b*) The answer in part (*a*) is just a little more than 2 units per minute. Show by geometrical evidence that this answer is reasonable.

$$\frac{dv}{dt} = -\frac{Gm \, M}{(4/100)^2} \; ($$

APPENDIX

Transformation of Coordinates

A1. *Introduction.*   When we derived the equations of the ellipse and the hyperbola in Chapter 7, we stated that experience indicates how to locate the axes in reference to the foci so that the resulting equation would be as simple as possible. Curiosity might prompt us to see what happens if we choose the axes in another position. However, more than a mere desire to satisfy curiosity recommends looking into the question of a change in the location of the axes. We no longer need to be assured that the knowledge of the relation between curve and equation is valuable for the mathematical treatment of physical problems and for visual aid in studying the behavior of formulas.

So far we know that first degree equations in x and y and straight lines are the algebraic and geometric counterparts of each other. We have also learned that the circle, parabola, ellipse, and hyperbola have second degree equations, at least for particular choices of axes. This work leaves open the question of what other curves may correspond to second degree equations in x and y. There is also the possibility that the study of what happens to the equation of a curve when the location of the axes is changed might shed light on the basic problem of coordinate geometry, namely, the relation between curves and equations.

A2. Rotation of Axes.   Because we know the full story of the general first degree equation

$$Ax + By + C = 0,$$

let us look into second degree equations in x and y. The most general equation of the second degree in x and y has the form

(1) $$Ax^2 + Bxy + Cy^2 + Dx + Ey + F = 0.$$

This equation looks formidable, and there seems to be no obvious way of determining what curve or curves it may represent for various values of the coefficients. One might pick particular values of A, B, C, and the other coefficients, solve for y as a function of x, make a table of values, and plot the corresponding points. However, such an approach is not likely to be fruitful not only because there is an infinite number of possible values for each of the coefficients, but because we know in fact that this equation includes parabolas, ellipses, and hyperbolas as special cases and we would only be confused by the variety of results. However, the thought that the equation of a curve depends on the location of the axes suggests approaching the problem of analyzing (1) by considering what happens when we change axes.

Suppose that we consider what happens when the axes are rotated through some angle θ. That is, suppose that we have already the set of x- and y-axes and that we introduce a new pair (Fig. 7A-1), the (x', y')-axes such that the x'-axis makes an angle θ with the x-axis. Moreover, to start with let us suppose that the origin is the same for both pairs. If we take any point P in the plane, its location with respect to the x- and y-axes is specified by the coordinates x and y of P, x being OM and y being PM. With respect to the (x', y')-axes, the *same* geometric point P has different coordinates, say (x', y'), x' being OM' and y', PM'. How are the coordinates (x, y) of P related to the coordinates (x', y') of P?

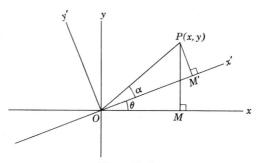

Figure 7A-1

Let us start with the x-value of P. If we introduce the angle α shown in the figure, we can say that

(2) $$x = OP \cos (\theta + \alpha).$$

We can use the trigonometric identity

$$\cos (A + B) = \cos A \cos B - \sin A \sin B$$

to rewrite (2) as

$$x = OP \cos \theta \cos \alpha - OP \sin \theta \sin \alpha.$$

However, $OP \cos \alpha$ is OM' or x' and $OP \sin \alpha$ is PM' or y'. Hence

(3) $$x = x' \cos \theta - y' \sin \theta.$$

Thus we see so far how x is related to x' and y'.

If in place of (2) we consider

(4) $$y = OP \sin (\theta + \alpha)$$

and apply the trigonometric identity

$$\sin (A + B) = \sin A \cos B + \cos A \sin B,$$

we obtain from (4) that

$$y = OP \sin \theta \cos \alpha + OP \cos \theta \sin \alpha.$$

Because $OP \cos \alpha$ is x' and $OP \sin \alpha$ is y',

(5) $$y = x' \sin \theta + y' \cos \theta.$$

Thus we have the following theorem:

Theorem: If (x, y) are the coordinates of a point relative to the (x, y)-axes and (x', y') the coordinates of the same point relative to (x', y')-axes which have the same origin but are rotated an angle θ with respect to the first pair of axes, then

(6)
$$x = x' \cos \theta - y' \sin \theta$$

$$y = x' \sin \theta + y' \cos \theta.$$

We see from (6) how the coordinates of a single point are related to the new coordinates under rotation. How does this help to analyze equation (1)? The equation represents a particular collection of points, those whose coordinates satisfy the equation. Suppose that we consider what happens to the coordinates of all these points. Because the equations (6) hold for any (x, y), we certainly can substitute them for the x and y of points belonging to (1). The algebra involved in simplifying the resulting equation is lengthy. However, only multiplication is utilized. If we substitute the values of x and y given by (6) into (1), carry out the indicated multiplications and rearrange the terms we obtain

(7) $[A \cos^2 \theta + B \sin \theta \cos \theta + C \sin^2 \theta]x'^2$

$+ [-2A \sin \theta \cos \theta + B(\cos^2 \theta - \sin^2 \theta) + 2C \sin \theta \cos \theta]x'y'$

$+ [A \sin^2 \theta - B \sin \theta \cos \theta + C \cos^2 \theta]y'^2$

$+ [D \cos \theta + E \sin \theta]x' + [-D \sin \theta + E \cos \theta]y' + F = 0.$

Equation (7) is certainly no improvement over (1). However, there is the chance that by picking θ properly we may obtain a simplification of (7). If we examine the equations of the parabola, ellipse, and hyperbola, which we have already encountered, we observe that they do not contain an xy-term. Perhaps we should choose θ so as to eliminate the $x'y'$-term in (7); we might then see more clearly what the equation represents. To eliminate the $x'y'$-term, we must have a θ for which

(8) $-2A \sin \theta \cos \theta + B(\cos^2 \theta - \sin^2 \theta) + 2C \sin \theta \cos \theta = 0.$

As an aid in determining the value of θ, we use the trigonometric identities

$$\sin 2\theta = 2 \sin \theta \cos \theta$$

$$\cos 2\theta = \cos^2 \theta - \sin^2 \theta.$$

Then (8) becomes

(9) $(C - A) \sin 2\theta + B \cos 2\theta = 0.$

Division by $\cos 2\theta$ gives

(10) $\tan 2\theta = \dfrac{B}{A - C}.$

Because A, B, and C are known from (1), we see that we can pick a θ which eliminates the $x'y'$-term in (7). Of course, there are many values of θ satisfying (10), but no matter what value $B/(A - C)$ might have we can find a value of 2θ lying between $0°$ and $180°$ and therefore a value of θ lying between $0°$ and $90°$. There is the special case in which $A - C = 0$, but in this case (9) tells us that $\cos 2\theta = 0$ and therefore $2\theta = 90°$.

For the value of θ which satisfies (9) the coefficients in (7) have definite values. We cannot make any significant statements as yet about these coefficients, but let us note for the moment that because the $x'y'$-term is eliminated (7) has the form

(11) $$A'x'^2 + B'y'^2 + D'x' + E'y' + F = 0.$$

To practice what we have learned so far, let us eliminate the xy-term from the equation

(12) $$3x^2 - 10xy + 3y^2 = 0.$$

We first use (10) to determine θ. Because our $A = 3$, $B = -10$, and $C = 3$, we see that

$$\tan 2\theta = \frac{-10}{3 - 3}.$$

Of course, division by 0 is meaningless, but what this equation tells us, in view of a previous remark, is that $2\theta = 90°$. We can see this in another way; by (10)

$$\cot 2\theta = \frac{A - C}{B}$$

and because $\cot 2\theta = 0$, $2\theta = 90°$. Hence $\theta = 45°$. Now $\sin 45° = \sqrt{2}/2$ and $\cos 45° = \sqrt{2}/2$. Then equations (6) become

$$x = x'\frac{\sqrt{2}}{2} - y'\frac{\sqrt{2}}{2}$$

$$y = x'\frac{\sqrt{2}}{2} + y'\frac{\sqrt{2}}{2}.$$

We substitute these values of x and y in (12). Thus

$$3\left(x'\frac{\sqrt{2}}{2} - y'\frac{\sqrt{2}}{2}\right)^2 - 10\left(x'\frac{\sqrt{2}}{2} - y'\frac{\sqrt{2}}{2}\right)\left(x'\frac{\sqrt{2}}{2} + y'\frac{\sqrt{2}}{2}\right)$$

$$+ 3\left(x'\frac{\sqrt{2}}{2} + y'\frac{\sqrt{2}}{2}\right)^2 = 0.$$

We carry out the indicated multiplications and obtain

(13) $$x'^2 - 4y'^2 = 0.$$

Of course, the $x'y'$-term should not appear in the result, and the fact that it does not is a partial check on the correctness of the algebra.

The curve corresponding to (13) consists of the two straight lines

$$x' - 2y' = 0 \quad \text{and} \quad x' + 2y' = 0.$$

In fact, we encountered an equation such as (13) in our discussion of the asymptotes of the hyperbola [see (38) of Chapter 7], and the argument given there applies here. Figure 7A-2 shows the curve of Equation (13). We should note that the curve—the two straight lines in this case—must be graphed with respect to the (x', y')-axes, which are turned 45° from the (x, y)-axes. Moreover, the graph of the original Equation (12) consists of the same two straight lines. In fact, having obtained the graph we could now forget about the (x', y')-axes and regard the two straight lines as the graph of (12) with respect to the (x, y)-axes.

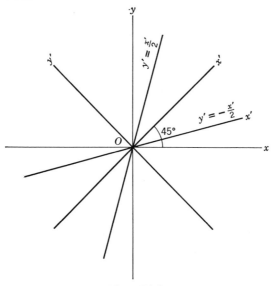

Figure 7A-2

In this example we found that $\theta = 45°$, and therefore we knew at once that $\sin \theta = \sqrt{2}/2$ and $\cos \theta = \sqrt{2}/2$. In other cases we may find $\tan 2\theta$ by using (10) and we may not be able to state at once what $\sin \theta$ and $\cos \theta$ are. We could of course go to the trigonometric tables to find 2θ; then θ, $\sin \theta$, and $\cos \theta$ can also be determined. However, there is no need to resort to trigonometric tables and to decimal expressions if one does not wish to. We know that $1 + \tan^2 A = \sec^2 A$ and $\cos A = 1/\sec A$. Hence

$$\cos 2\theta = \pm \frac{1}{\sqrt{1 + \tan^2 2\theta}}.$$

the signs of $\cos 2\theta$ and $\tan 2\theta$ must be the same. Next we may resort to the half-angle trigonometric identities to state that

$$\sin \theta = \sqrt{\frac{1 - \cos 2\theta}{2}}, \qquad \cos \theta = \sqrt{\frac{1 + \cos 2\theta}{2}}$$

to find the $\sin \theta$ and $\cos \theta$ we need to use formulas (6).

Exercises

1. Transform the following equations by rotating the axes through the indicated angle. Graph the curve and show both sets of axes:

(a) $x^2 + 4xy + y^2 = 16$; $45°$.
$\qquad$ Ans. $3x'^2 - y'^2 = 16$.
(b) $3x^2 - 4xy + 10 = 0$; $\tan \theta = 2$.

(c) $3x^2 - 3xy - y^2 = 5$; $\tan \theta = 3$.
(d) $x^2 + 4xy + 4y^2 = 0$; $\tan \theta = 2$.

2. Would you expect the equation $x^2 + y^2 = r^2$ to remain the same under a rotation of axes? If so, why?

3. Remove the xy-term from the following equations by rotating the axes. Graph the curve and show both sets of axes:

(a) $x^2 + 2\sqrt{3}xy - y^2 = 4$.
$\qquad$ Ans. $x'^2 - y'^2 = 2$.
(b) $17x^2 - 16xy + 17y^2 = 225$.
(c) $3x^2 - 4\sqrt{3}xy - y^2 = 9$.
$\qquad$ Ans. $-3x'^2 + 5y'^2 = 9$.
(d) $x^2 + 4xy + y^2 = 16$.

(e) $x^2 - 2xy + y^2 = 12$.
$\qquad$ Ans. $y'^2 = 6$.
(f) $xy = 12$.
(g) $25x^2 + 14xy + 25y^2 = 288$.
$\qquad$ Ans. $16x'^2 + 9y'^2 = 144$.

4. Could rotation of axes be used to simplify the general equation $Ax + By + C = 0$ of the straight line?

A3. Translation of Axes. Now let us consider whether we can carry further our analysis of the general second degree equation (1). We have found so far that we can, by rotation of axes, transform it to (11), namely,

(14) $$A'x'^2 + C'y'^2 + D'x' + E'y' + F = 0.$$

There is the possibility that by a further change in the location of the axes we can simplify (14). This suggestion arises from the following example.
Consider the equation

(15) $$(x - 3)^2 + (y - 2)^2 = 25.$$

The left-hand side is the square of the distance from (x, y) to $(3, 2)$, and this distance, according to the right side, is always 5. Hence the curve corresponding to (15) is a circle with center at $(3, 2)$ and radius 5. If we square the terms in (15), we obtain

(16) $$x^2 - 6x + y^2 - 4y - 12 = 0.$$

On the one hand we see that (16) is of the form (14). On the other, we know that the equation of a circle with center at the origin and radius 5 is

(17) $$x^2 + y^2 = 25.$$

If we chose axes in Fig. 7A-3 with origin at (3, 2) and parallel to the existing x- and y-axes, the equation of the circle would be (17) with respect to the new axes, whereas it is (16) or (15) with respect to the original axes.

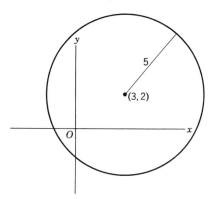

Figure 7A-3

The suggestion that we derive from this example is that we may be able to simplify (14) by introducing new axes parallel to the original ones but at some new origin (h, k), that is, by *translating* the axes. Let us try this. If we introduce new axes, the x''- and y''-axes of Fig. 7A-4, then for any point P with coordinates (x', y')

(18)
$$x' = x'' + h$$
$$y' = y'' + k.$$

Let us substitute these values of x' and y' in (14) and see if we can determine h and k so as to simplify the equation materially.

Figure 7A-4

Substitution of (18) in (14) gives

(19) $A'(x'' + h)^2 + C'(y'' + k)^2 + D'(x'' + h) + E'(y'' + k) + F = 0.$

Multiplication yields

(20) $A'x''^2 + 2A'x''h + A'h^2 + C'y''^2 + 2C'y''k + C'k^2 + D'x''$
$$+ D'h + E'y'' + E'k + F = 0.$$

We hope to eliminate the x''- and y''-terms. The coefficients of x'' and y'' are

$$2A'h + D' \quad \text{and} \quad 2C'k + E'.$$

Let us set them equal to 0. Thus

$$2A'h + D' = 0, \qquad 2C'k + E' = 0.$$

If A' and C' are not 0, we have

(21) $$h = -\frac{D'}{2A'}, \qquad k = -\frac{E'}{2C'}.$$

Thus we can determine h and k to eliminate the x''- and y''-terms in (20), and (20) reduces to

(22) $$A'x''^2 + C'y''^2 + G = 0,$$

where G is the sum of all the constant terms in (20).

Now we are on familiar ground. If $A' = C'$ and if G is opposite in sign to A' and C', Equation (22) represents a circle. If $A' \neq C'$ but are alike in sign and G is of opposite sign, Equation (22) represents an ellipse. If A' and C' are of opposite signs, whether numerically equal or not, Equation (22) represents a hyperbola.

The derivation of (21) presupposed that A' and C' are not 0. Now, both cannot be 0 because these A' and C' are the A' and C' of (14), and if they were both 0, (14) would be a straight line; because (14) represents the same curve as (1), the latter would represent a straight line and therefore would not be of the second degree. However, A' or C' of (20) may be 0. Let us suppose that $C' = 0$. Then we cannot determine k in (21), but we can determine h to eliminate the x'-term in (20). Then (20) reduces to

(23) $$A'x''^2 + E'y'' + H = 0,$$

where

(24) $$H = A'h^2 + D'h + E'k + F.$$

Because h is already fixed we can use (24) to determine k so that $H = 0$. Then (23) reduces to

(25) $$A'x''^2 + E'y'' = 0,$$

which is a parabola.

Likewise, if A' should be 0 but C' not 0 in (20), we could reduce (20) to

(26) $$C'y''^2 + D'x'' = 0,$$

which is again a parabola.

We note, incidentally, that instead of remembering (21) or the special cases such as (24), it is just as well, given (14), to make the substitution (18) and determine h and k directly.

Thus we have learned much about (1). Rotation of axes eliminates the xy-term. Then translation of axes reduces it to one of the standard forms that we have already encountered for the ellipse, parabola, or hyperbola. Our proofs did omit a couple of degenerate cases. For example, if E' were 0 in (23), we could not use (24) to determine k. But then if A' and H are of opposite signs, for example, if (23) degenerates to $3x''^2 - 7 = 0$, the graph consists of two coincident straight lines.

The grand conclusion that results from our analysis of (1) is that every equation of the second degree represents a parabola, ellipse (including the circle), or hyperbola, apart from a few degenerate cases. Moreover, by a rotation and translation of axes we can write the equation of the curve in one of the simplified forms that we learned earlier.

Exercises

1. Simplify each of the following equations by translating the axes. Graph the curves and show both sets of axes:

(a) $x^2 - y^2 + 32x + 4y + 40 = 0$.
      Ans. $x'^2 - y'^2 - 212 = 0$.

(b) $3x^2 + 4y^2 - 12x - 6y + 7 = 0$.

(c) $x^2 + 4y^2 + 10x - 12y + 14 = 0$.

(d) $x^2 + 6x + 4y + 8 = 0$.
      Ans. $x'^2 + 4y' = 0$.

(e) $4x^2 - 32x - 4y - 13 = 0$.
      Ans. $4x'^2 - 4y' = 0$.

(f) $y^2 - 6x - 10y + 19 = 0$.

(g) $x^2 - y^2 + 8x - 14y - 35 = 0$.
      Ans. $x'^2 - y'^2 - 2 = 0$.

(h) $x^2 + y^2 - 6x + 4y - 12 = 0$.

(i) $y^2 - 4x + 8 = 0$.
      Ans. $y'^2 = 4x'$.

(j) $y^2 - 8x - 6y + 17 = 0$.

2. Could translation of axes be applied to the equation $Ax + By + C = 0$ to simplify this equation?

3. Show that by translation of axes the equation

$$\frac{(x - 3)^2}{9} + \frac{(y + 2)^2}{4} = 1$$

can be reduced to the standard form of the ellipse, that is, $(x^2/a^2) + (y^2/b^2) = 1$.

4. (a) Show that the equation $y = ax^2 + bx + c$ can be reduced by translation of axes to the standard form $y = x^2/4p$ of the parabola.

(b) Find the coordinates of the focus, and vertex of the original parabola.

$$\text{Ans. Focus } \left(\frac{-b}{2a}, \frac{4ac - b^2 + 1}{4a} \right); \text{ vertex } \left(-\frac{b}{2a}, \frac{4ac - b^2}{4a} \right).$$

(c) Find the equation of the directrix of the original parabola

$$y = \frac{4ac - b^2 - 1}{4a}.$$

5. Determine the major and minor (transverse and conjugate) axes and the co-ordinates of the center of the following hyperbolas:

(a) $16x^2 - 25y^2 - 128x - 150y = 369.$ *Ans.* $a = 5, b = 4, (4, -3).$

(b) $36x^2 - 36y^2 - 288x - 360y + 972 = 0.$

(c) $9x^2 - 4y^2 + 54x + 16y = 79.$ *Ans.* $a = 4, b = 6, (-3, 2).$

(d) $16x^2 - 9y^2 + 192x + 72y = 278.$

(e) $25x^2 - 16y^2 + 200x + 160y = -400.$ *Ans.* $a = 5, b = 4, (5, -4).$

6. Determine the major and minor axes and the coordinates of the center of the following ellipses:

(a) $36x^2 + 25y^2 - 216x + 300y = -324.$ *Ans.* $a = 6, b = 5, (3, -6)$

(b) $16x^2 + 25y^2 - 96x - 100y - 156 = 0.$

(c) $9x^2 + 25y^2 + 36x + 150y + 36 = 0.$ *Ans.* $a = 5, b = 3, (-2, -3).$

(d) $9x^2 + 36y^2 + 54x - 216y + 81 = 0.$

(e) $49x^2 + 16y^2 - 396x - 96y - 244 = 0.$ *Ans.* $a = 7, b = 4, (2, 3).$

7. Reduce to standard form and graph the curve whose equation is

(a) $x^2 + 4xy + 4y^2 + 12x - 6y = 0.$ *Ans.* $y'' = \sqrt{5}x''^2/6.$

(b) $5x^2 + 6xy + 5y^2 + 22x - 6y + 21 = 0.$ *Ans.* $4x''^2 + y''^2 = 16.$

(c) $x^2 - 2xy + 4y^2 - 4 = 0.$

(d) $5x^2 + 4xy - y^2 + 24x - 6y - 5 = 0.$

(e) $x^2 - 2xy + y^2 - 5y = 0.$ *Ans.* $4y''^2 - 5\sqrt{2}x'' = 0.$

(f) $x^2 + 2xy + y^2 + 4x - 4y = 0.$

(g) $x^2 + 6x - 3y + 6 = 0.$ *Ans.* $x'^2 - 3y' = 0.$

(h) $13x^2 + 10xy + 13y^2 - 42x + 6y - 27 = 0.$

A4. Invariants. Coordinate geometry, useful as it is in furnishing equations for curves, also embarasses us with its abundance of equations for the same curve. We have seen that rotation of axes and then translation of axes give us two more equations for the very same curve with whose equation we begin. If we wished to determine some facts about the curve without having to go through rotation and translation of axes, it would certainly be desirable to do so by working with the original equation. Some of these facts can be so determined.

For example, given any second degree equation in x and y, we know now that it must represent a parabola, ellipse, hyperbola, or some degenerate case. Which curve it does represent can be determined without going through the processes of rotation and translation. We were able to show that the general equation (1), namely,

(26) $Ax^2 + Bxy + Cy^2 + Dx + Ey + F = 0$

can be transformed by rotation and translation into (22), that is,

(27) $A'x''^2 + C'y''^2 + G = 0,$

or into (24), that is,

(28) $$A'x''^2 + E'y'' = 0,$$

or into (25), which is

(29) $$C'y''^2 + D'x'' = 0,$$

or possibly into some degenerate case. By examining A' and C' we were able to state what curve we had. If we could relate A' and C' to A and C, we might be able to state, merely by examining the original Equation (26), what the curve is. How are A' and C' related to A and C?

We know from (7) and (11) that

(30) $$A' = A \cos^2 \theta + B \sin \theta \cos \theta + C \sin^2 \theta$$

(31) $$C' = A \sin^2 \theta - B \sin \theta \cos \theta + C \cos^2 \theta.$$

We see at once, by adding (30) and (31), that

(32) $$A' + C' = A + C.$$

This relation is useful but not sufficient. A review of the discussion following Equation (22) shows that we had to know whether $A' = C'$ or $A' \neq C'$ and, if the latter, whether A' and C' agreed or disagreed in sign. This information cannot be secured from (32). Hence we shall look for additional relations between the original and transformed coefficients. Since we do not know what relations beyond (32) may hold, let us explore a little bit.

We see from (30) and (31) that

$$A' - C' = A \cos 2\theta + B \sin 2\theta - C \cos 2\theta$$

or

(33) $$A' - C' = (A - C) \cos 2\theta + B \sin 2\theta.$$

This relation is not very useful because it involves θ. However, we know something essential about θ. We chose it to satisfy equation (9), namely,

(34) $$0 = (C - A) \sin 2\theta + B \cos 2\theta.$$

Now, if we square (33), we obtain

(35) $$(A' - C')^2 = (A - C)^2 \cos^2 2\theta + 2B(A - C) \sin 2\theta \cos 2\theta$$
$$+ B^2 \sin^2 2\theta.$$

If we square (34), we obtain

(36) $$0 = (C - A)^2 \sin^2 2\theta + 2B(C - A) \sin 2\theta \cos 2\theta + B^2 \cos^2 2\theta.$$

By adding (35) and (36), we obtain

(37) $$(A' - C')^2 = (A - C)^2 + B^2.$$

Equations (32) and (37) give two equations in the two unknowns A' and C' in terms of the known quantities A, B, and C, and therefore we could stop right here. However, we may be able to avoid the necessity of solving these two simultaneous equations every time we wish to know what A' and C' are. If we square (32), we obtain

(38) $$(A' + C')^2 = (A + C)^2.$$

And if we subtract (38) from (37), we obtain

(39) $$-4A'C' = B^2 - 4AC.$$

This single relation tells us all we need to know. Thus in the discussion following (22) we found that if A' and C' are alike in sign (whether equal or unequal), the curve is an ellipse (or the special case of a circle). But then $-4A'C'$ is negative. Hence

(40) if $B^2 - 4AC$ is negative, the curve is an ellipse.

If A' and C' are unlike in sign, we know from (22) that the curve is a hyperbola. But then $-4A'C'$ is positive. Hence

(41) if $B^2 - 4AC$ is positive, the curve is a hyperbola.

If A' or C' is 0, then (24) and (25) tell us that the curve is a parabola. In these cases $4A'C' = 0$, and therefore

(42) if $B^2 - 4AC = 0$, the curve is a parabola.

This listing of possibilities (40), (41), and (42) does not tell us what degenerate cases may arise, but it is rarely necessary to use such tests.

Thus we see from (40), (41), and (42) that we can tell from the original equation (26) exactly what curve we have. The answer to this question is often important in itself; it also serves as a check on what we obtain by rotation and translation if we have reason to go through these processes. Equation (39) serves still another purpose. The ellipse, hyperbola, and parabola are called conic sections because such curves can be obtained as the intersection of a cone and a plane (Fig. 7A-5) (we shall not examine this geometrical fact). The ellipse and hyperbola are called central conics because they have a center, the point of intersection of the axes of symmetry. If we start with the equation of a central conic, there is a slight reduction in the algebra of rotation and translation of axes if the translation is performed first. Equation (39) tells us which conic we are dealing with.

The relation (39) is significant for another reason. We know that in rotating the axes by some angle θ we fix θ so that $B' = 0$. Then we could write (39) as

(43) $$B'^2 - 4A'C' = B^2 - 4AC.$$

This equation says that the quantity $B^2 - 4AC$ remains the same or, one says, is *invariant* under rotation of axes. We found in (32) that the quantity

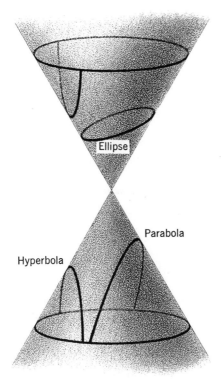

Ellipse

Parabola

Hyperbola

Figure 7A-5

$A + C$ is also invariant under rotation of axes. The entire subject of invariants under change of axes or under transformation of coordinates, is enormously important because such invariants express geometric properties of curves, that is, properties that are independent of the particular set of axes used to describe the equation of the curve.

Rotation and translation of axes are used to study equations of degrees higher than the second and to study the equations of other types of curves. We shall use these transformations in later work.

Exercises

1. Test the equations in Exercise 7 of Section A3 to determine what curves they represent. Check your results against the standard forms given in the answer.

2. If we multiply the equations of the straight lines $3x - 2y = 0$ and $4x - 5y = 0$, we obtain the equation $12x^2 - 23xy + 10y^2 = 0$. According to the argument given in Chapter 7 in connection with (38), the equation of the product should represent the two straight lines. However, by using the $B^2 - 4AC$ test we find that the equation represents a hyperbola. Explain the seeming contradiction.

3. (a) Would you expect the slope of a line to be invariant under rotation of axes?

   (b) To test whether the slope of a line is invariant under rotation of axes, we can take any line $y = mx + b$ and consider what happens to it under rotation of axes. Find the transformed equation and determine its slope.

$$\text{\textit{Ans.} } m' = \frac{m \cos \theta - \sin \theta}{\cos \theta + m \sin \theta}.$$

4. (a) Would you expect the angle between two lines to be invariant under rotation of axes?

   (b) Prove your conjecture by considering what happens under rotation of axes to $\tan \theta = (m_2 - m_1)/(1 + m_1 m_2)$. *Suggestion:* Use the result of Exercise 3b.

5. Would you expect the slope of a curve to be invariant under rotation of axes?

6. (a) Would you expect the slope of a line to be invariant under translation of axes?

   (b) Prove your conjecture by considering what happens to the slope of $y = mx + b$ under translation of axes.

7. Would you expect the angle between two lines to be invariant under translation of axes?

8. (a) Consider the quantity $x^2 + y^2$. Would you expect it to be invariant under rotation of axes? *Suggestion:* What is the geometric meaning of the quantity?

   (b) Prove that the quantity $x^2 + y^2$ is invariant under rotation of axes.

9. (a) Would you expect the quantity $x^2 + y^2$ to be invariant under translation of axes?

   (b) Prove your conjecture.

CHAPTER EIGHT

Maxima and Minima

1. *Introduction.* We mentioned at the outset of the discussion of the calculus that one of the major problems which troubled mathematicians of the seventeenth century was that of finding greatest or least values of varying quantities. The greatest range that could be obtained by varying the angle of elevation of a cannon and the greatest and least distance of a planet from the sun are examples of real problems of those times. Why should these problems have led to thinking about the calculus, that is, about instantaneous rates of change?

Physically, it was clear to the scientists that a rate of change was involved. Consider a ball thrown straight up into the air. As it rises, its velocity decreases; when it reaches the highest point, the maximum height, its velocity is 0 or else it would continue to rise. It then starts its downward motion. In other words, the velocity is 0 at the maximum height. But the velocity is the instantaneous rate of change of height with respect to time. Hence the instantaneous rate of change or the derivative is involved. We therefore expect that it is also involved in other maxima and minima problems.

Let us consider the problem of maximum range. The range of a shell fired from a cannon located at O (Fig. 8-1) depends on the angle A at which the cannon is inclined. It is intuitively clear that if the shell is fired at a very high angle or a very low angle, the range is small. Presumably, there is some value of A for which the range is a maximum. Let us suppose that we have the precise function which relates range and angle A. How should we proceed to find the value of A that yields maximum range? The motion of a ball thrown straight up furnishes a clue. Here the relevant function is the height of the ball as a function of the time, and at the maximum point the derivative of height with respect to time, the velocity, is 0. This suggests that to find the

Figure 8-1

205

maximum range we must find the derivative of the range with respect to A and set this derivative equal to 0.

More generally, if y is a function of x, it seems that to find the maximum value of y we must find $\dot{y}$ and set this equal to 0. With this clue in mind let us study the behavior of functions and see if we can find a method of determining maximum and minimum values of the dependent variable.

2. The Geometrical Approach to Maxima and Minima. Let us take a specific function, which is nevertheless representative of what happens generally, and study its geometrical behavior. Consider the function

$$y = \frac{x^3}{3} - 2x^2 + 3x + 2.$$

To obtain the graph of this function we make a table of x- and y-values, graph the points whose coordinates are given in the table, and join these points by a smooth curve (Fig. 8-2).

x	y
-1	$-3\frac{1}{3}$
0	2
1	$3\frac{1}{3}$
2	$2\frac{2}{3}$
3	2
4	$3\frac{1}{3}$
5	$\frac{26}{3}$

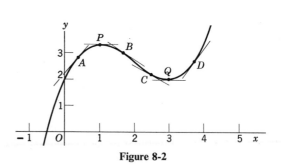

Figure 8-2

Judging by the graph, the function that we are studying seems to have a maximum value of about 3 near $x = 1$ and a minimum value of about 2 near $x = 3$. Because the behavior of the derivative of the function seems to be important in finding maximum and minimum values of functions, let us observe the behavior of the derivative near the maximum and minimum points. At a point such as A, to the left of the maximum point P, the derivative of y with respect to x, which is the slope of the curve at A, is positive. At a point such as B, the derivative is negative. At the maximum point P, the derivative seems to be 0, for the tangent line seems to be horizontal. Thus on the basis of the geometrical evidence we see that the derivative is 0 at the maximum point; it is positive at points to the left and negative at points to the right.

Now let us consider the behavior of the derivative near the minimum value of the function. At the point C to the left of the minimum point Q the derivative is negative; at Q the tangent is horizontal and therefore the derivative is 0; at D the derivative is positive. Hence at a minimum point, as at a maximum point, the derivative is 0, but in the case of a minimum the derived function changes from negative values at points to the left to positive values at points to the right.

The geometrical evidence suggests that we use the following algebraic procedure to determine the maximum and minimum values of a function. We have

(1)
$$y = \frac{x^3}{3} - 2x^2 + 3x + 2.$$

Then

(2)
$$\dot{y} = x^2 - 4x + 3.$$

We now find the values of x where $\dot{y} = 0$. Fortunately, we can write $\dot{y}$ as

(3)
$$\dot{y} = (x - 1)(x - 3),$$

and we see that

(4)
$$\dot{y} = 0 \quad \text{when} \quad x = 1 \quad \text{and when} \quad x = 3.$$

To determine whether $x = 1$ is the abscissa of a maximum point or a minimum point, we test the behavior of $\dot{y}$. It is apparent from (3) that when x is a little less than 1, the first factor is negative and the second is negative. Hence $\dot{y}$ is positive. However, when x is a little greater than 1, the first factor is positive and the second is negative. Hence $\dot{y}$ is negative. Thus $\dot{y}$ changes from positive to 0 to negative as x changes from values somewhat less than 1 to 1 and to values somewhat greater than 1. Then $x = 1$ should be the abscissa of the maximum point P. To find the y-value of P, that is, the maximum value of the function, we substitute $x = 1$ in (1) and obtain $y = 3\frac{1}{3}$.

To determine whether y is a maximum or a minimum at $x = 3$, we again observe the behavior of the derived function (3) for values of x near 3. For x somewhat less than 3, $\dot{y}$ is the product of a positive and a negative factor and therefore is negative. For x somewhat larger than 3, $\dot{y}$ is positive. Hence the derived function $\dot{y}$ changes from negative to positive as x passes through the value 3. Then $x = 3$ is the abscissa of a minimum value of the function. To find the value of y at $x = 3$, we substitute 3 for x in (1) and obtain $y = 2$.

We seem to have a procedure for finding the maximum and minimum values of a function. Before discussing the subject any further, it may be well to practice this procedure.

Exercises

1. Find the maximum and minimum values of the following functions:

(a) $y = 2x^3 - 9x^2 - 24x - 12$.
   Ans. Max., 1; min., -124.

(b) $y = -x^3 - 3x^2 + 9x + 15$.

(c) $y = x^4 - 2x^2$.
   Ans. Max., 0; min., -1.

(d) $y = x^2 + \dfrac{1}{x^2}$.

(e) $y = \dfrac{6x}{x^2 + 1}$.
   Ans. Max., 3; min., -3

There are a few additional considerations about maxima and minima which are important for the effective handling of the method. First, we did not really find the maximum or minimum values of the functions that we investigated above. Let us examine the function (1) and its graph (Fig. 8-2). For x greater than 3 the function increases continuously and becomes indefinitely large. In particular it becomes larger than the value $3\frac{1}{3}$ which we found to be the maximum value at $x = 1$. If we really want the maximum value of the function, then $3\frac{1}{3}$ is not the answer. In fact, because the function gets larger and larger as x increases to the right, the function has no maximum value. In what sense, then, is $3\frac{1}{3}$ the maximum value of the function? It is a *relative maximum;* that is, the value $3\frac{1}{3}$ is larger than the function values in the *immediate neighborhood* of $x = 1$. What we found, then, by our procedure is a relative maximum.

Likewise the y-value of 2 which occurs at $x = 3$ is not the minimum value of the function. In fact, for negative values of x the function values are not only less than 2 but they decrease more and more as x becomes more and more negative. The function in question has no minimum value, for it continues to decrease indefinitely as x becomes smaller. However, $y = 2$ is a *relative minimum;* that is, the y-value at $x = 3$ is smaller than y-values in the *immediate neighborhood* of $x = 3$.

To summarize, our procedure for finding the maximum and minimum values of a function is really a procedure for finding relative maxima and minima. It may seem then that our procedure is worthless. However, we shall see shortly that for scientific applications relative maxima and minima are very important.

There may, however, be problems in which the true or absolute maximum or minimum of a function is of interest. Let us note, first, that if we consider the function (1) over a definite interval of x-values, say from -2 to 5, the true or *absolute maximum* value of y in this interval is (Fig. 8-2) the y-value at $x = 5$ itself, namely $\frac{26}{3}$. The true or *absolute minimum* value of y in the same interval is $-\frac{20}{3}$, which occurs at $x = -2$. If instead of the interval -2 to 5 we consider the interval 0 to 3, we see that the relative maximum of $3\frac{1}{3}$ for y at $x = 1$ is also the absolute maximum for that interval. The absolute minimum is 2, which occurs at two values of x in the interval, namely, at $x = 0$ and at $x = 3$.

We can determine the absolute maxima and minima. Let us consider any finite interval of x-values. Such an interval is denoted by $a \leq x \leq b$, which means all x-values between a and b and including a and b. The absolute maximum must occur either at one or both ends of the interval or it must occur at some value x_0 interior to the interval. Thus in the case of the function (1) and the x-interval of -2 to 5, the absolute maximum occurs at the end value $x = 5$. If the x-interval is 0 to 3, the absolute maximum occurs at $x = 1$ which is inside or interior to the interval 0 to 3. If the absolute maximum occurs at an interior value x_0, it must also be a relative maximum because the function values on either side of x_0 must be smaller than at x_0. Hence the derivative $\dot{y}$ must be 0 at x_0, and we can use our procedure for relative maxima to find the absolute maximum. If the absolute maximum does not occur at an interior value, it must occur at an end value. Hence we have but to find the values of the function at the two end values and compare them with the values of the relative maxima to see which is the greatest value.

A second consideration is involved in the following examples. Let us seek the relative maxima and minima of the function

$$(5) \qquad\qquad y = x^3.$$

We first obtain

$$(6) \qquad\qquad \dot{y} = 3x^2$$

and set $\dot{y}$ equal to 0. We find, then, that $x = 0$ should be the abscissa of a relative maximum or minimum of the function. However (Fig. 8-3), the derivative is positive for x slightly less than 0 *and* for x slightly greater than 0. Thus the derivative does not change sign, and one of the conditions for a maximum or minimum is not fulfilled. This example shows that the vanishing of the first derivative at some value of x does not imply that the function has a maximum or a minimum at that value of x.

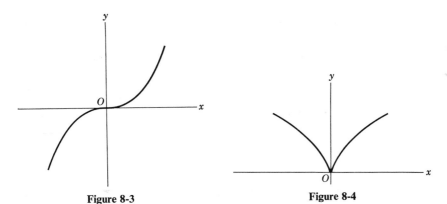

Figure 8-3   Figure 8-4

On the other hand, let us consider the function

$$(7) \qquad\qquad y = x^{2/3}.$$

Here

$$(8) \qquad\qquad \dot{y} = \tfrac{2}{3}x^{-1/3} = \frac{2}{3\sqrt[3]{x}}.$$

The derivative of the function is never 0. We might then be led to conclude that the function has no relative maximum or minimum. However, an examination of the function (Fig. 8-4) shows that it does indeed have a relative minimum at $x = 0$. The trouble here is that because the derivative does not exist at $x = 0$, it cannot give us information about the relative maxima and minima of the function.

3. *Analytical Treatment of Maxima and Minima.* So far our arguments have been based on graphs of particular functions; let us now try to be more analytical and more general. First, what do we mean by a relative maximum of a function relating y and x? A function has a *relative maximum* y_0 at $x = x_0$ if $y < y_0$ for all values of x less than and greater than x_0 at least in some small interval about x_0. A function has a *relative minimum* y_0 at $x = x_0$ if $y > y_0$ for all values of x less than and greater than x_0 at least in some small interval about x_0.

If a function does not have a relative maximum or relative minimum at $x = x_1$, what is its behavior? It may be increasing as x passes through x_1 or it may be decreasing. To be more precise, the function is said to be *increasing* at $x = x_1$ if for all x-values in some interval about x_1 it is true that when $x < x_1$ then $y < y_1$ and when $x > x_1$ then $y > y_1$ (Fig. 8-5a). Correspondingly, a function is said to be *decreasing* at x_1 if for all x-values in some interval about x_1, it is true that when $x < x_1$ then $y > y_1$ and when $x > x_1$ then $y < y_1$ (Fig. 8-5b).

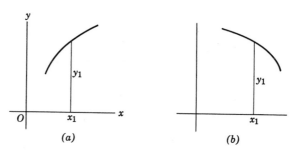

(a)   (b)

Figure 8-5

We may now prove the following theorem:

Theorem 1:   *If the derivative $\dot{y}$ is positive at $x = x_1$, the function is increasing at $x = x_1$. If the derivative $\dot{y}$ is negative at $x = x_2$, the function is decreasing at $x = x_2$.*

The proof is rather simple. Let $x = x_1$ be a value of x at which $\dot{y}$ is positive. Now

$$\dot{y} = \lim_{\Delta x \to 0} \frac{\Delta y}{\Delta x}.$$

If $\dot{y}$ is positive, $\Delta y/\Delta x$ must be positive for Δx sufficiently small because the quotient comes closer and closer to $\dot{y}$ as Δx approaches 0. Now let us consider $x_1 + \Delta x$ for small Δx. For negative Δx, $x_1 + \Delta x$ is to the left (Fig. 8-6) of x_1. The quantity Δy is, by definition, the value of y at $x_1 + \Delta x$ minus the value of y at x_1. If Δx is negative and $\Delta y/\Delta x$ is positive, Δy must be negative. This means that at $x_1 + \Delta x$, y must be less than at x_1. That is, y increases as x changes from $x_1 + \Delta x$ to x_1.

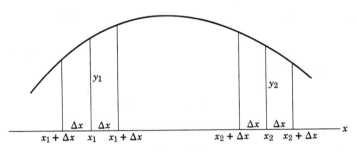

Figure 8-6

Now let us suppose that Δx is positive, so that $x_1 + \Delta x$ is to the right of x_1. The quantity Δy, which is the y-value at $x_1 + \Delta x$ minus its value at x_1, must now be positive because $\Delta y/\Delta x$ is positive. Hence y increases as x changes from x_1 to $x_1 + \Delta x$. We conclude then that at a point x_1 where $\dot{y}$ is positive the function increases as x changes from values less than x_1 to values greater than x_1.

A similar argument would show that at a point (x_2, y_2) where $\dot{y}$ is negative the function decreases as x changes from values less than x_2 to values greater than x_2.

We may now prove the following theorem:

Theorem 2: If y is a function of x and y has a relative maximum or minimum at $x = x_0$ and if $\dot{y}$ exists at x_0, then $\dot{y}$ is 0 at $x = x_0$.

If $\dot{y}$ is positive at $x = x_0$, then according to Theorem 1 the function must be increasing at x_0, and if $\dot{y}$ is negative at $x = x_0$, the function must be decreasing there. However, at a relative maximum or a relative minimum the function is neither increasing nor decreasing. Hence the derivative $\dot{y}$ (if it exists) must be 0 at x_0.

If a function has a relative maximum at x_0, the derivative must vanish there. However, the vanishing of the derivative, as we saw in the case of $y = x^3$, does not guarantee that the function has a relative maximum at x_0. What does guarantee it?

Theorem 3: If $\dot{y}$ is 0 at $x = x_0$ and if $\dot{y}$ changes from positive values to negative values as x passes through x_0, the function y has a relative maximum at x_0.

Because $\dot{y}$ is positive for $x < x_0$, then, by Theorem 1, y must be increasing at such values of x. Also, because $\dot{y}$ is negative for $x > x_0$, y must be decreasing for these values of x. This behavior of y is precisely what we mean by y having a relative maximum at $x = x_0$.*

There is, of course, the corresponding theorem about a relative minimum.

Theorem 4:   If $\dot{y}$ is 0 at $x = x_0$ and if $\dot{y}$ changes from negative to positive values as x passes through x_0, the function y has a relative minimum at x_0.

The proof here is practically the same as for Theorem 3 with appropriate changes corresponding to the fact that $\dot{y}$ now goes from negative to positive values.

Theorems 3 and 4 give what are called sufficient conditions for a relative maximum or minimum. That is, if the conditions are fulfilled the function has a relative maximum or minimum. If the derivative does not exist at some value of x in an interval under consideration, no information about relative maxima or minima can be deduced readily.

Let us summarize what the above theorems say. A function has a relative maximum (or minimum) at a value x_0 of x if the derivative is 0 there and if it changes sign as x changes from values less than x_0 to values greater than x_0. Also, as we saw in the preceding section, to obtain the absolute maximum (or minimum) of a function in an interval $a \leq x \leq b$, the values of the function at $x = a$ and $x = b$ must also be considered. The absolute maximum (or minimum) may occur at one or both of these end values or it may occur at an interior point. If it does occur at an interior point, it is a relative maximum (or minimum). To determine the absolute maximum (or minimum) in the interval, one must compare the values of the function at the relative maxima (or minima) and the values at the end points a and b.

Exercises

1. Find the relative maxima and minima and the absolute maxima and minima of
   (a) $y = -x^2 + 6x + 7$ over the interval $0 \leq x \leq 5$.

   Ans. Rel. max. 16; abs. max. 16; abs. min. 7.
   (b) $y = x^3 - 3x^2 + 4$ over the interval $-2 \leq x \leq 4$.
2. Find the relative maxima and minima of $y = (x - 1)^2(x + 1)^2$. Graph the function.   *Ans.* Max., 1; min., 0.
3. Find the relative maxima and minima of $y = 3 - (x - 1)^{2/3}$ by any method you find effective.
4. Show by exhibiting curves representing functions that
   (a) if $y = f(x)$ increases at each value of x of some interval (a, b) that $f'(x)$ is not necessarily an increasing function,
   (b) if $y = f(x)$ increases at each value of x of some interval (a, b) that $f'(x)$ can actually decrease,

---

* This proof is not complete because the notion of an increasing or decreasing function is defined over an interval rather than at a value of x. However, the proof is readily completed when the mean value theorem is available. See Chapter 12, Section 3, and Exercise 1 there.

$$y = 3 - (x-1)^{\frac{2}{3}}$$
$$\frac{dy}{dx} = 0 - \frac{2}{3}(x-1)^{-\frac{1}{3}}$$
$$\frac{dy}{dx} = -\frac{2}{3\sqrt[3]{x-1}}$$

(c) if $y = f'(x)$ is increasing at each value of x of some interval (a, b) that $f(x)$ may decrease.

5. We found in Theorem 1 that if $\dot{y}$ is positive at a value of x, then y is increasing there. Is the converse true? *Ans.* No.

4. *An Alternative Method of Determining Relative Maxima and Minima.* The use of the fact that the first derivative changes sign at a relative maximum or minimum can be replaced by a test which is sometimes more convenient.

Let us suppose that $\dot{y}$ is 0 at some value x_0 of x and that $\ddot{y}$ is a negative at this point (Fig. 8-7a). Now $\ddot{y}$ is itself the derived function of $\dot{y}$. Hence, by Theorem 1, the *derived function* $\dot{y}$ is a decreasing function at x_0. Because $\dot{y}$ is 0 at x_0 and is decreasing there, it must be changing from positive to negative values. However, the conditions of $\dot{y} = 0$ at x_0 and $\dot{y}$ changing from positive to negative are precisely the sufficient conditions of Theorem 3 that y have a relative maximum at x_0.

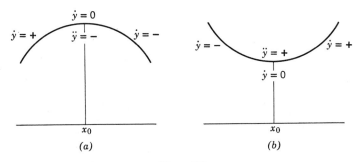

Figure 8-7

Likewise if $\ddot{y}$ is positive at x_0 (Fig. 8-7b), then $\dot{y}$ is an increasing function, and because it is 0 at x_0, it must be changing from negative to positive values as x passes through x_0. Then, by Theorem 4, y must have a relative minimum at x_0.

Thus our second test for the relative maxima and minima of a function runs as follows:

Theorem 5: *The function y has a relative maximum at $x = x_0$ if*

$$\dot{y} = 0 \quad \text{and} \quad \ddot{y} < 0 \quad \text{at} \quad x = x_0;$$

the function y has a relative minimum at $x = x_0$ if

$$\dot{y} = 0 \quad \text{and} \quad \ddot{y} > 0 \quad \text{at} \quad x = x_0.$$

If $\ddot{y}$ is 0 or does not exist at $x = x_0$, this test is not helpful.

The use of this theorem is illustrated by the following example. Suppose that we wish to determine the relative maxima and minima of the function

(9) $$y = x^3 - 3x^2 + 5.$$

We find $\dot{y}$, namely,

(10) $\dot{y} = 3x^2 - 6x.$

The function $\dot{y}$ is 0 when

$$3x^2 - 6x = 0$$

or when

$$x = 0 \quad \text{and} \quad x = 2.$$

Thus $x = 0$ and $x = 2$ are possible abscissas of relative maxima and minima. To determine what happens at these values of x we first find $\ddot{y}$. This is

$$\ddot{y} = 6x - 6.$$

Now when $x = 0$, $\ddot{y}$ is negative. Hence a relative maximum of the function occurs at $x = 0$. At $x = 2$, $\ddot{y}$ is positive. Hence a relative minimum of the function occurs at $x = 2$. The actual relative maximum and minimum values of the functions are obtained from (9). For $x = 0$, $y = 5$; for $x = 2$, $y = 1$.

Exercises

1. Use the second test to determine the relative maxima and minima of the functions:

(*a*) $y = x^3 - 3x^2 - 9x + 2.$
      Ans. Max., 7; min., −25.

(*b*) $y = x^2 + \dfrac{16}{x}.$ *Ans.* Min., 12.

(*c*) $y = (x + 1)^2(x - 2)^2.$
      Ans. Max., $\frac{81}{16}$; min., 0.

(*d*) $y = x^4 - 2x^3 - 2x^2 + 1.$

(*e*) $y = \dfrac{ax}{x^2 + a^2},$ a positive.
      Ans. Max., $\frac{1}{2}$; min., $-\frac{1}{2}$.

(*f*) $y = 3x^4 - 4x^3 - 36x^2 + 60.$
    Ans. Max., 60; min., −4 and −149.

(*g*) $y = x^4 - 2x^2 + 10.$

(*h*) $y = x^3 + 3x^2 + 9x + 6.$

2. What is the maximum slope of $y = -x^3 + 3x^2 + 9x - 27$?   *Ans.* 12.

5. *Some Applications of the Method of Maxima and Minima.* We have now a method of finding the relative maxima and minima of a function. In practical applications there is the additional step of formulating mathematically the function that expresses the physical quantity whose maximum or minimum value we seek. We shall examine a few physical applications.

One of the classic applications of the method was made by the mathematician Pierre de Fermat to derive what is called the law of refraction for light. First, let us be clear about the difference between reflection and refraction. When light strikes a mirror, whether the mirror is flat or curved (see Section 4 of Chapter 4), it is reflected in accordance with the principle that the angle of incidence, angle i of Fig. 8-8, equals the angle of reflection, angle r of the figure. (In our past work we used the complementary angles of i and r, which of course are also equal.) Thus under reflection the light goes back into

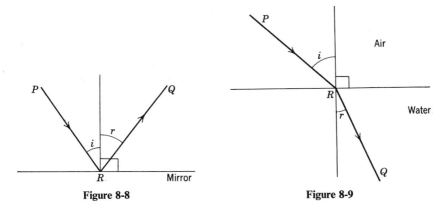

Figure 8-8   Figure 8-9

the medium from which it came; that is, in Fig. 8-8 it returns to the region above the mirror. In refraction there are two media, say air and water, and the light passes from one medium into the other. Thus (Fig. 8-9) the light ray emanating from P strikes the boundary between the air and the water at R, enters the water, and then travels through the water. What is remarkable about this process is that the light ray changes its direction as it enters the water, so that the path RQ is not a continuation of the straight line PR. The problem that baffled scientists and mathematicians from the time of Euclid until the seventeenth century was, how is the direction of RQ related to that of PR, or how is the angle of refraction r related to the angle of incidence i? There did not seem to be any simple relation between i and r.

In 1621 the Dutch mathematician Willebrord Snell and in 1637 René Descartes gave physical arguments to support their discovery of the correct law of refraction. Of course, physical arguments are more suspect than mathematical arguments, and in fact Descartes' argument was wrong even though his conclusion was correct. Fermat then took up the question of establishing mathematically the correct law of refraction.

The Alexandrian Greek mathematician and engineer Hero (first century) had proved in the case of reflection that the path $PR + RQ$ (Fig. 8-8) is the shortest path that light could take in going from P to *any* point of the mirror and then to Q; that is, the path that light actually takes so as to make angle i equal angle r is shorter than any other path from P to the mirror to Q. In the case of refraction (Fig. 8-9) light does not take the shortest path from P to Q because the shortest path is the straight-line path. However, it was known by Fermat's time that light travels with a finite velocity and that the velocity is a constant in a uniform medium. In the case of reflection the light goes back into the same medium from which it came and therefore, assuming that the atmosphere is of uniform character as it is over short distances, the velocity is constant over the entire path PRQ. Hence the fact that the light takes the shortest path under reflection also means that it takes the least time.

Fermat decided that light in traveling from one point to another always takes the path requiring least time, and he adopted this assertion as a basic physical principle or, one might say, as a physical axiom about light, just as Newton's laws of motion and of gravitation are physical axioms in the field of mechanics.

With the principle of least time as his physical axiom, Fermat established the correct law of refraction. Let us follow Fermat's derivation. Suppose that the light goes from P in the first medium to Q in the second. Because the points P and Q (Fig. 8-10) are given and fixed, the distance d between the feet

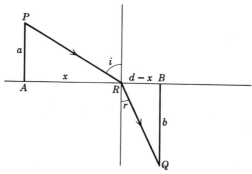

Figure 8-10

of perpendiculars from P and Q to the boundary of the medium is also fixed. This distance d is the distance AB in the figure. The light takes a straight-line path to *some* point R on the boundary, because medium 1 is homogeneous or uniform and the straight-line path takes least time. Likewise the light takes a straight-line path from R to Q in the homogeneous medium 2. What we do not know is where the point R lies on the boundary. Let us denote AR by x. Then $RB = d - x$. Let v_1 be the velocity of light in medium 1. In medium 2, the velocity is different, and therefore we denote it by v_2. Then the time light requires to travel from P to R and from R to Q is

$$t = \frac{PR}{v_1} + \frac{RQ}{v_2},$$

or, if a is the length PA and b is the length QB,

(11) $$t = \frac{\sqrt{a^2 + x^2}}{v_1} + \frac{\sqrt{b^2 + (d - x)^2}}{v_2}.$$

We can now find the value of x for which t is a minimum. To do this we first find dt/dx. To differentiate each radical, we use the chain rule. Thus

$$\frac{dt}{dx} = \frac{1}{v_1} \frac{1}{2} \frac{1}{\sqrt{a^2 + x^2}} 2x + \frac{1}{v_2} \frac{1}{2} \frac{1}{\sqrt{b^2 + (d - x)^2}} \frac{d}{dx} [b^2 + (d - x)^2]$$

$$= \frac{x}{v_1 \sqrt{a^2 + x^2}} + \frac{1}{v_2} \frac{1}{2} \frac{1}{\sqrt{b^2 + (d - x)^2}} [2(d - x)(-1)].$$

Then

(12)
$$\frac{dt}{dx} = \frac{x}{v_1\sqrt{a^2 + x^2}} - \frac{d - x}{v_2\sqrt{b^2 + (d - x)^2}}.$$

We now must set dt/dx equal to 0.   Thus

(13)
$$\frac{x}{v_1\sqrt{a^2 + x^2}} - \frac{d - x}{v_2\sqrt{b^2 + (d - x)^2}} = 0.$$

If there is a relative minimum at some value of x, this last equation must be satisfied at that value.   We could solve equation (13) for x, but fortunately there is a simpler way to obtain the result.

From Fig. 8-10 we see that

(14)
$$\sin i = \frac{x}{\sqrt{a^2 + x^2}} \quad \text{and} \quad \sin r = \frac{d - x}{\sqrt{b^2 + (d - x)^2}}.$$

Hence equation (13) says that

(15)
$$\frac{\sin i}{v_1} - \frac{\sin r}{v_2} = 0$$

or

(16)
$$\frac{\sin i}{\sin r} = \frac{v_1}{v_2}.$$

This is the law of refraction.   It tells us that the relation between i and r involves not only the sines of the angles but also the velocities of light in the two media.   This law is the basis for the design of all optical lenses.

We have not shown that equation (15) really yields a relative minimum of our original function (11).   However, by applying the first test we shall now see that·it does.   Let us note that in view of equation (14) the value of the derivative in (12) can be written as

(17)
$$\frac{dt}{dx} = \frac{\sin i}{v_1} - \frac{\sin r}{v_2}.$$

If the value of x is slightly less than the value determined by (13), we see from Fig. 8-10 that angle i and therefore $\sin i$ decreases, whereas angle r and therefore $\sin r$ increases.   Hence the value of dt/dx in (17) must be less than 0. Likewise if x is slightly greater than the value determined by (13), it is again evident fróm the figure that $\sin i$ increases and $\sin r$ decreases, and therefore dt/dx is greater than 0.   Hence dt/dx changes from a negative value to a positive one as x passes through the value determined by $dt/dx = 0$.   Then this value of x must be the value at which the function (11) is a relative minimum.

Let us consider next a problem which is simpler, but which involves another point.   Let us prove that of all rectangles with the same perimeter the square has maximum area. As a matter of fact, Fermat, who was one of the first to develop the calculus method of finding relative maxima and minima of functions, used this problem to show that the method works.

Let us denote by x and y the dimensions of any rectangle (Fig. 8-11). Then the area is given by

(18) $$A = xy.$$

However, we are interested only in rectangles with the same perimeter. Suppose that we denote this common perimeter by p. Then for all rectangles of perimeter p

(19) $$p = 2x + 2y.$$

Figure 8-11

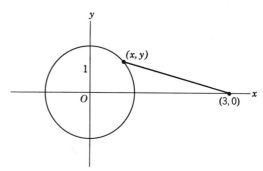

Figure 8-12

We may now state from (19) that

(20) $$y = \frac{p - 2x}{2}.$$

Then by substituting in (18) we obtain

$$A = x\left(\frac{p - 2x}{2}\right) = \frac{px}{2} - x^2.$$

We should now like to know, for what value of x is A a maximum? We can apply the standard method. We find $\dot{A}$ and set it equal to 0. Thus

$$\frac{p}{2} - 2x = 0$$

or

(21) $$x = \frac{p}{4}.$$

Because $\ddot{A}$ is -2, we see that the value $p/4$ furnishes a relative maximum. The rectangle of maximum area is a square.

Problems in which the function to be maximized or minimized involves two variables related by another equation often exhibit a peculiarity which is illustrated by the following example (Fig. 8-12). Suppose that we had to find the shortest distance from the point $(3, 0)$ to the circle $x^2 + y^2 = 1$. The answer happens to be geometrically evident. The point on the circle which is closest to $(3, 0)$ is clearly $(1, 0)$. However, let us apply the method of the calculus.

Let (x, y) be the coordinates of any point on the circle. Then the distance from $(3, 0)$ to the point (x, y) (see the Appendix to Chapter 3) is

$$(22) \qquad d = \sqrt{(x - 3)^2 + y^2}.$$

Our goal is to find the (x, y) for which d is a minimum. We note that the (x, y) that makes d a minimum also makes d^2 a minimum. Hence let us investigate the minimum of

$$(23) \qquad s = d^2 = (x - 3)^2 + y^2$$

or of

$$(24) \qquad s = x^2 - 6x + 9 + y^2.$$

As the problem now stands, s is a function of x and y. However, $x^2 + y^2 = 1$. Then choosing the positive x gives

$$x = \sqrt{1 - y^2}$$

and therefore

$$s = 1 - y^2 - 6\sqrt{1 - y^2} + 9 + y^2$$

or

$$(25) \qquad s = -6\sqrt{1 - y^2} + 10.$$

We now apply differentiation and find that

$$\dot{s} = \frac{6y}{\sqrt{1 - y^2}}.$$

We see that $\dot{s} = 0$ when $y = 0$. Moreover, $\dot{s}$ is negative for $y < 0$ and positive for $y > 0$. Hence $y = 0$ is the y-value of a relative minimum. Of course, when $y = 0$, $x = 1$. (We have already rejected negative values of x.) Thus $(1, 0)$ is the point on the circle that is at a minimum distance from $(3, 0)$, just as we expected.

In eliminating one of the variables from (24), we deliberately eliminated x and obtained (25). We could, however, eliminate y from (24). Using the fact that $y^2 = 1 - x^2$, we obtain instead of (25)

$$(26) \qquad s = x^2 - 6x + 9 + 1 - x^2$$

or

$$(27) \qquad s = -6x + 10.$$

Now let us differentiate. We find that

$$\dot{s} = -6.$$

Because the derivative is never 0, we might be tempted to conclude that there is no value of x that furnishes a minimum s. However, let us recall that our calculus method furnishes *relative* maxima or minima. There may very well be an absolute maximum or minimum. The x that we are concerned with can vary from -1 to 1. We see from (27) that when $x = 1$, s is least and is indeed 4. Also, when $x = 1$, $y = 0$. Hence again we find that $(1, 0)$ is the point on the circle which is least distant from $(3, 0)$.

Exercises

1. If the height of a ball above the ground is given by the formula $h = 80t - 16t^2$, find the maximum height the ball attains.   *Ans.* 100.

2. Show that of all rectangles with the same area the square has least perimeter.

3. Suppose that a rectangular plot is to be fenced off with one side along a river where no fencing is needed. What are the dimensions of the maximum area that can be fenced in with 100 feet of fencing?   *Ans.* 25 by 50.

4. Show that of all triangles with a given base and a given area, the isosceles triangle has the least perimeter. *Suggestion:* Let the given base be AB (Fig. 8-13). Choose an x-axis along AB and let the y-axis bisect AB. Because the areas are fixed, the altitude h must be the same for all triangles considered. Now show that for the triangle of least perimeter $CA = CB$.

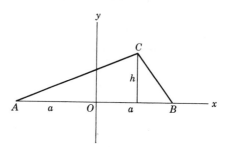

Figure 8-13

5. Show that of all triangles with a given base and a given perimeter, the isoceles triangle has the greatest area. *Suggestion:* Use Hero's formula for the area, namely, $A = \sqrt{s(s - a)(s - b)(s - c)}$ where a, b, and c are the sides and s is half the perimeter.

6. Find the dimensions of a rectangular plot containing 864 sq ft and requiring least fencing with the condition that a fence parallel to one pair of sides be included so as to divide the plot into two rectangles.   *Ans.* 24 by 36.

7. Find the dimensions of the rectangle of largest area whose diagonal is 10 feet.
                                                                  Ans. $5\sqrt{2}$ by $5\sqrt{2}$.

8. Find the dimensions of a cylindrical can containing 1 cu. ft. but with minimum surface area (including top and bottom).   *Ans.* $r = 1/\sqrt[3]{2\pi}$, $h = (2\pi)^{2/3}/\pi$.

9. Find the rectangle of given area which has the shortest diagonal.   *Ans.* Square.

10. Find the rectangle of maximum area inscribed in the circle $x^2 + y^2 = 1$.

11. Given a point R with coordinates (a, b) in the interior of the parabola $y^2 = 4px$, show that the shortest path from R to a point P of the parabola and from P to the focus $(p, 0)$ is the one determined by the point P which lies on the line through R parallel to the axis. (If we recall that light from the focus after reflection at the parabola goes out parallel to the axis, this problem shows that light takes the shortest path and, because it travels in one medium, it takes the least time.)

12. Suppose that two fixed masses m and M attract each other in accordance with the law of gravitation $F = GmM/r^2$. For what value of r is F least? Greatest?
Ans. None.

13. Can the value of the relative maximum of a function be less than a relative minimum of the function? *Suggestion:* Consider $y = x + (1/x)$. *Ans.* Yes.

14. Prove or disprove the assertion that if a function of x is 0 at $x = a$, the derivative must be 0 at $x = a$.

15. What conditions must any or all of the coefficients a, b, and c of the function $y = ax^2 + bx + c$ satisfy in order that the function have a relative maximum point? *Ans.* $a < 0$.

16. Given $y = x^3 + bx^2 + 3x + 5$, what condition must be imposed on b in order that the function have no relative maxima or minima? *Ans.* $|b| < 3$.

17. Find the maximum value of the function $y = x^3$ in the domain $-1 \leq x \leq 4$.
Ans. 64.

18. A 100-feet long straight fence is in place. We wish to add 200 more feet of fencing, so that the 100 feet are fully utilized and so that the 300 feet enclose a rectangle of maximum area. Find the dimensions of the rectangle of maximum area. *Ans.* 50 by 100.

19. Find the point on the parabola $y^2 = 4x$ which is at the shortest distance from $(1, 0)$. Carry out the work by eliminating y from the distance function and then by eliminating x. *Ans.* $(0, 0)$.

20. Find the point (x, y) on the ellipse $b^2x^2 + a^2y^2 = a^2b^2$ such that the distance to the focus $(c, 0)$ is a minimum. *Suggestion:* Express the distance as a function of x and work the problem. Then express the distance as a function of y and work the problem. *Ans.* $(a, 0)$.

21. A man is in a boat at P 1 mile from the nearest point A on the shore (Fig. 8-14). He wishes to go to B which is farther along the straight shore 1 mile from A. If he can row at 3 mi/hr and walk at 5 mi/hr, toward what point C between A and B should he row in order to reach B in least time. *Ans.* $AC = \frac{3}{4}$ mi.

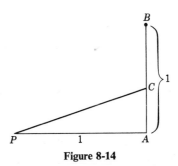

Figure 8-14

22. The conditions are the same as in Exercise 21, except that the man can row at 4 mi/hr. *Ans.* $C = B$.

23. The conditions are the same as in Exercise 21, except that the man can row at 5 mi/hr.   *Ans. C = B.*

24. Given the isosceles triangle ABC (Fig. 8-15), in which AB is 12 inches and the altitude CD is 3 inches, find the point P on CD such that the sum of the distances of P from the vertices is a minimum.   *Ans. The point C.*

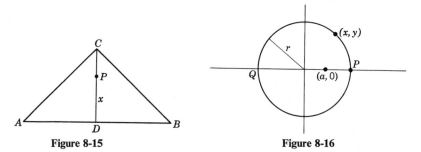

Figure 8-15   Figure 8-16

25. We shall "prove" that given a point inside a circle of radius r, there is no point on the circle which is nearest or farthest from the given point. We choose the origin of our coordinate system (Fig. 8-16) to be the center of the circle and we choose the x-axis so that it passes through the given point. Then the given point has coordinates $(a, 0)$. Let (x, y) be any point on the circle. The distance of (x, y) to $(a, 0)$ is given by $D = \sqrt{(x - a)^2 + y^2}$. Because D^2 is a maximum or a minimum when D is, we may as well consider D^2. Because $x^2 + y^2 = r^2$, $D^2 = (x - a)^2 + r^2 - x^2$. Then, if we denote D^2 by s, $\dot{s} = -2a$. This derivative is not 0 for any value of x, and therefore there is no maximum or minimum distance.

Intuitively it is evident, however, that P is the point on the circle at the minimum distance from $(a, 0)$ and Q is the point on the circle at the maximum distance from $(a, 0)$. What is wrong with the proof?

26. When measurements $m_1, m_2, \ldots, m_n$ of a certain length or other quantity are made, a common practice is to take the arithmetic mean $m = (m_1 + m_2 + \cdots + m_n)/n$ as the true value of the length. We call $m_1 - m, m_2 - m, \ldots, m_n - m$ the errors in the individual measurements. Show that the arithmetic mean makes the sum of the squares of the errors a minimum.

27. Use Fermat's principle of least time to deduce the law of reflection of light. *Suggestion:* Use the method in the text but remember that you are dealing here with reflection rather than refraction. In terms of Fig. 8-17, the answer is $\alpha = \beta$.

Figure 8-17

28. A pier is to be built at some point P along the shore CD of a river, so that merchandise can be unloaded from a ship on it and then trucked to towns A and B (Fig. 8-17). Where should P be located so that $AP + PB$ is least? *Suggestion:* In view of the fact that light travels at a constant velocity in a uniform or homogeneous medium, least time means least distance. Hence use the result of Exercise 27.

29. In Fig. 8-18 *CD* and *EF* are parallel shores of a river and *A* and *B* are towns each at some distance from the respective shores. The towns want to build a bridge *PQ* across the river and perpendicular to the shores so that the total distance from *A* to *B* is a minimum. Show that *P* must be chosen so that *AP* and *QB* are parallel.

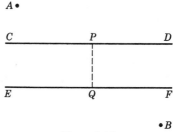

Figure 8-18

6. *Curve Tracing.* We have pointed out several times that the graph or curve of a formula is immensely useful in helping us to understand the behavior of the function. Up to now we have obtained the curves of formulas by relying largely on point-for-point plotting. For simple functions the graphs are readily obtained. However, for more complicated functions even the seemingly simple task of plotting points can be a problem. This process can be time-consuming and can lead to serious errors at that.

Let us consider the very simple function

$$(28) \qquad\qquad y = \frac{1}{x}.$$

By calculating values of y for various values of x and by plotting, we might obtain the four points shown as black dots on the right-hand portion of Fig. 8-19 and the four points similarly pictured on the left. Joining the four points on the right by a smooth curve and doing the same on the left gives correct portions of the full graph. However, we still do not know how the two portions should be joined. We might be tempted to join them by the broken line shown in the figure or perhaps, for art's sake, round out the junctions. In the case of this simple function we know the correct curve through previous contact with it. We can also see readily that as x approaches 0 through positive values, y becomes infinite through positive values, and as x approaches 0 through negative values, y becomes negatively infinite.

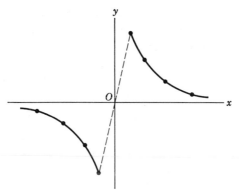

Figure 8-19

However, let us consider the relatively simple function

(29) $$y = 4x^3 - 15x^2 + 18x.$$

If we make a table of values for this function, we obtain the table shown below. By joining the four plotted points, we obtain

x	y
0	0
1	7
2	6
3	27

Figure 8-20

the broken-line curve shown in Fig. 8-20. This graph would lead us to believe that the function has a relative maximum at $x = 1$ and a relative minimum at $x = 2$. Actually, the relative minimum is not at $x = 2$ but at $x = \frac{3}{2}$, and we can determine this fact by means of our calculus method of determining relative maxima and minima. In other words, the calculus is an aid to graphing.

In this section we shall investigate how the calculus can help in graphing functions when we know the formula for the function. One aid, as the preceding example illustrates, is the determination of the relative maxima and minima of the function. There are others, which we consider next.

A helpful procedure is to find the first derivative and to note where it is positive and where negative. We know from our work on maxima and minima that where $\dot{y}$ is positive, the function must be increasing and where it is negative, the function must be decreasing. This in the example of (29), $\dot{y}$ is $12x^2 - 30x + 18$ and at $x = 2$, $\dot{y}$ is 6; therefore, the function must be increasing at $x = 2$.

Another aid in graphing is the determination of what is called the concavity of the graph. Figure 8-21 shows four ways in which a curve can lie in relation to its tangent. In the upper two cases the curve lies above its tangent. This means that the y-values of points on the curve are larger than the y-values of the tangent at P for the same x-values. The curve is then said to be *concave upward* at P. In the two lower cases shown in Fig. 8-21 the curve lies below its tangent at P, and the curve is said to be concave downward at P.

To know whether a curve is concave upward or downward at a point is certainly a help in graphing the curve. A useful test is the value of the second derivative at the point. Suppose that $\ddot{y}$ is positive at a point P. We proved earlier that if the derivative of a function is positive at a point, the function is increasing at that point. If $\ddot{y}$ is positive, the function $\dot{y}$ is increasing. However, $\dot{y}$ is the slope of the curve, and this is increasing at P. Hence the slope

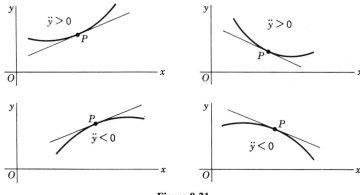

Figure 8-21

of the curve is less to the left of P and more to the right of P than it is at P. The curve then must have the shapes of either of the upper two cases in Fig. 8-21. (We must remember in the second case that as the angle of inclination of the tangent approaches 180°, the slope increases algebraically.)

Similarly, if $\ddot{y}$ is negative at P, $\dot{y}$ is a decreasing function. Hence the slope of the curve is greater to the left of P and less to the right of P than it is at P. Then the curve must behave as shown in the lower two cases of Fig. 8-21. Thus we can test readily for upward and downward concavity.

In this discussion of concavity we omitted consideration of the case in which $\ddot{y} = 0$ at a point on a curve. This case is of considerable interest. If $\ddot{y}$ is 0, we do not know whether $\dot{y}$ is increasing or decreasing, just as when $\dot{y}$ is 0, we do not know whether y is increasing or decreasing. In fact, usually when $\dot{y}$ is 0, y has a relative maximum or minimum. Hence when $\ddot{y}$ is 0, we should look into the possibility that $\dot{y}$ has a relative maximum or minimum. Figure 8-22 shows the most common situation. At the point Q and at all other points to the left of P, $\ddot{y}$ is positive and the curve is concave upward. At the point R and at all other points to the right of P, $\ddot{y}$ is negative and the curve

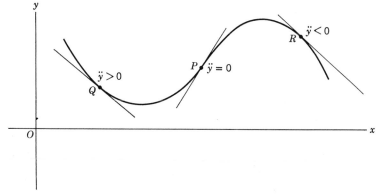

Figure 8-22

is concave downward. Alternatively, we may say that at points to the left of
P, the derived function $\dot{y}$ is an increasing function, and at points to the right
of P, $\dot{y}$ is a decreasing function. Then $\dot{y}$ has a relative maximum at P, and its
derivative, namely $\ddot{y}$, must be 0 at P. In other words, at a point at which $\ddot{y}$
is 0, it does seem as though $\dot{y}$ has a relative maximum or minimum. We must,
however, be careful. The vanishing of the derivative of a function is necessary
at a relative maximum or minimum but it is not sufficient. The derivative
must, in addition, change sign in passing through the relative maximum or
minimum point. In the present case, if $\ddot{y} = 0$ and if $\ddot{y}$ changes from positive
to negative as x passes through the value at P or if $\ddot{y}$ changes from negative
to positive, $\dot{y}$ has a relative maximum or minimum.

Thus at *a point at which $\ddot{y} = 0$ and changes sign, the first-derived function
has a relative maximum or minimum.* Moreover, the curve changes at that
point from concave upward to concave downward or the reverse. At such a
point the tangent *crosses* the curve, for at points immediately to the left the
curve must be above the tangent and at points immediately to the right, below
the tangent, or vice versa. A point at which $\ddot{y} = 0$ and changes from positive
to negative or negative to positive is called *a point of inflection.* The location
of such points is also an aid in graphing a function.

To tie together the various aids that the calculus offers toward graphing
functions, let us consider an example. Suppose that we know that the formula
representing some function is,

(30) $$y = \frac{2(x - 2)}{x^2}.$$

For a function such as (30), which we observe at once to have no value at
$x = 0$, it is well to determine exactly what the behavior is near $x = 0$. The
numerator approaches -4 as x approaches 0, and because the denominator
approaches 0, the value of the function becomes infinite as x approaches 0.
Moreover, whether x approaches 0 through negative values or through positive values, the function becomes negatively infinite. Hence we know already
that the function drops rapidly toward $-\infty$ as x approaches 0 through positive values as well as through negative values.

It is also useful to know where the curve cuts the x-axis; that is, the x-
intercepts. In the present case $y = 0$ when $x = 2$. Hence the curve cuts the
x-axis on the right of the y-axis but not on the left.

We note next that

(31) $$\dot{y} = \frac{-2x + 8}{x^3}.$$

Let us consider first the behavior of $\dot{y}$ for positive values of x. When x
increases from 0 to 2, $\dot{y}$ is always positive. Hence y increases steadily from
$x = 0$ to $x = 2$. The curve crosses the x-axis at $x = 2$ and, because $\dot{y}$ remains

positive until $x = 4$, the function still increases. At $x = 4$, $\dot{y} = 0$. Here we have a possible relative maximum or relative minimum of the function. Because $\dot{y}$ changes from positive to negative as x passes through 4, the value $x = 4$ is the abscissa of a relative maximum. When $x = 4$, $y = \frac{1}{4}$.

For $x > 4$, $\dot{y}$ is negative. Hence the function must decrease steadily. Yet we see from (30) that the function remains positive. Moreover, the denominator increases faster than the numerator, and the function values approach 0.

We know now the essential behavior of the function for positive x-values, but we may confirm what we have learned by testing for points or inflection. We find that

(32)
$$\ddot{y} = \frac{4x - 24}{x^4}.$$

Because $\ddot{y} = 0$ at $x = 6$, this value of x is a possible location of a point of inflection. We see that $\ddot{y}$ changes sign as x passes through the value 6, and therefore there is a point of inflection at $x = 6$. At the value 6 of x, y is $\frac{2}{9}$.

For negative values of x we note that $\dot{y}$ is always negative because the numerator is positive and the denominator is negative. A negative $\dot{y}$ means that the function is constantly decreasing *as x increases*. This means that as x increases from $-\infty$, that is, from large negative values, and approaches 0, the y-values decrease constantly. From what value do they start to decrease? When x is very large and negative, we see from (30) that y is negative and near 0 in value. Hence as x increases from $-\infty$ to 0, y starts from 0 and steadily decreases.

Figure 8-23 assembles all of the information that we have gathered about the graph. Of course, the graph is not exact. It gives the essential behavior of the function. To make the graph more accurate we would have to calculate the y-values for a number of x-values.

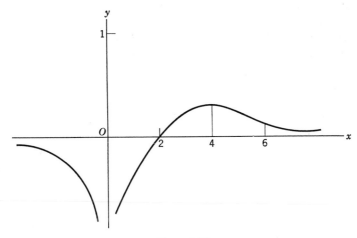

Figure 8-23

Exercises

1. Sketch the graphs of the following functions. Use all the information that you can obtain from studying the first and second derived functions of the functions.

   (a) $y = x^3 - 6x^2 + 9x + 1$.

   (b) $y = x^3 + 3x^2 + 3x + 5$.

   (c) $y = x^3 + 2x^2 + 3x + 5$.

   (d) $y = x^{5/3}$.

   (e) $y = \dfrac{1}{x^2 + 1}$.

   (f) $y = x^4$.

   (g) $y = x^4 - 4x^3$.

   (h) $y = \dfrac{x}{x^2 + 1}$.

   (i) $y = \dfrac{x(x - 3)}{(x + 3)^2}$.

   (j) $y = \dfrac{2x}{x + 4}$.

2. Given the function shown in Fig. 8-24, describe how the second derived function varies from A to B, B to C, ..., G to H, H to I.

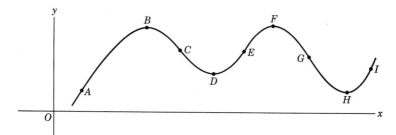

Figure 8-24

3. Show that the point of inflection of the general cubic polynomial function $y = ax^3 + bx^2 + cx + d$ is the average of the three zeros of the function (the three values of x at which y is 0). *Suggestion:* From algebra we know that $y = a(x - r_1)(x - r_2)(x - r_3)$. Two of the quantities r_1, r_2, and r_3 may be complex, but you may apply the calculus to the function.

4. The function $y = ax^3 + bx^2 + cx + d$ has a point of inflection and a horizontal tangent at the same value of x. Show that $b^2 - 3ac = 0$.

CHAPTER NINE

The Trigonometric Functions

1. Introduction. The power of mathematics grows as it develops more functions to represent and study physical phenomena. This power is greatly enhanced by the trigonometric functions because they represent periodic phenomena. The motion of a bob on a spring and the motion of a pendulum are obvious periodic phenomena, but many others, such as sound waves, alternating electric current, and radio waves, are also periodic, although this fact is not at once apparent. However, even if one recognizes that a phenomenon is periodic and that trigonometric functions should be involved, he must still answer the question of precisely which function represents that phenomenon and how one can extract physical information from the function. After presenting a few technical facts about the trigonometric functions we shall consider a few of these applications.

2. The Sinusoidal Functions. The basic periodic function is $y = \sin x$. To refresh our minds about this function, let us look at the graph in Fig. 9-1. As the function arises in trigonometry, x stands for the size of an angle, which is measured in degrees or in radians. Both units are shown in the figure. In the calculus the radian measure is preferred for a reason that will be evident shortly.

There is a common misconception about the function $y = \sin x$ which stems from the fact the x-values originate as a measure of angles. The function $v = 32t$ originally represented and still represents the velocity of a body

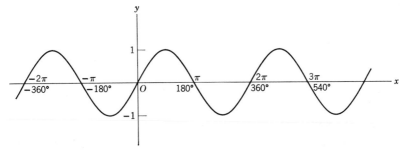

Figure 9.1 $y = \sin x$.

229

which is dropped and falls (in a vacuum) under the pull of the earth's gravity. The values of t in this application are time values and the v-values are, of course, velocity values. However, as a mathematical function the values of v and t are pure numbers and not time and velocity values. All one can say mathematically is that when $t = 1$, $v = 32$. Indeed, the same mathematical function might be used in a totally different physical context where t might represent any number of oxen and v the combined lengths of their tails. The same point applies to $y = \sin x$. As a mathematical function x and y represent pure numbers, and the fact that x originally represented the sizes of angles is irrelevant. If we choose to let the values of x represent, for example, values of time and the values of y to represent distance, we are entirely free to do so, and we shall do so when this interpretation fits the physical phenomenon under study. In other words, once we have some way of determining the y-value which belongs to a given x-value, we have a mathematical function that can be applied to any physical situation in which the function may be useful.

To obtain the value of y for a given value of x we do interpret x as the number of radians in an angle and then look up our trigonometric tables for the sine of the angle of that many radians or, if necessary, first convert the radians to degrees. This reversion to angles and sines of angles is utilized only because the values of y happen to be recorded in trigonometric tables.

The function $y = \sin x$ is periodic, that is, the y-values repeat in successive intervals the values that y takes on in the interval 0 to 2π. The interval 2π is called the period, a term which, incidentally, comes from the physical situation in which x represents time. (In applications in which x represents distance, the interval 2π is called the wavelength.) As Fig. 9-1 shows, the maximum y-value is 1, and this number is called the amplitude of the function.

The great usefulness of the trigonometric functions derives from the fact that for each of the six fundamental functions, $y = \sin x$, $y = \cos x$, $y = \tan x$, $y = \cot x$, $y = \sec x$, and $y = \csc x$, there is an infinitude of variations. We shall discuss these in connection with the function $y = \sin x$, but the same remarks apply to the other five functions.

A common variation of $y = \sin x$ is

$$(1) \qquad\qquad y = 2 \sin x$$

It is easy to see in this case how the second functions differs from the first. For each value of x, $2 \sin x$ is twice $\sin x$. Figure 9-2 shows the effect of the factor 2. The period of $y = 2 \sin x$ is still 2π, but the amplitude is 2. Of course, any number can occur in place of the 2, and so we already have the infinite number of functions $y = a \sin x$.

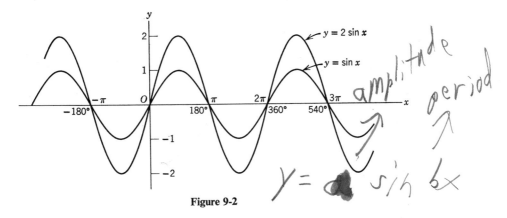

Figure 9-2

Another equally common variation of $y = \sin x$ is exemplified by

(2) $$y = \sin 2x.$$

The effect of the 2 in this function is different from that in $y = 2 \sin x$. In the case of (2), given any value of x, say $\pi/4$, we first multiply by 2, obtaining $\pi/2$, and then find $\sin \pi/2$, which is of course 1. That is, for $y = \sin 2x$ when $x = \pi/4$, $y = 1$. We can readily see that as x takes on the values from 0 to π, $2x$ takes on the values from 0 to 2π and $\sin 2x$ runs through the complete set of y-values that occur in the interval from 0 to 2π of $y = \sin x$. That is, y increases from 0 to 1, then decreases to 0, decreases still further to -1, and then increases to 0. This range of y-values is called a cycle. The behavior of $y = \sin 2x$ is represented in Fig. 9-3. We see that the amplitude is 1 but the period is π. It is worth remembering that the period can be obtained by dividing the normal period 2π by the coefficient of x. It is perhaps unnecessary to add that in place of the 2 in $y = \sin 2x$, any number can occur, so that there is another infinity of sinusoidal functions of the form $y = \sin bx$.

Figure 9-3

Another kind of variation on $y = \sin x$ is that which combines the two types we have discussed. It is generally represented by the formula $y = a \sin bx$. A few other variations are suggested in the exercises.

Exercises

1. Sketch on the same axes $y = \sin x$ and

    (a) $y = \sin 3x$.

    (b) $y = 3 \sin x$.

    (c) $y = 3 \sin 2x$.

    (d) $y = 2 \sin 4x$.

    (e) $y = \sin\left(x + \dfrac{\pi}{2}\right)$.

    (f) $y = \sin x + \dfrac{\pi}{2}$.

    (g) $y = \sin(x - 1)$.

    (h) $y = -2 \sin 3x$.

2. Sketch $y = x + \sin x$. *Suggestion:* Sketch $y = x$ and $y = \sin x$ on the same axes. Then at a number of values of x add the ordinates of the two curves. If one ordinate is positive and the other negative, you must of course add the signed values.

3. Sketch $y = x \sin x$.

4. Sketch $y = 3 \sin 2(x - 1) + 4$. *Suggestion:* Sketch in order $y = \sin x$, $y = \sin 2x$, $y = \sin 2(x - 1)$, $y = 3 \sin 2(x - 1)$, and $y = 3 \sin 2(x - 1) + 4$.

5. Sketch $y = x^2 + \sin x$.

3. Some Preliminaries on Limits.

In the calculus we are interested in what we can do with the derived functions and integrals of the trigonometric functions. To find the derivative of $y = \sin x$, we use the method of increments. In the course of this work we must determine certain limits and so we shall dispose of these now. The first is

(3)
$$\lim_{x \to 0} \frac{\sin x}{x}.$$

The determination of this limit is more difficult than that of, say,

(4)
$$\lim_{x \to 2} \frac{x^2 - 4}{x - 2}.$$

Here we can divide numerator and denominator by $x - 2$, which is certainly correct when $x \neq 2$; having obtained $x + 2$, we can see that the function approaches 4 as x approaches 2. For (3), however, where the same difficulty arises as in (4), namely, both numerator and denominator approach 0, it is not possible to divide numerator and denominator by some quantity in order to determine the limit readily. Moreover, substituting 0 for x in (3), which sometimes gives the same result as finding the limit as x approaches 0, does not help because in the present case it gives $0/0$.

Before trying to determine the limit of a function, it is wise to convince oneself that it does indeed have one. To obtain some indication of whether there may be a limit and what number to expect, we choose values of x and calculate the values of the fraction (3). Thereby we obtain the following table:

x	0.5	0.3	0.2	0.1	0.05	0.01
$\sin x$	0.479	0.2955	0.1987	0.0998	0.049979	0.00999998
$\dfrac{\sin x}{x}$	0.959	0.985	0.9933	0.9983	0.99958	0.999998

It seems quite clear that the limit in question is 1.

We shall prove that this is so. We may regard x as the size of a positive central angle of a circle (Fig. 9-4) of radius 1 and center 0. Let AD be the arc of the circle intercepted by the angle. At A we drop the perpendicular AB to the side OD of the angle and at D we erect the perpendicular to the side OD. This perpendicular meets OA in some point which we denote by E.

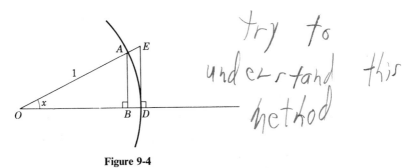

try to understand this method

Figure 9-4

We may now make a statement about areas:

(5) $\qquad$ area $OBA <$ area of sector $ODA <$ area $ODE.$

But

$$\text{area } OBA = \tfrac{1}{2}OB \cdot BA = \tfrac{1}{2}\cos x \sin x.$$

Further, the area ODA of the sector of the circle is that part of the entire area of the circle which the central angle x is of 2π. That is,

$$\text{area } ODA = \frac{x}{2\pi} \cdot \pi(1)^2 = \frac{x}{2}.$$

Finally,

$$\text{area } ODE = \tfrac{1}{2}ED \cdot OD = \tfrac{1}{2}\tan x = \frac{1}{2}\frac{\sin x}{\cos x}.$$

With these values of the individual areas the inequality (5) reads

$$\tfrac{1}{2}\cos x \sin x < \frac{x}{2} < \frac{1}{2}\frac{\sin x}{\cos x}.$$

If we divide the inequality by the positive quantity (sin x)/2 we obtain

(6) $$\cos x < \frac{x}{\sin x} < \frac{1}{\cos x}.$$

We recall from the study of trigonometry (see Fig. 9-5) that as x approaches 0, cos x approaches 1. However, we see from (6) that as x approaches 0, $x/\sin x$ always lies between two quantities, cos x which approaches 1 and $1/\cos x$ which must also approach 1 because cos x does. Hence

$$\lim_{x \to 0} \frac{x}{\sin x} = 1.$$

Because this limit is 1, it is also true that the reciprocal approaches 1, that is,

(7) $$\lim_{x \to 0} \frac{\sin x}{x} = 1.$$

We have considered the limit of (sin x)/x as x approaches 0 through positive values. However, when x is negative, we may use the fact that

(8) $$\frac{\sin x}{x} = \frac{\sin (-x)}{-x},$$

because sin $(-x) = -\sin x$. Moreover, if x is negative, $-x$ is positive. Because the right side of (8) deals with a positive variable and the fraction approaches 1 as x approaches 0 the left side of (8) also approaches 1.

We should note that the convenience of radian measure is utilized in the proof of (7). Had we used x-values which are associated with the degree measure of angles, our statement about the area of sector ODA would have had to be modified to read

$$\text{area } ODA = \frac{x}{360} \cdot \pi(1)^2,$$

and as a consequence the final result would have been

$$\lim_{x \to 0} \frac{180}{\pi} \frac{\sin x}{x} = 1.$$

When the values of x are associated with the radian measure of angles, we dispense with the factor $180/\pi$. Of course, nothing important in the calculus would really be affected if we did have to carry this factor.

There is one more limit that we shall utilize shortly, namely,

(9) $$\lim_{x \to 0} \frac{1 - \cos x}{x}.$$

The difficulty in evaluating this limit is the usual one—both numerator and denominator approach 0. However, the limit is readily evaluated. We utilize the trigonometry identity

(10)
$$\sin \frac{x}{2} = \sqrt{\frac{1 - \cos x}{2}}$$

so that

$$1 - \cos x = 2 \sin^2 \frac{x}{2}.$$

If we substitute this value in (9), we obtain

$$\lim_{x \to 0} \frac{2 \sin^2 \dfrac{x}{2}}{x}.$$

It is correct algebraically to write this last expression as

$$\lim_{x \to 0} \sin \frac{x}{2} \; \frac{\sin \dfrac{x}{2}}{\dfrac{x}{2}}.$$

If, for convenience, we regard $x/2$ as y, we see that we must determine the limit as y approaches 0 of a product one factor of which is $\sin y$ and the other $(\sin y)/y$. We know that the limit of a product of two functions is the product of the limits. However, as y approaches 0, $(\sin y)/y$ approaches 1 and $\sin y$ approaches 0. Hence the product of the limits is 0. Thus

(11)
$$\lim_{x \to 0} \frac{1 - \cos x}{x} = 0.$$

Exercises

1. Show that $\lim\limits_{x \to 0} \dfrac{1 - \cos x}{x} = 0$ by multiplying numerator and denominator by $1 + \cos x$ and then making any appropriate steps.

2. Evaluate the following limits:

(a) $\lim\limits_{x \to 0} \dfrac{\sin 2x}{x}$.   *Ans.* 2.   (d) $\lim\limits_{x \to 0} \dfrac{1 - \cos x}{x^2}$.

(b) $\lim\limits_{x \to 0} \dfrac{\sin ax}{x}$.   (e) $\lim\limits_{x \to 0} \dfrac{\tan x}{x}$.   *Ans.* 1.

(c) $\lim\limits_{\Delta x \to 0} \dfrac{\sin \Delta x}{\Delta x}$.   *Ans.* 1.

4. Differentiation of the Trigonometric Functions. To differentiate $y = \sin x$ we apply the method of increments. Let x_0 be the value of x at which we desire the derivative. Then

$$y_0 = \sin x_0.$$

If x changes to the value $x_0 + \Delta x$, then

$$y_0 + \Delta y = \sin (x_0 + \Delta x)$$

and

$$\frac{\Delta y}{\Delta x} = \frac{\sin (x_0 + \Delta x) - \sin x_0}{\Delta x}.$$

We cannot obtain the limit of the right side as Δx approaches 0 by merely inspecting the expression; hence we shall try to transform it on the chance that some other form may be more prespicuous. The presence of $\sin (x_0 + \Delta x)$ suggests that we try to use the identity

$$\sin (A + B) = \sin A \cos B + \cos A \sin B.$$

Then

$$\frac{\Delta y}{\Delta x} = \frac{\sin x_0 \cos \Delta x + \cos x_0 \sin \Delta x - \sin x_0}{\Delta x}.$$

Again, a direct evaluation of the limit of the fraction does not seem possible, and therefore we try collecting the terms in $\sin x_0$ and breaking up the fraction into two fractions. Thus

$$(12) \qquad \frac{\Delta y}{\Delta x} = \sin x_0 \cdot \frac{\cos \Delta x - 1}{\Delta x} + \cos x_0 \frac{\sin \Delta x}{\Delta x}.$$

To obtain $\dot{y}$ we must determine the limit of $\Delta y / \Delta x$ as Δx approaches 0. The right side is a sum of two terms, and according to the theorem that the limit of a sum is the sum of the limits we may consider each term separately. As for the term

$$(13) \qquad \sin x_0 \cdot \frac{\cos \Delta x - 1}{\Delta x},$$

the quantity $\sin x_0$ is a constant. A theorem on limits tells us that the limit of the product is the constant times the limit of the second factor. This limit is precisely the one we considered in (11), except for a factor of -1 and the fact that the x in (11) is the Δx in (13). Hence the limit of (13) is 0.

The term

$$(14) \qquad \cos x_0 \frac{\sin \Delta x}{\Delta x}$$

in (12) is again a constant times a function of Δx, and the limit of this term is the constant times the limit of $(\sin \Delta x)/\Delta x$. By (7) we see that the limit of (14) is $\cos x_0$.

We have, then, from the consideration of (13) and (14) that

$$\dot{y} = \lim_{\Delta x \to 0} \frac{\Delta y}{\Delta x} = \cos x_0.$$

This result holds at every value of x_0, and therefore we have that if $y = \sin x$ the derived function is

(15) $$\dot{y} = \cos x.$$

Now that we have the derived function in (15), the chain rule enables us to handle more complicated sine functions. Suppose that $y = \sin 3x$. To obtain dy/dx we regard $3x$ as u; we then have

(16) $$y = \sin u, \qquad u = 3x.$$

The chain rule states that

$$\frac{dy}{dx} = \frac{dy}{du} \cdot \frac{du}{dx}.$$

Hence from (15) we have

$$\frac{dy}{dx} = \cos u \cdot 3 = 3 \cos 3x.$$

In fact, no matter how complicated the function of x whose sine is being considered, we may always call it u and write $y = \sin u$ with u representing that function of x. Then

(17) $$\frac{dy}{dx} = \cos u \frac{du}{dx}.$$

The derivatives of the other five trigonometric functions are readily obtained. Let us remind ourselves first of the behavior of the function $y = \cos x$. This is shown in Fig. 9-5.

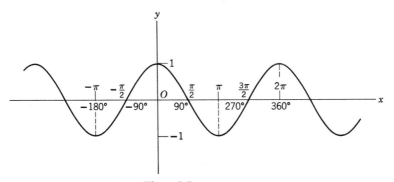

Figure 9-5 $y = \cos x$.

To obtain the derivative of $y = \cos x$, we can go through the method of increments, but it is easier to obtain it from (17). We know that we can relate cos x to sin x through the trigonometric identity

$$\cos x \equiv \sin\left(x + \frac{\pi}{2}\right).$$

This identity holds for every value of x. Hence to differentiate $y = \cos x$, we may differentiate $y = \sin(x + \pi/2)$. With the chain rule the result is immediate. We regard $x + \pi/2$ as u, so that

$$y = \sin u, \qquad u = x + \frac{\pi}{2}.$$

Then by (17)

$$\dot{y} = \cos u \cdot 1 = \cos\left(x + \frac{\pi}{2}\right).$$

But we have the identity

$$\cos\left(x + \frac{\pi}{2}\right) \equiv -\sin x.$$

Hence, if $y = \cos x$,

(18) $\dot{y} = -\sin x.$

As in the case of $y = \sin x$, if we have $y = \cos u$, where u is some function of x, we may apply the chain rule to write

(19) $$\frac{dy}{dx} = -\sin u \, \frac{du}{dx}.$$

For the function $y = \tan x$, whose behavior is shown in Fig. 9-6, the derived function is readily obtained. We have only to note that

$$y = \tan x = \frac{\sin x}{\cos x},$$

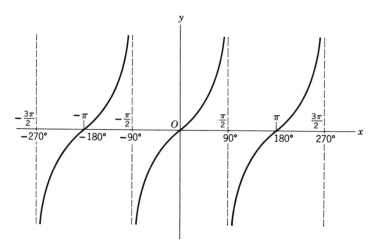

Figure 9-6 $y = \tan x.$

and we may now apply the theorem on the derivative of the quotient of two functions. We leave the details for an exercise and merely note the result. If $y = \tan x$, then

(20) $$\dot{y} = \sec^2 x.$$

Here we should note that the derived function exists at all values of x, except when x is an odd multiple of $\pi/2$ (see Fig. 9-8). As in the case of $y = \sin x$, if we have $y = \tan u$, where u is a function of x, then

(21) $$\dot{y} = \sec^2 u \, \frac{du}{dx}.$$

The case of $y = \cot x$ is practically the same as $y = \tan x$. The graph of the function is shown in Fig. 9-7. To obtain the derived function of $y = \cot x$,

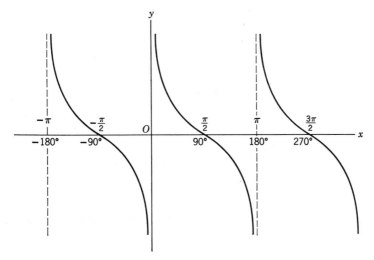

Figure 9-7 $y = \cot x$.

we have only to note that

(22) $$y = \cot x = \frac{\cos x}{\sin x}$$

and apply the theorem on the derivative of a quotient of two functions. Again we leave the details for an exercise and note the result. If $y = \cot x$, then

(23) $$\dot{y} = -\csc^2 x,$$

and if $y = \cot u$, where u is a function of x, then

(24) $$\dot{y} = -\csc^2 u \, \frac{du}{dx}.$$

The derived function in (23) fails to exist when x is any multiple of π (see Fig. 9-9).

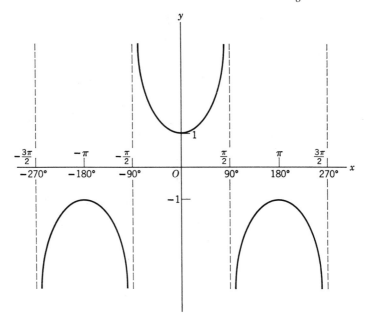

Figure 9-8 $y = \sec x$.

The derived function of $y = \sec x$, whose behavior is shown in Fig. 9-8, is also obtainable at once. Because

(25) $$y = \sec x = \frac{1}{\cos x},$$

the theorem on the derived function of a quotient of two functions can be applied and yields

(26) $$\dot{y} = \sec x \tan x.$$

Also, if $y = \sec u$, where u is a function of x, then

(27) $$\dot{y} = \sec u \tan u \frac{du}{dx}.$$

The derived function in (26) does not exist when x is an odd multiple of $\pi/2$.

Finally, we consider the sixth trigonometric function $y = \csc x$, whose behavior is shown in Fig. 9-9. The derived function is obtainable from the fact that

(28) $$y = \csc x = \frac{1}{\sin x}.$$

The result is

$$\dot{y} = -\csc x \cot x.$$

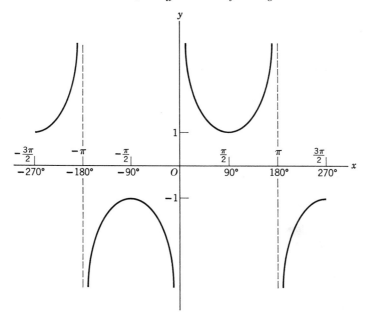

Figure 9-9 $y = \csc x$.

If $y = \csc u$, where u is a function of x, then

$$(30) \qquad\qquad \dot{y} = -\csc u \cot u \, \frac{du}{dx}.$$

The derived function in (29) fails to exist when x is any multiple of π.

Let us put together our results on the six functions. In all cases to be stated u is a function of x.

$$(31) \qquad\qquad \text{If } y = \sin u, \text{ then } \dot{y} = \cos u \, \frac{du}{dx}.$$

$$(32) \qquad\qquad \text{If } y = \cos u, \text{ then } \dot{y} = -\sin u \, \frac{du}{dx}.$$

$$(33) \qquad\qquad \text{If } y = \tan u, \text{ then } \dot{y} = \sec^2 u \, \frac{du}{dx}.$$

$$(34) \qquad\qquad \text{If } y = \cot u, \text{ then } \dot{y} = -\csc^2 u \, \frac{du}{dx}.$$

$$(35) \qquad\qquad \text{If } y = \sec u, \text{ then } \dot{y} = \sec u \tan u \, \frac{du}{dx}.$$

$$(36) \qquad\qquad \text{If } y = \csc u, \text{ then } \dot{y} = -\csc u \cot u \, \frac{du}{dx}.$$

Exercises

Exercises 1 to 6 round out details of the theory in the text.

1. Given that $\dfrac{\Delta y}{\Delta x} = \dfrac{\sin(x_0 + \Delta x) - \sin x_0}{\Delta x}$ use the identity

$$\sin A - \sin B = 2 \cos \frac{A+B}{2} \sin \frac{A-B}{2}$$

to find $\dot{y}$.

2. To differentiate $y = \cos x$, we might use a trigonometric identity and write $y = \sin\left(\dfrac{\pi}{2} - x\right)$. Obtain $\dot{y}$ from this form of $\cos x$.

3. Using the fact that $\tan x = \sin x / \cos x$, find $\dot{y}$ when $y = \tan x$.
4. Using the fact that $\cot x = \cos x / \sin x$, find $\dot{y}$ when $y = \cot x$.
5. Using the fact that $\sec x = 1/\cos x$, find $\dot{y}$ when $y = \sec x$.
6. Using the fact that $\csc x = 1/\sin x$, find $\dot{y}$ when $y = \csc x$.
7. Find the derived functions of each of the following functions:

(a) $y = \sin 2x$. Ans. $\dot{y} = 2 \cos 2x$.   (h) $y = \sin x \cot x$.
(b) $y = \cos 5x$.   (i) $y = \cos x \tan x$.
(c) $y = 3 \cos 2x$.   Ans. $\dot{y} = \cos x$.
                 Ans. $\dot{y} = -6 \sin 2x$.   (j) $y = \sqrt{1 - \cos^2 x}$.
(d) $y = 6 \tan 5x$.   (k) $y = \sqrt{1 + \tan^2 x}$.
(e) $y = \sec 4x$.   Ans. $\dot{y} = \sec x \tan x$.
                 Ans. $\dot{y} = 4 \sec 4x \tan 4x$. (l) $y = \sqrt{2 - \cos^2 x}$.
(f) $y = \sin x \cos x$.
                                                             Ans. $\dot{y} = \dfrac{\sin x \cos x}{\sqrt{1 + \sin^2 x}}$.
(g) $y = \dfrac{1}{\cos 2x}$.

                 Ans. $\dot{y} = \dfrac{2 \sin 2x}{\cos^2 2x}$.

8. Find the derived functions of each of the following functions:

(a) $y = \sin^3 x$.   (i) $y = x \cos \dfrac{1}{x}$.
                 Ans. $\dot{y} = 3 \sin^2 x \cos x$.
(b) $y = \sin^3 x \cos x$.   Ans. $\dot{y} = \cos \dfrac{1}{x} + \dfrac{1}{x} \sin \dfrac{1}{x}$.
(c) $y = \sin^3 2x$.
                 Ans. $\dot{y} = 6 \sin^2 2x \cos 2x$.
(d) $y = \sqrt[3]{\sin x}$.   (j) $y = \sqrt{\sin x^3}$.
(e) $y = \cos^2 2x$.   (k) $y = \cos(\sin x)$.
                 Ans. $\dot{y} = -4 \sin 2x \cos 2x$.   Ans. $\dot{y} = -\sin(\sin x) \cos x$.
(f) $y = \sin x^3$.   (l) $y = \sin^2 x + \cos^2 x$.
(g) $y = \tan 2x \cot 2x$.
                 Ans. $\dot{y} = 0$.   (m) $y = \dfrac{\sin 2x}{\tan x}$.

(h) $y = \sin \dfrac{1}{x}$.   Ans. $\dot{y} = -4 \sin x \cos x$.

9. Given $y = \sin x$, find $\ddot{y}$. *Ans.* $\ddot{y} = -\sin x$.

10. Given $y = \cos x$, find $\ddot{y}$.

11. Let us accept for the present the fact that the range of a projectile fired from a gun which is inclined at an angle A to the ground is given by the formula $R = (V^2/16) \sin A \cos A$, where V, the initial velocity of the projectile, is fixed. Find the value of A for which the range is maximum. *Ans.* $\pi/4$.

12. Find the value of $\lim\limits_{\Delta x \to 0} \dfrac{\sin(2x + 2\,\Delta x) - \sin 2x}{\Delta x}$.

13. Find the value of $\lim\limits_{x \to \pi/2} \dfrac{\sin x - 1}{x - \pi/2}$. *Ans.* 0.

14. A mass M is drawn up a straight incline of given height h by a mass m which is attached to the first mass by a string passing from it over a pulley at the top of the incline (Fig. 9-10) and which hangs vertically. Find the angle of the incline in order that the time of ascent be a minimum. *Suggestion:* The net force acting on M is $32m - 32M \sin A$. *Ans.* $\sin A = m/2M$.

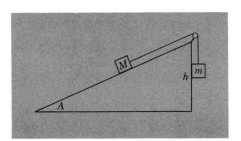

Figure 9-10

15. Given a point and a vertical line distant d from it, find the inclination of the straight line which would guide a particle acted on only by gravity from the point to the vertical line in the shortest time. *Ans.* $\pi/4$.

16. A swinging pendulum is 4 feet long and is rotating at the rate of 18°/sec when it makes an angle of 30° with the vertical. How fast is the end of the pendulum rising or falling at that moment? *Ans.* $\pi/5$ ft/sec.

17. An airplane, flying at an altitude of 2 miles, passes directly over an observer on the ground. A few moments later the observer notes that the airplane's angle of elevation is 30° and is decreasing at the rate of 15°/min. How fast is the plane traveling? *Ans.* $2\pi/3$ mi/min.

18. A revolving beacon 3600 feet off a straight shore makes 2 revolutions per minute. How fast does its beam sweep along the shore (a) at the point on the shore nearest the beacon? (b) at the point on the shore 4800 feet sway from the beacon? *Ans.* (a) $14{,}400\,\pi$ ft/min; (b) $25{,}600\,\pi$ ft/min.

19. A ferris wheel 50 feet in diameter makes 1 revolution every 2 minutes. If the center of the wheel is 30 feet above the ground, how fast is a passenger in the cab rising when he reaches a height of 40 feet? *Ans.* $5\sqrt{21}\,\pi$ ft/min.

20. A destroyer at A sights a battleship at B, two miles away (Fig. 9-11). The latter is sailing due east at 10 mi/hr and the former is capable of sailing at 8 mi/hr. In what direction should the destroyer sail to come as close as possible to the battleship? *Suggestion:* Suppose that the destroyer takes the direction θ and sails for some time t until it is closest to the battleship. The destroyer may then be at C and the battleship at D. The destroyer can do better by sailing in the direction ϕ, the angle determined by the straight line from A to D, for in that same time t it can travel the distance AC' equal to AC, and DC' is then less than DC. Hence it is necessary to consider only the situations in which the destroyer heads directly for the position of the battleship. However, this still leaves open a domain of possible values for ϕ, and the problem then becomes. which value of ϕ is best?   *Ans.* $\sin \phi = 0.8$.

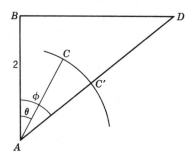

Figure 9-11

21. A steel girder 27 feet long is moved on rollers along a passageway and into a corridor 8 feet wide and at right angles to the passageway. How wide must be the passageway for the girder to go around the corner? *Suggestion:* Idealize the girder as the line segment AB of Fig. 9-12. As the girder is moved around the corner it is best to keep it touching the inner vertex at 0 and touching the outer wall of the corridor. Then θ varies as the girder is moved into the corridor. The largest value of x as θ varies from 90° to 0° is the required width of the passageway.   *Ans.* $5\sqrt{5}$.

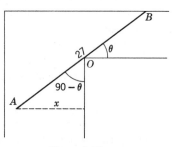

Figure 9-12

5. *Integration of the Trigonometric Functions.* Every new formula of differentiation gives us a new formula for integration. Thus from formulas

(31) to (36) we have, when u is a function of x,

(37) $\qquad$ if $\dot{y} = -\sin u \dfrac{du}{dx}$, $\qquad y = \cos u + C$,

(38) $\qquad$ if $\dot{y} = \cos u \dfrac{du}{dx}$, $\qquad y = \sin u + C$,

(39) $\qquad$ if $\dot{y} = \sec^2 u \dfrac{du}{dx}$, $\qquad y = \tan u + C$,

(40) $\qquad$ if $\dot{y} = -\csc^2 u \dfrac{du}{dx}$, $\qquad y = \cot u + C$,

(41) $\qquad$ if $\dot{y} = \sec u \tan u \dfrac{du}{dx}$, $\qquad y = \sec u + C$,

(42) $\qquad$ if $\dot{y} = -\csc u \underset{\underset{\text{cot}}{}}{\tan} u \dfrac{du}{dx}$, $\quad y = \csc u + C$.

As in the case of the algebraic functions, integration is more difficult than differentiation. Let us consider a few examples involving the trigonometric functions.

Given

$$\dot{y} = \cos 2x,$$

let us find y. We realize readily that if we think of $2x$ as u, we have $\dot{y} = \cos u$. If we had in addition the factor du/dx, we could integrate by applying (38). In the present case, because du/dx is 2, we write

$$\dot{y} = \tfrac{1}{2} \cos u \cdot 2.$$

Now, apart from the factor $\tfrac{1}{2}$, our derivative is in the form called for by (38). However, a constant factor can be kept separate and merely multiplied into the integral . Hence

$$y = \tfrac{1}{2} \sin u + C = \tfrac{1}{2} \sin 2x + C.$$

We may recall that the factor du/dx, which is 2 in this example, does not itself give rise to any term in the integral.

Let us consider next

$$\dot{y} = \cos^2 x \sin x.$$

If we regard $\cos x$ as u, we have

$$\frac{dy}{dx} = u^2 \cdot \sin x.$$

To have the proper du/dx, in view of the fact that $u = \cos x$, we need $-\sin x$. However, this is easily introduced, because it involves only multiplying and dividing by a constant factor.

Thus

$$\frac{dy}{dx} = -u^2(-\sin x) = -u^2 \frac{du}{dx}.$$

Now apart from the constant factor -1 we are in position to apply the generalized power rule of Chapter 7, Section 7. Then

$$y = -\frac{u^3}{3} + C = -\frac{\cos^3 x}{3} + C.$$

As a third example let us consider

(43) $$\dot{y} = \tan 2x \sec^2 2x.$$

The fact that the derived function of $\tan x$ is $\sec^2 x$ suggests setting

$$u = \tan 2x.$$

Then by (33)

(44) $$\frac{du}{dx} = \sec^2 2x \cdot 2.$$

With this choice of u as $\tan 2x$, we see from (43) and (44) that

$$\frac{dy}{dx} = \frac{1}{2} u \frac{du}{dx}.$$

Again, apart from the factor $\frac{1}{2}$, we are in position to apply the generalized power rule. From this we have

(45) $$y = \tfrac{1}{4} u^2 + C = \tfrac{1}{4} \tan^2 2x + C.$$

There is another way of doing the integration. Let us write (43) as

(46) $$\dot{y} = \sec 2x \sec 2x \tan 2x.$$

Now we try letting

$$u = \sec 2x.$$

Then by (35)

$$\frac{du}{dx} = \sec 2x \tan 2x \cdot 2.$$

We see then that we can write (46) as

$$\frac{dy}{dx} = \frac{1}{2} u \frac{du}{dx},$$

from which

(47) $$y = \tfrac{1}{4} u^2 + C = \tfrac{1}{4} \sec^2 2x + C.$$

If we compare (45) and (47), we see that we presumably have two different answers. However, there is the trigonometric identity

$$\sec^2 2x = 1 + \tan^2 2x.$$

Then

$$\tfrac{1}{4} \sec^2 2x = \tfrac{1}{4} + \tfrac{1}{4} \tan^2 2x.$$

Hence (47) becomes

$$y = \tfrac{1}{4} + \tfrac{1}{4} \tan^2 2x + C = \tfrac{1}{4} \tan^2 2x + C',$$

where C' is some new constant of integration. If we now compare with (45), we see that we have the same result.

In integrating trigonometric funtions we should keep in mind that the numerous identities of trigonometry often aid in transforming a given function into one which is identical in its values to the given one but more amenable to integration.

Exercises

1. Given the following derived functions, find y:

(a) $\dot{y} = \cos 3x$.

$$\text{Ans. } y = \frac{\sin 3x}{3} + C.$$

(b) $\dot{y} = \sin 4x$.

(c) $\dot{y} = \sin^2 x$.

$$\text{Ans. } y = \frac{x}{2} - \frac{\sin x \cos x}{2} + C.$$

(d) $\dot{y} = \cos^2 x$.

(e) $\dot{y} = \sin^2 x \cos x$.

$$\text{Ans. } y = \frac{\sin^3 x}{3} + C.$$

(f) $\dot{y} = \sin^2 3x \cos 3x$.

(g) $\dot{y} = \sec^3 x \tan x$.

$$\text{Ans. } y = \frac{\sec^3 x}{3} + C.$$

(h) $\dot{y} = \cot^4 x \csc^2 x$.

(i) $\dot{y} = \tan^3 2x \sec^2 2x$.

$$\text{Ans. } y = \frac{\tan^4 2x}{8} + C.$$

(j) $\dot{y} = \dfrac{\csc^2 2x}{\cot^3 2x}$.

(k) $\dot{y} = \sqrt{\cot^3 x}\, \csc^2 x$.

$$\text{Ans. } y = \frac{-2 \cot^{5/2} x}{5} + C.$$

(l) $\dot{y} = \csc^4 ax \cot ax$.

(m) $\dot{y} = \sec^5 x \tan x$.

$$\text{Ans. } y = \frac{\sec^5 x}{5} + C.$$

(n) $\dot{y} = \dfrac{\sec^2 x}{\sqrt{\tan x + 3}}$.

(o) $\dot{y} = x \cos x^2$.

2. Find the area bounded by the y-axis, $y = 8 \cos x$ and $y = \sec^2 x$.　　Ans. $3\sqrt{3}$.

3. If $\dot{y} = \sin x \cos x$, then by letting $u = \sin x$ we see that $y = (\sin^2 x)/2$. By letting $u = \cos x$, we see that $y = -(\cos^2 x)/2$. Then $(\sin^2 x)/2 = -(\cos^2 x)/2$. What is wrong?

4. If $y = f(x)$ is a periodic function, is $y = f'(x)$ necessarily periodic? Defend your answer.　　　　　　　　　　　　　　　　　　　　Ans. Yes.

5. Show by an example that if $y = f'(x)$ is periodic, then $y = f(x)$ need not be.

6. Applications of the Trigonometric Functions to Periodic Phenomena.
We have already stated that the trigonometric functions are immensely important

in the study of periodic phenomena, and we are now in a position to look at a few of them. We consider first the motion of a bob on a spring—an investigation launched by Robert Hooke as part of the seventeenth-century efforts to design simple, portable clocks.

Suppose that the upper end (Fig. 9-13) of the spring is fixed and a bob is attached to the lower end. The weight of the bob extends the spring. Because the spring is extended, it exerts a tension or pull upward, and this tension increases as the spring becomes more and more extended. The spring stretches to the point at which the upward tension in the spring just offsets the weight of the bob. The position of the bob at which the two forces, the upward pull of the spring and the downward pull of the weight, offset each other is called the equilibrium position. If no new forces are introduced, the bob stays in this equilibrium position indefinitely.

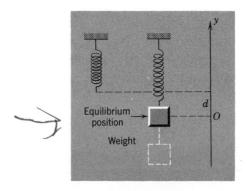

Figure 9-13

If the bob is pulled down still more and then released, it oscillates about the equilibrium position and, if air resistance (and strictly internal losses in the spring) are ignored, the bob continues to oscillate endlessly. We propose to study the motion of the bob mathematically. Our program is to obtain a function that describes its motion and then to try to learn some facts from the function which are not apparent from mere observation of the bob's motion.

We introduce a vertical coordinate line, the y-axis of Fig. 9-13, and choose the origin O to be the equilibrium position of the bob. Let us denote by d, which we take to be positive, the length by which the spring is extended when the bob is attached to it. After the bob is set in motion by pulling it down from the equilibrium position and then releasing it, its position, of course, varies continuously with time. The y-value of this varying position that the bob may have at any time t is called the displacement. When the bob is below the equilibrium position, the y-values are negative numbers; when above, they are positive.

Understand
research

d—(y)⟹ y is
it,ele ⟵

We seek the relation between displacement and time, that is, between y and t. To obtain the motion of the bob, we must have some physical principle or principles. In the present case we apply Hooke's law which says that the tension in the spring or force exerted by the spring is proportional to the extension or contraction of the spring beyond its normal length. To be specific, suppose that the bob is pulled down a distance y below the equilibrium position. Because this y-value is itself negative, the spring is extended to an amount $d - y$. Hooke's law states that the force exerted by the spring on the bob is

(48)
$$k(d - y)$$

where k is the proportionality constant and is positive. This constant has a direct physical meaning. Some springs are very "tight", that is, it is hard to extend them. Hence when extended they exert a strong force to contract. For such springs k is large. Alternatively, there are springs that are easily extended, and these exert a small restoring force. For such springs k is a small number. Thus k represents the "stiffness" of the spring and is called the spring constant.

One force acting on the bob is the pull of the spring. Also acting on the bob is the weight of the bob, $32m$, where m is the mass of the bob. In representing these forces mathematically, we must be careful about the signs. The significance of a force insofar as motion is concerned is that it causes acceleration. We know this through Newton's second law of motion which states that a force acting upon a mass gives it an acceleration. We have already pointed out that an acceleration in a given direction produces a velocity in that direction and the velocity produces a distance moved in that same direction. Then the positive direction of a force must be that which causes the distance traveled to be in the positive direction.*

Let us now look at the forces acting on the bob with a view to assigning the proper signs to them; let us keep in mind that we have chosen the upward direction to be the positive one for y. The spring force, by (48), is $k(d - y)$. When y is positive but less than d, and when y is negative, the quantity $k(d - y)$ is positive. However, for the values of y in question, the spring is extended and therefore pulls the bob upward. The force then is in the positive direction, and because $k(d - y)$ is positive, it has the correct sign. To check the sign let us consider the situation when y is positive and greater than d. Then $k(d - y)$ is negative. However, when $y > d$, the spring is contracted

---

* Likewise a negative force causes a negative acceleration, which causes the distance traveled to be in the negative direction. Nevertheless, even when a negative force and therefore a negative acceleration is acting, the actual motion may be upward. This can happen because some other velocities or accelerations may also be acting and may dominate. Thus when a ball is thrown up into the air and the upward direction is taken positive, there is a negative acceleration, due to gravity, always acting on the ball which causes the distance traveled to be downward. However, the initial velocity given to the ball by the hand is positive, and this dominates the motion during the upward motion of the ball.

beyond its normal length; it therefore seeks to expand and so presses downward on the bob. It causes the bob to travel downward and because the downward direction is negative, the sign of $k(d - y)$ is correct in this case too.

The only other force acting on the bob is the weight $32m$. This force always acts downward and, because it causes the bob to move downward, it should be negative. We represent this force then by $-32m$.

Thus the algebraic sum of the forces acting on the bob is

(49) $$k(d - y) - 32m.$$

When the bob is in the equilibrium position, the upward pull of the spring just offsets the downward pull of the weight. Consequently,

(50) $$kd = 32m.$$

Hence the *net force* acting on the bob is

$$-ky.$$

We note incidentally that equation (50) enables us to measure the spring constant k. If we attach a known weight to the spring, we can measure d and solve for k.

Now that we know the net force acting on the bob we may use Newton's second law of motion which states that $F = ma$, where F is the force in poundals, m is the mass in pounds, and a is the acceleration in feet per second per second. In the present case of straight-line motion, a is d^2y/dt^2 or $\ddot{y}$ and F is $-ky$. Hence

(51) $$m\ddot{y} = -ky.$$ $a = \ddot{y}$

Thus the implication of Hooke's law and Newton's second law of motion in calculus terms is a statement about the second derivative of y as a function of t.

This equation is of the same form as that encountered in dealing with escape velocity. We could solve the present one by the same trick, that is, by replacing d^2y/dt^2 by $v\,dv/dy$, where v is the velocity, but here we can do something simpler. If we examine (51), we see that it calls essentially for a function whose second derivative equals the function. This suggests sine or cosine. By mere trial we find that

$$y = \sin\sqrt{\frac{k}{m}}\,t \quad \text{and} \quad y = \cos\sqrt{\frac{k}{m}}\,t$$

will serve, for if

$$y = \sin\sqrt{\frac{k}{m}}\,t,$$

then

$$\dot{y} = \sqrt{\frac{k}{m}}\cos\sqrt{\frac{k}{m}}\,t$$

and

$$\ddot{y} = -\sqrt{\frac{k}{m}}\sqrt{\frac{k}{m}}\sin\sqrt{\frac{k}{m}}\,t = -\frac{k}{m}\sin\sqrt{\frac{k}{m}}\,t = -\frac{k}{m}\,y.$$

Likewise, $y = \cos\sqrt{k/m}\,t$ satisfies (51). Moreover, if we introduce a constant multiplier in either choice of y, we also obtain a function that satisfies (51). Finally, we can state that

(52)
$$y = A\sin\sqrt{\frac{k}{m}}\,t + B\cos\sqrt{\frac{k}{m}}\,t,$$

where A and B are any constants we choose, is also a solution of (51) because when we substitute this value of y in that equation, we see that the left side equals the right side.

Thus by trial we have obtained a function that satisfies (51). We do not know that this is the only function that can satisfy it, but at the moment we should be thankful that we have at least one; let us see if it tells us anything about the bob's motion. We shall return later (Chapter 10, Section 4) to the question of whether (52) is the unique solution, that is, the one and only one.

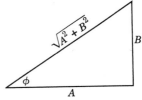

Figure 9-14

Formula (52) is the sum of a sine function and a cosine function of the same period. Such a sum is sinusoidal; we can see this in the following way. We multiply and divide through the right-hand side of (52) by $\sqrt{A^2 + B^2}$. Thus

(53) $\quad y = \sqrt{A^2 + B^2}\left(\dfrac{A}{\sqrt{A^2 + B^2}}\sin\sqrt{\dfrac{k}{m}}\,t + \dfrac{B}{\sqrt{A^2 + B^2}}\cos\sqrt{\dfrac{k}{m}}\,t\right).$

We now introduce an angle ϕ, which is defined as shown in Fig. 9-14; that is, ϕ is the angle for which

(54) $\qquad \cos\phi = \dfrac{A}{\sqrt{A^2 + B^2}}, \qquad \sin\phi = \dfrac{B}{\sqrt{A^2 + B^2}}.$

Such an angle can be defined for any value of A and B; of course, if A or B or both prove to be negative, ϕ is not an acute angle. Also, because A and B are constants, so is $\sqrt{A^2 + B^2}$, and we may as well replace it by the constant C. Then (53) becomes

$$y = C\left(\sin\sqrt{\frac{k}{m}}\,t\cos\phi + \cos\sqrt{\frac{k}{m}}\,t\sin\phi\right)$$

or by a trigonometric identity

(55)
$$y = C\sin\left(\sqrt{\frac{k}{m}}\,t + \phi\right).$$

Equation (55) is fully equivalent to (52). The constants A and B in (52), as yet undetermined, are replaced in (55) by the constants C and ϕ. Moreover, if we determine A and B from some physical facts, we can calculate C and ϕ. Conversely, if we know C and ϕ, we know $\sqrt{A^2 + B^2}$ and $\cos \phi$ and $\sin \phi$. Hence we can find A and B from (54).

The advantage of (55) as opposed to (52) is that we see at once that y is a sinusoidal function of t; that is, the curve is a sine curve of some period and amplitude. The amplitude is clearly C. The quantity ϕ is what is usually called a phase constant; that is, y is not 0 when t is 0, as in the simple sine function $y = \sin t$, but y is 0 in (55) when t is $-\phi/\sqrt{k/m}$ and of course whenever the argument $\sqrt{k/m}\,t + \phi$ is a multiple of π. The period T of (55) is, as in all sine curves, 2π divided by the coefficient of t; that is,

$$(56) \qquad T = \frac{2\pi}{\sqrt{\dfrac{k}{m}}} \quad \text{or} \quad T = 2\pi\sqrt{\frac{m}{k}}.$$

This means that for each increase in t of $2\pi\sqrt{m/k}$, the y-values go through one cycle of values. Or, in terms of time, it takes $2\pi\sqrt{m/k}$ seconds for the curve to go through one full cycle of sine values. If it takes this many seconds to go through one cycle, the number of cycles per second, or the frequency per second, is

$$(57) \qquad f = \frac{1}{2\pi\sqrt{\dfrac{m}{k}}} = \frac{1}{2\pi}\sqrt{\frac{k}{m}}.$$

Thus we have learned that the motion of the bob is sinusoidal. Moreover, we see from (56) that it takes $2\pi\sqrt{m/k}$ seconds to go through one cycle; that is, it takes this much time for the bob to make one complete oscillation, or one complete up and down motion. This last fact is rather remarkable, for it says that the period is *independent of the amplitude.* Thus regardless of whether the bob moves far up and down from its equilibrium position or just oscillates slightly above and below its equilibrium position the period is the same. This fact is very important in the use of springs in watches or clocks, because though air resistance and friction cause the motion to die down, that is, cause the amplitude to decrease, the period is not affected. Moreover, if we restore the amplitude by giving the bob an occasional push or pull, the period is still not affected. Hence the period can be used as a constant measure of time.

We learn also from (57) that we can fix the period or frequency as we wish. The frequency depends on k and m. This means that if we choose k and m properly, we can make f, say, 1 per second. If we pick a particular spring, k is fixed and, as we pointed out in connection with (50), can be measured.

Then we select m, the mass of the bob, so that

$$\frac{1}{2\pi} \sqrt{\frac{k}{m}} = 1.$$

It is of interest to find out how the constants A and B of (52) or the C and ϕ of (55), which are in effect the constants of integration, are determined in a particular situation. Suppose that we work with A and B. When we considered the motion of a ball thrown up into the air, we found that the initial velocity and the position from which we measured height determined the constants of integration. The situation is similar here. We start the bob off by pulling it down some distance, say D, and then let it go. If we agree to measure time from the instant it is released, we have that at $t = 0$, $y = -D$. If we substitute these values in (52), we obtain

$$(58) \qquad -D = A \sin \left(\sqrt{\frac{k}{m}} \cdot 0 \right) + B \cos \left(\sqrt{\frac{k}{m}} \cdot 0 \right).$$

This tells us that $B = -D$.

If the bob is merely released after it is pulled down, the velocity $\dot{y} = 0$ when $t = 0$. This second condition is met by first obtaining $\dot{y}$ from (52). Thus

$$(59) \qquad \dot{y} = A \sqrt{\frac{k}{m}} \cos \sqrt{\frac{k}{m}} t - B \sqrt{\frac{k}{m}} \sin \sqrt{\frac{k}{m}} t.$$

Because $\dot{y} = 0$ when $t = 0$,

$$0 = A \sqrt{\frac{k}{m}} \cos \left(\sqrt{\frac{k}{m}} \cdot 0 \right) - B \sqrt{\frac{k}{m}} \sin \left(\sqrt{\frac{k}{m}} \cdot 0 \right).$$

Then

$$A = 0.$$

Thus the final description of the motion for the initial conditions specified above is

$$(60) \qquad y = -D \cos \sqrt{\frac{k}{m}} t.$$

The amplitude of the motion is precisely the distance down to which the bob is pulled before being released. Figure 9-15 shows the graph of the motion called for by (60). Of course, the bob's motion is up and down.

We can start the bob's motion differently. We can pull it down to a distance $-D$ below the equilibrium position and then give it an upward velocity of, say, v_0. Time can still be measured from the instant the bob is pushed upward at $y = -D$. The first condition still requires that (58) hold, so that $B = -D$. However, to meet the condition on the initial velocity we now use (59) and

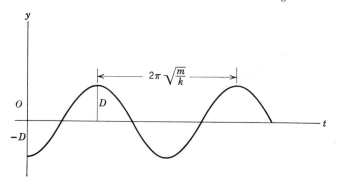

Figure 9-15

require that $\dot{y} = v_0$ when $t = 0$.   Hence

$$v_0 = A\sqrt{\frac{k}{m}} \cos\left(\sqrt{\frac{k}{m}} \cdot 0\right) - B\sqrt{\frac{k}{m}} \sin\left(\sqrt{\frac{k}{m}} \cdot 0\right).$$

From this equation we see that

$$A = v_0\sqrt{\frac{m}{k}}\,.$$

Now our description of the motion is

(61) $$y = v_0\sqrt{\frac{m}{k}} \sin\sqrt{\frac{k}{m}}\,t - D\cos\sqrt{\frac{k}{m}}\,t.$$

Exercises

1. Suppose that we use the representation (55), namely,

$$y = C\sin\left(\sqrt{\frac{k}{m}}\,t + \phi\right),$$

to represent the motion of the bob. Use the initial conditions that y is $-D$ and $\dot{y}$ is 0 at $t = 0$ to determine C and ϕ.   *Ans.* $C = -D$, $\phi = \pi/2$.

2. Use the representation (52) of the bob's motion and determine A and B under the initial conditions that the bob is at the equilibrium position when $t = 0$ but is given an initial velocity of 5 ft/sec. What is the amplitude of the motion?

3. What is the amplitude of the motion represented by (61)? *Suggestion:* Utilize the form (55).

4. Consider the motion of the bob given by (60). When is the velocity of the bob greatest? When is the acceleration of the bob greatest?

5. Suppose that the effect of gravity is ignored in the motion of a bob on a spring. How is (51) affected? What can you say about the solution of the equation in this case?   *Ans.* $d = 0$; (51) remains same but y is measured from end of unextended spring.

6. A mass weighing $\frac{1}{4}$ pound and attached to one end of a spring is in equilibrium when the extension of the spring is 4 inches. The mass is raised 2 inches from its equilibrium position and then released. Find the displacement of the mass t seconds after the start of the motion.

7. An elastic string stretches $\frac{1}{2}$ inch for every pound of mass attached to one end. If the upper end is fixed and a mass of 3 pounds is attached to the lower end and suddenly released, how far will the mass fall before reversing its motion and what is the period of oscillation of the mass?   *Ans.* 3 in.; 0.393 sec.

8. A spring, one end of which is fixed, stretches $\frac{1}{2}$ inch for every pound of mass attached to the free end. A 4-pound mass is attached to the free end and allowed to reach the equilibrium position. The mass is then struck so as to give it instantaneously an upward velocity of 1 ft/sec. Find the function relating displacement and time of motion of the mass.

9. A particle is attached to the middle of a uniform elastic string which is stretched between two points A and B on a smooth horizontal table (Fig. 9-16). If the particle is pulled to some point in the line AB and then released, determine its subsequent motion. Assume that the displacement of the particle is small enough to keep the two parts of the string taut. *Suggestion:* If the length AB is $2a$, if the unstretched length of the string is $2l$, $l < a$, and if the displacement of the particle at any instant is x, the two forces acting on the particle are $k(a - l - x)$ and $k(a - l + x)$. These forces oppose each other.

Figure 9-16

10. The balance wheel of a watch oscillates sinusoidally; that is, the angular displacement of any point on the rim is a sinusoidal function of the time. The maximum angular displacement of any point is $\pi/2$ and the period is $\frac{1}{2}$ second. Find the angular velocity and angular acceleration of any point (and therefore of the wheel) 2 seconds after it passes through the equilibrium position.
     Ans. $2\pi^2/\text{sec}$; 0.

Our second application of the trigonometric function is to the study of the motion of a simple pendulum. This device, like that of a bob on a spring, was investigated during the seventeenth century as a possible standard of time, and the principal men in this work were Galileo and Huygens. The device is still important today, although its use in clocks is out of date. The simple pendulum consists of a string suspended from a fixed point T (Fig. 9-17) and a bob attached to the other end. The equilibrium position of the pendulum is, of course, that in which the string is vertical. When the bob is pulled to one side and released, it continues to swing forward and back and, were there no air resistance, would continue this motion indefinitely.

When the bob is in any position to the right or left of its equilibrium position, it is said to be displaced; this displacement can be represented mathematically by the arc length s, which is measured positive to the right of 0 and

negative to the left. Alternatively, the displacement of the bob can be represented by the angle θ which the string in any position makes with the vertical.
The angle θ is taken to be positive when the bob is to the right of 0 and negative when the bob is to the left of 0. Because $s = l\theta$, where l is the constant
length of the string, we can readily convert from one variable to the other.
Our first objective is to find the function that relates displacement and time.

What force keeps the bob moving? The answer is that the force of gravity,
which in this case is the weight of the bob, gives the bob an acceleration.
The weight, if m is the mass of the bob, is $32m$. Let us see how this force acts
on the bob. Suppose that it is in a typical position, P in Fig. 9-17. The force

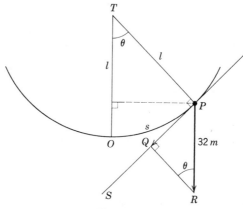

Figure 9-17

of gravity pulls straight down, whereas the bob moves along a circular arc.
Hence we must determine what component of the force of gravity is effective
in causing motion along the circle. The direction of the motion when the bob
is at $\overset{\cdot}{P}$ is tangential to the circle, and so we must ask for the component of
gravity along the tangent PS. Let PR be a vector that represents the force of
gravity. The component of PR along PS is obtained by dropping a perpendicular from R onto PS thus obtaining PQ. The angle at R is readily seen to be
equal to θ, and therefore the component is

$$PQ = 32m \sin \theta.$$

This component is directed toward the left when s or θ is positive. However,
a positive force must be that which causes s or θ to increase. Hence we must
write

$$PQ = -32m \sin \theta.$$

This force is the only one acting along the circle.

As in the case of the motion of the bob on the spring, we now utilize Newton's second law of motion, $F = ma$, to state that

(62) $$ma = -32m \sin \theta.$$

The acceleration is the second derivative of the distance traveled by the bob; that is, $a = d^2s/dt^2$ or $\ddot{s}$. Hence (62) becomes

(63)
$$m\ddot{s} = -32m \sin \theta.$$

To obtain an equation in two variables, we use the fact that

$$s = l\theta.$$

Because θ is also a function of t and l is a constant,

$$\dot{s} = l\dot{\theta};$$

by differentiating once more, we obtain

$$\ddot{s} = l\ddot{\theta}.$$

Then (63) becomes, after dividing through by m and by l,

(64)
$$\ddot{\theta} = \frac{-32}{l} \sin \theta.$$

We would, of course, like to know the functional relation between θ and t which satisfies (64). Actually, the integration of (64) to find $d\theta/dt$ as a function of t could be performed, but the step from $d\theta/dt$ as a function of t to θ as a function of t involves a difficulty that cannot be overcome at this time. (See Chapter 20, Section 12). Our alternative move at present is one which is commonly employed in the application of mathematics to physical problems, namely, we make a reasonable approximation. For the pendulum motion, that occurs in a clock, the angle θ does not become very large. We proved earlier that

$$\lim_{\theta \to 0} \frac{\sin \theta}{\theta} = 1.$$

This means that for θ-values near 0, $\sin \theta$ and θ must be nearly equal in value. In fact, our table in Section 3 shows that for θ equal to 0.3 radians or less, $\sin \theta$ and θ differ at most in the third decimal place. Now 0.3 radians is more than 17°. Hence it would appear that the error committed in replacing $\sin \theta$ by θ when θ is small could not be very much. Therefore, we replace $\sin \theta$ by θ in (64) and consider the equation

(65)
$$\ddot{\theta} = -\frac{32}{l} \theta.$$

We now compare (65) with (51) which reads

$$\ddot{y} = -\frac{k}{m} y.$$

These two equations are precisely the same except for the symbols. There is therefore no need to repeat the steps by which we determined the solution of (51). We have but to change the symbols in (52) and write

(66) $$\theta = A \sin \sqrt{\frac{32}{l}}\, t + B \cos \sqrt{\frac{32}{l}}\, t.$$

Moreover, we may take over at once from (56) the conclusion that the period T of a pendulum is given by

(67) $$T = 2\pi \sqrt{\frac{l}{32}}$$

and that the number of oscillations per second or the frequency per second of the pendulum is, in view of (57),

(68) $$f = \frac{1}{2\pi} \sqrt{\frac{32}{l}}.$$

The conclusions we drew about the motion of the bob on the spring also apply to the pendulum, except that an approximation is made in deriving the results for the pendulum. We see, in particular, that the period and frequency are independent of the amplitude of the motion. Hence in the case of the pendulum, too, the decrease in amplitude caused by air resistance does not affect the period, and if the amplitude is maintained, as it is in pendulum clocks, by periodically giving the pendulum a little "push," the period is not affected. We see also that the period can be adjusted by varying the length l of the string.

There is an additional point about the pendulum that does not apply to the bob on the spring. The period of the pendulum depends on the quantity 32, which is the acceleration due to gravity. If a pendulum clock has been set so that its period is 1 second and it is then taken to another location where the acceleration due to gravity is no longer 32—the top of a mountain, for example, the period no longer is 1 second. This dependence of the period on the acceleration of gravity is a defect in pendulum clocks. However, it is an ill wind that blows no good. If we carried through the mathematical work on the pendulum using g for the acceleration of gravity in place of 32, the formula for the period would be

(69) $$T = 2\pi \sqrt{\frac{l}{g}}.$$

Now suppose that the period of a pendulum is measured at some location by another timepiece; then (69) can be used to determine the acceleration of gravity at that location. The pendulum is, in fact, one of the most sensitive devices for measuring the acceleration of gravity.

We still must see how (66) can be adjusted to the initial data of any particular problem. Suppose that the bob of a pendulum is pulled aside, so that θ is 0.1 radian, and then released and suppose that time is measured from the

instant the pendulum is released. These physical conditions mean in mathematical terms that $\theta = 0.1$ when $t = 0$ and that $\dot{\theta}$, which is the instantaneous
rate of change of θ with respect to t or what is called the *angular velocity*, is
0 when $t = 0$. If we substitute $\theta = 0.1$ and $t = 0$ in (66), we obtain

$$0.1 = A \sin 0 + B \cos 0$$

or

$$B = 0.1.$$

To use the initial conditions on the angular velocity, we first find $\dot{\theta}$. This is

$$\dot{\theta} = A\sqrt{\frac{32}{l}} \cos \sqrt{\frac{32}{l}}\, t - B\sqrt{\frac{32}{l}} \sin \sqrt{\frac{32}{l}}\, t.$$

Because $\dot{\theta} = 0$ when $t = 0$,

$$0 = A\sqrt{\frac{32}{l}} \cos 0 - B\sqrt{\frac{32}{l}} \sin 0.$$

Then

$$A = 0.$$

Thus the function which represents the motion in this case is

(70)
$$\theta = 0.1 \cos \sqrt{\frac{32}{l}}\, t.$$

Exercises

1. Given the equation $\ddot{y} = -ky$, write out at once the functional relation between
   y and t.   *Ans.* $y = A \sin \sqrt{k}t + B \cos \sqrt{k}t$.
2. Suppose that the bob of a pendulum is pulled to the right so that $\theta = 0.1$ and
   is then given an initial angular velocity of -0.05 rad/sec. Find the function
   relating θ and t.
3. Suppose that a pendulum is in the equilibrium position and is given an initial
   velocity of 0.1 rad/sec to the right. Find the function relating θ and t.

   $$\text{\textit{Ans.} } \theta = 0.1 \sqrt{\frac{l}{32}} \sin \sqrt{\frac{32}{l}}\, t.$$

4. What function relates the displacement s of the pendulum and time t?
5. Discuss the variation in the angular velocity of the pendulum motion whose
   equation is given in (70).
6. Suppose that the period of a pendulum is half of what you would like it to be.
   How would you change l to obtain the desired period?
7. How does the period of a pendulum depend on the mass of the bob?
8. Suppose that you wish to hit a target which moves like the bob of a pendulum.
   At what point in its path would you seek to hit it and why? *Ans.* When $v = 0$.

9. A pendulum oscillates in a vertical plane about a fixed horizontal axis O. From the equilibrium position to the position of maximum deflection of $\theta = \pi/16$ radians, it takes $\frac{2}{3}$ seconds.

(*a*) What is the equation of motion of the pendulum?

$$Ans. \ \theta = \frac{\pi}{16} \sin \frac{3}{4} \pi t.$$

(*b*) Where will the pendulum have its maximum angular velocity and what is it?

$$Ans. \ \dot{\theta}_{max} = \tfrac{3}{64} \, \pi^2/\text{sec}.$$

10. What is the linear velocity, that is, the velocity along the circular path, of the bob of the pendulum whose motion is described by (70)?

We consider next a third "application" of the trigonometric functions. Suppose that a straight tunnel is dug through the earth from point U to point V (Fig. 9-18). An object is placed just inside the tunnel at U and then released. What is its subsequent motion?

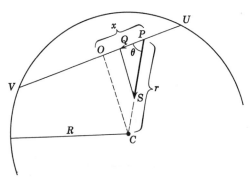

Figure 9-18

Of course, if the object is to move from U, some force must act on it to provide acceleration and thus permit it to gain velocity. This force is the force of gravity. The force of gravity of the entire earth acts differently on objects inside the earth than on objects outside. We recall that the usual formula for the force with which an object of mass M attracts another of mass m external to the first one is

(71)
$$F = \frac{GMm}{r^2}.$$

When the mass m is inside the earth, the earth's gravitational force is given by

(72)
$$F = \frac{GM}{R^3} mr$$

where G is the usual gravitational constant, M is the mass of the earth, R is the radius of the earth, m is the mass being attracted, and r is the distance of the mass m from the center of the earth. This force, too, acts to pull objects toward the center of the earth. As we shall see later (Chapter 16, Section 7), formula (72) is a consequence of (71). Since G, M, and R are constants, let us write for convenience

(73) $$F = kmr$$

where k is GM/R^3.

The object is free to move along the tunnel UV. Hence we should first determine how effective the force of gravity is along the tunnel. Suppose that the object of mass m is at P. The force of gravitation pulls it in the direction PC, where C is the center of the earth. Let PS represent the direction and magnitude of the force F given by (73). The effectiveness of this force in causing the object at P to move along the tunnel is the component of PS in the direction UV. As usual, to obtain this component we drop a perpendicular from S onto UV; this determines the point Q. The length PQ is the component of PS along UV, and PQ equals $|PS| \cos \theta$ where $|PS|$ is the magnitude of the vector PS and θ is the angle shown in Fig. 9-18.

To study the motion of the mass m along the tunnel, it is desirable to introduce coordinates that indicate its position. The most convenient way to do this is to choose the midpoint O of UV as the origin and let distances from O along UV be denoted by x, x being positive in the direction OU and negative in the direction OV.

When the object is at P, the distance PC is r and OP is x. From Fig. 9-15 it is at once evident that

$$\cos \theta = \frac{x}{r}.$$

Because PQ is $|PS| \cos \theta$ and, by (73), $|PS|$ is kmr, then $PQ = kmx$. However, PQ acts to decrease x. Hence we must write

$$PQ = -kmx.$$

Newton's second law of motion is, of course, $F = ma$. In the present case the acceleration is d^2x/dt^2 or $\ddot{x}$. Hence

$$m\ddot{x} = -kmx$$

or

(74) $$\ddot{x} = -kx.$$

What function relates x and t? We need but compare (74) with (51). The two are identical if k here replaces the k/m there. We know then from (52) that

(75) $$x = A \sin \sqrt{k}t + B \cos \sqrt{k}t.$$

We now fix A and B to meet the initial conditions of our present problem. At time $t = 0$ the object is at U. Suppose that the distance OU is x_0. Then at time $t = 0$, $x = x_0$. Because the object is just placed at U, it has no initial velocity; that is, at $t = 0$, $\dot{x}$ is 0. The first initial condition yields from (75)

$$x_0 = A \sin 0 + B \cos 0.$$

Hence

$$B = x_0.$$

From (75) we obtain by differentiation

$$\dot{x} = A\sqrt{k} \cos \sqrt{k}t - B\sqrt{k} \sin \sqrt{k}t.$$

The initial condition that $\dot{x} = 0$ when $t = 0$ yields

$$0 = A\sqrt{k} \cos 0 - B\sqrt{k} \sin 0,$$

so that

$$A = 0.$$

The resulting function is then

(76) $$x = x_0 \cos \sqrt{k}t.$$

The motion of the object placed at U is now clear. The object oscillates back and forth from U to V to U. We can even calculate the period of the motion. Formula (56) applied to the present case, where k replaces the k/m in (56), becomes

$$T = \frac{2\pi}{\sqrt{k}}.$$

However, $k = GM/R^3$ and, as we may recall from formula (65) of Chapter 6, $GM = 32R^2$. Hence $k = 32/R$. Then

(77) $$T = 2\pi\sqrt{\frac{R}{32}}.$$

If we use $4000 \cdot 5280$ for R, then $T = 5100$ seconds or 85 minutes.

Formulas (76) and (77) are interesting not only because of what they do say but also because of what they do not say. Neither involves a particular location for the tunnel UV. If we choose any two points on the earth's surface and connect them by a tunnel, the resulting motion is still described by (76) and the resulting period by (77). Formula (76) involves the length of the tunnel, because x_0 is half the length, but the period of the motion is the same no matter where the tunnel is located.

The subject of motion in a tunnel through the earth has an interesting variation. Instead of building a straight tunnel from U to V, we might fashion a curved tunnel (Fig. 9-19). Then the acceleration at the outset, being directed more toward the center of the earth, is greater and an object sliding along the tunnel acquires more velocity sooner than in a straight tunnel. Of course, the path is longer for a curved tunnel, and therefore the gain in velocity can be offset by the increased length of path. What path requires least time? This question cannot be answered by the methods of the ordinary calculus—it is a problem belonging to the subject of the calculus of variations—but the answer, which was supplied by Newton, is worth noting.

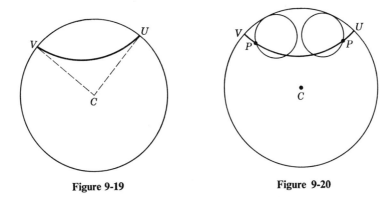

Figure 9-19   Figure 9-20

Newton showed that the best path is an arc of a hypocycloid joining U and V. A hypocycloid is the path traced by a definite point P of a small circle rolling on the inside of a larger circle (Fig. 9-20). In the case of a tunnel through the earth, the larger circle is the circumference of the earth and the size of the smaller circle depends on the location of U and V. The hypocycloid starts out with a vertical drop (that is, the tangent at U goes through the center of the earth), and so an object sliding along it has the maximum possible acceleration at the outset.

The following data give some idea of what can be gained by using a hypocycloidal path. Suppose that a straight tunnel is dug between New York and San Francisco. Along the surface of the earth the two cities are about 2,575 miles apart, but the tunnel would be 2,530 miles long (Fig. 9-21). At the midpoint the tunnel would be 206 miles below the surface; the maximum

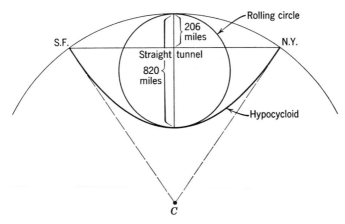

Figure 9-21

velocity acquired by the object, which would be at the midpoint, would be 1.57 mi/sec; and a one-way journey, according to (77), would take about $42\frac{1}{2}$ minutes. The hypocycloidal path would be 2940 miles long. At the midpoint the tunnel would be 820 miles below the surface; the velocity of the object at that point would be 3 mi/sec; and the one-way journey would take 26 minutes.

Exercises

1. How do you account physically for the fact that the period of the motion is the same whether the tunnel UV (Fig. 9-18) is a short one or even as long as the one through the center of the earth?

2. Suppose that a straight tunnel is bored from London to Paris, a distance of 200 miles, and an object is placed inside the tunnel at London. What is the maximum velocity that the object acquires during its journey?   *Ans.* $100\sqrt{k}$.

3. Suppose that an object is placed in the tunnel UV (Fig. 9-18) at a point two-thirds of the way from U to O and then released. What function describes its motion and what is the period of the motion?

$$\text{\textit{Ans.} If } OU = x_0, \text{ then } x = \frac{x_0}{3}\cos\sqrt{k}t; \quad 2\pi/\sqrt{k}.$$

4. Suppose that an object is placed at the center of the tunnel UV (Fig. 9-18) and then released. What is its subsequent motion?   *Ans.* No motion.

5. Suppose that an object is placed at any distance $\bar{x}$ from the center of the tunnel UV (Fig. 9-18) and then released. Graph the period of the motion as a function of $\bar{x}$. Of course, $\bar{x}$ can vary from $-x_0$ to x_0, where x_0, as in the text, is one half of UV. The results of Exercises 3 and 4 would come in handy here.

6. A circularly cylindrical block of wood 1 foot in diameter and weighing 100 pounds floats in water with its axis vertical (Fig. 9-22). The cylinder is depressed

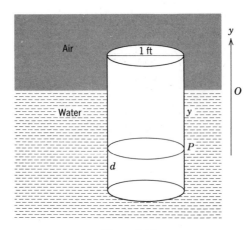

Figure 9-22

2 feet and then released. What function describes its subsequent motion? *Suggestion:* This problem involves Archimedes' principle which states that an object immersed (partly or entirely) in water is buoyed up by a force that is equal to the weight of the displaced water. Suppose that, when the cylinder just floats in the water, d feet of it are immersed (this is the equilibrium position). The volume of displaced water is then $\pi(\frac{1}{2})^2 d$ and, because water weighs 62.5 lb/cu ft, the weight of the displaced water is $\pi(\frac{1}{2})^2 d(62.5)$ pounds. Since the cylinder weighs 100 pounds (in air) and because it floats, the weight of the cylinder must just equal the weight of the displaced water. Then

(*a*) $100 = (\frac{1}{2})^2(62.5)\pi d = 15.6\pi d$.

Introduce a vertical coordinate axis and let the origin O be at the water's surface. Let the cylinder now be depressed, so that the point P which in the equilibrium position is at the surface is now y feet below. Then $d - y$ feet of its length are in water (y is positive upward). Gravity still exerts a force of 100 pounds downward, but the upward (buoyant) force of the displaced water is now $15.6\pi(d - y)$. The net force on the cylinder is now

(*b*) $15.6\pi(d - y) - 100$.

In view of (*a*), the net force is

(*c*) $-15.6\pi y$.

This net force causes acceleration and therefore an up and down motion of the bob. Now use Newton's second law of motion. Note that the mass of the cylinder is also 100 pounds and the net force of the water, which should be in poundals, is 32 times the quantity in (*c*).

Ans. The diff. equation is $100\ddot{y} = -32 \cdot 15.6\pi y$.

7. Suppose that a tunnel similar to that discussed in the text is dug through the moon. Given that the mass of the moon is $\frac{1}{81}$ of that of the earth, the radius of the moon is $\frac{3}{11}$ of that of the earth and the acceleration of gravity on the surface of the moon is $\frac{1}{6}$ that on the surface of the earth, if an object is placed at one end of the tunnel and released, what is the period of the motion in the tunnel?

Ans. $T = 6\sqrt{2}\pi/\sqrt{11k}$.

The applications that we have considered—the motion of a bob on a spring, the motion of a simple pendulum, and motion along a tunnel in the earth—illustrate some important applications of the calculus of trigonometric functions. But they also show something more. The same mathematical technique applies to a variety of different physical situations, so that if one masters the technique, he can immediately obtain insight into a variety of situations. In all of the above applications the fundamental physical fact, when expressed in mathematical terms, is that some function y of the independent variable x satisfies the equation

(78)
$$\frac{d^2 y}{dx^2} = -Ky$$

and, as we have seen, the function turns out to be of the form

(79)
$$y = A \sin \sqrt{K}x + B \cos \sqrt{K}x$$

or

(80) $$y = C \sin (\sqrt{K}x + \phi).$$

We then fix the constants A and B or the constants C and ϕ to suit particular conditions of the physical situation. Motions obeying the differential equation (78) or its consequence (79) are called *simple harmonic motions*.

Exercises

1. The amplitude of a body undergoing simple harmonic motion is a and its period is τ. Find its maximum velocity.   *Ans.* $2\pi a/\tau$.

2. The maximum velocity of a body undergoing simple harmonic motion is 2 ft/sec and its period is $\frac{1}{5}$ second. What is its amplitude?   *Ans.* $1/5\pi$ ft.

$$\frac{dy}{dx} = C\sqrt{K}\cos\left(\sqrt{K}x + \phi\right)$$

$$\frac{d^2y}{dx^2} = 0 = -CK\sin\left(\sqrt{K}\,x + \phi\right)$$

$$0 = -a\,\frac{2\pi}{\tau}\sin\,\sin\left(\frac{2\pi}{\tau} + \phi\right) \qquad \frac{2\pi}{\phi} = \tau$$

$$0 = \sin(---) \qquad\qquad \phi = \frac{2\pi}{\tau}$$

$$\therefore \sin = 1$$

$$v = -a\,\frac{2\pi}{\tau}$$

The Inverse Trigonometric Functions

1. The Notion of an Inverse Function. Functions are, of course, used to express relationships between variables, and it is helpful both from the standpoint of physical meaning and mathematical technique to designate one variable as the independent variable and the other as the dependent variable. Thus in studying the relation between the velocity of a body which is dropped near the surface of the earth and the time of fall, that is, the function $v = 32t$, it is usually desirable to regard the time as the independent variable and the velocity as the dependent variable. Certainly, to answer the question of what velocity is acquired in a given number of seconds of fall, the choice of t as the independent variable is helpful.

However, one may be interested in determining how many seconds are required for the velocity to reach 100 ft/sec, 200 ft/sec, etc. To answer this question it is more convenient to write the formula as $t = v/32$, substitute the given values of v, and then calculate t. That is, it is more convenient to regard v as the independent variable and t as the dependent variable. One says that $t = v/32$ is the *inverse function* of $v = 32t$.

Let us look at the concept of inverse function graphically. If we graph the independent variable along the horizontal axis and the dependent variable along the vertical axis, the graph of $v = 32t$ looks as shown in Fig. 10-1, and the graph of $t = v/32$ appears as in Fig. 10-2. Actually, either graph represents both the original function and its inverse. Just as we can choose a value of t, find the point on either graph that has this t-value, and then find the corresponding value of v, so we can choose a value of v, go over to the point on the graph having this v-value, and find the corresponding value of t.

As far as the basic relation between t and v is concerned, both functions $v = 32t$ and $t = v/32$ say the same thing and both graphs illustrate the same relation. The choice of one function and graph rather than the other is merely a matter of convenience in answering particular questions.

A slight difficulty arises when we consider such functions as

(1) $$d = \frac{v^2}{64}.$$

This function tells us the distance d that a dropped body has fallen when it

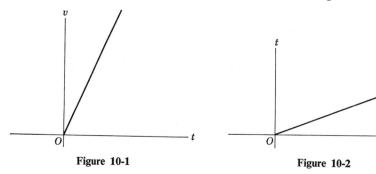

Figure 10-1   Figure 10-2

has acquired a given velocity v; thus, by the time the body has acquired a velocity of, say 10 ft/sec, it has fallen $\frac{25}{16}$ feet. We may be interested in how much velocity a body acquires in falling a given number of feet. In this case it is more convenient to express v as a function of d. If, however, we proceed to solve for v, we find, first, that

(2) $$v^2 = 64d.$$

This function is called multiple-valued, because to each value of d there are two values of v, namely,

(3) $$v = +8\sqrt{d} \quad \text{and} \quad v = -8\sqrt{d}.$$

We pointed out in Chapter 2 that the calculus cannot work effectively with multiple-valued functions. Given a value of d, we must know which value of v is to be taken or, if we want the instantaneous rate of change of v with respect to d, we must know which of the two single-valued functions in (3) we should differentiate. In simple falling-body problems, we would most likely use $v = 8\sqrt{d}$, because we usually take distance and velocity to be positive.

Which function is in the inverse function to $d = v^2/64$? Let us look at the situation graphically. The original function is shown in Fig. 10-3 and the multiple-valued function $v^2 = 64d$ is graphed in Fig. 10-4. In the domain 0

Figure 10-3   Figure 10-4

to $-\infty$ for v, the original function d increases from 0 to ∞. This behavior of v and d is also shown in the lower half of Fig. 10-4, although there d is the independent variable. As v varies from 0 to ∞ in the original function, d increases from 0 to ∞. This relation is shown in the upper half of Fig. 10-4 where, again, d is shown as the independent variable.

The graphs suggest the following. We can and do define the inverse function of $d = v^2/64$ to be the multiple-valued function $v^2 = 64d$ or $v = \pm 8\sqrt{d}$. This function is said to have two branches: $v = 8\sqrt{d}$ and $v = -8\sqrt{d}$. The first branch serves as the inverse function to $d = v^2/64$ when v runs from 0 to ∞, and the second branch serves as the inverse function to $d = v^2/64$ when v varies from $-\infty$ to 0.

In other words, when the original function rises and falls or falls and rises, we must break up the entire domain of the independent variable into separate domains, in each of which the function is continually increasing or continually decreasing. In each separate domain the original function has a distinct inverse function. The collection of separate inverse functions belongs to one multiple-valued function, just as $v = 8\sqrt{d}$ and $v = -8\sqrt{d}$ belong to $v^2 = 64d$. The multiple-valued function is the inverse function to the entire original function.

2. The Inverse Trigonometric Functions.   As in the case of the algebraic functions, it is often convenient to utilize the inverse functions of the trigonometric functions. Let us first acquire a little information about the inverse trigonometric functions.

We start with the original function $y = \sin x$. Its graph is repeated here (Fig. 10-5) for convenience. We now wish to define the inverse function of $y = \sin x$. By definition, this inverse function assigns to each value of y the

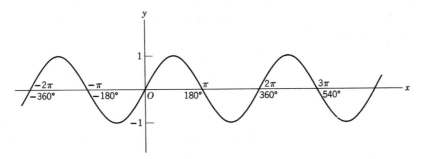

Figure 10-5

value or values of x which correspond to y in $y = \sin x$. We cannot solve $y = \sin x$ for x, at least not so as to express the solution in terms of available notation, and therefore we introduce a new one. We write

(4)
$$x = \sin^{-1} y.$$

This is read "x is the inverse sine function of y." This inverse function is multiple-valued, because to each value of y there is an infinite number of values of x. However, in view of what we pointed out about inverse functions for functions that increase and decrease, we may be able to break up the domain of x into a number of separate domains, so that in each domain there is just one x for a given y. Thus consider the domain $-\pi/2$ to $\pi/2$ for x; here $y = \sin x$ always increases, and we can now say that as y varies from -1 to 1, x varies from $-\pi/2$ to $\pi/2$. In other words, if we restrict x to the range $-\pi/2$ to $\pi/2$, there is only one branch of the inverse function. We can also limit x to the domain $\pi/2$ to $3\pi/2$; then we can say that as y varies from -1 to 1, x varies from $3\pi/2$ to $\pi/2$. This range of x-values furnishes another branch of the inverse function $x = \sin^{-1} y$.

Because we must work with single-valued functions, it is necessary to restrict the domain of x-values. When the x-range is $-\pi/2$ to $\pi/2$, the corresponding branch of (4) is called the principal branch and the values of x are called the principal values. When the function $x = \sin^{-1} y$ is used without mention of the range of x-values, it is understood that the principal branch is meant. Then for the principal branch of

$$x = \sin^{-1} y$$

as y varies from -1 to 1, x varies from $-\pi/2$ to $\pi/2$.

The notation $\sin^{-1}$ is both good and bad. It is suggested by the fact that the inverse of the number 2, say, is 2^{-1}. On the other hand, we do *not* mean $1/\sin y$ by $\sin^{-1} y$. Rather, we mean to denote the inverse function to $y = \sin x$ in the sense of inverse function already discussed. An alternative notation, $x = \arcsin y$, which is an abbreviation for x is the arc (or angle) whose sine is y, is really preferable to avoid ambiguity but takes more time and space to write. We use the notation in (4) because it is standard. If we really wish to denote $1/\sin y$ in terms of negative exponents, we write $(\sin y)^{-1}$ or $\csc y$.

The function (4) is the inverse function to $y = \sin x$. However, mathematicians like to use x for the independent variable and y for the dependent variable, so that we write

(5) $$y = \sin^{-1} x$$

for the inverse function. For the principal branch the domain of x is -1 to 1 and the range of y is $-\pi/2$ to $\pi/2$. Figure 10-6 shows the graph of $y = \sin^{-1} x$.

To each trigonometric function there is an inverse function, which is multiple-valued. The problem of choosing the principal branch is the same as for $y = \sin x$; that is, we must choose a domain of x in which the original function is either continually increasing or continually decreasing and define the principal branch for that domain of x. Let us dispose of the details.

$\sin^{-1} = \arcsin y$

Principal branch of
$y = \sin^{-1} x$
$-1 \le x \le +1$
$0 \le y \le \pi$

$-1 \le x \le +1$

principal branch
of $y = \sin^{-1} x$
$-1 \le x \le +1$
$-\dfrac{\pi}{2} \le y \le +\dfrac{\pi}{2}$

Figure 10-6. $y = \sin^{-1} x$.

For the function $y = \cos x$, which is illustrated in Figure 9-5, we can introduce the inverse function

$$x = \cos^{-1} y,$$

or, letting x denote the independent variable and y the dependent variable,

(6) $$y = \cos^{-1} x$$

Figure 10-7 illustrates this function. To choose a principal branch, we note that for $y = \cos x$, y decreases from 1 to -1 as x increases from 0 to π. In this domain of x-values there is only one value of x for each value of y. Hence the principal branch of $y = \cos^{-1} x$ is chosen to be from -1 to 1 for x and, as x varies from -1 to 1, y varies from π to 0. As in the case of (5), when no range of y is mentioned, the principal values are understood to be the ones to be used.

For the function $y = \tan x$, whose behavior is shown in Fig. 9-6, the inverse function is

$$x = \tan^{-1} y$$

or, using the more customary convention regarding independent and dependent variable,

(7) $$y = \tan^{-1} x.$$

The graph of this function is shown in Fig. 10-8. The principal branch is the one for which, as x varies from $-\infty$ to ∞, y varies from $-\pi/2$ to $\pi/2$.

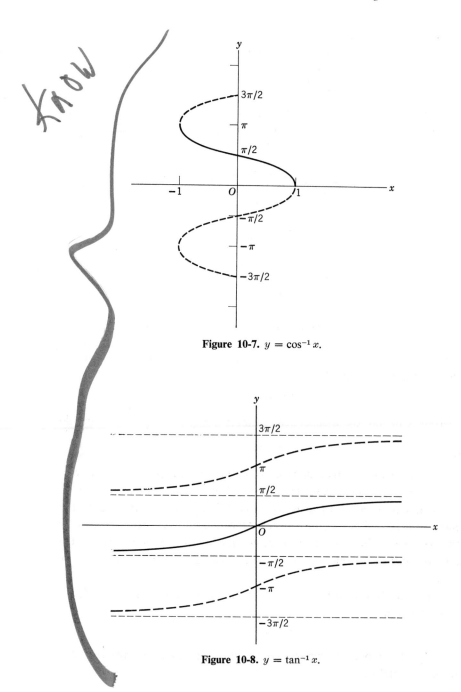

Figure 10-7. $y = \cos^{-1} x$.

Figure 10-8. $y = \tan^{-1} x$.

The function $y = \cot x$, which is graphed in Fig. 9-7, has as its inverse function

(8) $$y = \cot^{-1} x$$

whose graph is shown in Fig. 10-9. The principal branch is that for which, as x varies from $-\infty$ to ∞, y varies from π to 0.

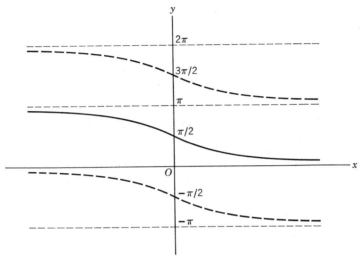

Figure 10-9. $y = \cot^{-1} x$.

The definition of the inverse function of $y = \sec x$ presents a bit of a problem. The inverse function

(9) $$y = \sec^{-1} x$$

is illustrated in Fig. 10-10. There is no way of selecting a principal branch so that, as x increases continuously from $-\infty$ to ∞, y will continually

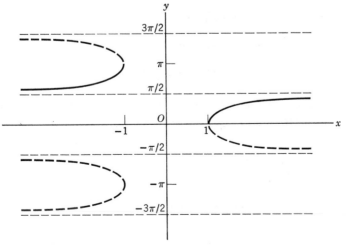

Figure 10-10. $y = \sec^{-1} x$.

increase or continually decrease. Guided by the desirable relation that

$$\sec^{-1} x = \cos^{-1}\left(\frac{1}{x}\right),$$

that is, that the angle whose secant is x equals the angle whose cosine is $1/x$, we define the principal branch of (9) to be the one for which, as x varies from $-\infty$ to -1, y varies from $\pi/2$ to π, and as x varies from 1 to ∞, y varies from 0 to $\pi/2$.

The same problem presents itself in defining the inverse function of $y = \csc x$. The graph of

(10) $y = \csc^{-1} x$

is shown in Fig. 10-11. There is no way of choosing a principal branch so that, as x varies from $-\infty$ to ∞, y will continually increase or continually

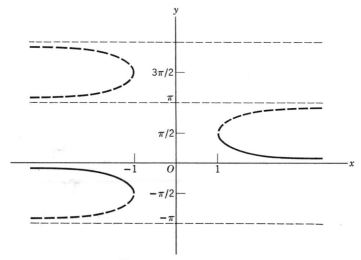

Figure 10-11. $y = \csc^{-1} x$.

decrease. Because it is desirable that

$$\csc^{-1} x = \sin^{-1}\left(\frac{1}{x}\right),$$

we define the principal branch to be the one for which, as x varies from $-\infty$ to -1, y varies from 0 to $-\pi/2$, and as x varies from 1 to ∞, y varies from $\pi/2$ to 0.

Exercises

1. What is the inverse function of the function $y = (x - 1)(x - 2)$?

$$Ans. \ x = \frac{3 + \sqrt{1 + 4y}}{2} \text{ and } x = \frac{3 - \sqrt{1 + 4y}}{2}.$$

Also, prob. 11, 16 p. 243

2. Find the values of:

(a) $\sin^{-1} 0.5$.　　　　　*Ans.* $\pi/6$.　　(e) $\tan^{-1}(-1)$.　　　*Ans.* $-\pi/4$.

(b) $\sin^{-1}(-0.5)$.　　　　　　　　　　　(f) $\sin^{-1}(-0.3)$.

(c) $\cos^{-1}(0.5)$.　　　　*Ans.* $\pi/3$.　　(g) $\cos^{-1}(0.7)$.　　　*Ans.* $45° 34'$.

(d) $\cos^{-1}(-0.5)$.　　　　　　　　　　(h) $\cos^{-1}(-1)$.

3. What is

(a) $\lim\limits_{x\to\infty} \tan^{-1} x$;　　*Ans.* $\pi/2$.　　(b) $\lim\limits_{x\to-\infty} \tan^{-1} x$?

4. Evaluate:

(a) $\sin(\sin^{-1} 0.5)$.　　　*Ans.* 0.5.　　(e) $\sin(\sec^{-1}(-2))$.　*Ans.* 0.8660.

(b) $\cos(\sin^{-1} 0.5)$.　　　　　　　　　(f) $\cos(\sec^{-1} 2)$.

(c) $\sec(\sin^{-1} 0.5)$.　　　*Ans.* 1.15.　　(g) $\sin(2 \sin^{-1} 0.5)$.　*Ans.* $\sqrt{3}/2$.

(d) $\sin(\sec^{-1} 2)$.　　　　　　　　　(h) $\cos(2 \sin^{-1} 1)$.

3. The Differentiation of the Inverse Trigonometric Functions.   The calculus is concerned with the use of derivatives and integrals of functions. Let us then consider the question, what is the derivative of $y = \sin^{-1} x$? Because this is a new type of function, it would be natural to try to find its derivative by applying the method of increments. This approach proves to be difficult. However, an inverse function is intimately related to its original function, and perhaps we can learn something about the derivative of the inverse function from that of the original function.

Let us consider

(11) $$y = \sin x$$

and its inverse function

(12) $$x = \sin^{-1} y.$$

In the present discussion of the inverse function we use y for the independent variable and x for the dependent variable to help keep in mind how these variables relate to the original function.

What we seek in terms of the notation in (12) is

$$\lim_{\Delta y \to 0} \frac{\Delta x}{\Delta y}$$

where Δy is the increment in y at some value y_0 and Δx is the corresponding increment in x at the value $x_0 = \sin^{-1} y_0$. Because Δx and Δy are numbers and not 0,

(13) $$\frac{\Delta x}{\Delta y} = \frac{1}{\dfrac{\Delta y}{\Delta x}}.$$

Moreover, as Δy approaches 0, Δx approaches 0 because they are related by the function (12) and, as in the case for any continuous function (see Chapter

6 Section 2), when the value $y_0 + \Delta y$ of the independent variable approaches y_0, the corresponding values $x_0 + \Delta x$ of the dependent variable approach x_0. However, the y and x in (12) are the same as the y and x in (11), and for (11) we know that as Δx approaches 0, Δy approaches 0. Hence to speak of Δy approaching 0 for the difference quotient $\Delta x/\Delta y$ is equivalent to speaking of Δx approaching 0 for the difference quotient $\Delta y/\Delta x$. Because the left and right sides of (13) are equal for all Δx and Δy as both of these approach 0 simultaneously,

$$(14) \qquad \lim_{\Delta y \to 0} \frac{\Delta x}{\Delta y} = \lim_{\Delta x \to 0} \frac{1}{\dfrac{\Delta y}{\Delta x}} .$$

Finding the limit of the right side of (14) calls for finding the limit of the quotient of two functions, namely, 1 and $\Delta y/\Delta x$. However, the limit of a quotient is the quotient of the limits provided that the limit of the denominator is not 0 (Chapter 6, Theorem 7). Hence

$$(15) \qquad \frac{dx}{dy} = \frac{1}{\dfrac{dy}{dx}}$$

or in the Newtonian notation

$$\dot{x} = \frac{1}{\dot{y}},$$

where, of course, $\dot{x}$ is the derivative of the inverse function and $\dot{y}$ is the derivative of the original function. Of course, (15) also holds for the derived functions wherever both exist.

This result is of general use in the calculus and we state it more formally for future reference.

Theorem: If y is a function of x and x as a function of y is the inverse function corresponding to some domain of x-values of the original function, then

$$(16) \qquad \dot{x} = \frac{1}{\dot{y}} \quad \text{or} \quad \frac{dx}{dy} = \frac{1}{\dfrac{dy}{dx}}$$

provided that $\dot{y}$ or dy/dx is not 0.

The statement of the result (16) in the Leibnizian notation can be misleading. It appears that all we are saying, for example, is that

$$\frac{7}{3} = \frac{1}{\dfrac{3}{7}}.$$

However, (16) is not that simple because neither dx/dy nor dy/dx is a quotient, and we must go through a proof involving limits, as we did, in order to establish (16). The Leibnizian notation may help us to remember the result,

$$\frac{dx}{dy} \neq \text{quotient, rather a limit of a quot}$$

as it does in the case of the chain rule, but it is deceptive as to the thought behind the symbols.

Let us see how this theorem can be used to find the derived functions of the inverse trigonometric functions. We return to (11) and (12), namely, $y = \sin x$ and its inverse function $x = \sin^{-1} y$. According to (16),

$$\frac{dx}{dy} = \frac{1}{\frac{dy}{dx}}.$$

The dy/dx refers to the derived function of the original function. Because this is $y = \sin x$, we have

$$\frac{dx}{dy} = \frac{1}{\cos x}.$$

The independent variable in the inverse function is y, and we want to express the derived function of the inverse function in terms of its independent variable, as we did for all other functions that we have studied. We know that

$$\frac{1}{\cos x} = \frac{1}{\pm\sqrt{1 - \sin^2 x}} = \frac{1}{\pm\sqrt{1 - y^2}}.$$

Thus we have the result in terms of y, but there is still the question of which sign to take for the radical. We must recall here that we chose as the principal branch of $x = \sin^{-1} y$ the range $-\pi/2$ to $\pi/2$ for x. In this interval $\cos x$ is always positive. We must then choose the positive radical. Our result is

$$\frac{dx}{dy} = \frac{1}{\sqrt{1 - y^2}}.$$

If we represent the independent variable in the inverse function by x and the dependent variable by y, our result can be formulated thus:

Theorem: If $y = \sin^{-1} x$, then in the interval $-\pi/2$ to $\pi/2$ for y

(17)
$$\frac{dy}{dx} = \frac{1}{\sqrt{1 - x^2}}.$$

Let us determine next the derived function of the inverse cosine function. The original function is $y = \cos x$, and we write the inverse function as $x = \cos^{-1} y$, again to keep the identities of the x's and y's clear. In view of (16),

$$\frac{dx}{dy} = \frac{1}{\frac{dy}{dx}} = -\frac{1}{\sin x}.$$

To express dx/dy in terms of the independent variable of the inverse function, we do much the same as we did in the case of the inverse sine function. Thus

$$-\frac{1}{\sin x} = -\frac{1}{\pm\sqrt{1 - \cos^2 x}} = -\frac{1}{\pm\sqrt{1 - y^2}}.$$

To determine which sign to use we note that the x-values of $y = \cos x$ are restricted to the interval 0 to π for the purpose of defining the principal branch of the inverse function. In this interval $\sin x$ is positive. Hence we must use the positive sign for the *radical*. Our result then is

$$\frac{dx}{dy} = -\frac{1}{\sqrt{1 - y^2}}.$$

If we represent the independent variable in the inverse function by x and the dependent variable by y, our result is the following:

Theorem: If $y = \cos^{-1} x$, then in the interval 0 to π for y

18)
$$\frac{dy}{dx} = -\frac{1}{\sqrt{1 - x^2}}.$$

We determine next the derived function of the inverse tangent function. The original function is $y = \tan x$ and the inverse function is $x = \tan^{-1} y$. By (16)

$$\frac{dx}{dy} = \frac{1}{\dfrac{dy}{dx}} = \frac{1}{\sec^2 x}.$$

To write the result in terms of the independent variable y of the inverse function, we note that

$$\frac{1}{\sec^2 x} = \frac{1}{1 + \tan^2 x} = \frac{1}{1 + y^2}.$$

Then

$$\frac{dx}{dy} = \frac{1}{1 + y^2}.$$

If we represent the independent variable in the inverse function by x and the dependent variable by y, we have the following theorem:

Theorem: If $y = \tan^{-1} x$, then

(19)
$$\frac{dy}{dx} = \frac{1}{1 + x^2}.$$

This result holds for every branch of $y = \tan^{-1} x$.

We should, of course, remember in connection with each differentiation formula that *the chain rule extends the scope of these formulas* immeasurably.

Thus suppose that we wish to find the derived function of

(20) $$y = \cos^{-1}\frac{1}{x}.$$

Before we differentiate, let us note the domain of values for x. Because the cosines of angles can vary only from -1 to $+1$, x in (20) can vary from $-\infty$ to -1 and from 1 to ∞. To use the chain rule, we let

$$u = \frac{1}{x}.$$

Then (20) becomes

$$y = \cos^{-1} u, \qquad u = \frac{1}{x}.$$

By the chain rule and by (18),

$$\frac{dy}{dx} = \frac{dy}{du} \cdot \frac{du}{dx} = -\frac{1}{\sqrt{1-u^2}} \cdot \frac{-1}{x^2} = \frac{1}{\sqrt{1-\left(\frac{1}{x}\right)^2}} \frac{1}{x^2}.$$

To simplify the result we can write first

$$\frac{dy}{dx} = \frac{1}{\sqrt{\dfrac{(x^2-1)}{x^2}}} \frac{1}{x^2}.$$

Now we must be careful. The radical must yield a positive quantity because this is what we have agreed to mean by it. When both roots are possible, we have written $\pm\sqrt{}$ and when the negative root is called for, we have written $-\sqrt{}$. Hence in taking the x^2 out of the radical we *cannot* write

$$\frac{dy}{dx} = \frac{1}{\dfrac{1}{x}\sqrt{x^2-1}} \frac{1}{x^2}$$

because when x is negative, as it can be, the value of the left factor is negative. Rather, we must write

$$\frac{dy}{dx} = \frac{1}{\dfrac{1}{|x|}\sqrt{x^2-1}} \frac{1}{x^2}.$$

To simplify further, we note that $1/x^2$ is always positive. $|x|$ is also always positive. Hence the division of $|x|$ into x^2 must yield $|x|$. Thus the final result is

(21) $$\frac{dy}{dx} = \frac{1}{|x|\sqrt{x^2-1}}.$$

For convenient reference we list our results on the differentiation of the inverse trigonometric functions. Although we did not derive the last three of these, the method of deriving them is exactly the same as that employed for the first three. *It is understood in these formulas that u is a function of x.*

(22)   If $y = \sin^{-1} u$, then $\dfrac{dy}{dx} = \dfrac{1}{\sqrt{1 - u^2}} \dfrac{du}{dx}$.

(23)   If $y = \cos^{-1} u$, then $\dfrac{dy}{dx} = -\dfrac{1}{\sqrt{1 - u^2}} \dfrac{du}{dx}$.

(24)   If $y = \tan^{-1} u$, then $\dfrac{dy}{dx} = \dfrac{1}{1 + u^2} \dfrac{du}{dx}$.

(25)   If $y = \cot^{-1} u$, then $\dfrac{dy}{dx} = -\dfrac{1}{1 + u^2} \dfrac{du}{dx}$.

(26)   If $y = \sec^{-1} u$, then $\dfrac{dy}{dx} = \pm\dfrac{1}{u\sqrt{u^2 - 1}} \dfrac{du}{dx}$.

The plus sign holds if $u > 1$ and the minus sign for $u < -1$. The formula presupposes that for $1 < u < \infty$, y runs from 0 to $\pi/2$ and for $-\infty < u < -1$, y runs from $\pi/2$ to π.

(27)   If $y = \csc^{-1} u$, then $\dfrac{dy}{dx} = \mp\dfrac{1}{u\sqrt{u^2 - 1}} \dfrac{du}{dx}$.

In this formula we use the upper sign if $u > 1$ and the lower sign if $u < -1$. The formula presupposes that for $-\infty < u < -1$, y runs from 0 to $-\pi/2$ and for $1 < u < \infty$, y runs from $\pi/2$ to 0.

Exercises

1. Deduce the derived function for $y = \cot^{-1} x$.
2. Differentiate each of the following functions:

(a) $y = \sin^{-1} \dfrac{x}{3}$.

Ans. $\dot{y} = \dfrac{1}{\sqrt{9 - x^2}}$.

(b) $y = \cos^{-1} x^2$.

(c) $y = \tan^{-1} \dfrac{1}{x}$.

Ans. $\dot{y} = -\dfrac{1}{x^2 + 1}$.

(d) $y = \sin^{-1} \dfrac{x - 1}{x}$.

(e) $y = (\sin^{-1} x)^2$.

Ans. $\dot{y} = 2(\sin^{-1} x)/\sqrt{1 - x^2}$.

(f) $y = \tan^{-1} \sqrt{x^2 + 1}$.

(g) $y = \sin^{-1} (\cos x)$.

Ans. $\dot{y} = 1$.

(h) $y = \tan^{-1} \sqrt{x - 1}$.

(i) $y = \sec^{-1} 3x$.

3. Draw the graph of $y = \cos^{-1}(1/x)$ and check whether (21) has the right sign.

4. Draw the graph of $y = \cos^{-1}(\sin x)$ as x varies from 0 to 2π.

5. Determine the point of inflection of

(a) $y = \sin^{-1} x$. *Ans.* $x = 0$. (c) $y = \tan^{-1} 2x$. *Ans.* $x = 0$.

(b) $y = \sin^{-1} 2x$.

6. If $x = g(y)$ is the inverse function of $y = f(x)$, determine whether $d^2y/dx^2 = 1/d^2x/dy^2$. *Suggestion:* Because $\dot{y}$ is a function of x and x is a function of y, differentiate $\dot{y} = 1/\dot{x}$ with respect to x, but use the chain rule on the right side.

Ans. $\ddot{y} = -\ddot{x}/\dot{x}^3$.

7. Evaluate

(a) $\lim\limits_{x \to 0} \dfrac{\tan^{-1} x}{x}$. *Ans.* 1. (b) $\lim\limits_{x \to 1} \dfrac{\tan^{-1} x - \dfrac{\pi}{4}}{x - 1}$. *Ans.* $\frac{1}{2}$.

8. A particle P moves (Fig. 10-12) along the line $x = a$ with constant speed v. If the line OP joining the particle to the origin makes an angle θ with the x-axis, find the angular velocity and angular acceleration of the line OP in terms of v, a, and θ. *Suggestion:* The problem calls for $\dot{\theta}$ and $\ddot{\theta}$. Introduce the quantity y shown in the figure and find an expression for θ.

$$\text{Ans. } \dot{\theta} = \frac{v}{a}\cos^2 \theta, \qquad \ddot{\theta} = -\frac{2v^2}{a^2}\sin \theta \cos^3 \theta.$$

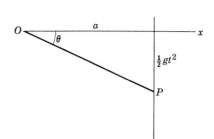

Figure 10-12   Figure 10-13

9. A particle P falls down (Fig. 10-13) the straight line $x = a$ starting from the axis of x. If its distance from the x-axis is $\frac{1}{2}gt^2$ when it has been moving t seconds, find the angular velocity and angular acceleration of the line OP. *Suggestion:* The problem calls for $\dot{\theta}$ and $\ddot{\theta}$. Find an expression for θ.

$$\text{Ans. } \dot{\theta} = \frac{4agt}{4a^2 + g^2t^4}, \qquad \ddot{\theta} = \frac{4ag(4a^2 - 3g^2t^4)}{(4a^2 + g^2t^4)^2}.$$

4. Integration Involving the Inverse Trigonometric Functions. Because new techniques of differentiation generally yield new techniques of integration, we should see to what extent our power to integrate is increased by formulas (22) to (27) for the inverse trigonometric functions. The surprising fact about the derived functions of the inverse trigonometric functions is that they do not involve trigonometric functions or their inverses but algebraic functions. We are enabled thereby to integrate new types of algebraic functions, and we shall examine one or two in a moment. The integration of functions that are themselves inverse trigonometric functions can be carried out but requires a technique that we shall study later, namely, integration by parts.

Let us note first the integration formulas that result from inverting the differentiation formulas (22) to (27). With the understanding that u is a function of x, we have

(28) $\quad$ if $\dfrac{dy}{dx} = \dfrac{1}{\sqrt{1-u^2}}\dfrac{du}{dx}$, then $y = \sin^{-1} u + C$;

(29) $\quad$ if $\dfrac{dy}{dx} = -\dfrac{1}{\sqrt{1-u^2}}\dfrac{du}{dx}$, then $y = \cos^{-1} u + C$;

(30) $\quad$ if $\dfrac{dy}{dx} = \dfrac{1}{1+u^2}\dfrac{du}{dx}$, then $y = \tan^{-1} u + C$;

(31) $\quad$ if $\dfrac{dy}{dx} = -\dfrac{1}{1+u^2}\dfrac{du}{dx}$, then $y = \cot^{-1} u + C$;

(32) $\quad$ if $\dfrac{dy}{dx} = \pm\dfrac{1}{u\sqrt{u^2-1}}\dfrac{du}{dx}$, then $y = \sec^{-1} u + C$;

(33) $\quad$ if $\dfrac{dy}{dx} = \mp\dfrac{1}{u\sqrt{u^2-1}}\dfrac{du}{dx}$, then $y = \csc^{-1} u + C$.

In the last two formulas the upper sign holds if $u > 1$ and the lower sign holds if $u < -1$.

As a simple application of these formulas, let us consider the problem of integrating

$$\dot{y} = \frac{2x}{\sqrt{1-x^4}}.$$

As we know from past work on differentiation, a given derived function may not seem to fall directly under one of the known integration formulas, but by the proper choice of u as a function of x it can be so handled. In the present case the $2x$ in the numerator suggests that it may play the role of du/dx, and therefore we choose $u = x^2$. Then

$$\frac{dy}{dx} = \frac{1}{\sqrt{1-u^2}}\frac{du}{dx}.$$

We may now state by virtue of (28) that

$$y = \sin^{-1} u + C = \sin^{-1} x^2 + C.$$

Let us consider another example of integration, namely, to find y as a function of x when

(34) $$\dot{y} = \frac{1}{\sqrt{a^2 - b^2 x^2}}.$$

Remember chair rule

We assume that a and b are positive. The troublesome quantity in this derived function is the a^2, for if it were just 1, we could let $u = bx$ and then manage to apply (28). However, a slight algebraic step removes the difficulty. We write

(35)
$$\dot{y} = \frac{1}{a\sqrt{1 - \dfrac{b^2}{a^2}x^2}}.$$

We would now like to let $u = bx/a$, but to use (28) we need the proper du/dx. This is b/a. Hence we write (35) as

$$\dot{y} = \frac{1}{b}\frac{1}{\sqrt{1 - \dfrac{b^2}{a^2}x^2}}\frac{b}{a}.$$

The factor $1/b$ can be ignored for the moment because it is a constant factor. With the understanding that $u = bx/a$,

$$\dot{y} = \frac{1}{b}\frac{1}{\sqrt{1 - u^2}}\frac{du}{dx}.$$

We may then apply (28) and state that

(36)
$$y = \frac{1}{b}\sin^{-1} u + C = \frac{1}{b}\sin^{-1}\frac{bx}{a} + C.$$

Exercises

1. Integrate the following derived functions:

(a) $\dot{y} = \dfrac{x}{\sqrt{1 - x^4}}.$

  Ans. $y = \frac{1}{2}\sin^{-1} x^2 + C.$

(b) $\dot{y} = \dfrac{x^2}{\sqrt{1 - x^6}}.$

  Ans. $y = \frac{1}{3}\sin^{-1} x^3 + C.$

(c) $\dot{y} = \dfrac{1}{a^2 + x^2}.$

  Ans. $y = \frac{1}{a}\tan^{-1}\frac{x}{a} + C.$

(d) $\dot{y} = \dfrac{1}{a^2 + b^2 x^2}.$

(e) $\dot{y} = \dfrac{1}{2x\sqrt{x^2 - 1}}.$

(f) $\dot{y} = \dfrac{1}{\sqrt{5 - 4x^2}}.$

  Ans. $y = \frac{1}{2}\sin^{-1}\frac{2x}{\sqrt{5}} + C.$

(g) $\dot{y} = \dfrac{1}{16 + 9x^2}.$

  Ans. $y = \frac{3}{4}\tan^{-1}\frac{3x}{4} + C.$

(h) $\dot{y} = \dfrac{1}{\sqrt{16 - 9x^2}}.$

  Ans. $y = \frac{1}{3}\sin^{-1}\frac{3x}{4} + C.$

(i) $\dot{y} = \dfrac{1}{2x\sqrt{4x^2 - 1}}.$

2. Find the area between the curve $y = 1/(9 + x^2)$, the x-axis, and the lines $x = \pm \sqrt{3}$.   *Ans. $\pi/9$.*

Our ability to integrate the types of algebraic expressions in formulas (28) to (33) empowers us to dispose of some unfinished business. In Chapter 9 we had occasion to integrate an equation of the form

(37) $$\ddot{y} = -Ky,$$

where $\ddot{y}$ is the second derivative of y with respect to t and K is positive. This equation arose in the motion of the bob on the spring, the motion of the pendulum, and the motion of an object along a tunnel through the earth. We found by mere trial that there is an integral of the form [see (52) of Chapter 9]

(38) $$y = A \sin \sqrt{K}\, t + B \cos \sqrt{K}\, t.$$

Of course, the K here is the quantity k/m in the reference just cited. The point we did not settle in the preceding chapter is that (38) is the *only* solution of (37). We shall now pursue two objectives. We shall find (38) by a systematic process and determine that (38) is indeed the only solution of (37).

Our first step is one we have made in other applications [see Chapter 7, step (70)]. We multiply both sides of (37) by $2\dot{y}$. Then

(39) $$2\dot{y}\ddot{y} = -2Ky\dot{y}.$$

Now y is some function of t (although we do not know the precise form of this function). For this function, no matter what it turns out to be, the left side of (39) and the right side are identical functions of t. Hence the integrals of these two functions can differ at most by a constant. Let us then integrate each side separately and equate the results.

On the left side we regard $\dot{y}$ as u. Then $\ddot{y} = du/dt$. We have then

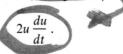

$$2u \frac{du}{dt}.$$

To integrate with respect to t, we have precisely the form required for the chain rule, namely, a function of u, multiplied by du/dt. According to the procedure for reversing the chain rule, we integrate the function of u with respect to u. The integral then is u^2 or $\dot{y}^2$.

On the right side we have a similar situation. If we think of y as u, again we have, apart from the constant factor $-2K$, a function of u multiplied by du/dt. Thus the chain rule can be applied. We integrate the function of u, which is u itself, with respect to u and obtain $u^2/2$, and in view of the factor $-2K$ we get $-Ku^2$ or $-Ky^2$.

We may therefore state that

(40) $$\dot{y}^2 = -Ky^2 + C.$$

We wish, however, to find y as a function of t. We have that

(41) $$\dot{y} = \pm\sqrt{C - Ky^2}.$$

Unfortunately, the right side is a function of y rather than of the independent variable t. Hence ordinary integration seems to be impossible. However, here we can use another device that is very much worth noting. The quantity $\dot{y}$ is, of course, dy/dt, and it refers to y as a function of t. We can, however, think of the *inverse* function where t is a function of y. Moreover, we know from (16) that

$$\frac{dt}{dy} = \frac{1}{\dfrac{dy}{dt}}.$$

Then we have from (41) that

(42) $$\frac{dt}{dy} = \pm\frac{1}{\sqrt{C - Ky^2}}.$$

Now that we have the derived function expressed as a function of the independent variable, there is some hope of carrying out the integration.

The right side of (42) is in the form of (34) if we think of a in (34) as $\sqrt{C}$ and b in (34) as $\sqrt{K}$. Hence in view of (36)

(43) $$t = \pm\frac{1}{\sqrt{K}}\sin^{-1}\frac{\sqrt{K}}{\sqrt{C}}y + D,$$

where D is another constant of integration. Because we want to obtain y as a function of t, we solve for y as follows. From (43)

$$\pm\sqrt{K}(t - D) = \sin^{-1}\frac{\sqrt{K}}{\sqrt{C}}y$$

or

$$\frac{\sqrt{K}}{\sqrt{C}}y = \sin\{\pm\sqrt{K}(t - D)\}$$

or

(44) $$y = \frac{\sqrt{C}}{\sqrt{K}}\sin\{\pm\sqrt{K}(t - D)\}.$$

This result can be written in a simpler form. The quantity K is given to start with. But C is a constant of integration and therefore is fixed by the initial conditions. We can replace $\sqrt{C}/\sqrt{K}$ by a new constant, say E, and fix it when the initial conditions are applied. The same argument applies to $\sqrt{K}\,D$, which we therefore replace by F. Then

$$y = \pm E\sin(\sqrt{K}\,t - F).$$

By agreeing that E can take on positive or negative values we eliminate the need to write the $+$ and $-$ signs in front, so that

$$(45) \qquad\qquad y = E \sin(\sqrt{K}\, t - F).$$

We have but to compare (45) with the result (55) of Chapter 9 to see that the result is the same. Of course, the quantity F here is the quantity $-\phi$ there. Because both are arbitrary and are fixed by initial conditions, it does not matter which way we write this constant.

Thus what we should see is that equation (37), which we integrated by trial and error in the preceding chapter, can be integrated by two successive antidifferentiation processes, and the two constants of integration, which we previously introduced on the trail-and-error basis, arise through the two successive antidifferentiations. Moreover, because two integrals of a given derived function can differ at most by a constant and we used this fact in integrating (37), the result (45) is unique.

5. Change of Variable in Integration. When we integrated the derived function

$$(46) \qquad\qquad \dot{y} = \frac{2x}{\sqrt{1 - x^4}}$$

in the preceding section, we found that by letting $u = x^2$ we could apply the chain rule. As a matter of fact, in all applications of the chain rule whether for differentiation or integration the key step is to let u be some function of x; then the rule itself says that

$$(47) \qquad\qquad \frac{dy}{dx} = \frac{dy}{du}\frac{du}{dx}.$$

We may characterize this process of introducing u by saying that we *substitute a new variable u for a function of x.*

In the integration of roots of algebraic expressions, of which (46) is typical, another process is often employed which is actually only a minor modification of the use of substitution but is sufficiently different to warrant attention and even to justify the introduction of a new name. We could illustrate this new process by working with the derived function in (46), but for the sake of variety let us integrate

$$(48) \qquad\qquad \dot{y} = \sqrt{a^2 - x^2}.$$

We note, first, that this derived function occurs neither among the formulas (28) to (33) nor among previously established formulas for integration.

The troublesome element in (48) is, of course, the presence of the square root, and therefore it seems wise to see what we can do about eliminating it. Toward this end the trigonometric functions seem to be helpful. Thus, suppose that we let

(49)
$$x = a \sin \theta$$

and substitute this value of x in (48). Then

(50)
$$\frac{dy}{dx} = \sqrt{a^2 - a^2 \sin^2 \theta} = a\sqrt{1 - \sin^2 \theta} = a \cos \theta.$$

We now have the derived function in a simpler form but as a function of θ.
Hence so far we cannot integrate with respect to x. However, the chain rule
states that

$$\frac{dy}{d\theta} = \frac{dy}{dx}\frac{dx}{d\theta}.$$

If we *multiply dy/dx* in (50) by $dx/d\theta$, we can state that the result is $dy/d\theta$.
Because, by (49),

$$\frac{dx}{d\theta} = a \cos \theta,$$

we have from (50)

$$\frac{dy}{d\theta} = a \cos \theta \cdot a \cos \theta = a^2 \cos^2 \theta.$$

To integrate $\cos^2 \theta$ the simplest method is to use the identity

$$\cos \theta = \pm\sqrt{\frac{1 + \cos 2\theta}{2}}.$$

Hence

$$\frac{dy}{d\theta} = \frac{a^2}{2} + \frac{a^2}{2} \cos 2\theta,$$

and therefore

(51)
$$y = \frac{a^2}{2}\theta + \frac{a^2}{4} \sin 2\theta + C.$$

We have the integral as a function of θ, whereas we were concerned with y
as a function of x. However, from (49) we obtain

$$\theta = \sin^{-1}\frac{x}{a}.$$

To replace θ by x in (51), we need also the value of $\sin 2\theta$. Because

$$\sin \theta = \frac{x}{a}$$

and

$$\sin 2\theta = 2 \sin \theta \cos \theta$$

or

$$\sin 2\theta = 2\frac{x}{a}\sqrt{1 - \frac{x^2}{a^2}} = 2\frac{x}{a^2}\sqrt{a^2 - x^2},$$

we have from (51) that

(52) $$y = \frac{a^2}{2} \sin^{-1} \frac{x}{a} + \frac{x}{2} \sqrt{a^2 - x^2} + C.$$

Thus we have integrated (48).

The key idea in the integration is to let

(53) $$x = a \sin \theta,$$

and then to replace x by this function of the new variable θ, whereas in the usual method of substitution we replace a function of x by u. The consequence as far as the use of the chain rule is concerned is the following. When using the method of substitution, we consider the derived function as it stands, and if by introducing u as a function of x we have the form

$$\frac{dy}{dx} = \frac{dy}{du} \frac{du}{dx},$$

we can state that

$$\frac{dy}{du} = f(u)$$

where $f(u)$ is that part of the derived function other than du/dx. However, when we replace x by a function of θ, we use the chain rule in the form

$$\frac{dy}{d\theta} = \frac{dy}{dx} \frac{dx}{d\theta}$$

and we *multiply* the given dy/dx by $dx/d\theta$ to get $dy/d\theta$.

For the sake of identification let us say that when we replace x by a function of θ, we make a *change of variable* and when we introduce u as a function of x, we use *substitution of a new variable*. These two methods, substitution and change of variable, are and are not essentially different. From the standpoint of what we do to carry out the integration, there is a difference. In substitution, after introducing u as a function x, we do *not* change the given derived function (except for algebraic steps that leave its value unchanged) and merely single out the dy/du. In change of variable, where x is replaced by a function of θ, we multiply dy/dx by $dx/d\theta$ to obtain $dy/d\theta$. From the standpoint of the underlying theory, the methods of substitution and change of variable are essentially the same. Both are applications of the chain rule.

There is one more point to note about the use of change of variable. We first obtained y in (51) as a function of θ and

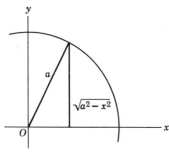

Figure 10-14

then, because θ is a function of x, we obtained y as a function of x in (52). However, suppose that we wish to find the area in the first quadrant (Fig. 10-14) bounded by the circle

$$x^2 + y^2 = a^2.$$

Because $\dot{A} = y$, our derived function is

$$\dot{A} = \sqrt{a^2 - x^2},$$

and according to (48) and (51)

(54)
$$A = \frac{a^2}{2} \theta + \frac{a^2}{2} \sin 2\theta.$$

We may think that we must reexpress A as a function of x and then substitute the end values for x in the function of x. However, we know that

$$x = a \sin \theta.$$

The end values for x are $x = 0$ and $x = a$. We can now argue that

$$\text{when } x = 0, \quad \theta = 0$$

and

$$\text{when } x = a, \quad \theta = \frac{\pi}{2}.$$

If we substitute $\pi/2$ for θ in (54), we obtain

$$A = \frac{a^2}{2} \cdot \frac{\pi}{2}.$$

If we substitute 0 for θ in (54), we obtain

$$A = 0.$$

Then the area in question is the difference in the two values of A or

$$A = \frac{\pi a^2}{4}.$$

We have, of course, ignored the constant of integration in (54) because it is canceled in the subtraction.

The point, then, of this calculation is that if we wish to evaluate the integral (54) at specific values of x, we do not need to reexpress the integral as a function of x; we find the values of θ corresponding to the values of x and use (54) directly.

Exercises

1. Integrate $\dot{y} = \sqrt{a^2 - x^2}$ by using the change of variable $x = a \cos \theta$.

$$Ans. \ y = -\frac{a^2}{2}\left(\cos^{-1}\frac{x}{a} - \frac{x\sqrt{1 - (x^2/a^2)}}{a}\right) + C.$$

2. Find the area in the first quadrant of the ellipse $(x^2/a^2) + (y^2/b^2) = 1$.

Ans. $\pi ab/4$.

3. Integrate by making a change of variable for x in terms of some appropriate function of θ:

(a) $\dot{y} = \dfrac{1}{\sqrt{9 - x^2}}$.

Ans. $y = -\cos^{-1}\dfrac{x}{3} + C$.

(b) $\dot{y} = \dfrac{1}{\sqrt{16 - 9x^2}}$.

(c) $\dot{y} = \dfrac{1}{16 + 9x^2}$.

Ans. $y = \dfrac{1}{12}\tan^{-1}\dfrac{3x}{4} + C$.

(d) $\dot{y} = \sqrt{9 - x^2}$.

(e) $\dot{y} = \dfrac{1}{(a^2 + x^2)^{3/2}}$.

Suggestion: Let $x = a \tan \theta$.

Ans. $y = \dfrac{x}{a^2\sqrt{a^2 + x^2}} + C$.

(f) $\dot{y} = \dfrac{1}{(a^2 - x^2)^{3/2}}$.

(g) $\dot{y} = \dfrac{x^2}{\sqrt{16 - x^2}}$.

Ans. $y = 8\sin^{-1}\dfrac{x}{4}$

$-\dfrac{x}{2}\sqrt{16 - x^2} + C$.

(h) $\dot{y} = \dfrac{x^2}{(25 - x^2)^{3/2}}$.

Ans. $\dfrac{x}{\sqrt{25 - x^2}} - \sin^{-1}\dfrac{x}{5} + C$.

(i) $\dot{y} = \dfrac{\sqrt{25 - x^2}}{x^2}$.

4. Calculate the area of the portion of the ellipse $9x^2 + 16y^2 = 144$ between the y-axis and $x = 2$.   *Ans.* $\pi + 3\sqrt{3}/2$.

There is one caution about integrating a function of x by introducing a new variable, whether by substitution or by change of variable. Suppose that we denote the new variable by t. *Then x must be a (continuous) single-valued function of t and dx/dt must also be continuous in the domain of t values that corresponds to the domain of x-values over which one wishes to consider the integral.* Let us see why this must be so by using a simple example. Suppose that we wish to calculate the area between $y = x^2 + 1$, $x = -1$, $x = 4$, and the x-axis (Fig. 10-15). This problem can be handled at once. We know that

(55) $$\dot{A} = x^2 + 1$$

so that

$$A = \dfrac{x^3}{3} + x.$$

We need not bother with the constant of integration, because in the method of finding areas we must only substitute 4 for x, then substitute -1 for x, and subtract the second result from the first. Thus

(56) $$A = \tfrac{64}{3} + 4 - (-\tfrac{1}{3} - 1) = \tfrac{80}{3}.$$

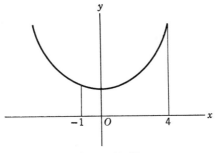

Figure 10-15

Suppose that we decide to perform the integration by introducing a new variable and that we use the change of variable $x = \sqrt{t}$. Then from (55)

$$\frac{dA}{dx} = t + 1.$$

However, by the chain rule

$$\frac{dA}{dt} = \frac{dA}{dx} \cdot \frac{dx}{dt} = (t + 1)(\tfrac{1}{2}t^{-\frac{1}{2}}) = \tfrac{1}{2}t^{\frac{1}{2}} + \tfrac{1}{2}t^{-\frac{1}{2}}.$$

We may integrate A with respect to t and obtain

(57) $$A = \tfrac{1}{3}t^{\frac{3}{2}} + t^{\frac{1}{2}}.$$

Now suppose that we decide to find the end values for t and use (57) to evaluate A. Because $t = x^2$, when $x = -1$, $t = 1$, and when $x = 4$, $t = 16$. Hence we substitute these values of t in (57). Then

(58) $$A = (\tfrac{1}{3} \cdot 16^{\frac{3}{2}} + 16^{\frac{1}{2}}) - (\tfrac{1}{3} \cdot 1^{\frac{3}{2}} + 1^{\frac{1}{2}}) = 24.$$

The result in (58) does not agree with that in (56), because the domain for the new variable t, namely from 1 to 16, does not correspond to the domain -1 to 4 for x. In fact, if we substitute 1 for t in $x = \sqrt{t}$, we obtain $+1$ for x and not -1.

Figures 10-16 and 10-17 tell the story. In the domain -1 to 0 for x, it is true that $t = x^2$, but the inverse function is $x = -\sqrt{t}$; in the domain 0 to 4 for x, the inverse function is $x = \sqrt{t}$. This point is precisely the one we made earlier in this chapter, namely, that if the original function falls and rises (is not monotonic), we must break it up into intervals in which it is monotonic and define a separate branch of the inverse function for each domain in which this original function is monotonic. In the range of -1 to 4 for x, x is not a single-valued function of t, as Fig. 10-17 shows.

Figure 10-16

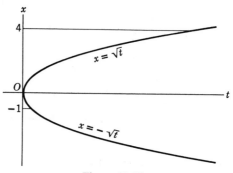

Figure 10-17

Let us redo the problem by change of variable, but this time let us be careful about the inverse functions. We can calculate the desired area by calculating the area from -1 to 0 for x and then from 0 to 4 for x (see Fig. 10-15). Now in any case

$$\dot{A} = x^2 + 1.$$

In the interval -1 to 0 for x, we use the change of variable $x = -\sqrt{t}$. Then

$$\frac{dA}{dx} = t + 1$$

and, as before,

$$\frac{dA}{dt} = \frac{dA}{dx} \cdot \frac{dx}{dt}.$$

But now

$$\frac{dx}{dt} = -\tfrac{1}{2}t^{-\frac{1}{2}}$$

so that

$$\frac{dA}{dt} = (t + 1)(-\tfrac{1}{2}t^{-\frac{1}{2}}).$$

Then

(59) $$A = -\tfrac{1}{3}t^{\frac{3}{2}} - t^{\frac{1}{2}}.$$

When $x = -1$, $t = 1$, and when $x = 0$, $t = 0$. If we substitute 0 for t, then 1 for t, and subtract the second result from the first, we obtain for this portion of the area

(60) $$A = 0 - (-\tfrac{1}{3} - 1) = \tfrac{4}{3}.$$

The calculation of the area from $x = 0$ to $x = 4$ is made by using the inverse function $x = \sqrt{t}$, which yields

(61) $$A = \tfrac{1}{3} \cdot 16^{\frac{2}{3}} + 16^{\frac{1}{2}} = \tfrac{76}{3}.$$

The sum of the results in (60) and (61) is $\tfrac{80}{3}$ as in (56).

6. Time of Motion Under Gravitational Attraction. The inverse trigonometric functions are helpful in carrying further the study of motion in a straight line caused by gravitational attraction. In Chapter 7, Section 8, we found the velocity which an object acquires when it starts from rest at a distance r_1 from the center of the earth (Fig. 10-18) and falls to a distance r. To produce this motion, gravity introduces an acceleration

$$a = -\frac{GM}{r^2},$$

where G is the gravitational constant, M is the mass of the earth, and r is the variable distance of the falling object from the center of the earth. The velocity v acquired by the object is given by

(62)
$$\frac{v^2}{2} = \frac{GM}{r} - \frac{GM}{r_1}.$$

Figure 10-18

We can now ask the question, how long does it take the object to fall from the distance r_1 to the distance r? There is a possibility of answering this question because v in (62) is dr/dt, and if we could find r as a function of t or t as a function of r we could calculate the time in question.

Equation (62) tells us that

$$v = \pm\sqrt{2GM} \, \sqrt{\frac{1}{r} - \frac{1}{r_1}}.$$

We shall use the minus sign because the acceleration downward was taken to be negative (in Chapter 7) and the velocity acquired then must also be negative. Also, because $v = dr/dt$, we have

$$\frac{dr}{dt} = -\sqrt{2GM} \, \sqrt{\frac{1}{r} - \frac{1}{r_1}}.$$

We again face the fact that the right side is a function of the dependent variable rather than of the independent variable, and therefore we work with t as a function of r. By using (16) we have

(63)
$$\frac{dt}{dr} = -\frac{1}{\sqrt{2GM}} \, \frac{1}{\sqrt{\dfrac{1}{r} - \dfrac{1}{r_1}}}.$$

The problem now is how to integrate the function of r on the right side. As it stands, there is no apparent antidifferentiation theorem that seems to be applicable. Let us try rewriting by combining the fractions in the radical. Then

$$\frac{dt}{dr} = -\frac{1}{\sqrt{2GM}} \, \sqrt{\frac{rr_1}{r_1 - r}}.$$

There is still no clearly applicable integration process, but the presence of the square root and the knowledge that some root expressions can be handled by a trigonometric change of variable suggest trying

$$(64) \qquad\qquad r = r_1 \sin^2 \theta.$$

Replacing r by its value in terms of θ gives

$$(65) \qquad \frac{dt}{dr} = -\frac{1}{\sqrt{2GM}} \frac{r_1 \sin \theta}{\sqrt{r_1} \cos \theta} = -\frac{\sqrt{r_1}}{\sqrt{2GM}} \frac{\sin \theta}{\cos \theta}.$$

In place of dt/dr we now want $dt/d\theta$ because the right side is a function of θ.

But

$$\frac{dt}{d\theta} = \frac{dt}{dr} \cdot \frac{dr}{d\theta}$$

and

$$\frac{dr}{d\theta} = 2r_1 \sin \theta \cos \theta.$$

If, therefore, we multiply the right side of (65) by $2r_1 \sin \theta \cos \theta$, the left side becomes $dt/d\theta$. That is,

$$\frac{dt}{d\theta} = -\frac{\sqrt{r_1}}{\sqrt{2GM}} \frac{\sin \theta}{\cos \theta} (2r_1 \sin \theta \cos \theta)$$

or

$$(66) \qquad\qquad \frac{dt}{d\theta} = -\frac{2}{\sqrt{2GM}} r_1^{3/2} \sin^2 \theta.$$

We now have an integrable function on the right. Then, using the formula $\sin^2 \theta = \frac{1}{2} - \frac{1}{2} \cos 2\theta$, we obtain

$$(67) \qquad\qquad t = -\frac{\sqrt{2}}{\sqrt{GM}} r_1^{3/2} \left(\frac{\theta}{2} - \frac{1}{4} \sin 2\theta \right) + C.$$

We can now replace θ by its value in terms of r by means of (64). According to (64),

$$\theta = \sin^{-1} \sqrt{\frac{r}{r_1}},$$

where we use the plus sign for the radical because r can vary only from r_1 to some lower value and so $\sin \theta$ can be taken to be positive for that range of r. Also,

$$\sin 2\theta = 2 \sin \theta \cos \theta,$$

and by using (64) and the relation $\cos \theta = \sqrt{1 - \sin^2 \theta}$,

$$\sin 2\theta = 2\sqrt{\frac{r}{r_1}} \sqrt{1 - \frac{r^2}{r_1^2}}.$$

If we substitute these values of θ and $\sin 2\theta$ in (67), we obtain

$$(68) \qquad t = -\frac{\sqrt{2}}{\sqrt{GM}} r_1^{3/2} \left(\frac{1}{2} \sin^{-1} \sqrt{\frac{r}{r_1}} - \frac{1}{2} \sqrt{\frac{r}{r_1}} \sqrt{1 - \frac{r^2}{r_1^2}} \right) + C.$$

Now let us agree to fix C so that $t = 0$ when $r = r_1$. Then

$$0 = - \frac{\sqrt{2}}{\sqrt{GM}} r_1^{3/2} \left(\frac{\pi}{4} \right) + C.$$

With this value of C,

(69) $\qquad t = - \frac{\sqrt{2}}{\sqrt{GM}} r_1^{3/2} \left(\frac{1}{2} \sin^{-1} \sqrt{\frac{r}{r_1}} - \frac{1}{2} \sqrt{\frac{r}{r_1}} \sqrt{1 - \frac{r^2}{r_1^2}} - \frac{\pi}{4} \right).$

This formula also presupposes that $v = 0$ when $r = r_1$ because this condition was used in Chapter 7, Section 8, to derive (62).

The result (69) is useful if we are interested in the functional relation between t and r. However, if we wish only to calculate the value of t for a specific motion from $r = r_1$ to $r = r_2$, say, we can work with t as a function of θ as given by (67). We would usually fix the constant of integration in (67) so that $t = 0$ when $r = r_1$, that is, when the object is at the point from which it starts to fall. However, when $r = r_1$, we see from (64) that $\sin^2 \theta = 1$ and $\theta = \pi/2$. We substitute 0 for t and $\pi/2$ for θ in (67) and obtain

(70) $\qquad 0 = - \frac{\sqrt{2}}{\sqrt{GM}} r_1^{3/2} \frac{\pi}{4} + C.$

Then using this value of C in (67) gives

(71) $\qquad t = - \frac{\sqrt{2}}{\sqrt{GM}} r_1^{3/2} \left(\frac{\theta}{2} - \frac{1}{4} \sin 2\theta - \frac{\pi}{4} \right).$

If we wish to calculate the time of fall to some point r_2, we must use (64) to calculate the corresponding value of θ and then substitute this value of θ in (71). Furthermore, if we wish to calculate the time of fall from a distance r_2 to a distance r_3, we can find the corresponding values of θ in (64) and substitute them in (67). The difference in the corresponding t-values is the answer. The constant of integration will be canceled in the calculation and therefore need not be determined.

Exercises

For convenient reference we list the following values: $G = 1.07 \cdot 10^{-9}$, $M = 13.1 \cdot 10^{24}$ pounds, $GM = 14 \cdot 10^{15}$, $R = 21 \cdot 10^6$ feet, $GM/R^2 = 32$ ft/sec².

1. Calculate the time required to reach the earth's surface by an object which is dropped from a height of 2000 miles above the earth's surface.

   Ans. 1250 sec approx.

2. Suppose that we use the acceleration of 32 ft/sec² in place of the true gravitational acceleration and that an object falls from a height of 2000 miles above the earth's surface. Will the object take more or less time to fall to the surface than if accelerated by the true acceleration? Calculate the time of fall and compare with the answer to Exercise 1.

3. Suppose that an object is shot up from the earth's surface to just reach a height of 100,000 feet, that is, so that its velocity is 0 when it reaches that height. Calculate the time of flight. *Ans. 98 sec approx.*

4. Find the time required for an object to reach the moon 240,000 miles away if the object is shot up with just enough velocity to reach the moon. The moon's gravitational attraction is not to be considered. *Ans. 4 days, 20 hours.*

5. Suppose that an object is shot up with the escape velocity. How long does it take to reach a height r. *Suggestion:* Neither formula (67) nor (69) is useful because if we let r_1 become infinite we cannot evaluate t. It is best to rederive the formula for velocity (in place of (62) so that the velocity is fixed at the surface of the earth). This was done in Exercise 15 of Chapter 7, Section 8. Now let the initial velocity at the surface of the earth become the escape velocity and derive an expression for the time of flight to height r. Fix the constant of integration so that $t = 0$ at the surface of the earth.

$$Ans. \ t = \frac{\sqrt{2}}{3\sqrt{GM}} r^{3/2} - \frac{\sqrt{2}}{3\sqrt{GM}} R^{3/2}.$$

6. Two identical spheres each of mass 2000 pounds and radius 1 foot are placed with their centers 6 feet apart. If they are attracted to each other by their mutual force of gravitation, how long will it take for them to come into contact? *Suggestion:* Because the same force acts on each sphere, they will meet halfway between the two points at which they started. Choose an origin there; let x be the variable distance from this origin to the center of either sphere, and let m be the mass of either sphere. Then the motion of each sphere is given by $m\ddot{x} = -Gm^2/4x^2$. When they come into contact, $x = 1$. You can use the theory of the text, except that $Gm/4$ replaces G there. *Ans. $t = 2$ hrs approx.*

7. A body of unit mass is attracted to a center by the gravitational force of a mass M located at the center. Suppose that the unit mass is released at infinity with 0 velocity. (This means that as the distance from the center becomes infinite, the velocity approaches 0.) Let us agree to measure time from the instant the body reaches the center.

(a) Find the formula for the distance from the center as a function of time. *Ans. $r = (-\frac{3}{2})^{2/3}(2GM)^{1/3}t^{2/3}$.*

(b) How long does it take the body to travel the infinite distance from infinity to the center? *Ans. ∞.*

(c) What is the velocity of the body when it reaches the center? *Ans. ∞.*

(d) Does the solution to (a) have mathematical meaning for positive t?

(e) What physical meaning does the solution to (a) have for positive t?

(handwritten at top) $y = \log a$ iff $x = a^y$

Logarithmic and Exponential Functions

(handwritten notes)

① $\log_a xy = \log_a x + \log_a y$

② $\log_a \frac{x}{y} = \log_a x - \log_a y$

③ $\log_a x^n = n \log_a x$

④ $\log_b x = \frac{\log_a x}{\log_a b} = \frac{\log_a x}{\log_a b}$

$\log x = a^x$

1. Introduction. Suppose that there are 100 bacteria in a culture and that each bacterium doubles on the average once every hour; then at the end of one hour there are 200 bacteria, at the end of two hours, 400, and so on. The number N of bacteria present after t hours might then be represented by the formula:

$$(1) \qquad\qquad N = 100 \cdot 2^t.$$

Of course, this formula is at best a mathematical idealization of the actual physical situation. For many values of t, N turns out to be a whole number plus a decimal. This decimal part has no physical significance. Apart from this fact, however, the formula appears to be a realistic description of the increase in the number of bacteria. It represents, as it should, a steady increase in the number N as t increases. Moreover, the formula gives the correct number at positive integral values of t. Of course, we do not know whether the formula describes accurately what "on the average" means, but we shall soon look into phenomena of this nature.

Formula (1) is an example of an exponential function. What characterizes exponential functions is that the independent variable, t in formula (1), occurs as an exponent, whereas, for example, in $y = x^n$ the independent variable is the base and the exponent n is constant. This example also shows that to represent some physical phenomena we seem to need a greater variety of functions than we have studied so far. The diversity of natural phenomena is almost endless, and mathematics must supply a multiplicity of types of functions to represent and deduce knowledge about these happenings. In this chapter we shall study exponential functions and the closely related logarithmic functions; we shall also see how useful they can be. We begin with logarithmic functions because it is more convenient to do so.

2. A Review of Logarithms. The concept of logarithms is probably not new, for the reader has undoubtedly met them in connection with arithmetic calculation. Nevertheless, let us review the essential facts. The ordinary or common logarithm of a number is the exponent to which 10 must be raised to obtain the number. Thus the logarithm of 100 is 2 because $100 = 10^2$ and the logarithm of 0.1 is -1 because $0.1 = 10^{-1}$. The annoying fact about logarithms is that most numbers do not have integral logarithms. Thus the logarithm of 5 (which for the present we take from a table) is 0.6990 because $5 = 10^{0.6990}$; that is, we would have to raise 10 to 699th power and then take the 1000th root of that power to obtain 5, a process that, fortunately, we do not have to carry out. (Actually, the logarithm is an infinite decimal and therefore the answer would not be exactly 5.)

Logarithms exist for all positive numbers.* For convenience in determining and calculating with logarithms, we first consider the logarithms of numbers between 1 and 10. These logarithms are always between 0 and 1. Then the whole-numbered part of the logarithm, called the characteristic, is 0 and the rest of it, called the mantissa, is some decimal. Thus for 5 the logarithm is 0.6990; here 0 is the characteristic and .6990 is the mantissa. Now let us consider a number greater than 10. Since

$$50 = 5 \cdot 10 = 10^{0.6990}\, 10^1 = 10^{1.6990},$$

the logarithm of 50 has the characteristic 1 and the mantissa .6990. Any number greater than 10 is some positive integral power of ten times a number between 1 and 10, and so the logarithm of that number has a positive integral part and a decimal, which is also the mantissa of the corresponding number between 1 and 10. As another example, because

$$325 = 3.25 \cdot 10^2$$

and because (again resorting to a table)

$$3.25 = 10^{0.5119},$$

$$325 = 10^{0.5119} \cdot 10^2 = 10^{2.5119}.$$

Thus the mantissa of 325 and 3.25 is the same, but the characteristic of 325 is 2, whereas that of 3.25 is 0.

For numbers between 0 and 1 it is still true that each is some power of 10 multiplied by a number between 1 and 10. Thus

$$0.325 = 3.25 \cdot 10^{-1}$$

and because

$$3.25 = 10^{0.5119},$$

it follows that

$$0.325 = 10^{0.5119} \cdot 10^{-1}.$$

But now we must be careful. The logarithm 0.5119 is a positive number, whereas the logarithm -1 is negative. For purposes of *arithmetic* it is better not to add these numbers and to write

$$0.325 = 10^{\bar{1}.5119}.$$

---

* There are logarithms for negative and even complex numbers, but they are not considered in elementary calculus.

By putting the minus sign over the 1 we indicate that only the 1 is negative. If we are not interested in using logarithms to do arithmetic, we can just as well calculate $-1 + 0.5119$, which is -0.4881, and write

$$0.325 = 10^{-0.4881}.$$

Then the logarithm of 0.325 is -0.4881, a negative number. Moreover, the closer a number is to 0, the more negative is its logarithm. For example, because

$$0.000001 = 10^{-6},$$

the logarithm of 0.000001 is -6.

We repeat that the numbers between 0 and 1 have negative logarithms and the closer the number is to 0 the more negative its logarithm. As the numbers increase from 1 onward, their logarithms are positive and increase. A graph (Fig. 11-1) shows how the logarithms of numbers increase with the numbers. The numbers from 0 on are plotted along the x-axis, and the y-value corresponding to each x-value is the logarithm of that x-value.

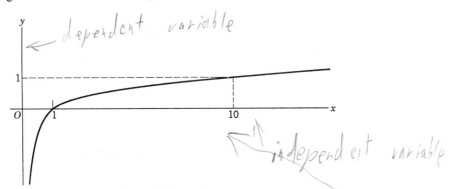

Figure 11-1. $y = \log_{10} x$.

The graph thrusts to the force what has been implicit in the subject of logarithms from the outset—there is a functional relation between numbers and their logarithms. We can, in fact, let x stand for any positive number and y for any logarithm. Then the formula

(2) $y = \log x$

represents the relation between numbers and their logarithms.

Review Exercises on Logarithms

1. Given $\log 7 = 0.8451$, find the following:

(a) $\log 70$.   *Ans.* 1.8451.   (d) $\log 0.07$.
(b) $\log 700$.   (e) $\log 0.007$.   *Ans.* $-3 + 0.8451$.
(c) $\log 0.7$.   *Ans.* $-1 + 0.8451$.

2. Given $\log 7 = 0.8451$ and $\log 9 = 0.9542$, find the following:

    (*a*) $\log 63$.   *Ans.* 1.7993.   (*d*) $\log 9^2 \cdot 7$.

    (*b*) $\log 7^3$.   (*e*) $\log 21$.

    (*c*) $\log (90/7)$.   *Ans.* 1.1091.

3. The Derived Functions of Logarithmic Functions.

In the calculus we are naturally interested in what we can do with the derivative and integral of the logarithmic function. Let us look first into the derivative. When we have no prior theorems to tell us how to differentiate a given function, we fall back on the definition of the derivative, which means applying the method of increments. At a value x_0 of x we have

$$(3) \qquad\qquad\qquad y_0 = \log x_0.$$

If x changes to the value $x_0 + \Delta x$, y changes to $y_0 + \Delta y$, and

$$(4) \qquad\qquad\qquad y_0 + \Delta y = \log (x_0 + \Delta x).$$

Then subtraction of (1) from (2) gives

$$\Delta y = \log (x_0 + \Delta x) - \log x_0,$$

and therefore

$$(5) \qquad\qquad\qquad \frac{\Delta y}{\Delta x} = \frac{\log (x_0 + \Delta x) - \log x_0}{\Delta x}.$$

We wish, of course, to find the limit of $\Delta y / \Delta x$ as Δx approaches 0. However, the limit of the quotient on the right side of (5) is not evident, and so we shall try to change the form of it in the hope that the limit may be more apparent. We shall use the fact that the logarithm of the quotient of two numbers is the logarithm of the numerator minus the logarithm of the denominator. If we first put the factor $1/\Delta x$ in (5) in front of the expression and then use the fact just cited, we obtain

$$(6) \qquad\qquad \frac{\Delta y}{\Delta x} = \frac{1}{\Delta x} \log \left(\frac{x_0 + \Delta x}{x_0} \right) = \frac{1}{\Delta x} \log \left(1 + \frac{\Delta x}{x_0} \right).$$

This form is not an improvement because as Δx approaches 0, the quantity in parentheses approaches 1, its logarithm approaches 0, and the entire right side approaches $0/0$. Let us try another transformation. Because the logarithm of a power is the exponent times the logarithm of the base (for example, $\log 9^3 = 3 \log 9$), we may write (6) as

$$(7) \qquad\qquad\qquad \frac{\Delta y}{\Delta x} = \log \left(1 + \frac{\Delta x}{x_0} \right)^{1/\Delta x}.$$

This form seems equally useless, for as Δx approaches 0, the quantity in parenthesis approaches 1 and the exponent becomes infinite; thus it is not at all clear what the entire power approaches.

We shall investigate the right side of (7). It is easier to do so after making the following change: we raise the number

$$\left(1 + \frac{\Delta x}{x_0}\right)^{1/\Delta x}$$

to the power x_0 and compensate by dividing the logarithm by x_0; that is,

(8)
$$\frac{\Delta y}{\Delta x} = \frac{1}{x_0} \log \left(1 + \frac{\Delta x}{x_0}\right)^{x_0/\Delta x}.$$

The point in making this change is that if we now let $\Delta x/x_0$ be t, we can consider the simpler expression

(9)
$$(1 + t)^{1/t}$$

and see what happens as t approaches 0. To get some idea of how this quantity varies with t, we do a little arithmetic. The results, which can be obtained by arithmetic but are more readily obtained by using logarithms, are

t	1	0.5	0.25	0.1	0.03	0.01	0.001	0.0001
$(1 + t)^{1/t}$	2	2.250	2.441	2.5	2.6786	2.7048	2.7169	2.7181

Because Δx may be negative as well as positive, we consider also some negative values of t. The results are

t	−0.01	−0.001	−0.0001
$(1 + t)^{1/t}$	2.7320	2.7196	2.7184

It seems from these tables that, as t approaches 0,

$$(1 + t)^{1/t}$$

approaches a definite number whose value to three decimal places is 2.718. Further calculations would show that there is an unending number of digits in the decimal part of the number, but that it does not become so large as 2.719 or less than 2.718. These calculations do not really prove that the expression (9) has a limit as t approaches 0, for there is a chance that for very small t the expression may, for example, suddenly start to increase rapidly and even become infinite. There is, however, a geometric argument that does convince us that (9) approaches a limit. The limit, if it exists, of $\Delta y/\Delta x$ in (8) is the derivative of $y = \log x$ and therefore is the slope of the curve in Fig. 11-1 at (x_0, y_0). However, the curve clearly has a definite slope at each point. Hence lim $\Delta y/\Delta x$ as Δx approaches 0 exists, and because $1/x_0$ is merely a constant factor

(10)
$$\lim_{t \to 0} (1 + t)^{1/t}$$

$$P = \lim_{t \to 0} (1 + t)^{\frac{1}{t}}$$

does exist. For the present we shall rely on this geometric argument (which is not a rigorous proof) to establish the fact that the limit in (10) does exist.

This limit has an unending number of digits in the decimal part, as, for example, $\sqrt{2}$ and π have. Because it is not possible to write out the exact number, it is designated by e in honor of the mathematician Leonhard Euler, who made fundamental contributions to the calculus and, for that matter, to all other branches of the mathematics and physics of the eighteenth century.

We may now return to (8). In view of the value of t, we can say that

(11)
$$\left(1 + \frac{\Delta x}{x_0}\right)^{x_0/\Delta x}$$

approaches e as Δx approaches 0. Then the logarithm of (11) should approach $\log e$ because, judging at least by the graph in Fig. 11-1, when x approaches a definite number, $\log x$ approaches the logarithm of that number. Then we have from (8)

(12)
$$\dot{y} = \lim_{x \to 0} \frac{\Delta y}{\Delta x} = \frac{1}{x_0} \log e.$$

We could use this result for the derivative of the logarithmic function. However, the quantity $\log e$, which means, of course, the logarithm of the number $2.718\ldots$, then always occurs as a multiplier of the essential quantity $1/x_0$. To avoid carrying this constant, $\log e$, it is customary in the calculus and in higher mathematics to introduce another system of logarithms. The usual or common system employs 10 as the base, and, as we know, the logarithm of any number is the exponent to which we must raise 10 so that the resulting power equals the number. Although 10 is indeed the best base for calculations with logarithms, it is possible to use other bases. In particular, it is possible to choose e itself as the base. In this natural or Naperian system the logarithm of a number is the exponent to which e must be raised so that the power equals the number. For example, it happens to be arithmetically correct that

$$10 = e^{2.3026}$$

(we give only four decimal places in the exponent). Then the logarithm of 10 to the base e is 2.3026, whereas the logarithm of 10 to the base 10 is 1. All of the theorems that we learn about logarithms to base 10 apply to logarithms to base e, because these theorems are really a translation of theorems on exponents. Thus the theorem that if a and b are positive numbers,

$$\log (ab) = \log a + \log b$$

holds for base e because, if we suppose that l_1 is the logarithm of a to the base e,

$$a = e^{l_1}.$$

Likewise, if l_2 is the logarithm of b to the base e,

$$b = e^{l_2}.$$

Then

$$ab = e^{l_1} \cdot e^{l_2} = e^{l_1 + l_2},$$

and therefore the logarithm of ab is the sum of the logarithms of a and b. Of course, the rules for finding the characteristic and mantissa of a logarithm are different for base e than for base 10.

How do we obtain the logarithms of numbers to base e? There is a very simple relation between the logarithms of numbers to base e and the logarithms of numbers to base 10. Suppose that N is any (positive) number and l is its logarithm to base e. This means that $N = e^l$. Suppose that m is the logarithm of N to the base 10. This means that $N = 10_m$. Then

$$e^l = 10^m.$$

Now let us take the logarithm to base e of both sides of this equality. Then

$$\log_e e^l = \log_e 10^m.$$

Because the logarithm of a power is the exponent times the logarithm of the base, we have

$$l \log_e e = m \log_e 10.$$

Now $\log_e e$ is 1 because $e^1 = e$. In view of the meanings of l and m, this equation says that

(13) $$\log_e N = \log_{10} N \cdot \log_e 10.$$

Equation (13) tells us that to obtain the logarithm of a number N to the base e we should take the logarithm of that number to base 10 and multiply it by the logarithm of 10 to base e. All we need, then, to obtain logarithms of numbers to base e is the constant factor $\log_e 10$ and an ordinary logarithm table.

How can we obtain $\log_e 10$? Suppose that we let N be e in (13). Then

(14) $$1 = \log_{10} e \cdot \log_e 10.$$

Thus $\log_e 10$ is $1/\log_{10} e$, and the latter can be found by using the ordinary logarithm tables. It turns out that

$$\log_e 10 = 2.3026.$$

Despite the fact that logarithms to base e can be calculated by using (13), tables of logarithms to base e have been made up and a brief one is appended to this book. Actually, logarithms to the base e are more readily calculated than common logarithms, and in modern times the latter are computed from the former. (See Chapter 20.)

$\log_e N = \log_{10} N \cdot \ln e$ ''

If we agree hereafter that by logarithms we mean logarithms to base e, our logarithm function is

(14) $$y = \log x, \qquad \dot{y} = \frac{1}{x} \log e$$

with base e understood (Fig. 11-2). Then (12) says, because $\log_e e = 1$, that

(15) $$\dot{y} = \frac{1}{x_0}. \qquad \therefore \ \dot{y} = \frac{1}{x_0}(1) = \frac{1}{x}$$

The derived function is, of course,

(16) $$\dot{y} = \frac{1}{x}.$$

We note for the logarithmic function, as for the inverse trignometric functions, that the derived function is an algebraic function.

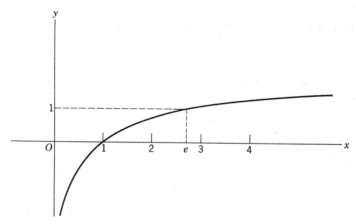

Figure 11-2. $y = \log_e x$.

Formula (16) also provides a new integral. Previously (Chapter 6, Section 7) we proved that if

$$\dot{y} = x^n,$$

then

(17) $$y = \frac{x^{n+1}}{n+1} + C$$

for all positive and negative integral and fractional values of n, except $n = -1$. When $n = -1$, we have formula (16), and we now see that when

(18) $$\dot{y} = \frac{1}{x}, \qquad y = x^{-1}$$

then

$$y = \frac{x^0}{0} + C$$

(19) $$y = \log x + C, \qquad x > 0.$$

Let us not forget the ubiquitous chain rule. If

$$y = \log u,$$

where u is a positive function of x, that is, a function whose values are positive, then

(20) $$\dot{y} = \frac{1}{u}\frac{du}{dx}.$$

Conversely, if (20) holds, then

(21) $$y = \log u + C, \qquad u > 0.$$

There is one point about the passage from (18) to (19) that is worthy of note. The function $\log x$ is defined or has meaning only for positive values of x. However, the derivative $\dot{y} = 1/x$ is defined for positive and negative values of x. If we were given $\dot{y} = 1/x$ and were interested in some application with negative values of x, could we still integrate this $\dot{y}$? The answer is yes, because if x stands for negative numbers, then $-x$ is positive. We can write

(22) $$\dot{y} = \frac{1}{x} = \frac{1}{-x}(-1).$$

We may now think of $-x$ as u, which meets the condition in (20) that u be positive, and the following factor, (-1) in (22), is du/dx. Hence

$$y = \log u + C$$

or

(23) $$y = \log(-x) + C \quad \text{for } x < 0.$$

We may also generalize the inverse of the chain rule. If

$$\dot{y} = \frac{1}{u}\frac{du}{dx}$$

when u is a negative function of x, then we may set

$$u = -v,$$

where v is a positive function of x. We have that

$$\frac{du}{dx} = -\frac{dv}{dx}.$$

Now

(24) $$\dot{y} = \frac{1}{u}\frac{du}{dx} = \frac{1}{-u}\left(-\frac{du}{dx}\right) = \frac{1}{v}\frac{dv}{dx}.$$

Because v is a positive function, we may use (21) and write

(25) $$y = \log v + C = \log(-u) + C \quad \text{for } u < 0.$$

Let us put these various results together for convenient reference.

(26)   If $y = \log x$, $x > 0$,   then $\dot{y} = 1/x$.

(27)   If $\dot{y} = 1/x$, then $y = \log x + C$ when $x > 0$ and $y = \log(-x) + C$
when $x < 0$.

We may express (27) in the form;

(28)   If $\dot{y} = 1/x$, $y = \log|x| + C$, whether x is positive or negative.

Next, if $y = \log u$ where u is a positive function of x, then

(29) $$\frac{dy}{dx} = \frac{1}{u}\frac{du}{dx}.$$

If

$$\frac{dy}{dx} = \frac{1}{u}\frac{du}{dx},$$

then

(30) $y = \log u + C$ for $u > 0$ and $y = \log(-u) + C$ for $u < 0$.

We may express (30) in the form: if for positive or negative u

$$\frac{dy}{dx} = \frac{1}{u}\frac{du}{dx},$$

then

(31) $$y = \log|u| + C,$$

Exercises

1. Estimate the integral part of the following:

(a) $\log_e 3$.   *Ans.* 1.   (c) $\log_e 100$.   *Ans.* 5.
(b) $\log_e 9$.   (d) $\log_e 1$.

2. Suppose that 2 is used as the base of a system of logarithms. What then are
the following:

(a) $\log 8$.   *Ans.* 3.   (c) $\log 1$.
(b) $\log 16$.   (d) $\log \frac{1}{2}$.   *Ans.* −1.

3. Look up in the table of natural logarithms the following quantities:

(a) $\log 3$.   *Ans.* 1.0986.   (d) $\log 0.1$.
(b) $\log 5$.   (e) $\log 0.5$.   *Ans.* −0.6931.
(c) $\log 10$.   *Ans.* 2.3026.

4. Find the numbers whose natural logarithms are the following:

(a) −0.5108.   (c) 3.4012.
(b) 0.7885.   *Ans.* 2.2.   (d) 4.3820.   *Ans.* 80.

$$Log_{(10)} N \cdot Log_{(a)} 10 = Log_{(a)} N$$

5. On the same set of axes sketch $y = \log_{10} x$ and $y = \log_e x$.

6. On the same set of axes sketch the following pairs of curves. Base e is understood.

(*a*) $y = \log x$ and $y = 3 \log x$.

(*b*) $y = \log x$ and $y = \log x + 2$.

(*c*) $y = \log x$ and $y = \log (x + 3)$.

(*d*) $y = \log x$ and $y = 3 \log (x + 2)$.

(*e*) $y = \log x$ and $y = \log (5 - x)$ for $x < 5$.

7. Given the function $y = \log_a x$, where the notation indicates the logarithm to base a, find $\dot{y}$. *Suggestion:* Rewrite $y = \log_a x$ in terms of $\log_e x$.

Ans. $\dot{y} = 1/x \log_e a$.

8. Find $\dot{y}$ when y has the following values:

(*a*) $y = \log x^2$.   *Ans.* $\dot{y} = 2/x$.

(*b*) $y = (\log x)^2$.

(*c*) $y = \log \dfrac{x}{1 + x}$.

Ans. $\dot{y} = 1/(x + x^2)$.

(*d*) $y = \log \sin x$.

(*e*) $y = \log (x^2 + 3x)$.

Ans. $\dot{y} = \dfrac{2x + 3}{x^2 + 3x}$.

(*f*) $y = x \log x$.

(*g*) $y = x \log x - x$.

Ans. $\dot{y} = \log x$.

(*h*) $y = \dfrac{\log x}{x}$.

(*i*) $y = \log (\log x)$.

Ans. $\dot{y} = 1/x \log x$.

9. Is there something especially worth noting in the result of Exercise 8(*g*)?

10. Find y when $\dot{y}$ has the following values:

(*a*) $\dot{y} = \dfrac{1}{3x}$.

Ans. $y = \frac{1}{3} \log x + C$.

(*b*) $\dot{y} = \dfrac{1}{x + 2}$.

(*c*) $\dot{y} = \dfrac{2x}{x^2 + 1}$.

Ans. $y = \log (x^2 + 1) + C$.

(*d*) $\dot{y} = \dfrac{x}{x^2 + 1}$.

(*e*) $\dot{y} = \dfrac{x - 3}{x^2 - 6x + 10}$.

Ans. $y = \frac{1}{2} \log (x^2 - 6x + 10) + C$.

(*f*) $\dot{y} = \dfrac{\cos x}{\sin x}$.

Ans. $y = \log |\sin x| + C$.

(*g*) $\dot{y} = \dfrac{\sin x}{\cos x}$.

Ans. $y = -\log |\cos x| + C$.

(*h*) $\dot{y} = \tan x$.

(*i*) $\dot{y} = \cot x$.

Ans. $y = \log |\sin x| + C$.

(*j*) $\dot{y} = \dfrac{\sin x}{1 - \cos x}$.

(*k*) $\dot{y} = \dfrac{\sec^2 x}{\tan x}$.

Ans. $y = \log |\tan x| + C$.

(*l*) $\dot{y} = \dfrac{1}{x \log x}$.

11. Find the area under the curve $y = 1/x$ and from $x = 1$ to $x = 10$.   *Ans.* 2.3026.

12. Show by mathematical induction that

$$\frac{d^n}{dx^n} \log x = (-1)^{n-1} \frac{(n-1)!}{x^n}.$$

The left-hand side means the nth derivative of $\log x$ and $(n-1)!$ means $1 \cdot 2 \cdot 3 \cdots (n-1)$.

13. Evaluate $\displaystyle\lim_{x \to 1} \frac{\log x}{x-1}$.   *Ans.* 1.

4. Exponential Functions and Their Derived Functions. We have often converted from statements about logarithms to statements about exponents. It is apparent therefore that exponential functions are closely related to logarithmic functions. In fact, the statement

(32) $y = \log x$ $\{ x = e^y$

means

(33) $x = e^y.$

Because the same x and y are involved in (32) and (33) but (33) expresses the relation with y as the independent variable, (33) is the inverse function of (32). A glance at Fig. 11-2 shows that there is a unique x for each y, so that we do not have the problem of multiple values. If we write x for the independent and y for the dependent variable, the exponential function is

(34) $y = e^x;$

its graph is shown in Fig. 11-3. This graph, of course, is only Fig. 11-2 with the x- and y-axes interchanged.

To find the value of y in (34) for various values of x we could work backwards in the table of natural logarithms; that is, because (34) says that x is

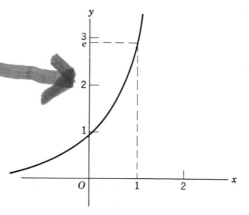

Figure 11-3. $y = e^x$.

the natural logarithm of y, we could look up the x-value in the logarithm table and find the number, the y-value, which has that logarithm. However, because the exponential function is widely used, a separate table of e^x and even e^{-x}-values has been prepared and a brief one is included in the Appendix to this book.

Exercises

1. On the same set of axes sketch each of the following pairs of curves:

(a) $y = e^x$ and $y = 3e^x$.

(b) $y = e^x$ and $y = e^{-x}$.

(c) $y = e^x$ and $y = e^{(x+2)}$.

(d) $y = e^x$ and $y = e^x + 2$.

(e) $y = e^x$ and $y = x + e^x$.

(f) $y = e^x$ and $y = e^{3x}$.

(g) $y = e^x$ and $y = e^{-3x}$.

The calculus is, of course, concerned with differentiation and integration. Let us see what these processes amount to for exponential functions. Because the basic exponential function is the inverse of the basic logarithmic function and because we have a theorem on the derivative of inverse functions, let us approach the derivative of the basic exponential function in this way. To keep the relation between x and y clear we write the original function as

$$(35) \qquad y = \log x$$

and the inverse function as

$$(36) \qquad x = e^y.$$

We know from the theorem on the derived function of an inverse function that

$$\frac{dx}{dy} = \frac{1}{\dfrac{dy}{dx}}.$$

Since the derived function of (35) is $1/x$,

$$\frac{dx}{dy} = \frac{1}{1/x} = x = e^y.$$

If now we write the inverse function with y as the dependent variable and x as the independent one, we have the following result. If

$$y = e^x,$$

then

$$(37) \qquad \dot{y} = e^x.$$

Peculiarly, the derivative of e^x is e^x.

$y = a^y$

$\dot{y} = a^y \log_e a \, \dfrac{dy}{dx}$

deriv. of $e^x = e^x$

Of course, the chain rule helps us to extend the utility of the result (37). If $y = e^u$, where u is any function of x, then

(38)
$$\frac{dy}{dx} = e^u \frac{du}{dx}.$$

Thus we can now differentiate a variety of exponential functions.

We also have at once the integration formulas:

(39)   if $\dot{y} = e^x$ then $y = e^x + C$

and

(40)   if $\dot{y} = e^u \frac{du}{dx}$ then $y = e^u + C.$

To apply (40) we can proceed as follows. Suppose that

(41)
$$\dot{y} = xe^{-x^2}.$$

If we let $u = -x^2$, then $du/dx = -2x$. We rewrite (41) as

$$\frac{dy}{dx} = -\tfrac{1}{2}e^{-x^2}(-2x).$$

With our choice of u

$$\frac{dy}{dx} = -\tfrac{1}{2}e^u \frac{du}{dx}.$$

Apart from the constant factor we may say that $y = e^u + C$ and, because a constant factor also multiplies the integral,

$$y = -\tfrac{1}{2}e^u + C = -\tfrac{1}{2}e^{-x^2} + C.$$

Exercises

1. Find $\dot{y}$ when y has the following values:

(a) $y = e^{x^2}$.   *Ans.* $\dot{y} = 2xe^{x^2}$.

(b) $y = e^{-2x}$.

(c) $y = e^{-1/x}$.

             Ans. $\dot{y} = (1/x^2)e^{-1/x}$.

(d) $y = e^{\sin x}$.

(e) $y = e^x \log x$.

(f) $y = x^2 e^{-x}$.

        Ans. $\dot{y} = (2x - x^2)e^{-x}$.

(g) $y = e^{-x} \cos 2x$.

(h) $y = (e^x)^2$.   *Ans.* $\dot{y} = 2e^{2x}$.

(i) $y = \dfrac{e^x - e^{-x}}{e^x + e^{-x}}$.

(j) $y = \log \dfrac{e^x}{1 + e^x}$.

        Ans. $\dot{y} = 1/(1 + e^x)$.

2. Find the slope of $y = e^x$ at $x = 0$.

3. Graph the function $y = e^{-x^2}$.

4. Find y when $\dot{y}$ has the following values:

(a) $\dot{y} = e^{-x}$. *Ans.* $y = -e^{-x} + C$.

(b) $\dot{y} = xe^{x^2}$.

(c) $\dot{y} = e^{\sin x} \cos x$.

       Ans. $y = e^{\sin x} + C$.

(d) $\dot{y} = \dfrac{e^{-1/x}}{x^2}$.

5. Graph the function $y = e^{-x}$.

6. Graph the function $y = e^{-x} \sin x$.

7. Show that if a phenomenon obeys the law $y = e^{kx}$, then for successive values of x that are in arithmetic progression the corresponding values of y are in geometric progression. *Suggestion:* Suppose that the successive values of x are $0, h, 2h, \ldots$, and calculate the corresponding values of y.

8. Evaluate $\lim\limits_{h \to 0} \dfrac{e^h - 1}{h}$.

       Ans. 1.

9. Find y when $\dot{y}$ has the following values:

(a) $\dot{y} = \dfrac{e^x - e^{-x}}{e^x + e^{-x}}$.

       Ans. $y = \log(e^x + e^{-x})$.

(b) $\dot{y} = \dfrac{e^{2x} - 1}{e^{2x} + 1}$.

(c) $\dot{y} = \dfrac{e^{2x}}{1 + e^{2x}}$.

       Ans. $y = \frac{1}{2} \log(1 + e^{2x})$.

10. Show that $y = De^{kx}$ satisfies the equation $\dot{y} = ky$.

5. *Problems of Growth and Decay.* One class of applications employing the exponential and logarithmic functions deals with quantities that increase or decrease continuously at a rate that is some constant times the amount present at any time. Thus the temperature in a steel bar may decrease at any instant at a rate of 0.1 per minute times the actual temperature at that instant. Such rates of change are instantaneous rates, and therefore the calculus is involved. We are already accustomed to the notion of an instantaneous rate of change and the idea itself may no longer disturb us, but the notion of an instantaneous rate that is some constant times the amount already present calls for an understanding of the significance of the constant that may not be intuitively apparent.

Let us therefore begin with a more familiar situation. Suppose that we deposit 1 dollar in a bank that pays 4 per cent interest per year and compounds the interest annually. This means that the bank adds 4 cents to the account at the end of the first year. Then the total amount to the credit of the depositor at that time is 1.04. At the end of the second year the bank pays 4 per cent interest on $1.04. Hence the amount at the end of the second year is

$$1.04 + (1.04)(0.04) = 1.04(1 + 0.04) = (1.04)^2.$$

At the end of the third year the bank pays 4 per cent on the amount present, namely $(1.04)^2$. Hence the amount at the end of the third year is

$$(1.04)^2 + (1.04)^2(0.04) = (1.04)^3.$$

At the end of n years the amount A accumulated is

(42) $$A = (1.04)^n.$$

We should note that under annual compound interest the bank pays interest on the *amount present*, but it pays this interest once a year; the rate of 0.04 is *not* applied continuously to the amount present. Moreover, if formula (42) is to fit the actual situation, the values of n must be positive integers.

Now suppose that the bank pays 4 per cent per year compounded quarterly. This means that the annual rate is divided by 4 and the interest of 1 per cent is paid at the end of each quarter year on the amount present at that time. The amount accumulated at the end of n years is readily calculated by the same argument that led to (42), except that now the interest rate is $0.04/4$ and the number of times it is compounded is $4n$. Hence the amount accumulated at the end of n years is

(43) $$A = \left(1 + \frac{0.04}{4}\right)^{4n}.$$

If, instead of quarterly, the interest is compounded r times a year at the rate of 4 per cent per year, the amount accumulated at the end of n years is

(44) $$A = \left(1 + \frac{0.04}{r}\right)^{rn}.$$

We now ask the seemingly pointless question: suppose that r becomes infinite, that is, suppose that the interest is compounded *continuously* at the rate of 4 per cent per year; how much money is accumulated at the end of n years? What we want is the value of A in (44) as r becomes infinite. We can write (44) in the form

$$A = \left[\left(1 + \frac{0.04}{r}\right)^{r/0.04}\right]^{0.04n}.$$

If we let $0.04/r$ be t, then the quantity in the brackets looks familiar; in fact, it is what we encountered in (9), where $t = 0.04/r$. Because r becoming infinite is equivalent to t approaching 0, we have that

$$\lim_{r \to \infty}\left[\left(1 + \frac{0.04}{r}\right)^{r/0.04}\right]^{0.04n} = \lim_{t \to 0}[(1 + t)^{1/t}]^{0.04n} = e^{0.04n}.$$

Then

(45) $$A = e^{0.04n}$$

There are several features of this result that warrant attention. First, in formula (42), n is a number of years but limited to a positive integer (or zero).

In (43) n is still a number of years but, because the formula represents quarterly compounding, it is logical to ask how much money is accumulated at the end of 6 quarters for example. In this case n is one and one half years or $\frac{3}{2}$. In other words, n can take on values such as $\frac{1}{4}$, $\frac{2}{4}$, and $\frac{3}{4}$. For the case of compounding r times a year, when (44) obtains, it is logical to ask how much money is accumulated in any number of intervals. Thus if r were 13, and we wanted to know how much money accumulated after 16 intervals, we would let n be 16/13. The permissible values of n, in other words, are $m/13$ where m is any positive interger. In the case of (45), where the money is compounded continuously, it is logical to ask how much money is accumulated at any time. Hence n can be any positive real number. To emphasize the fact that n can now stand for any interval of time, we write (45) as

(46)
$$A = e^{0.04t}.$$

The next point to note about (46) is the rather surprising result that 1 dollar bearing interest at the rate of 4 per cent per year but compounded *continuously* throughout the year amounts to $e^{0.04}$ at the end of 1 year. The table of the exponential function shows that $e^{0.04} = 1.0408$. Hence 1 dollar invested at the rate of 4 per cent per year compounded continuously produces 1.0408. This amount is not much more than 1.04 but, of course, if 1 million dollars is so invested, the return is $1,040,800 in 1 year instead of $1,040,000, and the difference between 4 per cent per year compounded only at the end of the year and 4 per cent per year compounded continuously is $800. Moreover, if the million dollars is left to accumulate interest for 10 years at the rate of 4 per cent per year compounded continuously, it amounts to

$$1 \cdot 10^6 \, e^{0.04(10)},$$

and because $e^{0.4}$ is 1.4918, the amount accumulated is $1,491,800, whereas if the interest were 4 per cent per year compounded annually for 10 years the amount accumulated, according to (42), would be

$$1 \cdot 10^6 (1.04)^{10}$$

or $1,480,244.

Let us return to reality. The most important point about the above discussion is that continuous compounding of interest at the rate of 0.04 per year is an example of the phenomenon in which a quantity changes continuously at a rate that is applied constantly to the amount present at any instant. Moreover, a rate of 0.04 *per year applied continuously* to the amount present is equivalent to the rate of 0.0408 applied at the end of each year

Let us now look at the problem of continuous compounding of interest in another way. To say that interest is continuously compounded means that at any instant of time the interest is being applied to the amount present. If A is the amount present at any instant, the amount that is added in time Δt, if the annual rate is 0.04 and if Δt is measured in years is $A(0.04) \, \Delta t$. Then

$\Delta A = A(0.04)\, \Delta t$ and $\Delta A/\Delta t = 0.04A$. The instantaneous rate of increase of A is, by definition, dA/dt or $\dot{A}$. Hence

(47) $$\dot{A} = 0.04A.$$

Let us see what this equation implies about the relation between A and t.

We can integrate this equation readily. By the theorem on inverse functions it can be written as

$$\frac{dt}{dA} = \frac{1}{0.04}\,\frac{1}{A}.$$

Then by (27)

$$t = \frac{1}{0.04}\log A + C.$$

We could evaluate the constant of integration at once, but we save time later if we first rewrite the equation as

$$\log A = 0.04t - 0.04C.$$

By the definition of logarithms to base e,

$$A = e^{0.04t - 0.04C} = e^{0.04t} \cdot e^{-0.04C}.$$

For the moment C is some unknown constant that is still to be determined. Then so is $e^{-0.04C}$. Let us call the latter D. Hence

(48) $$A = De^{0.04t}.$$

Suppose that 1 dollar was invested to start with. Then when $t = 0$, $A = 1$. Hence $D = 1$ and

(49) $$A = e^{0.04t}.$$

This is the same result as (46).

We see, then, that continuous compounding at the rate of 0.04 per year means, in view of (47), that the instantaneous rate of change of A is some constant times A, and this constant is the annual rate. There is another point to be noted about the statement of the rate of change. We stated that the money is compounded *continuously at the rate of* 4 *per cent per year* of the amount present. The phrase "per year" is essential. It is because the 0.04 is a rate per year that we must interpret the t in (49) as standing for a quantity in terms of years.

Let us now return to the problem of what happens to a steel bar which is initially at $100°$ and which loses heat continuously at the rate of 0.1 per minute of the amount present. If the bar lost 0.1 of its existing temperature *at the end of* each minute, it would have a temperature of $90°$ at the end of 1 minute, a temperature of $81°$ at the end of the second minute, and so on. However, the condition is that the loss of 0.1 of the existing temperature be continuous. A continuous loss of temperature at the rate of 0.1 per minute

$$\Delta A = 0.04\, A_0\, \Delta t$$

times the temperature present means that the instantaneous rate of change of temperature equals 0.1 times the temperature. In symbols, if T is the temperature,

$$\dot{T} = 0.1T.$$

This statement is not quite correct. Because the temperature is decreasing, its derivative must be negative. Then we must state that

$$\dot{T} = -0.1T.$$

Our problem now is to find the functional relation between T and t.

This equation is of exactly the same form as (47). The -0.1 here corresponds to 0.04 there and, of course, T here corresponds to A there. In view of (48) we can state at once that

(50) $$T = De^{-0.1t}.$$

To fit this formula to the specific situation in which the temperature is $100°$ at the outset, we can agree that if time is measured from the instant when the temperature is $100°$, then when $t = 0$, $T = 100°$. If we substitute these values in (50), we have

$$100 = De^{-0.1(0)}.$$

Then $D = 100$ and

(51) $$T = 100e^{-0.1t}.$$

This formula tells us how the temperature of the body decreases with time. The unit of t must be minutes because the rate of 0.1 is 0.1 per minute.

To calculate T at various values of t, we could utilize common logarithms. Thus at $t = 3$, say,

(52) $$T = 100e^{-0.3}.$$

Now

$$\log_{10} T = \log_{10} 100 - 0.3 \log_{10} e.$$

Because e is about 2.718, we could complete the calculation by using the table of common logarithms. However, with a table of the exponential function available we only need to look up $e^{-0.3}$. The rest of the arithmetic is obvious. In the present case, the value of T in (52) is about $74.1°$. When $t = 10$, since $e^{-1} = 0.368$, $T = 36.8°$ approximately.

Phenomena such as the continuous compounding of money and the loss of heat in an object are examples of exponential growth and decay, respectively. In these examples we knew the rate at which the continuous change is taking place. However, there are situations in which we know that a quantity is changing continuously at a rate that is some constant times the amount present but do not know the constant. Such a situation is sometimes stated in the language of proportion; that is, one is told that some quantity y is changing continuously at a rate with respect to time which is proportional to the amount present. In symbols, this statement is written as

$$\frac{dy}{dt} = ky,$$

where k is unknown. However, enough information may be given to determine k and also y as a function of t. Let us consider some examples.

Let us examine first a problem in the growth of a population. If the physical conditions in an area are stable, we might expect that the birth and death rates would remain constant and that there would be some net rate, say a rate of growth, if the birthrate exceeds the death rate. It may be sufficient in some population studies to know that if there are 3 births per one hundred of population per year and 1 death per hundred per year, the net rate of increase is 2 people per hundred per year. We can then write a formula for the population in t years. In fact, if the population is 500 at $t = 0$, then

$$P = 500 + 500(0.02)t.$$

However, in other such studies it may be necessary to take into account that the population increases *continuously* at some annual rate applied to the existing population. This fact is certainly pertinent in a large population because births and deaths are continually taking place. Let us see what can be done with the assumption of a continuous change whose rate is proportional to the number present at any time.

The statement that the population changes continuously at some annual rate applied to the existing population or that the instantaneous rate of change of population is proportional to the existing population can be expressed in mathematical language as

(53) $$\frac{dP}{dt} = kP$$

where P is the population, t is the time in years, and k is the proportionality constant whose value we do not know. Now (58) leads, in the same way as (47) led to (48), to

(54) $$P = De^{kt}.$$

Suppose that we know that the population was 10,000 twenty years ago and is 20,000 today. Let us agree to measure time from the instant when the population was 10,000. Then at $t = 0$, $P = 10,000$. This implies that D in (54) is 10,000. So far then

(55) $$P = 10,000e^{kt}.$$

Because our unit of time is years, we can say that at $t = 20$, $P = 20,000$. From (55) we have

$$20,000 = 10,000e^{k \cdot 20}.$$

Then

$$2 = e^{20k},$$

and by taking the logarithms of both sides

$$20k \log e = \log 2.$$

This statement is correct in base 10 or base e. If we choose base e, then, because $\log_e e = 1$,

(56) $$k = \frac{\log_e 2}{20} = \frac{0.693}{20} = 0.0347.$$

If we choose base 10, then

$$k = \frac{1}{20} \frac{\log_{10} 2}{\log_{10} e} = \frac{1}{20} \frac{0.3010}{0.4343} = 0.0347.$$

This value of k is the rate per year which operates continuously. By substituting this value in (55) we obtain the precise law of population growth. We can then use this law to calculate the population to be expected at some time in the future. Of course, the law is an idealization. Strictly the population does not change continuously because the values of P must be integral.

We consider one more phenomenon in which the exponential function rules. We know that the air above us exerts a pressure on us as surely as if a weight were placed directly on our heads. This air pressure decreases with altitude simply because there is less air pressing down on us at higher altitudes. We seek now to determine the variation of pressure with height above the surface of the earth.

The term pressure is used to denote the weight or force acting on a square unit of area. Hence let us take a square unit of area (Fig. 11-4) at some height

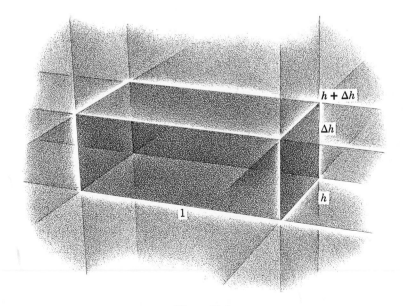

Figure 11-4

h and let p be the air pressure on the unit area at level h. At the height $h + \Delta h$, the pressure on the unit area is a little less than at h because the air between h and $h + \Delta h$ is not involved. The weight of the air in the box-shape volume is the density, that is, the weight per unit volume multiplied by the volume. If we denote the density in this volume, by some average value $\bar{\rho}$, the weight is $\bar{\rho} \cdot 1^2 \cdot \Delta h = \bar{\rho} \, \Delta h$. Then we may say that if Δp is the change in air pressure from the level h to the level $h + \Delta h$,

$$(57) \qquad\qquad \Delta p = -\bar{\rho} \, \Delta h.$$

We must now call upon a physical principle which states that the density of the air is proportional to the pressure. This principle is quite reasonable because the number of molecules of air crowded into the box between h and $h + \Delta h$ depends on the pressure above it. Of course, this argument does not tell us that the density is a constant times the pressure; the density might very well vary with the square of the pressure, but nature often favors us by being as simple as possible.* Then

$$\bar{\rho} = k\bar{p}$$

where k is the proportionality constant. If we substitute (58) in (57), we have

$$\Delta p = -k\bar{p} \, \Delta h.$$

We divide both sides by Δh and let Δh approach 0. Then $\bar{p}$, which is an average pressure for the region between h and $h + \Delta h$, must approach the pressure at h. That is,

$$(58) \qquad\qquad \dot{p} = -kp.$$

We know now [cf. (47) and (48)] that the solution of this equation is

$$p = De^{-kh}.$$

Moreover, if $h = 0$ is the height at the earth's surface and p_0 is the pressure at the earth's surface, then

$$(59) \qquad\qquad p = p_0 e^{-kh}.$$

---

* The assertion that the density is proportional to the pressure can be deduced from the chemical law for gases which states that for perfect gases

$$pv = nRT,$$

or that the pressure times the volume equals the number n of molecules (divided by a constant) times the gas constant R times the temperature T. If we assume that the temperature is constant with height, then because R is a constant, we have that

$$p = K\frac{n}{v}$$

where K is RT. Now n/v is proportional to the density by the very meanings of n and v. Hence $\rho = kp$.

To determine k we can use chemical constants for air as measured in the laboratory or we can use a barometer to measure the pressure at, say, 1 mile above the earth's surface. If the unit of h is taken to be miles, we know what p is when h is 1, and knowing p_0 we can calculate k, which is a rate per mile. We may then use (59) to calculate the pressure at other heights.

Exercises

1. The more general statement of how an object loses heat, known as Newton's law of cooling, is that the rate of decrease of temperature of an object is continuous and proportional to the difference between the temperature of the object and that of the surrounding medium. Suppose that the surrounding medium is so vast that the heat it absorbs from the object does not appreciably change the medium's temperature so that it remains constant. Suppose that the object is initially at a temperature of 100° and loses temperature continuously at the rate of 1/100 per minute of the difference between its temperature at time t and the constant temperature T_0 of the surrounding medium. Derive the formula that relates the temperature of the object and time.
   Ans. $T - T_0 = (100 - T_0)e^{-0.01t}$.

2. Suppose that an object loses temperature at the rate of 0.01 of the existing temperature not continuously but at the end of each minute. If the temperature is initially 100°, derive the formula that relates the temperature of the object and the time? *Ans.* $T = 100(0.99)^t$. To fit the physical situation t can take on only the values 0, 1, 2, ...

3. Suppose that an object, initially at a temperature of 100°, loses temperature continuously at the rate of 0.01° per minute. Derive the formula that relates the temperature and the time? *Ans.* $T = 100 - 0.01t$.

4. Suppose that the population of a town increases at the net rate *per year* of 0.03466 of its population *at the beginning* of the year. Find the formula that relates the population and time. *Ans.* $P = P_0(1.03466)^t$.

5. Suppose that the population of a town was 5000 twenty years ago and that it increased continuously at a rate proportional to the existing population. Suppose that the population reached 15,000 at the end of the twenty years. What formula relates the population and the time? *Ans.* $P = 5000e^{0.06t}$.

6. A steel ball heated to a temperature of 100° is placed in a medium which is held at a constant temperature of 40°. At the end of 2 minutes the temperature of the ball is 80°. At what time will the temperature be 43°? *Suggestion:* See Exercise 1. *Ans.* 14.8 min.

7. Sugar in water dissolves continuously at a rate proportional to the undissolved amount. If the amount of sugar is initially 200 grams and 100 grams are dissolved in 2 minutes, how long does it take to dissolve 150 grams? How long does it take to dissolve all 200 grams? *Ans.* 4.1 sec; ∞.

8. Suppose that the population of a town increases at an annual rate of r people per hundred per year. Find the equivalent rate if the same population is assumed to increase continuously and at a rate proportional to the existing population. *Ans.* $k = \log_e (1 + r)$.

9. Bacteria in a culture increase continuously at a rate proportional to the number already attained. If the proportionality constant is 0.2 per minute, find the number of bacteria in t minutes if there are 100 to start with.

Ans. $N = 100e^{0.2t}$.

10. A beam of light passing through water loses intensity continuously at a rate that is proportional to the intensity present at a given depth. If the proportionality constant is denoted by k, that is, if k is the percentage of loss per foot of depth, and if the intensity is reduced by $\frac{1}{2}$ after the light passes through 10 feet of water, how much is k?   *Ans.* $k = -0.07$.

11. A radioactive substance such as uranium emits particles from the nucleus of each atom. After emitting this particle the atom is no longer uranium (it becomes thorium). We say then that the uranium atom has decayed or disintegrated. There are billions of atoms even in a small amount of uranium, and in any small interval of time some of the atoms disintegrate. Because some disintegration is continually taking place, it is reasonable to speak of the instantaneous rate of change with respect to time of the number of atoms of uranium. Moreover, even though two different atoms may emit particles at quite different instants, the number of atoms is so large that we can assume that the rate at which the atoms emit is proportional to the number of atoms present. Then if N is the number of uranium atoms present at time t, the rate of decrease of N per unit of time (in years) is

$$\dot{N} = -kN$$

where k is the proportionality constant. If there are 10^{12} uranium atoms present at $t = 0$, and if half of these are present after 4,500,000,000 years, find the value of k.   *Ans.* $k = 1.6 \cdot 10^{-10}$.

12. In a certain chain of nuclear reactions that take place in a nuclear reactor plutonium decays to uranium 235 and the uranium decays to thorium. The amount of uranium at any time is given by $u = P(1 - e^{\lambda t})$ where P is the original amount of plutonium. The amount of uranium that has decayed at any time t is given by $U = u(1 - e^{-\lambda t})$. Let us assume that $P = 3400$ grams and that $\lambda = \frac{1}{10} \log 2$. If the amount of uranium present at any time exceeds what is called the critical mass, namely 800 grams, the reactor will explode. Is the reactor safe?   *Ans.* Disaster.

13. A tank contains 100 gallons of salt water in which 150 pounds of salt is dissolved. Salt water containing one pound of salt per gallon enters continuously at the rate of 2 gal/min. If the mixture in the tank is kept uniform by stirring and the mixed salt water flows out continuously at the rate of 2 gal/min, what is the amount of salt in the tank at the end of 1 hour. *Suggestion:* Let Q be the number of pounds of salt in the tank at the end of t minutes. Show that $\dot{Q} = 2 - 2Q/100$. Find Q as a function of t.   *Ans.* 115 lb.

14. A fishtank, which holds 10 gallons, contains impure water, that is, a mixture of impurities and water. A filter is placed in the tank which draws out the impure water continuously at the constant rate of 10 gal/hr and replaces it at the same rate by pure water. How long does it take to replace half of the impure water by pure water? *Suggestion:* Let $y =$ the number of gallons of impurity present.   *Ans.* 0.7 hr.

15. The half-life of a radioactive mass of atoms $N(t)$, which disintegrate according to the law $N(t) = N(0)e^{-kt}$ where t is time in years, is the time required for $N(t)$ to equal $N(0)/2$. Find the half-life in terms of k. *Ans.* $0.693/k$.

16. **(a)** A quantity of radium atoms disintegrates according to the law $N(t) = N(0)e^{-0.000433t}$, the number 0.000433 meaning the per cent of atoms per year. How many of the original number $N(0)$ are left after 100 years?

Ans. $0.958N(0)$.

(b) What is the half-life of radium? *Ans.* About 1600 years.

6. *Motion in one Direction in a Resisting Medium.* When Galileo investigated the laws of falling bodies in the early part of the seventeenth century, he neglected air resistance because it is a secondary effect compared to the action of gravity. Had he undertaken to consider this effect, he might have been frustrated in any case, because the mathematics required to handle it was not available. One hundred years later, by which time the calculus had been founded, the mathematicians were empowered and proceeded to tackle problems of motion in resisting media. Such problems, which include the motion of raindrops, meteorites, ships, trains, and automobiles, have always been important, and today are even more important in view of the greater variety of motions that modern man initiates.

To consider motions in media that offer resistance, say, air or water, we must know something about the kind of resistance that takes place. This information is not derived from mathematics but from physical investigations. Perhaps the first point to note is that the resistance of the medium is a force, which acts in conjunction with other forces such as the force of gravity. Second, the resistance that an object experiences in falling through air or in being propelled through water depends on many factors, for example, the density of the medium, the shape and size of the object, the smoothness of the surface of the object, and its velocity. If it is necessary to obtain a precise expression for the resistance of the medium, all of these factors must be taken into account, as is done, for example, in the design of airplanes. However, of all these factors the *velocity* of the object as it moves through the medium is usually the most important in determining what resistance the object will encounter. In our introduction to the problem of motion in resisting media we consider the dependence of the resistance only on the velocity of the moving object. The other factors will be contained in a proportionality constant. This simplification or idealization is a very realistic one, as we shall soon see.

How, then, does the resistance depend on the velocity? For comparatively small speeds, say up to about a few hundred feet per second, it is physically reasonable to suppose that the resistance offered by the medium is proportional to the velocity of the moving object; for higher speeds the resistance is proportional to the square of the velocity. These are the physical facts; however, for the purpose of getting to know how to treat motions in resisting media we shall not worry much about the proper range of the actual speeds.

Let us consider first a rather simple situation. Suppose that an object is projected along smooth ground and that the resistance of the air is *proportional to the velocity* of the object. The action of gravity can be neglected because the surface opposes downward motion. What formula relates the velocity of the object and time and what formula relates the distance traveled and time?

When we say that the object is projected along smooth ground we mean that the object is launched with some initial velocity and thereafter is subject to the resistance that slows down its motion. Suppose that the body is projected to the right, which we take to be the positive direction. Then the air resistance acts to the left and slows down the object. We can obtain the mathematical representation of this motion in either of two ways. We can argue that at any instant the object loses velocity at a rate that is proportional to the velocity. The instantaneous loss in velocity is dv/dt or $\dot{v}$. Because this is proportional to the velocity, we have so far that $\dot{v} = kv$. If the object is moving to the right, v is positive; however, the resistance acts to the left, so that

$$(60) \qquad\qquad\qquad \dot{v} = -kv,$$

where k is a positive constant. To see that the minus sign is necessary we can also argue that v is positive but is decreasing. Hence dv/dt must be negative, and therefore we must interpose the minus sign if the right side is to equal the left side.

The second method of deriving (60), which is worth noting because it is more useful in later problems, argues that there is a resistive force acting to the left which is proportional to the velocity. This force is $-Kv$. According to Newton's second law of motion, this force must equal the mass of the object times its acceleration, and therefore

$$m\dot{v} = -Kv.$$

If we divide both sides by m and replace K/m by k, we again obtain (60).

The form of equation (60) is quite familiar, and by now we know that the integral is

$$(61) \qquad\qquad\qquad v = De^{-kt}.$$

To determine D we must know some physical facts. If, for example, we know that the object was launched with an initial velocity of 100 ft/sec and if we measure time from the instant the object is launched, then at $t = 0$, $v = 100$. These values substituted in (61) yield $D = 100$, and therefore the final formula for the velocity as a function of the time is

$$(62) \qquad\qquad\qquad v = 100e^{-kt}.$$

Of course, to calculate v for various values of t we must know k. This quantity can be obtained from measurements of actual resistance experienced by objects in the medium in question; alternatively, by measuring v at a definite value of t one can calculate k. Figure 11-5 shows how v varies with t.

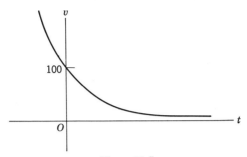

Figure 11-5

From (62) we can derive the formula for distance traveled in time t. If x is the distance traveled in time t, then $v = dx/dt = \dot{x}$, so that

(63) $$\dot{x} = 100e^{-kt}.$$

The exponential factor on the right is of the form e^u where $u = -kt$. To apply the inverse of the chain rule we need du/dt, which is $-k$. Hence we write (63) as

$$\frac{dx}{dt} = -\frac{100}{k} e^{-kt}(-k).$$

Now we can apply (40). Then

(64) $$x = -\frac{100}{k} e^u + C = -\frac{100}{k} e^{-kt} + C.$$

Again we need some physical information to determine C. If, for example, we measure distance traveled from the position of the object at time $t = 0$, then $x = 0$ when $t = 0$. If we substitute these values in (64), we have that

$$0 = -\frac{100}{k} + C.$$

Then

$$x = -\frac{100}{k} e^{-kt} + \frac{100}{k}$$

or

(65) $$x = \frac{100}{k} (1 - e^{-kt}).$$

It is helpful to see what this result means geometrically. The graph of this function is best obtained by first determining the graph of $x = -e^{-kt}$, which is shown in Fig. 11-6*a*. By adding 1 to each *x*-value in this graph we obtain Fig. 11-6*b*. If we now "stretch" each ordinate by the factor $100/k$, we obtain the graph of (65) shown in Fig. 11-6*c*. We note that as *t* becomes infinite, that is, as *t* takes on larger and larger values without bound, *x* approaches $100/k$. This fact is also apparent in (65) because $e^{-kt} = 1/e^{kt}$. In other words, the object approaches a fixed point $100/k$ feet away from the starting point more and more closely as *t* becomes infinite, but never quite reaches this point.

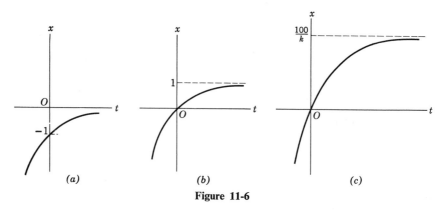

Figure 11-6

As another example of motion in a resisting medium let us consider the motion of an object of mass *m* falling downward in air. If the motion takes place near the surface of the earth, we can take the acceleration of gravity to be 32 ft/sec². We assume that the resistance of the air is *proportional to the velocity*. The force of gravity acts on the object, and the amount of this force is the weight of the object or $32m$. To keep the signs straight, we must take the positive direction of force to be the positive direction of the distance. Let us take downward direction as positive. Hence the force of gravity is $+32m$. The magnitude of the air resistance is Kv, where we take *K* to be positive, and because this force acts to resist the motion, its direction is upward. Hence the force of the air resistance is $-Kv$. The net force acting on the object is

$$32m - Kv.$$

By Newton's second law of motion this force is the mass of the object times the acceleration; hence

$$m\dot{v} = 32m - Kv.$$

If we divide both sides of this equation by *m* and replace K/m by another constant *k*, our equation becomes

(66) $$\dot{v} = 32 - kv.$$

The integration of this equation seems to pose a problem. Since the right side is a function of the *dependent* variable, let us write it as

(67) $$\frac{dt}{dv} = \frac{1}{32 - kv}.$$

It seems likely that we can apply formula (30) if we can choose a suitable u. We let

$$u = 32 - kv.$$

Then

$$\frac{du}{dv} = -k.$$

We therefore write (62) in the form $dt/dv = (dt/du)(du/dv)$, that is,

$$\frac{dt}{dv} = -\frac{1}{k}\frac{1}{u}(-k).$$

The constant $-1/k$ can be ignored for the moment while we apply (30). Then

$$t = -\frac{1}{k}\log u + C = -\frac{1}{k}\log(32 - kv) + C.$$

Because we want v as a function of t, we solve for v. First,

$$\log(32 - kv) = -kt + kC$$

or

$$32 - kv = e^{-kt+kC} = e^{-kt}e^{kC} = De^{-kt},$$

where $D = e^{kC}$. Thus we obtain

(68)
$$v = \frac{32}{k} - \frac{D}{k}e^{-kt}.$$

To determine D we need some physical information. Suppose that the object is just dropped from some point above the surface of the earth. This means in mathematical terms that $v = 0$ when $t = 0$ if time is measured from the instant the object is dropped. If we substitute these values in (68), we find that $D = 32$. Then

(69)
$$v = \frac{32}{k}(1 - e^{-kt}).$$

Again, it is instructive to picture the relation between v and t. Let us recall that positive v is directed downward. We first graph $v = -e^{-kt}$ as shown in Fig. 11-7a. We then add 1 to each v-value and obtain Fig. 11-7b. Finally, we multiply each v-value by $32/k$ and obtain Fig. 11-7c.

The surprising fact which the last figure reveals but which can also be deduced from (69) is that the velocity of the falling object does not increase indefinitely; it approaches a limiting value of $32/k$ as t becomes infinite. This limiting value is called the *terminal velocity*. The terminal velocity itself can be deduced without the use of (69). As the object falls under gravity, its velocity increases. However, because the air resistance increases with the

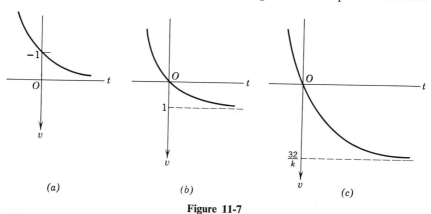

Figure 11-7

velocity, the resistance also increases. Yet the resistance cannot become greater than the weight of the object, for the weight is the only downward force; when the resistance becomes equal to the weight, there will be no downward force and therefore no acceleration. Then the velocity will not increase any further. Hence the maximum resistive force $Kv = 32m$. But $K = km$, so that maximum $v = 32/k$. Of course, this argument does not tell us how v varies with t or any other facts about the motion.

The fact that there is a finite terminal velocity is very important in some situations. Suppose that a man drops out of an airplane and opens his parachute immediately. Then the air resistance is considerable. Let us suppose that the value of k in this case is $\frac{1}{2}$. The man's downward velocity is 0 at the outset and increases thereafter, but it never becomes larger than $32/\frac{1}{2}$ or 64 ft/sec. He may then land without injuring himself.

Having obtained (69), we may as well see if we can find the formula that relates distance fallen and time of fall. We let y represent the variable distance; the downward direction has already been chosen to be the positive one. Let us rewrite (69) as

(70)
$$\dot{y} = \frac{32}{k} - \frac{32}{k} e^{-kt}.$$

The integration here is practically straightforward. The first term on the right is a constant and the second can be handled in the same way as (63). Then

$$y = \frac{32}{k} t + \frac{32}{k^2} e^{-kt} + C.$$

If we measure distance from the position of the object at $t = 0$, then at this instant $y = 0$. It follows that $C = -32/k^2$, and

(71)
$$y = \frac{32}{k} t + \frac{32}{k^2} e^{-kt} - \frac{32}{k^2}.$$

To obtain a sketch of the graph of (66), we first sketch (Fig. 11-8) $y = (32/k^2)e^{-kt}$. We then subtract from this sketch the constant value $-32/k^2$. This *raises* the first sketch by a constant amount. We then graph independently but on the same set of axes the function $y = 32t/k$. This is a straight line whose slope depends, of course, on the value of k. Now, according to (71), the y we seek is the sum of the y-values on the second sketch and the y-values on the straight line. Hence, as t increases from 0 onward, we estimate what the sum of these y-values is and thus obtain the final graph which is the final curve in Fig. 11-8.

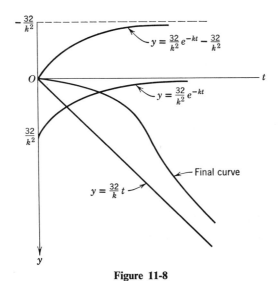

Figure 11-8

We note from the graph that the object does not fall quite as far during the first few seconds as it does later in the same period of time. This is, of course, understandable because the object starts with 0 velocity and takes time to gain appreciable velocity. However, it soon acquires a velocity close to the terminal velocity of $32/k$ and thereafter falls at almost this velocity.

Exercises

1. Suppose that an object is launched horizontally over some smooth surface with an initial velocity of 100 ft/sec and that the air resistance varies as the square of the velocity. We may neglect gravity for the reason given in the text. Find the formula that relates velocity and time. Compare the result with (62).
   Ans. $v = 100/(1 + 100kt)$.

2. Under the conditions of Exercise 1 and using the result obtained there, find the formula that relates distance traveled and time of travel. Compare the result with (65).
   Ans. $x = (1/k) \log (1 + 100kt)$.

3. According to the result of Exercise 2 when an object travels subject to a resistance that varies as the square of the velocity, the distance traveled becomes infinite with increasing time. The text showed that when the resistance of the medium is proportional to the velocity, the distance traveled approaches a finite limit with increasing time. Because the resistance of the medium seems to be greater in Exercise 2, we would expect the distance traveled to be less than in the text example. How would you explain this paradox. *Suggestion:* Consider what happens when v becomes less than 1.

4. A particle starts from the origin with velocity V and moves along a horizontal smooth surface in a medium whose resistance is proportional to $\sqrt{v}$, where v is the variable velocity. Find the following:

   (a) The relation between velocity and time.   *Ans.* $v = (\sqrt{V} - kt/2)^2$.

   (b) The relation between distance and time.

   (c) The relation between velocity and distance.   *Ans.* $x = 2(V^{3/4} - v^{3/4})/3k$

   (d) How far does the particle move   *Ans.* $2V^{3/4}/3k$.

5. A man rowing at v_0 ft/sec in still water rests his oars. Thereafter the resistance of the water, which we may assume to be proportional to the velocity, slows down his speed. Find the formulas for the velocity and distance traveled t seconds later.   *Ans.* $v = v_0 e^{-kt}$; $x = (v_0/k)(1 - e^{-kt})$.

6. Using the relation $dv/dt = v\,dv/dx$ and the conditions of Exercise 5, find the formula for the velocity v in terms of the distance x traveled after the oars are rested.   *Ans.* $v = v_0 - kx$.

7. Suppose that we redo the problem considered in the text of an object falling from some height in a medium whose resistance is proportional to the velocity, but that this time we take the upward direction as positive. Derive the formula that relates velocity and time. *Suggestion:* The difficulty lies in the integration. Watch out for the logarithm of negative quantities. When $y < 0$, $\log |y| = \log - y$.

8. Compare the result (69) with the corresponding formula for an object that falls straight down under the action of gravity in a vacuum.

9. Suppose that an object is thrown downward with an initial velocity of 1000 ft/sec in a medium whose resistance is proportional to the velocity. Find the expression for the velocity as a function of time.   *Ans.* $v = 1000e^{-kt}$.

10. Suppose that an object is thrown downward with an initial velocity V in a medium whose resistance is proportional to the velocity.

    (a) Find the expression for the velocity as a function of time and discuss the motion for the cases $V > 32/k$, $V = 32/k$, and $V < 32/k$.

$$\textit{Ans. } v = \frac{32}{k} - \left(\frac{32}{k} - V\right)e^{-kt}$$

    (b) What is the terminal velocity in each case? Explain physically why the answers are correct.   *Ans.* $32/k$.

11. Using the result of Exercise 9, find the expression for the distance fallen as a function of time t.

$$\textit{Ans. } y = -\frac{1}{k}1000e^{-kt} + \frac{1000}{k}.$$

12. A body falls from rest in a medium whose resistance is proportional to the velocity. If the terminal velocity is 12 ft/sec, find the velocity and distance fallen after 2 seconds. *Ans.* $v = 12(1 - e^{-16/3})$; $y = 12(2 + \frac{3}{8}e^{-16/3}) - \frac{9}{2}$.

13. An aviator drops out of an airplane and falls freely for 10 seconds (during which time we may suppose the air resistance to be negligible). He then opens his parachute and the air resistance becomes proportional to his velocity. Find the formula that expresses his velocity as a function of time from the instant he opens his parachute.

$$Ans. \ v = \frac{32}{k} - \left(\frac{32}{k} - 320\right)e^{-kt}.$$

14. A torpedo is ejected under water with an initial velocity V. It is known experimentally that the resistance of the water is $0.0068v^2$. If the torpedo must strike with a velocity of at least $V/2$ to cause damage, what is the maximum effective striking distance? *Suggestion:* See Exercises 1 and 2. *Ans.* 1019 ft.

15. Exercise 14 can be done by following the procedures of Exercises 1 and 2 and then calculating the time at which v becomes $V/2$. However, because we are interested in the relation between distance traveled and velocity, we can use an old device, namely, $dv/dt = (dv/dx)(dx/dt) = v \, dv/dx$. Redo Exercise 14 by this method.

16. Suppose that a body has acquired a downward velocity v_0 and that thereafter the velocity is proportional to the distance traveled. Find the formulas for distance traveled, velocity, and acceleration as functions of time. Distance and time are measured from the instant and place where the object already has the velocity v_0. *Ans.* $y = (1/k)v_0(e^{kt} - 1)$.

17. Suppose that an object is dropped and falls freely in a vacuum and suppose that we consider, as Galileo seriously did for a while, that the velocity acquired by the object is proportional to the distance fallen. Show that this assumption leads to an absurdity.

18. Suppose that a body has acquired a downward velocity v_0 and that thereafter the increase in its velocity is proportional to the distance traveled. Measure time and distance from the instant and place where the object has acquired the velocity v_0 and find the formula for the distance traveled as a function of time. *Suggestion:* Use at once the fact that $dv/dt = v \, dv/dy$.

$$Ans. \ y = \frac{1}{2\sqrt{k}}(e^{\sqrt{k}t} - v_0^2 e^{-\sqrt{k}t} + v_0^2 - 1).$$

7. Up and Down Motion in Resisting Media. The motions in resisting media that we have considered so far are motions in one direction, that is, either horizontally or downward. Let us consider next an object of mass m that is projected upward with some initial velocity, say 1000 ft/sec. We suppose that the air resistance is *proportional to the velocity*. The object, of course, rises and then falls. What function relates velocity and time and what function relates height above the ground and time?

Let us choose the upward direction as positive. The force of gravity acts continuously in the downward direction and therefore is represented by

$-32m$. The resistance of the medium acts downward when the object is rising and upward when it is falling. This reversal of the direction in which the air resistance acts raises the question of its sign. When the object rises, its velocity v is positive, and therefore the air resistance is $-Kv$. When the object falls, v itself is negative, so that $-Kv$ is positive and represents an upward force. Thus $-Kv$ is the correct representation of the air resistance for both the upward and the downward motion. The net force acting on the object at any instant is

$$-32m - Kv,$$

and by Newton's second law of motion we have that at any instant

$$m\dot{v} = -32m - Kv.$$

If we divide both sides by m and replace K/m by k, we obtain

(72) $$\dot{v} = -32 - kv.$$

To integrate we may use the method already applied to (66). That is, we can write (72) in the form

$$\frac{dt}{dv} = -\frac{1}{32 + kv}$$

and, if we again introduce

$$u = 32 + kv,$$

we can write

$$\frac{dt}{dv} = -\frac{1}{k}\frac{1}{u}\frac{du}{dv}.$$

Then by (30)

$$t = -\frac{1}{k}\log u + C$$

or

(73) $$-kt + C' = \log u$$

where $C' = kC$. In view of the value of u,

$$\log(32 + kv) = -kt + C'.$$

Then by the meaning of the logarithm

(74) $$32 + kv = e^{-kt+C'} = De^{-kt},$$

where $D = e^{C'}$.

To determine the constant of integration we use the physical fact that at $t = 0$, the instant at which the object is thrown up, $v = 1000$. Then

$$32 + k \cdot 1000 = D.$$

With this value of D substituted in (74), we have that

(75) $$v = -\frac{32}{k} + \frac{32 + 1000k}{k}e^{-kt}.$$

Thus we have obtained the formula for the velocity as a function of the time.

A graph of (75) is instructive. The graph of the second term on the right is an exponentially decaying function which, at the value $t = 0$, is $(32 + 1000k)/k$. We subtract the constant value $32/k$ from this graph and obtain the result shown in Fig. 11-9.

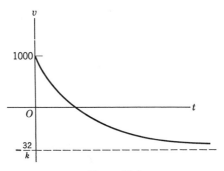

Figure 11-9

Having obtained the formula for the velocity as a function of the time, we can now reasonably ask for the relation between height above the ground and time. If we denote height above the ground by y, we have from (75) that

$$\dot{y} = -\frac{32}{k} + \frac{32 + 1000k}{k} e^{-kt}.$$

To find y we have but to integrate in a straightforward manner. Then

$$(76) \qquad y = -\frac{32}{k} t - \frac{32 + 1000k}{k^2} e^{-kt} + C$$

At $t = 0$ the object is at the ground so that $y = 0$; by substituting these values in (76), we find that

$$C = \frac{32 + 1000k}{k^2}.$$

With this value of C, (76) becomes

$$(77) \qquad y = -\frac{32}{k} t + \frac{32 + 1000k}{k^2} (1 - e^{-kt}).$$

A graph of (72) is helpful in interpreting its significance. To obtain a sketch we might pick a possible value of k, say $k = 0.5$. We start by sketching $y = -e^{-kt}$; we then add 1 to each y-value of this graph to obtain the graph of $y = 1 - e^{-kt}$; next we "stretch" each y-value of the latter graph by the factor $(32 + 1000k)/k^2$. Then we graph separately but on the same set of axes $y = (-32/k)t$ and by adding ordinates of these last two graphs at a number of values of t we obtain the result shown in Fig. 11-10.

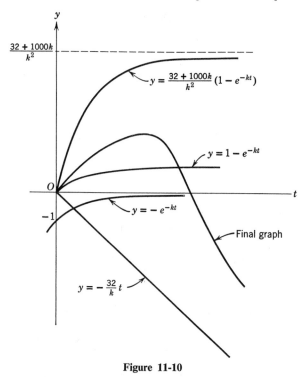

Figure 11-10

Because motion in a resisting medium is more realistic than motion in a vacuum, we should explore the implications of the major results (75) and (77). Some pertinent questions are considered in the exercises.

Exercises

1. What is the physical significance of the value of t where the curve cuts the t-axis in Fig. 11-9?

2. Suppose that an object is thrown straight up with an initial velocity of 1000 ft/sec and that air resistance is neglected. What formula relates velocity and time? How does the graph of this formula compare with that in Fig. 11-9?

$$Ans. \quad v = 1000 - 32t.$$

3. Suppose that an object is projected upward with an initial velocity of 1000 ft/sec and that air resistance is proportional to the velocity. Find the time t_1 at which it reaches maximum height.   *Ans.* $t_1 = (1/k) \log [1 + (1000/32)k]$.

4. Under the conditions of Exercise 3 find the maximum height y_1 reached by the object.   *Ans.* $y_1 = (1000/k) - (32/k^2) \log [1 + (1000k/32)]$.

5. Suppose that an object is projected upward with an initial velocity of 1000 ft/sec and air resistance is neglected. Find the time to reach maximum height and the maximum height.   *Ans.* 125/4 sec; 15,625 ft.

6. Compare the results of Exercise 5 with those of Exercises 3 and 4. For the purposes of comparison, use the value of 0.5 for k.

7. The point of Exercises 5 and 6 is that it takes less time for an object to reach its maximum height when air resistance is taken into account than when it is not. Because air resistance slows up the object, how do you account for the seeming contradiction?

8. It is not possible with the present means at our disposal to find the time of flight of an object that is projected upward under the conditions in Exercise 3, that is, the time elapsed from the instant the object starts upward to the instant it returns to the ground.* However, if we call T the time of flight, we can show readily that the velocity with which the object returns to the ground is $32T - 1000$. Use (75) and (77) to show that this result is correct. Also, how does this result compare with the analogous one in the case of no air resistance?

We consider next the motion of a body projected *upward* in a medium whose resistance is *proportional to the square of the velocity*. Let us take the upward direction as positive. During the upward motion the resistance is downward and so is $-Kv^2$, where K is a positive constant. Then the differential equation, much as in the case when the resistance is proportional to the velocity, is

$$(78) \qquad m\dot{v} = -32m - Kv^2.$$

Here, however, we encounter a peculiar feature. The differential equation represents the situation at any instant during the upward motion because then v is positive and in any case v^2 is positive so that $-Kv^2$ represents a downward force. However, during the downward motion the air resistance acts upward and therefore should be represented by a positive term. But the term $-Kv^2$ is still negative because v is squared. Hence (78) represents the *upward* motion only. We can use it to find the formulas representing this motion and answer a few questions about it. The downward motion must be considered separately, which we shall do later.

We proceed to derive the formula for velocity. By dividing through by m we obtain

$$(79) \qquad \dot{v} = -32 - kv^2$$

where $k = K/m$. The right side is a function of v rather than t. Hence we consider the inverse function, that is, t as a function of v; by using the theorem on the derived function of an inverse function we have that

$$(80) \qquad \frac{dt}{dv} = -\frac{1}{32 + kv^2}.$$

The form of the right side suggests possible use of formula (30) of Chapter 10. However, the right side is not quite in the correct form. We can, of course, write it as

$$\frac{dt}{dv} = -\frac{1}{32} \cdot \frac{1}{1 + \dfrac{k}{32}v^2}$$

---

* In our work on infinite series (Chapter 20) we shall learn additional techniques.

and thus be closer to the form that we seek to utilize. Furthermore, we can introduce the substitution

$$u = \sqrt{\frac{k}{32}}\, v$$

and obtain

(81)
$$\frac{dt}{dv} = -\frac{1}{32} \cdot \frac{1}{1+u^2} \cdot$$

However, the left side is dt/dv, whereas the right side is a function of u. Because

$$\frac{du}{dv} = \sqrt{\frac{k}{32}},$$

we can write (81) as

$$\frac{dt}{dv} = -\frac{1}{32}\sqrt{\frac{32}{k}}\, \frac{1}{1+u^2}\sqrt{\frac{k}{32}}\cdot$$

Then by formula (30) of Chapter 10,

$$t = -\frac{1}{\sqrt{32k}}\tan^{-1} u + C$$

or

$$t = -\frac{1}{\sqrt{32k}}\tan^{-1}\sqrt{\frac{k}{32}}\, v + C.$$

To obtain v as a function of t the following simple steps suffice. First,

$$-\sqrt{32k}\, t + C' = \tan^{-1}\sqrt{\frac{k}{32}}\, v$$

where $C' = \sqrt{32k}\, C$. Then

$$\sqrt{\frac{k}{32}}\, v = \tan\left(-\sqrt{32k}\, t + C'\right)$$

and, finally,

(82)
$$v = \sqrt{\frac{32}{k}}\tan\left(-\sqrt{32k}\, t + C'\right).$$

To determine the constant of integration, let us suppose that the object is projected upward with an initial velocity of 1000 ft/sec and that time is measured from the instant the object is launched. Then when $t = 0, v = 1000$. Substitution of these values in (82) gives

$$1000 = \sqrt{\frac{32}{k}}\tan C'.$$

Thus the quantity C' is

$$C' = \tan^{-1}\sqrt{\frac{k}{32}}\, 1000.$$

Were we applying our theory to an actual situation, we would have to know k in order to calculate C'. To save writing, let us introduce α for C' just to suggest that we have calculated C'. Thus

(83)
$$\alpha = \tan^{-1}\sqrt{\frac{k}{32}}\ 1000,$$

and now we may write (82) as

(84)
$$v = \sqrt{\frac{32}{k}}\ \tan\left(\alpha - \sqrt{32k}\ t\right).$$

We have the formula that expresses the velocity of the object as a function of time. Let us see if the formula makes sense physically. To be specific, let us suppose that $k = 0.005$. Then according to (83)

$$\alpha = \tan^{-1}\sqrt{\frac{0.005}{32}}\ 1000 = \tan^{-1}\frac{1000}{80} = \tan^{-1} 12.5$$

or

$$\alpha = 85°\ 25' = 1.491 \text{ radians approximately.}$$

Now (84) reads

$$v = 80 \tan (1.491 - 0.4t).$$

We see that as t increases, the quantity in parentheses decreases, and so the velocity v decreases. Moreover, when t is about 3.7 seconds, the quantity is 0 and v is 0. Thus it takes about 3.7 seconds for the object to reach its maximum height. If the object had been projected upward with a velocity of 1000 ft/sec and there were no air resistance, its velocity would be given by the formula

$$v = 1000 - 32t,$$

and we see that when $v = 0$, $t = 31$ seconds approximately. Thus the effect of an air resistance of $0.005v^2$ is considerable.

Having obtained the formula for the velocity as a function of time, let us see if we can obtain the formula for the height y attained by the object as a function of time. We have from (84) that

(85)
$$\dot{y} = \sqrt{\frac{32}{k}}\ \tan\left(\alpha - \sqrt{32kt}\right).$$

To integrate this function, we must use the device of regarding $\tan x$ as $\sin x/\cos x$. Thus

(86)
$$\dot{y} = \sqrt{\frac{32}{k}}\ \frac{\sin\left(\alpha - \sqrt{32kt}\right)}{\cos\left(\alpha - \sqrt{32kt}\right)}.$$

The numerator is almost the derivative of the denominator, which suggests (30). In fact, if we let

$$u = \cos\left(\alpha - \sqrt{32kt}\right),$$

then

$$\frac{du}{dt} = \sqrt{32k}\ \sin\left(\alpha - \sqrt{32kt}\right).$$

By multiplying and dividing the right side of (86) by $\sqrt{32k}$, we obtain

(87) $$\frac{dy}{dt} = \frac{1}{k} \frac{1}{\cos(\alpha - \sqrt{32kt})} \sqrt{32k} \sin(\alpha - \sqrt{32kt}).$$

With our choice of u, (87) is in the form

$$\frac{dy}{dt} = \frac{1}{k} \frac{1}{u} \frac{du}{dt},$$

so that by (30)

$$y = \frac{1}{k} \log u + C$$

or

$$y = \frac{1}{k} \log \cos(\alpha - \sqrt{32kt}) + C.$$

To fix the constant of integration, we measure height from the ground up. Then at $t = 0$, $y = 0$ and

$$C = -\frac{1}{k} \log \cos \alpha.$$

Finally,

(88) $$y = \frac{1}{k} \log \cos(\alpha - \sqrt{32kt}) - \frac{1}{k} \log \cos \alpha.$$

To obtain an idea of what this function looks like, let us use our previous value of $k = 0.005$. Then, as before, $\alpha = 1.491$ radians and log cos $1.491 = 8.90260 - 10 = -1.0974$. Hence

$$y = 200 \log \cos(1.491 - 0.4t) - 200(-1.0974)$$

or

(89) $$y = 200 \log \cos(1.491 - 0.4t) + 219.5.$$

We can readily analyze this formula. As t increases from 0 to $1.491/0.4$, the quantity in parentheses decreases; hence the cosine value increases and approaches 1 and its logarithm (which is negative because the cosine values are fractions) approaches 0. Then y approaches the constant 219.5. We know from our discussion of the velocity function that when $t = 1.491/0.4$ the object is at the highest point. Hence the maximum height attained is 219.5 feet.

We may recall that our original equation (79) represents the motion only on the upward path. We can now see that this confirmed by the solution. If we let t in (89) increase beyond the value 1.491.4, the quantity in parentheses becomes negative, but the cosine of a negative quantity is the same as the cosine of the corresponding positive quantity. Then as t increases beyond $1.491/0.4$, the first term on the right decreases (because the logarithm of a fraction is negative) from 0 to smaller and smaller negative values. When t reaches $2(1.491/0.4)$, the angle is -1.491 radians and the value of 200 log cos (-1.491) is -219.48. Then the value of y is 0. In fact, as t increases from $1.491/0.4$ to $2(1.491/0.4)$, the y-values repeat in opposite order the values that y has when t increases from 0 to $1.491/0.4$. This means that the variation of y with t is symmetric (Fig. 11-11) about the line $t = 1.491/0.4$. However, this fact is not in accord with the physics, because, although gravity aids the motion on the way down in precisely the opposite way in which it hinders the motion on the way up, the air resistance hinders the motion both on the way up and on the way down. Hence the motion should not proceed in the down-ward direction in the manner exactly opposite to that in the upward direction. Thus if we had been careless and had not noticed that the differential equation (79) does not represent the motion downward or had not checked on the physical significance of our result (89), we might have assumed that (89) represented the downward as well as the upward motion and so might have drawn the wrong conclusions from the mathematics.

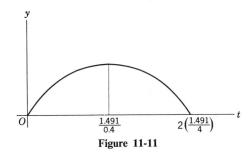

Figure 11-11

Exercises

1. Suppose that an object is projected upward with an initial velocity of 1000 ft/sec and there is no air resistance. Calculate the maximum height attained and compare the result with that in the text where the air resistance is $0.005v^2$.

Ans. 15,625 ft.

2. Suppose that an object is projected upward with an initial velocity of 1000 ft/sec in a medium whose resistance is proportional to the square of the velocity. Calculate the time t_1 to reach maximum height.

$$Ans.\ t_1 = \frac{1}{\sqrt{32k}} \tan^{-1}\left(\sqrt{\frac{k}{32}}\,1000\right).$$

3. Under the conditions of Exercise 2 calculate the maximum height y_1 attained by the object.

$$Ans.\ y_1 = \frac{1}{2k} \log\left[1 + (1000)^2\,\frac{k}{32}\right].$$

4. Suppose that an object is projected upward in a medium whose resistance is kv^2 and the initial velocity is v_0. How is (84) modified to suit this initial condition? How is (88) modified to suit this initial condition?

$$Ans.\ \alpha = \tan^{-1}\left(\sqrt{\frac{k}{32}}\,v_0\right).$$

5. To find the relation between height and velocity of a body that is projected upward with an initial velocity of 1000 ft/sec in a medium whose resistance is proportional to the square of the velocity, we can eliminate t between (84) and (88). Alternatively, we can start with (79) and use the now familiar fact that $dv/dt = v\,dv/dy$, where y is the vertical distance. Use this fact and find the relation between y and v.

$$\textit{Ans. } y = -\frac{1}{2k}\log\frac{32 + kv^2}{32 + k1000^2}.$$

6. Suppose that an object is projected upward in a medium whose resistance is 1/450 times the square of the velocity. The initial velocity is 40 ft/sec. Calculate the following:

(*a*) The time it takes to reach maximum height.   *Ans.* 1.20 sec.
(*b*) The greatest height the body will reach.   *Ans.* 23.5 ft.

We have found that we can represent the upward motion of an object in a medium whose resistance is proportional to the *square of the velocity*, but that the *downward* motion requires special treatment. Let us consider this problem. It is convenient to take the downward direction as positive. Then the force of gravity is $32m$ and the air resistance, which is directed upward, is $-Kv^2$. On the basis of Newton's second law of motion we may state that

$$m\dot{v} = 32m - Kv^2$$

or, after dividing through by m, that

(90) $$\dot{v} = 32 - kv^2,$$

where $k = K/m$. Because the right side is a function of the dependent variable, we consider instead the equation

(91) $$\frac{dt}{dv} = \frac{1}{32 - kv^2}.$$

The technique of integration that we have thus far acquired does not enable us to integrate the right side of (91). Instead of trying to integrate the particular function in (91), let us try to integrate a general function of the type represented by (91). Suppose that

(92) $$\frac{dy}{dx} = \frac{1}{a^2 - x^2}.$$

We do not know how to integrate (92), but we do know some algebra. We know, for example, that the denominator can be factored into $(a - x)(a + x)$ and we also know that a fraction of the form

(93) $$\frac{1}{(a - x)(a + x)}$$

could originate by adding fractions of the form

(94) $$\frac{A}{a - x} \quad \text{and} \quad \frac{B}{a + x}.$$

If we could reexpress (93) as a sum of fractions of the form in (94), we would be able to integrate, because we know how to handle these fractions.

Let us assume that

(95)
$$\frac{1}{a^2 - x^2} \equiv \frac{A}{a - x} + \frac{B}{a + x}.$$

We use the identity sign because A and B are to be determined in such a way that the left side equals the right side for all values of x except a and $-a$. Now let us determine the A and the B for which (95) holds. We can clear of fractions; that is, we can multiply both sides by $(a - x)(a + x)$. Then

(96)
$$1 \equiv A(a + x) + B(a - x).$$

For the proper A and B, (95) holds for all values of x except $x = a$ and $x = -a$. However, surprisingly, (96) holds for all values of x including a and $-a$. The reason is that (96) certainly holds for an infinite number of values of x because (95) does. Moreover, (96) is an equality of two polynomials. A theorem of algebra states that if two polynomials of the nth degree are equal for more than n-values, they are equal for all values.*

Because (96) holds for all values of x, let us set $x = a$. Then

$$A = \frac{1}{2a}.$$

If we set $x = -a$ in (96), we obtain

$$B = \frac{1}{2a}.$$

Then, in view of (95),

(97)
$$\frac{1}{a^2 - x^2} \equiv \frac{1}{2a(a - x)} + \frac{1}{2a(a + x)}.$$

We may now dispense with our assumption that (95) is correct by merely adding the two fractions on the right side of (97) to see that the sum is the left side.

Let us return to the integration problem in (92). In view of (97), we have that

$$\frac{dy}{dx} = \frac{1}{2a}\frac{1}{a - x} + \frac{1}{2a}\frac{1}{a + x}.$$

Now we can say that

$$y = -\frac{1}{2a}\log(a - x) + \frac{1}{2a}\log(a + x)$$

or

$$y = \frac{1}{2a}\log\frac{a + x}{a - x} + C.$$

* The proof of this theorem of algebra is simple. If two nth degree polynomials in x are equal for more than n-values of x, the difference of the two polynomials, which is at most an nth degree polynomial, vanishes for more than n values of x or has more than n-roots. This is impossible unless the difference is identically zero.

We have proved a theorem on integration, which we state explicitly for future reference.

Theorem: If

(98)
$$\frac{dy}{dx} = \frac{1}{a^2 - x^2},$$

then

(99)
$$y = \frac{1}{2a} \log \frac{a + x}{a - x} + C.$$

Moreover, if u is a function of x and if we have

(100)
$$\frac{dy}{dx} = \frac{1}{a^2 - u^2} \frac{du}{dx},$$

then, in view of the chain rule,

(101)
$$y = \frac{1}{2a} \log \frac{a + u}{a - u} + C.$$

The method we used to obtain (99) is called the method of partial fractions. The two fractions on the right side of (97) are said to be the partial fractions of the left side.

Now we can integrate (91), which reads

$$\frac{dt}{dv} = \frac{1}{32 - kv^2}.$$

We let

$$u = \sqrt{k}v.$$

Then

(102)
$$\frac{dt}{dv} = \frac{1}{32 - u^2}.$$

This derivative is neither in the form (98) nor (100). We can, however, put it into the form (100) because

$$\frac{du}{dv} = \sqrt{k}.$$

We therefore write (102) in the form

$$\frac{dt}{dv} = \frac{1}{\sqrt{k}} \cdot \frac{1}{32 - u^2} \cdot \sqrt{k}.$$

Now our derivative, apart from the constant factor $1/\sqrt{k}$, is in the form (100) where $a = \sqrt{32}$, y happens to be t, and x happens to be v. Then by (101)

$$t = \frac{1}{\sqrt{k}} \frac{1}{2\sqrt{32}} \log \frac{\sqrt{32} + u}{\sqrt{32} - u} + C$$

or

(103)
$$t = \frac{1}{2\sqrt{32k}} \log \frac{\sqrt{32} + \sqrt{k}v}{\sqrt{32} - \sqrt{k}v} + C.$$

We may as well determine the constant of integration at this point. We are considering the motion of an object that falls downward in a medium whose resistance is proportional to the square of the velocity. Suppose that time is measured from the instant the object starts to fall and suppose that the object starts from rest. Then $v = 0$ when $t = 0$. We see from (103) that $C = 0$, and therefore

$$(104) \qquad t = \frac{1}{2\sqrt{32k}} \log \frac{\sqrt{32} + \sqrt{k}v}{\sqrt{32} - \sqrt{k}v}.$$

To express v as a function of t, we first multiply through by $2\sqrt{32k}$. Then

$$\frac{\sqrt{32} + \sqrt{k}v}{\sqrt{32} - \sqrt{k}v} = e^{2\sqrt{32k}t}.$$

If we multiply both sides by the denominator, we see that we have a first degree equation in v. We collect terms involving v and obtain

$$\sqrt{\frac{k}{32}}\, v + \sqrt{\frac{k}{32}}\, e^{2\sqrt{32k}t}\, v = e^{2\sqrt{32k}t} - 1.$$

Then

$$(105) \qquad v = \sqrt{\frac{32}{k}} \frac{e^{\sqrt{32k}t} - 1}{e^{2\sqrt{32k}t} + 1}.$$

Thus we have obtained the velocity as a function of time.

We can draw an interesting conclusion from (105). Suppose that t becomes larger and larger. Then the numerator and the denominator in (89) become more nearly equal. In fact, for large t the exponential terms become so large that the subtraction of 1 in the numerator and the addition of 1 in the denominator have almost no effect on the value of the fraction. This can be expressed in the language of the calculus as

$$\lim_{t \to \infty} \frac{e^{2\sqrt{32k}t} - 1}{e^{2\sqrt{32k}t} + 1} = 1.$$

Then the velocity approaches the value $\sqrt{32/k}$ as t becomes infinite. This limiting velocity is the terminal velocity for the case in which the resistance of the medium is proportional to the square of the velocity. It is independent of the height from which the object falls and also independent of the initial velocity, although our derivation assumed a zero initial velocity.

Having found the formula for velocity, let us see if we can find the formula for the distance fallen in terms of the time. Let y represent the variable distance which, in view of our choice of direction for acceleration, is positive in the downward direction. From (105) we have

$$(106) \qquad \dot{y} = \sqrt{\frac{32}{k}} \frac{e^{2\sqrt{32k}t} - 1}{e^{2\sqrt{32k}t} + 1}.$$

Integration of the right side of (106) appears to be a formidable task. However, luck is with us. As (106) now stands, the method of integration is not obvious. If we multiply numerator and denominator by $e^{-\sqrt{32k}\,t}$, however, we obtain

$$(107) \qquad \dot{y} = \sqrt{\frac{32}{k}\,\frac{e^{\sqrt{32k}\,t} - e^{-\sqrt{32k}\,t}}{e^{\sqrt{32k}\,t} + e^{-\sqrt{32k}\,t}}}.$$

Now if we let

$$u = e^{\sqrt{32k}\,t} + e^{-\sqrt{32k}\,t},$$

then

$$\frac{du}{dt} = \sqrt{32k}(e^{\sqrt{32k}\,t} - e^{-\sqrt{32k}\,t}).$$

Aside from the factor $\sqrt{32k}$, which is a constant, this du/dt is precisely the numerator in (107). We can, of course, multiply and divide by the constant, so that (107) takes the form

$$\frac{dy}{dt} = \sqrt{\frac{32}{k}} \cdot \frac{1}{\sqrt{32k}} \cdot \frac{1}{u}\frac{du}{dt}.$$

Then by (30)

$$y = \frac{1}{k}\log u + C$$

or

$$(108) \qquad y = \frac{1}{k}\log (e^{\sqrt{32k}\,t} + e^{-\sqrt{32k}\,t}) + C.$$

To determine the constant of integration, we use the physical fact that $y = 0$ when $t = 0$; this is correct if we measure distance from the point at which the object begins to fall. If we substitute these values of y and t in (108), we find that

$$C = -\frac{1}{k}\log 2.$$

Then

$$y = \frac{1}{k}\log (e^{\sqrt{32k}\,t} + e^{-\sqrt{32k}\,t}) - \frac{1}{k}\log 2$$

or

$$(109) \qquad y = \frac{1}{k}\log \left(\frac{e^{\sqrt{32k}\,t} + e^{-\sqrt{32k}\,t}}{2}\right).$$

This is the formula for the distance fallen in t seconds if we measure distance from the point at which the object starts to fall. To sum up, in (105) and (109) we have obtained the velocity and distance fallen of an object that starts from rest and falls in a medium whose resistance is proportional to the square of the velocity.

Our entire discussion of motion in resisting media illustrates a very important feature of applied mathematics. As we noted at the beginning of Section 6, when Galileo decided to study motion he consciously neglected air resistance. When he was challenged about this neglect, he answered that we must first consider the primary phenomenon and then, if necessary, consider any additional factors. Galileo initiated what is still today regarded as the sound approach to the problems of applied mathematics and mathematical physics. One always idealizes a physical problem, which means neglecting any effects or subsidiary phenomena that may not matter for the usefulness of the desired results. If, however, the results are not accurate enough for the application, one must seek a better idealization, that is, one which hews closer to reality. Thus including resistance of the medium gives a better idealization than the assumption of no resistance for motions in the atmosphere and in water. A better idealization may also mean the need to employ more advanced mathematical techniques, as we can see by comparing what we did in Chapter 3 with the work in this section. Practical application may require even a third or fourth improvement in the idealization. For example, we ignored the shape of the moving object; in fact, we lumped such factors as shape, size, and frictional effects due to the surface of the object together in the value of the constant K and took into account only the effect of velocity on resistance. Such an idealization would not suffice if one were designing the wings of an airplane.

Exercises

1. Use the value of 0.005 for k and calculate the velocity and distance fallen by an object that starts from rest and falls for 3.7 seconds in a medium whose resistance is $0.005v^2$. We may recall from the text that 3.7 seconds is the time it takes the object to reach the maximum height of 219.5 feet, if it is projected upward with an initial velocity of 1000 ft/sec. Hence the purpose of this exercise is to see how much velocity the object acquires by falling downward for the same amount of time as it took to reach the maximum height and to see how the distance it falls during the 3.7 seconds compares with the distance it rose during that time. *Ans.* 72 ft/sec; 170.9 ft.

2. Suppose that an object starting from rest falls 219.5 feet in a medium whose resistance is $0.005\ v^2$. How long does it take to fall that distance?
   Suggestion: We are given k and y in (109), and our goal is to find t. Let $a = e^{\sqrt{32kt}}$. Then note that $e^{-\sqrt{32kt}} = 1/a$. Find a and then t. Do you expect the result for t to be more or less than 3.7 seconds, which is the time it takes to *rise* 219.5 feet, and what physical argument can you give to support your expectation? *Ans.* 4.38 sec.

3. Having found the time required to fall 219.5 feet under the conditions of Exercise 2, use that result to find the velocity that the object acquires in falling that distance. This velocity should be compared with the velocity of 1000 ft/sec

with which the object was projected upward so as to reach the maximum height of 219.5 feet.   *Ans.* 75.2 ft/sec.

4. If we were interested in finding the formula that relates velocity and distance fallen by an object which starts from rest and falls in a medium whose resistance is kv^2, we could take the value of t given by (104), substitute this in (109), and then simplify the resulting relation between y and v. We can, however, proceed as follows: In (90) we may use the fact that $dv/dt = (dv/dy)(dy/dt) = v(dv/dy)$. Then our differential equation becomes

$$v\frac{dv}{dy} = 32 - kv^2.$$

Find y as a function of v.   *Ans.* $y = \dfrac{1}{2k} \log \dfrac{32}{32 - kv^2}.$

5. Suppose that a raindrop falls from a cloud with an initial velocity v_0 in a medium whose resistance is kv^2. Find the distance fallen as a function of v.

$$\textit{Ans. } y = \frac{1}{2k} \log \frac{32 - kv_0{}^2}{32 - kv^2}.$$

6. Using the result of Exercise 5, solve for v as function of y and then find the terminal velocity. Note that the terminal velocity is by definition the velocity approached as t becomes infinite. But by (109) we see that as t becomes infinite, Is the terminal velocity independent of the initial velocity v_0?

$$\textit{Ans. } v = \sqrt{\frac{32e^{2ky} + kv_0{}^2 - 32}{ke^{2ky}}}.$$

7. An object that falls from rest in a medium whose resistance is proportional to the square of the velocity has a terminal velocity of 16 ft/sec. How long does it take to acquire a velocity of 15.8 ft/sec.?   *Ans.* 1.267 sec.

8. Suppose that an object is shot up from the ground with a velocity of 80 ft/sec in a medium whose resistance is 1/200 of the square of the velocity. Find the velocity with which the object returns to the ground and the time required for the up and down motions.

   Ans. Velocity on reaching ground, $40\sqrt{2}$ ft/sec; time to reach maximum height, 1.96 sec; time for downward motion, 2.2 sec.

9. A parachute jumper falls in a medium whose resistance is proportional to the square of the velocity. If he does not open his parachute, $k = 0.0015$. If he does open it, $k = 0.142$. Compare the terminal velocities in the two cases.
                                        Ans. 170 ft/sec; 15 ft/sec.

10. With the data of the Exercise 9 determine for both cases how far the parachute jumper falls by the time he reaches a velocity of 95 per cent of the terminal velocity.   *Ans.* 915.8 ft; 8.7 ft.

11. A particle is projected upward with an initial speed V in a medium whose air resistance is kv^2 where v is the velocity. Find the velocity of the particle when it falls back to its starting point. *Suggestion:* By using the result of Exercise 4 of the preceding list we learn the maximum height the particle will attain. It will then fall from that height to the ground starting with a zero initial velocity.   *Ans.* $v = V/\sqrt{1 + (kV^2/32)}.$

8. *Hyperbolic Functions.* In formula (109) of Section 7 we found that an object which falls from rest in a medium whose resistance is proportional to the square of the velocity falls the distance

(110)
$$y = \frac{1}{k} \log \left(\frac{e^{\sqrt{32k}\,t} + e^{-\sqrt{32k}\,t}}{2} \right)$$

where t is the time. The quantity in parenthesis has a form that occurs often in mathematics; mathematicians have therefore introduced a name for such

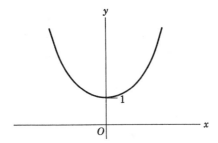

Figure 11-12. $y = \cosh x$.

expressions. Specifically, we introduce a new function called hyperbolic cosine of x and abbreviated to cosh x (pronounced as spelled). By definition

(111)
$$y = \cosh x = \frac{e^x + e^{-x}}{2}.$$

The graph of $y = \cosh x$ is shown in Fig. 11-12. The derivative of this function also occurs frequently; it is called the hyperbolic sine of x and is abbreviated to sinh x (pronounced like "cinch"). Then

(112)
$$y = \sinh x = \frac{e^x - e^{-x}}{2}.$$

The graph of $y = \sinh x$ is shown in Fig. 11-13.

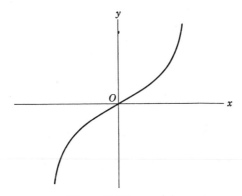

Figure 11-13. $y = \sinh x$.

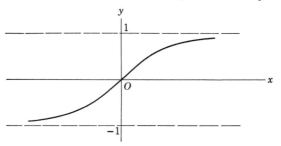

Figure 11-14. $y = \tanh x$.

These two functions are analogous to the ordinary sine and cosine functions, although there are differences. Thus, whereas

$$\frac{d}{dx} \cos x = -\sin x.$$

we have

(113) $$\frac{d}{dx} \cosh x = \sinh x.$$

Just as it is convenient in ordinary trigonometry to introduce four additional functions that can be defined in terms of sin x and cos x, so for the hyperbolic functions we introduce four additional functions, namely,

$$\tanh x = \frac{\sinh x}{\cosh x}, \qquad \coth x = \frac{1}{\tanh x},$$

(114)

$$\operatorname{sech} x = \frac{1}{\cosh x}, \qquad \operatorname{csch} x = \frac{1}{\sinh x}.$$

The graph of $y = \tanh x$ is shown in Fig. 11-14. and for handy reference we include the graphs of $y = \coth x$, $y = \operatorname{sech} x$, and $y = \operatorname{csch} x$ (Figs. 11-15 through 11-17).

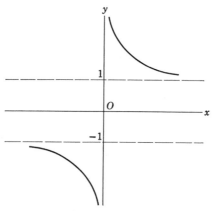

Figure 11-15. $y = \coth x$.

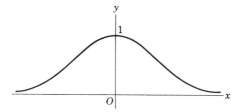

Figure 11-16. $y = \text{sech } x$.

For these six hyperbolic functions, as for the ordinary trigonometric functions, many identities hold. For example, we see immediately from the definitions of the hyperbolic functions that

$$\sinh x = -\sinh (-x),$$

(115) $$\cosh x = \cosh (-x_e),$$

$$\cosh^2 x = \sinh^2 x = 1.$$

As these examples show, some of the identities are entirely analogous to those for the ordinary trigonometric functions, whereas others differ somewhat. We leave for the exercises the establishment of a few other identities for the hyperbolic functions.

The term hyperbolic functions suggests that somehow the hyperbola is involved. Let us recall that the familiar trigonometric functions are defined in terms of ordinate, abscissa, and distance of any point P in the coordinate plane that lies on the terminal side of the angle when the initial side (Fig. 11-18) is the positive x-axis. As the angle A varies, point P on the terminal side can always be taken to have the same distance from the origin. Hence these points lie on a circle and the ordinary functions are often called the circular functions to distinguish them from the hyperbolic functions. The latter can be defined in terms of properties of the hyperbola but because the definitions are not often used we shall not look into them.

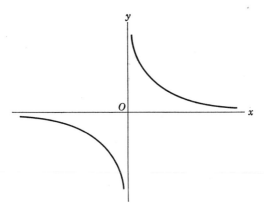

Figure 11-17. $y = \text{csch } x$.

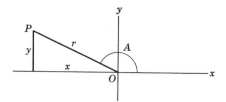

Figure 11-18

Just as the ordinary or circular trigonometric functions give rise to inverse functions, so do the hyperbolic functions. Thus to the function

$$y = \sinh x$$

there corresponds the inverse hyperbolic function

(116) $$x = \sinh^{-1} y.$$

To write down the inverse function is not enough. We must also ascertain that there is a unique x for each y or at least a unique x for each y in some domain. However, Fig. 11-13 shows that this is the case for every value of y.

Because $y = \sinh x$ has a meaning in terms of the exponential functions, let us see if we can obtain some corresponding meaning for $x = \sinh^{-1} y$. We know that

$$y = \sinh x = \frac{e^x - e^{-x}}{2}.$$

Let us see if we can solve for x in terms of y. We let

$$e^x = z.$$

Then

$$e^{-x} = \frac{1}{z}$$

and

$$y = \frac{z - \dfrac{1}{z}}{2}.$$

This equation is easily solved for z and yields

$$z = y \pm \sqrt{y^2 + 1}.$$

We seem to have a choice here, but if we wish to stick to real values of our variables then because z or e^x is necessarily positive,

$$z = y + \sqrt{y^2 + 1}.$$

In view of the value of z

$$x = \log (y + \sqrt{y^2 + 1}).$$

This function is defined for every real value of y.

Because it is customary to use x for the independent variable and y for the dependent variable, we now write

(117) $$y = \sinh^{-1} x = \log{(x + \sqrt{x^2 + 1})}$$

and this function is defined for every real x (Fig. 11-19).

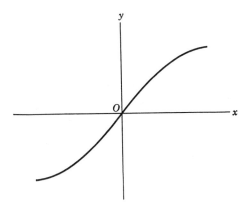

Figure 11-19. $y = \sinh^{-1} x$.

We may define an inverse hyperbolic function for each of the original hyperbolic functions. Thus to $y = \cosh x$ there corresponds

$$x = \cosh^{-1} y.$$

As in the case of $x = \sinh^{-1} y$, we can find an expression for $x = \cosh^{-1} y$ in terms of the logarithmic function. Here we find by the above method that

$$x = \log{(y \pm \sqrt{y^2 - 1})}.$$

In this case we must be careful as to which of the two functions we choose. The graph of $y = \cosh x$ (Fig. 11-12) shows that there are two values of x for each value of y greater than 1. The two choices for x show up in the above equation by the presence of $\pm \sqrt{y^2 - 1}$. We use for the principal branch

$$x = \log{(y + \sqrt{y^2 - 1})} \quad \text{for} \quad y \geq 1.$$

If we now revert to the use of x and y as independent and dependent variables, respectively, we have for the principal branch

(118) $$y = \cosh^{-1} x = \log{(x + \sqrt{x^2 - 1})} \quad \text{for} \quad x \geq 1.$$

Figure 11-20 shows the graph of the double-valued function. The principal branch is the upper half and the logarithmic expression in (118) represents only this half.

Corresponding to the function $y = \tanh x$, there is the inverse function

$$x = \tanh^{-1} y.$$

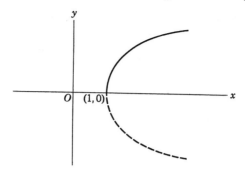

Figure 11-20. $y = \cosh^{-1} x$.

To obtain an expression for x in terms of ordinary functions, we go back to

$$y = \tanh x = \frac{\sinh x}{\cosh x} = \frac{e^x - e^{-x}}{e^x + e^{-x}}.$$

If we use our earlier device of letting $e^x = z$ and solve for z, we find that

$$z^2 = \frac{1 + y}{1 - y}.$$

and because $z^2 = e^{2x}$,

$$x = \tfrac{1}{2} \log \frac{1 + y}{1 - y}.$$

This function is defined for all y between -1 and $+1$. With the usual use of x and y, we write

(119) $\qquad y = \tanh^{-1} x = \tfrac{1}{2} \log \dfrac{1 + x}{1 - x} \quad$ for $-1 < x < 1$.

Figure 11-21 shows the graph of this function.

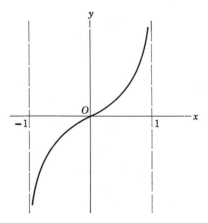

Figure 11-21. $y = \tanh^{-1} x$.

We see from the manner in which we have treated the first three inverse hyperbolic functions that we can make the analogous definitions for the last three. For reference we note that

(120) $y = \coth^{-1} x = \frac{1}{2} \log \dfrac{x+1}{x-1}$ for $x < -1$ and $x > 1$.

Figure 11-22 shows the graph of this function.

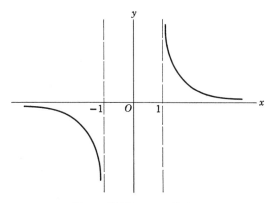

Figure 11-22. $y = \coth^{-1} x$.

Furthermore, we have

(121) $y = \operatorname{sech}^{-1} x = \log \dfrac{1 + \sqrt{1 - x^2}}{x}$ for $0 < x \leq 1$.

The graph of this function is shown in Fig. 11-23; the principal branch in the upper half of the graph and the logarithmic expression in (121) represents only this half.

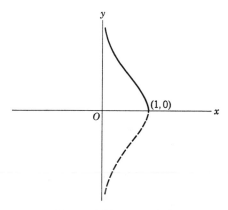

Figure 11-23. $y = \operatorname{sech}^{-1} x$.

Finally, we have the function

(122) $$y = \operatorname{csch}^{-1} x = \log\left(\frac{1}{x} + \frac{\sqrt{1 + x^2}}{|x|}\right) \quad \text{for } x \neq 0.$$

The graph of this function is given by Fig. 11-24.

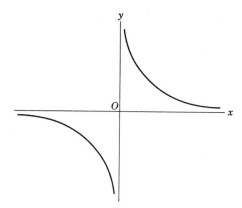

Figure 11-24. $y = \operatorname{csch}^{-1} x$.

We can obtain the formulas for the derivatives of the inverse hyperbolic functions in several ways. The easiest say would be to use the logarithmic expressions in formulas (117) to (122). For reference we note the results:

(123) $$\frac{d(\sinh^{-1} x)}{dx} = \frac{1}{\sqrt{1 + x^2}};$$

(124) $$\frac{d(\cosh^{-1} x)}{dx} = \frac{1}{\sqrt{x^2 - 1}}$$

$$\text{for } x \geq 1 \quad \text{and for the principal branch;}$$

(125) $$\frac{d(\tanh^{-1} x)}{dx} = \frac{1}{1 - x^2} \quad \text{for } |x| < 1;$$

(126) $$\frac{d(\coth^{-1} x)}{dx} = \frac{1}{1 - x^2} \quad \text{for } |x| > 1;$$

(127) $$\frac{d(\operatorname{sech}^{-1} x)}{dx} = -\frac{1}{x\sqrt{1 - x^2}}$$

$$\text{for } 0 < x < 1 \quad \text{and for the principal branch;}$$

(128) $$\frac{d(\operatorname{csch}^{-1} x)}{dx} = -\frac{1}{|x|\sqrt{1 + x^2}}.$$

Of course, the chain rule extends the usefulness of these formulas in the usual way.

We see from the discussion of the hyperbolic functions and their inverse functions that they are no more than special combinations of exponential functions and logarithmic functions. Nevertheless, it is easier to work with the hyperbolic and inverse hyperbolic functions as such. For example, let us use them to express some of the quantities we encountered in the study of objects falling in resisting media. Thus formula (109) for the distance fallen in a medium whose resistance is proportional to the square of the velocity can be written as

(129)
$$y = \frac{1}{k} \log \cosh \sqrt{32kt}.$$

Also, because

$$\tanh x = \frac{e^x - e^{-x}}{e^x + e^{-x}} = \frac{e^{2x} - 1}{e^{2x} + 1},$$

we can write formula (105) for the velocity acquired in falling from rest in a medium whose resistance is proportional to the square of the velocity as

(130)
$$v = \sqrt{\frac{32}{k}} \tanh \sqrt{32kt}.$$

We can now bring together conveniently the results of the up and down motion in a medium whose resistance is proportional to the square of the velocity. In our study of the upward motion we found (see Exercise 2, page 337) that if a body is projected upward with an initial velocity V, then the time t_1 to reach maximum height is given by

(131)
$$t_1 = \frac{1}{\sqrt{32k}} \tan^{-1} \sqrt{\frac{k}{32}} V$$

and maximum height y_1 is given by (see Exercise 3, page 337).

(132)
$$y_1 = \frac{1}{2k} \log \left(1 + \frac{k}{32} V^2\right).$$

If we wish to calculate the time t_2 required for the object to fall back to the ground, we can use (129), where the distance y is given by (132), and our problem is to find t_2. That is, t_2 is given by the equation

$$\frac{1}{2k} \log \left(1 + \frac{k}{32} V^2\right) = \frac{1}{k} \log \cosh \sqrt{32kt_2}.$$

To solve for t_2, we multiply by k and write

$$\log \left(1 + \frac{k}{32} V^2\right)^{\frac{1}{2}} = \log \cosh \sqrt{32kt_2}$$

or

(133)
$$\left(1 + \frac{k}{32} V^2\right)^{\frac{1}{2}} = \cosh \sqrt{32kt_2}.$$

We could, of course, write our answer as

$$t_2 = \frac{1}{\sqrt{32k}} \cosh^{-1}\left(1 + \frac{k}{32}V^2\right)^{1/2},$$

but we can put the answer in a simpler form. We know from (115) that

$$\sinh^2 x = \cosh^2 x - 1.$$

Then

$$\sinh^2 \sqrt{32k}t_2 = \cosh^2 (\sqrt{32k}t_2) - 1,$$

and in view of (133)

$$\sinh^2 \sqrt{32k}t_2 = 1 + \frac{k}{32}V^2 - 1 = \frac{k}{32}V^2.$$

Then

$$\sinh \sqrt{32k}t_2 = \sqrt{\frac{k}{32}}V$$

and

(134) $$t_2 = \frac{1}{\sqrt{32k}} \sinh^{-1}\sqrt{\frac{k}{32}}V,$$

or, in view of (117),

(135) $$t_2 = \frac{1}{\sqrt{32k}} \log\left(\sqrt{\frac{k}{32}}V + \sqrt{\frac{k}{32}V^2 + 1}\right).$$

We now compare (131) with (134) or (135) and see that the time t_1 to reach maximum height is by no means the same as the time t_2 to fall from maximum height to the ground.

Exercises

1. Establish the following identities:

(*a*) $\tanh x = -\tanh(-x)$.

(*b*) $\sinh x = \dfrac{2 \tanh \dfrac{x}{2}}{1 - \tanh^2 \dfrac{x}{2}}$.

(*c*) $\sinh x = \dfrac{\tanh x}{\sqrt{1 - \tanh^2 x}}$.

(*d*) $\sinh 2x = 2 \sinh x \cosh x$.

(*e*) $\cosh 2x = \cosh^2 x + \sinh^2 x$.

(*f*) $\cosh 2x = 2 \cosh^2 x - 1$.

(*g*) $\cosh 2x = 1 + 2 \sinh^2 x$.

(*h*) $\tanh 2x = \dfrac{2 \tanh x}{1 + \tanh^2 x}$.

(*i*) $\sinh(x \pm y) = \sinh x \cosh y \pm \cosh x \sinh y$.

(*j*) $\cosh(x \pm y) = \cosh x \cosh y \pm \sinh x \sinh y$.

2. Show that the following relations hold:

(*a*) $\dfrac{d}{dx}(\sinh x) = \cosh x$.

(*b*) $\dfrac{d}{dx}(\tanh x) = \operatorname{sech}^2 x\, dx$.

(*c*) $\dfrac{d}{dx}(\coth x) = -\operatorname{csch}^2 x$.

3. Show that the following relations hold:

(a) $\dfrac{d}{dx}(\sinh^{-1} x) = 1/\sqrt{1 + x^2}$.

(c) $\dfrac{d}{dx}(\tanh^{-1} x) = 1/(1 - x^2)$.

(b) $\dfrac{d}{dx}(\cosh^{-1} x) = 1/\sqrt{x^2 - 1}$.

4. (a) We found that if a body is projected upward with an initial velocity V in a medium whose resistance is proportional to the square of the velocity, the time to fall from the maximum height to the ground is given by $t_2 = (1/\sqrt{32k})\sinh^{-1}\sqrt{k/32}\,V$. Show that the velocity the object acquires in falling from maximum height to the ground is given by $v_2 = \sqrt{32/k}\tanh(\sinh^{-1}\sqrt{k/32}\,V)$.

(b) Now show that the answer to part (a) can be expressed as

$$v_2 = \sqrt{\frac{32}{k}}\left(1 + \frac{32}{kV^2}\right)^{-\frac{1}{2}}.$$

Suggestion: Convert the $\sinh^{-1}$ to an equivalent $\tanh^{-1}$. Note that the velocity v_2 when the object reaches the ground is quite different from the velocity V with which the object is shot up.

5. Suppose that an object is shot up with an initial velocity V in a medium whose resistance is proportional to the square of the velocity. Write an expression for the total time of flight.

$$\text{\it Ans. } T = \frac{1}{\sqrt{32k}}\left[\tan^{-1}\sqrt{\frac{k}{32}}\,V + \cosh^{-1}\left(1 + \frac{k}{\sqrt{32}}V^2\right)^{\frac{1}{2}}\right].$$

9. *Logarithmic Differentiation.* We return for a moment to the pure technique of differentiation. We can now dispose of one more case of the power rule that we were unable to treat earlier. We proved that if

(136) $$y = x^n$$

and n is a rational number, that is, an integer or quotient of two integers, positive or negative, or zero,

$$\dot{y} = nx^{n-1}.$$

These proofs do not apply to cases such as

$$y = x^{\sqrt{2}}$$

because the exponent here is an irrational number, that is, neither a whole number nor a ratio of two whole numbers. The question then is, what is the derivative of x^n when n is irrational?

Let us note first that we limit the function to values of x greater than 0. The reason is that if x should be negative, the meaning of a negative number raised to an irrational exponent becomes complicated. The difficulty here is basically of the same kind as that involved in $(-2)^{1/2}$; that is, we run into complex numbers.

To differentiate the function in (136), we first take the logarithm of both sides. Then

$$\log y = n \log x.$$

To help our thinking we may introduce the variable u such that

$$u = \log y = n \log x.$$

Then u is a function of x for which we may assert

(137)
$$\frac{du}{dx} = n \frac{1}{x}.$$

But

$$\frac{du}{dx} = \frac{du}{dy} \frac{dy}{dx} = \frac{1}{y} \frac{dy}{dx}.$$

By equating the two results for du/dx we have

$$\frac{1}{y} \frac{dy}{dx} = n \frac{1}{x}.$$

Multiplication of both sides by y and replacement of y by x^n yields

(138)
$$\dot{y} = nx^{n-1}.$$

Thus we see that the same power rule applies when n is an irrational number as when it is rational. Of course, the corresponding integral, namely, if

$$\dot{y} = nx^{-n-1}$$

then

(139)
$$y = x^n + C,$$

applies when n is irrational, as does the chain rule in the case of

$$y = u^n$$

where n is irrational and u is a positive function of x.

The device of taking the logarithm of y in the function $y = f(x)$ that we wish to differentiate before differentiating is known as logarithmic differentiation. Its utility extends beyond the proof of the power rule for irrational n. Let us consider, for example, the function

(140)
$$y = x^x, \qquad x > 0.$$

This function is not a power of x in the usual sense, for in $y = x^n$ the exponent is a constant. Nor is (140) an exponential function in the usual sense, for in e^x or a^x the base is constant. Nevertheless, (140) is a function of x, and it is

meaningful to ask for its derivative. By the technique of logarithmic differentiation we can obtain it immediately. For

$$\log y = x \log x.$$

Then, in the same way,

$$\frac{1}{y}\frac{dy}{dx} = x \cdot \frac{1}{x} + \log x$$

or

$$\frac{dy}{dx} = y(1 + \log x)$$

or

$$\frac{dy}{dx} = x^x(1 + \log x).$$

The device of logarithmic differentiation proves useful especially when we
must differentiate functions of the form

$$y = u^v$$

where u and v are functions of x.

Exercises

1. Find $\dot{y}$ when y has the following values:

(a) $y = (x^2)^x$.   *Ans.* $\dot{y} = (2 + 2\log x)(x^2)^x$.

(b) $y = (x^2)^{2x}$.

(c) $y = \dfrac{\sqrt{2x + 5}}{\sqrt{x^2 + 7}}$.   *Ans.* $\dot{y} = \left(\dfrac{1}{2x + 5} - \dfrac{x}{x^2 + 7}\right)\dfrac{\sqrt{2x + 5}}{\sqrt{2x + 7}}$.

(d) $y = (x^2 + 1)^6(3x^3 - 5)^4(x^4 - 2x)^3$.

Differentials and the Law of the Mean

1. Differentials. Suppose that we are working with the function $y = x^2$ and wish to calculate Δy when $x = 5$ and $\Delta x = 0.2$. The need to do this might arise in experimental or engineering work where the value of x has been measured and found to be 5 with a possible error of as much as 0.2. One might then wish to know how much y could be in error because of the error in x. We can, of course, calculate Δy. For any x it is $(x + \Delta x)^2 - x^2$, so that

$$(1) \qquad \Delta y = 2x\,\Delta x + (\Delta x)^2.$$

We observe that when Δx is small, 0.2 in our case, $(\Delta x)^2$ is much smaller. A good approximation, then, to Δy is given by $2x\,\Delta x$; to have a notation for this approximation we shall use dy. Then

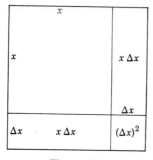

Figure 12-1

$$(2) \qquad dy = 2x\,\Delta x.$$

We can picture (Fig. 12-1) what the approximation amounts to. The function $y = x^2$ can represent the area of a square of side x, and Δx can represent an increase in x. We see then what $2x\,\Delta x$ and $(\Delta x)^2$ are. Certainly, for small Δx, the latter is much smaller than the former.

The advantage gained in approximating Δy by dy is minor for the function $y = x^2$, but only because the function is so simple. For even a slightly more complicated function the advantage can be considerable. Let us take $y = x^4$. Here

$$(3) \qquad \Delta y = 4x^3\,\Delta x + 6x^2(\Delta x)^2 + 4x(\Delta x)^3 + (\Delta x)^4.$$

For small Δx, not only is $(\Delta x)^2$ smaller, but $(\Delta x)^3$ and $(\Delta x)^4$ are even smaller. Hence the approximation dy, where

$$(4) \qquad dy = 4x^3\,\Delta x,$$

should be good, and we see here how much simpler it would be to calculate dy as opposed to Δy. When we consider how much more complicated than even $y = x^4$ are the functions that we deal with in the calculus, we must agree that there is some point to having a useful approximation to Δy.

Let us try to see what the proper generalization of (2) and (4) might be. We usually introduce Δy to calculate the derivative of the function. We then divide Δy by Δx and take the limit as Δx approaches 0. Were we to do this in (1) and in (3), we would find that the derivative is the coefficient of the term containing Δx in (1) and (3). For example, (3) can be written as

(5) $\qquad \Delta y = \dot{y}\,\Delta x +$ terms involving higher powers of Δx.

Equation (5) suggests that if we start with any function $y = f(x)$ and form Δy, we obtain

(6) $\qquad\qquad\qquad \Delta y = f'(x)\,\Delta x + \epsilon\,\Delta x,$

where ϵ is some quantity that approaches 0 when Δx does. (Mathematicians love to use Greek letters, such as epsilon here, because Greek letters seem more mysterious and more impressive to nonmathematicians and suggest that mathematicians are deep thinkers.) As a matter of fact, Δy must have the form in (6) because we know that $\Delta y/\Delta x$ is not $f'(x)$ but is $f'(x)$ plus some quantity that approaches 0 as Δx does. If the difference

$$\frac{\Delta y}{\Delta x} - f'(x)$$

did not approach 0 as Δx does, the quotient would not approach the derivative.

Because (6) is the correct form of Δy for any function, then from the very nature of ϵ we see that

(7) $\qquad\qquad\qquad dy = f'(x)\,\Delta x$

is a good approximation to Δy for small Δx. The quantity dy is called the *differential* of y. It is customary when working with differentials to write dx in place of Δx, although both have the identical meaning, namely, a change in x. Thus (7) is usually written as

(8) $\qquad\qquad\qquad dy = f'(x)\,dx.$

We note that the quotient of dy and dx is the derivative; we shall say more about it later.

Let us see what dy means geometrically. Suppose that we are at point P on the curve (Fig. 12-2a and b) of $y = f(x)$. If we change x by some amount Δx or dx, then y changes by some amount Δy, which is shown in the two figures. As for dy, in view of (8), the quotient dy/dx must equal the derivative at P and the derivative is the slope of the tangent line at P. However, the slope of a line is the tangent of the angle of inclination A. Then dy must be the length shown in each of the two figures. We could say that dy is in the increment in the function represented by the tangent line at P, or that if the function $y = f(x)$ were replaced by its tangent line at P, dy would be the increment in the function representing the tangent line corresponding to the increment dx in x. We see that for the function $y = f(x)$, dy is not the same as Δy; however, for small dx, dy is a good approximation to Δy.

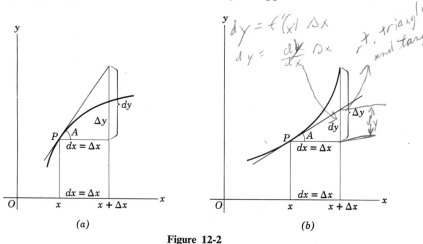

Figure 12-2

Let us return to an observation made earlier, namely, that the quotient of the differentials dy and dx at a value of x is the derivative of the function at that value of x. We have learned that the derivative $\dot{y}$ or $f'(x)$ of a function $y = f(x)$ is the *limit of a quotient*, namely, the quotient $\Delta y/\Delta x$, but we have emphasized that the derivative is not itself a quotient. That is, we cannot take the limit of Δy and divide it by the limit of Δx to obtain the derivative, because this procedure leads to $0/0$. However, once the notion of the derivative of a function is established, it is possible to *define*, as we did, a new quantity, namely, dy, so that the quotient dy/dx does equal the derivative. The notation dy/dx, then, has two meanings. So far we have used it as an alternative notation for $\dot{y}$ and in this sense it is *not* a quotient but the limit of $\Delta y/\Delta x$ as Δx approaches 0. From now on it also means the quotient of dy and dx, where dy is defined in (8) or (7) and dx is an alternative symbol for Δx.

The use of dy/dx is a bit confusing, particularly because in the sense of a derivative it is not a quotient. Why have we used it in that sense? The reason is largely historical and not without interest. When Leibniz attempted to define the derivative he realized that $\Delta y/\Delta x$ was not the correct quantity. He thought, however, that when Δx was sufficiently small and yet not zero, the quotient $\Delta y/\Delta x$ reached a value that was the derivative, that is, it yielded the slope of the tangent to the curve. When Δx and Δy were such sufficiently small quantities, Leibniz denoted them by dy and dx, and thus the derivative

was truly a quotient for him. He called *dy* and *dx* infinitesimals. We might wonder how Leibniz could have been so crude because, surely, we see clearly that no matter how small Δx is, $\Delta y/\Delta x$ is not exactly the value of the derivative. However, we must remember that the limit concept was not yet fashioned in the early days of the calculus, although Newton working independently, had the beginnings of a grip on this idea. Moreover, Leibniz believed that a continuous curve was really a series of very small line segments and that the tangent to the curve and the curve coincided over such a segment, the segment *PQ* of Fig. 12-3. (Of course, the segment in this figure is much enlarged over what Leibniz took its size to be.) In this view, if *dx* were no greater than the change in *x*-value between the two ends of the segment, Δy, the change in *y*-value of the curve, and *dy*, the change in *y*-value on the tangent line, would be equal.

Figure 12-3

We might think that the concept of infinitesimals, because it is based on such crude thinking, would have been abandoned long ago. But Newton and Leibniz quarreled. The Continental mathematicians, who were far more numerous and more active than the English mathematicians, were partial to Leibniz's ideas and notation and ignored Newton's work. For about 150 years the proper foundation for the derivative and other calculus concepts was not laid, and Leibniz's notation and use of differentials became standard in the calculus. Hence to read calculus books and more advanced works using the calculus we must at least become familiar with the notation employed.

However, there is some advantage to Leibniz's notation. Aside from the fact that *dy/dx* indicates what the independent and dependent variables are, now that *dy* and *dx* are properly defined as separate quantities, it is often convenient, when *dy* and *dx* are being used separately and the quotient does occur, to use the fact that *dy/dx* is the derivative. Otherwise, to indicate the derivative we would be obliged to replace this quotient by $\dot{y}$ or $f'(x)$. The use of *dy* itself as a separate concept is certainly advantageous, as our opening remarks on approximation indicated.

Exercises

1. Find *dy* for each of the following functions:

(*a*) $y = x^3$.   *Ans.* $dy = 3x^2\, dx$.
(*b*) $y = \sqrt{x}$.
(*c*) $y = x^{3/2}$.   *Ans.* $dy = \frac{3}{2}\sqrt{x}\, dx$.
(*d*) $y = \sin x$.
(*e*) $y = \cos x$.
        Ans. $dy = -\sin x\, dx$.

(*f*) $y = \log x$.
(*g*) $y = e^x$.
(*h*) $y = e^{2x}$.   *Ans.* $dy = 2e^{2x}\, dx$.
(*i*) $y = (x^2 + 1)^4$.

2. Compute $\sqrt{101}$ approximately. *Suggestion:* Compute dy for the function $y = \sqrt{x}$ when $x = 100$ and $dx = 1$.   *Ans.* 10.05.

3. Calculate $\sin 59°$ approximately, knowing that $\sin 60° = \sqrt{3}/2$. Remember that the calculus formulas presuppose radian measure for angles.

Ans. 0.8573.

4. What approximate error would arise in the volume of a sphere of radius 3 inches if the radius were in error by 0.2 inch?   *Ans.* 7.2π.

5. The width of a river is calculated by measuring the angle of elevation from a point on one bank of the top of a tree 50 feet high and directly across on the opposite bank. The angle is 45° with a possible error of 20'. Find the possible error in the calculated width of the river.   *Ans.* 100/173 ft.

6. The period of a pendulum is given by the formula $T = 2\pi\sqrt{l/32}$ where l is the length of the pendulum in feet and T is in seconds. Suppose that the pendulum consists of a steel wire and bob and the wire expands by 1 per cent of its length because the temperature of the environment increases.

   (a) What is the approximate error in the period?   *Ans.* $\frac{1}{2}\%$.

   (b) What is the approximate error per second?   *Ans.* 0.005.

   (c) What is the approximate error in the reading of this pendulum clock in one day?   *Ans.* 7.2 sec.

7. Suppose that you are planning to construct a machine that would calculate

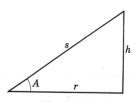

Figure 12-4

r (Fig. 12-4) either by using the values of s and A so that $r = s \cos A$ or by using the values of h and A so that $r = h \cot A$. Let us suppose further that it is possible to obtain the values of s and h quite accurately, but that the values of A for small angles cannot be obtained accurately. Which method of calculating r would you use to achieve better accuracy? *Suggestion:* Consider dr in each case.   *Ans.* $r = s \cos A$.

8. With reference to Fig. 12-4, suppose that to calculate s you have the choice of measuring h and A so that $s = h \csc A$ or of measuring r and A so that $s = r \sec A$. As in the preceding exercise, we suppose that lengths can be measured quite accurately, but that the measures of small angles cannot be obtained accurately. Which method of calculating s would you use?

Ans. $s = r \sec A$.

9. A pendulum clock is observed to lose 20 seconds a day when taken to a different locality. If the loss is due to the change in the value of g, find the approximate difference in g-values between the two localities. *Suggestion:* Because the acceleration of gravity is not necessarily 32 ft/sec², you must use the formula $T = 2\pi\sqrt{l/g}$.   *Ans.* $g/2160$.

10. If the pendulum of a clock is normally 3 feet long and the length increases by $\frac{1}{8}$ inch, how many minutes a day will the clock lose.

11. Using the formula $T = 2\pi\sqrt{l/g}$ for the period of a pendulum, where g has replaced 32, calculate the following:

   (a) Find the percentage change in T if the pendulum is removed to a place where the value of g is 0.2 per cent less.   *Ans.* $\frac{1}{10}\%$.

(b) Suppose that T remains constant but the value of l is in error by about 0.5 per cent. What is the percentage error in the value of g.

(c) Find the percentage error in the value of g if the period is in error by 0.1 per cent. *Ans.* 0.2%.

12. A given quantity of metal is to be cast in the form of a solid right circular cylinder of radius 5 inches and height 10 inches. If the radius is made $\frac{1}{20}$ of an inch too large, what is the error in the height?

13. Find the approximate difference that 1 minute of angle makes in log tan x when $x = 60°$. *Ans.* 0.0029.

14. The range R of a projectile fired at an angle A to the ground and with an initial velocity V is given by $R = (V^2/g) \sin 2A$, g being the acceleration of gravity. Show that for a small change in g, the percentage change in R is equal to the percentage change in g.

15. Give two interpretations of the notation dy/dx.

2. Differential Notation in Differentiation and Integration.

Because the differentials dy and dx have been used since the seventeenth century, it has been customary to phrase the operation of differentiation in terms of differentials. Thus given the function $y = \sin x$, for example, one can ask for the differential dy, and the answer, in view of (8), is

$$(9) \qquad\qquad dy = \cos x \, dx.$$

On the other hand,

$$(10) \qquad\qquad \dot{y} = \cos x.$$

The two statements (9) and (10) are entirely equivalent, for we can divide both sides of (9) by dx, and the quotient of the differentials dy and dx is, by their very definition, $\dot{y}$. Thus finding the differential dy of a function of x involves no new technique.

The differential form is used not only as an alternative to the derivative but also in integration. Up to now the problem of integration or antidifferentiation has been phrased thus: given that

$$(11) \qquad\qquad \dot{y} = \cos x,$$

find y. By reversing differentiation we know that

$$y = \sin x + C.$$

In terms of differentials the same problem is stated thus: given

$$(12) \qquad\qquad dy = \cos x \, dx,$$

find y. Because (12) says the same thing as (11), the process of antidifferentiation is also the same. One can say immediately that

$$y = \sin x + C.$$

Thus, as in the case of differentiation, the use of differentials introduces no new difficulty in integration.

A notation that is used in connection with integration is so much associated with the differential notation that we should become familiar with it. Suppose again that we are given

$$(13) \qquad \dot{y} = \cos x$$

and that we wish to find y. Before actually carrying out the integration, one can write

$$(14) \qquad y = \int \cos x + C.$$

The new symbol, $\int$, which is an elongated capital S, here states only that y is the function whose derivative is $\cos x$. The next step usually is to find y, and this is done in the same way as before; that is,

$$(15) \qquad y = \sin x + C.$$

The integral sign is usually used with the differential notation largely for historical reasons. Thus if we are given either

$$\dot{y} = \cos x$$

or

$$(16) \qquad dy = \cos x \, dx$$

we write first

$$(17) \qquad y = \int \cos x \, dx + C$$

and then by integration obtain

$$(18) \qquad y = \sin x + C.$$

The integral sign is for present purposes not really needed. We can go directly from (13) to (15) or from (16) to (18). However, we shall find it valuable later and so may as well become accustomed to using it.

Exercises

1. Evaluate the following:

(a) $y = \int \sin x \, dx.$

   Ans. $y = -\cos x + C.$

(b) $y = \int x^2 \, dx.$

(c) $y = \int e^x \, dx.$

(d) $y = \int \sec^2 x \, dx.$

   Ans. $y = \tan x + C.$

(e) $y = \int x^{3/2} \, dx.$

(f) $y = \int \sqrt{8x} \, dx.$

   Ans. $y = \dfrac{2\sqrt{8}}{3} x^{3/2} + C.$

The differential form of expression does have some value in mechanizing the process of integration. Let us consider the methods that we learned earlier under the names of substitution and change of variable. First, let us review how we previously integrated a derived function such as

(19) $$\dot{y} = (x^2 + 1)^5 x.$$

The substitution

(20) $$u = x^2 + 1$$

converts (19) into

(21) $$\frac{dy}{dx} = u^5 x$$

Because we use the generalized power rule, we want the factor following u^5 to be du/dx. By (20), $du/dx = 2x$. Hence if we write (21) as

$$\frac{dy}{dx} = \tfrac{1}{2}u^5 \cdot 2x,$$

we see that we have it in the form called for by the generalized power rule so that

$$y = \frac{1}{2}\frac{u^6}{6} + C$$

and since $u = x^2 + 1$,

$$y = \tfrac{1}{12}(x + 1)^6 + C.$$

Now let us do the same problem using the integral sign and the differential notation. From (19) we can say that

$$dy = (x^2 + 1)^5 x \, dx$$

and that

$$y = \int (x^2 + 1)^5 x \, dx.$$

We again introduce the substitution $u = x^2 + 1$ so that

(22) $$y = \int u^5 x \, dx.$$

We still wish the integrand, that is, the quantity to be integrated, to be of the form

$$u^n \frac{du}{dx}.$$

Because $u = x^2 + 1$, $du/dx = 2x$. Hence we write (22) as

(23) $$y = \int \tfrac{1}{2}u^5 \cdot 2x \, dx.$$

We know that the factor $\frac{1}{2}$ plays no role in the integration process. Hence it is convenient to put it outside the integral sign. That is, we write (23) as

$$y = \tfrac{1}{2}\int u^5 \cdot 2x \, dx.$$

Because the integrand is of the form $u^n \, du/dx$, we have by the generalized power rule that

$$y = \frac{1}{2}\frac{u^6}{6} + C$$

or in terms of x,

$$y = \tfrac{1}{12}(x^2 + 1)^6 + C.$$

We can go one step further. Starting from (23) and noting that since $u = x^2 + 1$, $du = 2x \, dx$, we have

$$y = \int \frac{1}{2} u^5 \, du = \frac{1}{2}\frac{u^6}{6} + C = \frac{(x^2 + 1)^6}{12} + C.$$

Thus the use of differentials makes the application of the chain rule automatic.

What this example of *integration by substitution* then amounts to in general terms is that if we have to evaluate

$$y = \int f(x) \, dx$$

and if by a substitution $u = \phi(x)$, where $\phi(x)$ is some function of x, we can write our integrand in the form

(24) $$y = \int g(u) \frac{du}{dx} \, dx,$$

we can integrate $g(u)$ *with respect to u* and then substitute the value of u in terms of x into the result. In our example the function $\phi(x)$ is $x^2 + 1$ and the function $g(u)$ is u^5.

Now let us see how integration by a *change of variable* is carried out with the new differential notation and the use of the integral sign. Suppose that we are given

(25) $$\dot{y} = \frac{x}{\sqrt{1 + x}}.$$

First, let us carry out the integration as we used to do it. We can make the change of variable

$$x = u^2 - 1.$$

Then

$$\frac{dy}{dx} = \frac{u^2 - 1}{u}.$$

Because the left side is dy/dx but the function to be integrated is a function of u, we apply the chain rule in the form

(26) $$\frac{dy}{du} = \frac{dy}{dx}\frac{dx}{du}.$$

In the present example $dx/du = 2u$ so that

$$\frac{dy}{du} = \frac{u^2 - 1}{u} \cdot 2u = 2(u^2 - 1).$$

Then by integrating with respect to u

(27) $$y = 2\frac{u^3}{3} - 2u + C$$

or, because $u = \sqrt{x + 1}$,

(28) $$y = \tfrac{2}{3}(x + 1)^{3/2} - 2\sqrt{x + 1} + C$$

Now let us do the same problem by using the integral sign and the differential notation. From (25) we have that

$$dy = \frac{x}{\sqrt{1 + x}}\,dx$$

or

(29) $$y = \int \frac{x}{\sqrt{1 + x}}\,dx.$$

We make the change of variable

$$x = u^2 - 1$$

so that

$$y = \int \frac{u^2 - 1}{u}\,dx.$$

The integrand, $(u^2 - 1)/u$, is really dy/dx but expressed as a function of u. To integrate a function of u we need dy/du. Therefore, we apply the chain rule in the form

$$\frac{dy}{du} = \frac{dy}{dx}\frac{dx}{du}.$$

This means that we must multiply the integrand by dx/du. To do this we replace the dx there by $(dx/du)\,du$ and since $dx/du = 2u$

$$y = \int \frac{u^2 - 1}{u}\,2u\,du = \int 2(u^2 - 1)\,du.$$

The factor 2 can be taken outside the integral sign and by integrating we obtain (27) and (28).

The point of this example of change of variable is the following: If $y = \int f(x)\,dx$ and if one makes the *change of variable* $x = \psi(u)$ so that $f(x)$ becomes $h(u)$, then

$$(30) \qquad\qquad y = \int f(x)\,dx = \int h(u)\frac{dx}{du}\,du.$$

The right-hand side is a function of u and is integrated with respect to u.

We note that in both (24) and (30) we handle the integrand exactly as we handled the derivatives before we used the integral sign and differential notation. However, if we use the latter to make a *change of variable* the dx in $y = \int f(x)\,dx$ reminds us to replace dx by $(dx/du)\,du$, so that here the presence of the differential dx is truly helpful. Even in the case of substitution of a new variable the fact that we obtain a function of u followed by a dx, as in (17), reminds us that some further step is necessary, namely, we must make certain that the integrand also contains the du/dx before we can reduce to an integral with respect to u. Note that under substitution the original integrand must supply the $g(u)\,du/dx$ in (24). No factors involving x should be introduced to obtain this form. On the other hand, under change of variable we actually multiply the integrand by $(dx/du)\,du$ to obtain the proper integrand as a function of u.

Fundamentally integration by substitution and integration by change of variable are the same process. In the former case we replace some function of x by u and in the latter we replace x by some function of u. We could do substitution as a change of variable. Thus to carry out

$$(31) \qquad\qquad y = \int (x^2 + 1)^5 x\,dx,$$

instead of letting $x^2 + 1$ be u we could let

$$x = \sqrt{u - 1}.$$

Then (31) becomes

$$(32) \qquad\qquad y = \int u^5 \sqrt{u - 1}\,dx.$$

The integrand is still dy/dx expressed as a function of u. To make the integrand dy/du we must multiply it by dx/du. However,

$$\frac{dx}{du} = \frac{1}{2\sqrt{u - 1}}.$$

Then from (32)

$$y = \int u^5 \sqrt{u - 1}\,\frac{1}{2\sqrt{u - 1}}\,du.$$

This simplifies to

$$y = \int \tfrac{1}{2} u^5 \, du,$$

and now by integrating we obtain the same result as by the method of substitution.

Likewise we could have carried out the integration of (29), which is

$$y = \int \frac{x}{\sqrt{1 + x}} \, dx,$$

by making the substitution

$$u = \sqrt{1 + x}$$

in place of the change of variable

$$x = u^2 - 1.$$

In practice, however, one or the other of the two methods is usually easier to perform and we naturally choose the easier method.

Exercises

1. Evaluate the following integrals by either the method of substitution or the method of change of variable:

(a) $y = \int \sqrt{1 + 3x} \, dx.$

  Ans. $y = 2(1 + 3x)^{3/2}/9 + C.$

(b) $y = \int (x^2 + 5)^{1/2} x \, dx.$

(c) $y = \int \sin^2 x \cos x \, dx.$

  Ans. $y = \dfrac{\sin^3 x}{3} + C.$

(d) $y = \int \dfrac{dx}{1 + 2x}.$

  Ans. $y = \tfrac{1}{2} \log |1 + 2x| + C.$

(e) $y = \int \dfrac{\sin x}{4 + 3 \cos x} \, dx.$

(f) $y = \int \sin^2 x \, dx.$

(g) $y = \int e^{2x} \, dx.$

(h) $y = \int (x^3 - 4)^3 x^2 \, dx.$

  Ans. $y = (x^3 - 4)^4/12 + C.$

(i) $y = \int (1 - x^2)^{1/2} \, dx.$

  Ans. $y = \dfrac{\cos^{-1} x}{2} - \dfrac{x\sqrt{1 - x^2}}{2} + C.$

(j) $y = \int (1 - x^2)^{3/2} \, dx.$

(k) $y = \int \dfrac{x}{\sqrt{1 + x^2}} \, dx.$

(l) $y = \int \dfrac{x}{1 + x^2} \, dx.$

(m) $y = \int \dfrac{dx}{a^2 \sin^2 x + b^2 \cos^2 x}.$

  Suggestion: Let $u = \dfrac{a}{b} \tan x.$

  Ans. $y = \dfrac{1}{ab} \tan^{-1}\left(\dfrac{a}{b} \tan x\right) + C.$

(n) $y = \int \dfrac{x + 1}{\sqrt{1 - x^2}} \, dx.$

  Ans. $y = \cos^{-1} x - \sqrt{1 - x^2} + C.$

3. *The Mean Value Theorem of the Differential Calculus.* The differential *dy* of a function $y = f(x)$ is defined, as we know, by the equation

(33) $dy = f'(x)\, dx.$

For small Δx

(34) Δy is approximated by $f'(x)\, dx.$

Can we obtain a better approximation? The answer to this question is a theorem that is of considerable use in building the calculus.

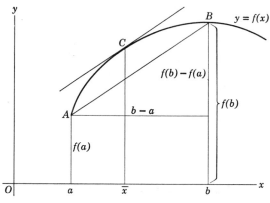

Figure 12-5

Suppose that we state the problem a little more broadly. The quantity Δy is $f(x + \Delta x) - f(x)$. Instead of considering the values x and $x + \Delta x$, let us consider any two values of x, say a and b. Then in place of $f(x + \Delta x) - f(x)$ we have $f(b) - f(a)$. In place of Δx we have $b - a$. Our question, then, is whether we can find an approximation to $f(b) - f(a)$ which is better than $f'(a)(b - a)$. Suppose that we look at the problem geometrically. Figure 12-5 shows a curve of a typical function, the values a and b of x, and $f(a)$ and $f(b)$. We see from the figure that

(35) $\dfrac{f(b) - f(a)}{b - a} = $ slope of line $AB.$

However, it is also apparent from the figure that the tangent to the curve at point C is parallel to the secant AB. Then the slope of the tangent is the same as the slope of the secant. But the slope of the tangent is algebraically the derivative of the function at C. We do not know the abscissa of C, but we do know that it lies between a and b. Let us denote this abscissa by $\bar{x}$. Then what we have learned is that

(36) $f(b) - f(a) = f'(\bar{x})(b - a), \qquad a < \bar{x} < b.$

In other words, we have an exact expression for $f(b) - f(a)$, except that we do not know precisely where $\bar{x}$ lies between a and b. Moreover, $b - a$ need not be small.

We should note that there may be more than one value $\bar{x}$ for which (36) is correct. Figure 12-6 shows a curve for which there are two points C and C' between $x = a$ and $x = b$ at which the slope of the tangent equals the slope of the secant line AB. Hence the abscissa of C or of C' can be used as the $\bar{x}$ for which (36) holds.

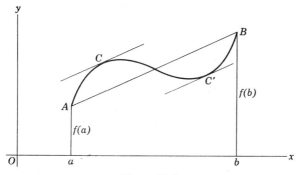

Figure 12-6

In relying upon geometric evidence to prove (36) we have made some assumptions. First, the curve joining A and B must be continuous. Figure 12-7 shows a curve that is discontinuous between A and B; in this case there is no value of x *between* A and B at which the slope of the tangent equals the slope of the secant AB. Secondly, the curve must have a definite slope at each

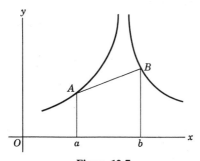

Figure 12-7

point between A and B; that is, $f'(x)$ must exist at each value of x between A and B. As Fig. 12-8 shows, nowhere between a and b does the slope of the curve equal the slope of the secant AB; the reason is that the slope changes abruptly at C and therefore fails to take on enough values between A and B to yield a point on the curve at which the slope equals that of the secant AB.

These considerations yield a theorem called the *mean value theorem of the differential calculus* or *the law of the mean of the differential calculus*.

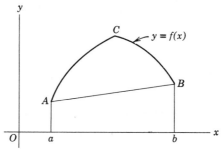

Figure 12-8

Theorem: If $f(x)$ is continuous in the interval $a \leq x \leq b$ and if $f'(x)$ exists at each value of x for which $a < x < b$, then there exists at least one value $\bar{x}$ of x between a and b such that

(37)
$$f(b) - f(a) = f'(\bar{x})(b - a).$$

There is a special case of (37) that is worth noting. Suppose for the function $y = f(x)$ that $y = 0$ at $x = a$ and at $x = b$; that is, $f(a) = 0$ and $f(b) = 0$. Then we see from (37) that the left side is 0. On the right side we have a product of two factors. One of these, $b - a$, cannot be 0 because b and a are two different values of x. Then the second factor $f'(\bar{x})$ must be 0. Thus the derivative of $y = f(x)$ must vanish at some value of x, namely $\bar{x}$, which we know to lie between a and b. Figure 12-9 illustrates what we have just proved. We see that the y-values are 0 at $x = a$ and $x = b$ and that the slope of the curve is 0 between a and b; in fact, for the particular function graphed in this figure there are three points on the curve at which the slope is 0 between a and b, which means that there are three values of x that can serve as the $\bar{x}$ at which $f'(\bar{x}) = 0$.

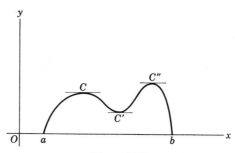

Figure 12-9

The special result we have just obtained is known as *Rolle's theorem.* It is named after Michel Rolle (1652–1719) who first proved it in 1691. The formal statement of Rolle's theorem is as follows.

Theorem: If $y = f(x)$ is continuous throughout the interval $a \leq x \leq b$, if it vanishes at $x = a$ and $x = b$, and if the derivative $f'(x)$ exists at each value

of x between a and b, then there is at least one value of x, say $\bar{x}$, at which
$f'(\bar{x}) = 0$.

In our order of events we first proved the law of the mean and then derived Rolle's theorem as a special case. It is perhaps worth noting that one can start by proving Rolle's theorem and then prove the more general result, the law of the mean, on the basis of Rolle's theorem. The two results do not differ essentially. If one rotated the axes and curve of Fig. 12-9 so as to obtain Fig. 12-10, the former x-axis would be a secant and the tangents at C, C', and C'', which were originally parallel to the x-axis, would still be parallel to the secant.*

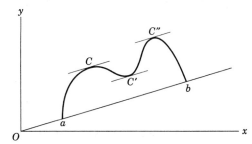

Figure 12-10

The mean value theorem will be useful to us in several connections later, but we can also make immediate use of it. Our first application here is to dispose of a question that we have left unanswered for a considerable time. We previously proved by a geometrical argument (Chapter 6, Section 6) that given a derived function, any two integrals can differ at most by a constant. That is, given

$$\dot{y} = f(x),$$

we showed that all integrals can be obtained by antidifferentiation and then by the addition of some constant. We can and do now prove this fact on the basis of the mean value theorem, although of course the latter was established here only by an intuitive argument.

Suppose that $F(x)$ and $G(x)$ have the same derivative $f(x)$ over some interval $a \leq x \leq b$. Then consider the function

$$H(x) = F(x) - G(x).$$

Let c be any value of x in the interval $a \leq x \leq b$. We apply the mean value theorem to $H(x)$ using the values $x = a$ and $x = c$. Then

(38) $$H(c) - H(a) = H'(\bar{x})(c - a),$$

* Of course, this rough indication of the relation between the two theorems presupposes that the rotation does not convert a single-valued function into a multiple-valued function.

where $\bar{x}$ lies between a and c. Now $H(x) = F(x) - G(x)$, and because $F(x)$ and $G(x)$ have the same derivative everywhere in (a, b), $H'(\bar{x}) = 0$. Then $H(c) - H(a) = 0$ and

$$H(c) = H(a)$$

or, by the definition of $H(x)$,

(39) $$F(c) - G(c) = F(a) - G(a).$$

The quantity a is fixed, and therefore $F(a) - G(a)$ is some fixed quantity that we shall denote by C. However, c was *any* value of x in (a, b). Hence, by (39), $F(x)$ and $G(x)$ can differ only by the constant C. Thus $F(x)$ and $G(x)$, which are any two integrals of $f(x)$, can differ only by a constant C.

Exercises

1. Show by use of the mean value theorem that if $f'(x) > 0$ for all x in the interval (a, b), then $f(b) > f(a)$.

2. Given the function $y = x^2$ and the values $x = 1$ and $x = 4$, find the value $\bar{x}$ at which the mean value theorem holds. Illustrate the result graphically.

Ans. $\bar{x} = \frac{5}{2}$.

3. Do the same as in Exercise 2 but for the function $y = x^3$.   *Ans.* $\bar{x} = \sqrt{7}$.

4. Show that if we choose $a = -1$ and $b = 1$, the mean value theorem cannot hold for the function $y = 1/x$; that is, there is no $\bar{x}$ satisfying the theorem. Why does the mean value theorem not hold in this case?

5. Show by use of the mean value theorem that for positive x, $x > \sin x$. You may use the fact that $|\cos x| \leq 1$.

6. Show by use of the mean value theorem that $\log(1 + h) > h/(1 + h)$ and that $h > \log(1 + h)$ for $h > 0$.

7. Show by use of the mean value theorem that $e^x > 1 + x$ for all $x > 0$.

8. Show that for the parabola $y = ax^2 + bx + c$, the value of $\bar{x}$ for which the mean value theorem (37) holds is $\bar{x} = (b + a)/2$.

4. Indeterminate Forms. In Chapter 11 we showed [see formula (65)] that if an object is set into motion along a smooth ground with an initial velocity of 100 ft/sec but the air resists the motion with a force proportional to the velocity, the object will travel a distance x in time t given by the formula

(40) $$x = \frac{100}{k}(1 - e^{-kt}).$$

The quantity k is the proportionality constant, and the smaller the k, the less is the resistance of the air. We would expect on physical grounds that when k is 0, the formula would yield the one which holds when there is no air resistance, in which case the formula for x in terms of t is $x = 100t$. Unfortunately the substitution of 0 for k in (40) yields the meaningless form $\frac{0}{0}$.

It is possible, however, that as k approaches 0, the limit of the right side of (40) does exist and may have the value of 100t. Hence let us see what happens to the formula for x in (40) as k approaches 0. However, the numerator and the denominator both approach 0 as k does, and in such a case we cannot argue that the limit of the entire expression is the limit of the numerator divided by the limit of the denominator. The problem that we face then is to find the limit of a quotient of two functions when the numerator and the denominator both approach 0 as the independent variable, k in the above example, approaches 0.

The function of k given in (40) is called an indeterminate form, because the function takes the form $\frac{0}{0}$ when k is 0. The words "indeterminate form" are actually misleading because they suggest that the form has a value at $k = 0$ but that the value is indeterminate. This is not the case. If a quotient of two functions has the form $\frac{0}{0}$ for some value, say, a of the independent variable, the quotient has no value at the value a of the independent variable. However, the quotient may very well have a *limiting value* as the independent variable approaches a, and we may seek that value because it may supply us with useful information. Thus if we can prove that the limit as k approaches 0 of the right side of (40) is 100t, we shall know that when the air resistance approaches 0 the motion becomes more and more like the motion with no air resistance.

Actually, we have been working with indeterminate forms right along. The derivative of a function $y = f(x)$ is, by definition,

$$(41) \qquad\qquad \lim_{\Delta x \to 0} \frac{\Delta y}{\Delta x}$$

where $\Delta y/\Delta x$ is a function of Δx. We know that if we were to substitute 0 for Δx in the expression for $\Delta y/\Delta x$, we would obtain $\frac{0}{0}$ because Δy is 0 when Δx is 0. However, we were able to evaluate the limit (41) for a great variety of functions. Thus we can say that we have already evaluated many indeterminate forms. Now we can use this knowledge to evaluate rather easily many other indeterminate forms that do not arise as difference quotients.

Let us consider the general problem exemplified by the above problem of motion. Suppose that we have the expression

$$F(x) = \frac{f(x)}{g(x)}$$

and we know that for $x = a, f(a) = 0$ and $g(a) = 0$, but that we should like to evaluate

$$\lim_{x \to a} \frac{f(x)}{f(x)} \;.$$

To do this we shall prove that

$$(42) \qquad\qquad \lim_{x \to a} \frac{f(x)}{g(x)} = \lim_{x \to a} \frac{f'(x)}{g'(x)} \;.$$

The proof of this assertion is readily made with the help of a slight extension of the mean value theorem known as the *generalized mean value theorem*.

Theorem: If $f(x)$ and $g(x)$ are continuous in $a \leq x \leq b$ and are differentiable in $a < x < b$, if $g(b) \neq g(a)$ and if $g'(x) \neq 0$, then there exists at least one value $\bar{x}$ such that

(43) $$\frac{f(b) - f(a)}{g(b) - g(a)} = \frac{f'(\bar{x})}{g'(\bar{x})}$$

and $a < \bar{x} < b$. *

The essence of this theorem is (43) and the assertion that $a < \bar{x} < b$. To prove it we are tempted to apply the mean value theorem to $f(x)$ separately and to $g(x)$ separately and to divide the results. However, this would give $f'(\bar{x}_1)/g'(\bar{x}_2)$, for the right-hand side of (43), whereas (43) asserts that the *same* $\bar{x}$ can be used in numerator and denominator. Nevertheless, it does seem likely that the law of the mean or possibly the special case, Rolle's theorem, could be used to prove (43). To obtain the same $\bar{x}$ in the numerator and denominator we probably should work with a function that involves $f(x)$ and $g(x)$ simultaneously. However, to enable us to apply the law of the mean or Rolle's theorem to the desired function, the function must satisfy the hypotheses of whichever theorem we use. The construction of the desired function is not immediately obvious but fortunately is not difficult. We set up the new function

(44) $G(x) = [g(b) - g(a)][f(x) - f(a)] - [g(x) - g(a)][f(b) - f(a)].$

We see by substitution that $G(a) = 0$ and $G(b) = 0$. Then Rolle's theorem applies to $G(x)$ and there exists an $\bar{x}$ for which $G'(\bar{x}) = 0$ and $a < \bar{x} < b$. However,

$$G'(x) = [g(b) - g(a)]f'(x) - g'(x)[f(b) - f(a)],$$

and because $G'(\bar{x}) = 0$, simple algebra yields

(45) $$\frac{f(b) - f(a)}{g(b) - g(a)} = \frac{f'(\bar{x})}{g'(\bar{x})}.$$

Of course, to carry out the algebra we need the fact that the denominators in (45) are not 0.

Now we can establish (42). This equation presupposes that $f(a) = 0$ and $g(a) = 0$. Because b in (45) is any value of x, provided only that $\bar{x}$ lies between a and x, we can replace b by x in (45) and use the facts on $f(a)$ and $g(a)$. Then

(46) $$\frac{f(x)}{g(x)} = \frac{f'(\bar{x})}{g'(\bar{x})}.$$

* If $g'(x) \neq 0$, then $g(b) \neq g(a)$ by the mean value theorem. However, this simplication of the hypotheses is a detail.

Now $\bar{x}$ depends on x and since the left and right sides of (46) are equal for all x near a,

$$\lim_{x \to a} \frac{f(x)}{g(x)} = \lim_{x \to a} \frac{f'(\bar{x})}{g'(\bar{x})} .$$

However if

$$\lim_{x \to a} \frac{f'(x)}{g'(x)}$$

exists, then $f'(\bar{x})/g'(\bar{x})$ must approach the same limit because the $\bar{x}$ are just values of x that approach a as x does. Then

(47) $$\lim_{x \to a} \frac{f(x)}{g(x)} = \lim_{x \to a} \frac{f'(x)}{g'(x)} .$$

This is the statement in (42). Let us note this basic result on indeterminate forms as a theorem:

Theorem: Suppose that $f(x)$ and $g(x)$ are continuous in some interval $a \leq x \leq b$, the derivatives $f'(x)$ and $g'(x)$ exist in $a < x < b$, and $g'(x)$ does not vanish in $a < x < b$. Then, if $f(a) = 0$ and $g(a) = 0$,

(48) $$\lim_{x \to a} \frac{f(x)}{g(x)} = \lim_{x \to a} \frac{f'(x)}{g'(x)}$$

when the right-hand limit exists.

The result (48) tells us that we can evaluate the limit called for on the left side by calculating the limit on the right side of it exists. If in addition to the hypotheses on $f(x)$ and $g(x)$ that we have already made in order to establish (48) we add that $f'(x)$ and $g'(x)$ approach $f'(a)$ and $g'(a)$, respectively, and if $g'(a)$ is not 0, we can derive a better result. Because the limit of a quotient is the limit of the numerator divided by the limit of the denominator provided that the limit of the denominator is not 0,

(49) $$\lim_{x \to a} \frac{f'(x)}{g'(x)} = \frac{\lim\limits_{x \to a} f'(x)}{\lim\limits_{x \to a} g'(x)} .$$

However, as x approaches a, $f'(x)$ approaches $f'(a)$. Likewise, as x approaches a, $g'(x)$ approaches $g'(a)$. Then from (48) and (49)

(50) $$\lim_{x \to a} \frac{f(x)}{g(x)} = \frac{f'(a)}{g'(a)} .$$

This form of the result, as opposed to (48), is more often used in practice. It says that to find the limit of $f(x)/g(x)$ as x approaches a, when $f(a)$ and $g(a)$ are 0, we should differentiate the numerator $f(x)$, differentiate the denominator $g(x)$, and evaluate $f'(a)/g'(a)$. The results (48) and (50) are usually credited to G. F. A. L'Hospital (1661–1704), a pupil of the superb

Swiss mathematician John Bernoulli, and are known as L'Hospital's rule. However, the idea is due to Bernoulli.

Before we apply the result (50) let us see what it means geometrically. We are dealing with two functions $f(x)$ and $g(x)$ that have the value 0 at $x = a$. Hence the curves of $y = f(x)$ and $y = g(x)$ must cross the x-axis (Fig. 12-11) at $x = a$. This is point P in the figure. Let x be an arbitrary value near $x = a$

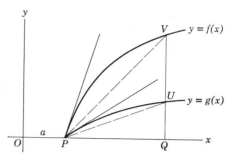

Figure 12-11

so that $QU = g(x)$ and $QV = f(x)$. The evaluation of the indeterminate form $f(x)/g(x)$ then amounts to asking what the ratio of QV to QU becomes as Q moves toward P. Now

$$\frac{QV}{QU} = \frac{QV/PQ}{QU/PQ}.$$

However, QV/PQ is the slope of the secant PV and QU/PQ is the slope of the secant PU. As Q approaches P, these secants approach the tangents to the respective curves so that QV/PQ approaches the slope of the tangent to the curve of $y = f(x)$ and QU/PQ approaches the slope of the tangent to $y = g(x)$. Hence what (50) says in geometrical terms is that the ratio of $f(x)$ and $g(x)$, that is, the ratio QV/QU, approaches, as Q approaches P, the ratio of the slopes of the two tangent lines at P.

We can now answer the question that we raised in connection with formula (40). What is

$$\lim_{k \to 0} \frac{100(1 - e^{-kt})}{k} \, ?$$

We know already that the numerator and denominator are 0 for $k = 0$. Hence let us apply (50). By differentiating numerator and denominator *with respect to k*, we have

$$\frac{100(te^{-kt})}{1}$$

and we evaluate this expression at $k = 0$. The result is $100t$. We are now certain that the motion in the resisting air approaches the motion in a resistanceless medium as k approaches 0.

Let us consider another example. The function

$$\frac{e^x - 1}{\log (1 + x)}$$

has no value when $x = 0$ because both numerator and denominator are 0. However, we might have reason to evaluate

(51) $$\lim_{x \to 0} \frac{e^x - 1}{\log (1 + x)}.$$

Direct inspection of this quotient does not tell us what the limit is. Hence we apply (50). We differentiate numerator and denominator of (51) and obtain

$$\frac{e^x}{1/(1 + x)} \quad \text{or} \quad (1 + x)e^x.$$

If we now substitute $x = 0$, we obtain 1, and this is the value of the expression in (51).

From the basic results (48) and (50) we can derive new ones that help us to evaluate other kinds of indeterminate forms. Thus in applying (48) it can happen that in evaluating

$$\lim_{x \to a} \frac{f'(x)}{g'(x)}$$

both $f'(x)$ and $g'(x)$ approach 0 as x approaches a and so the limit of the entire quotient is not discernible. We may then reapply the rule (48) for evaluating a $\frac{0}{0}$ form and determine

$$\lim_{x \to a} \frac{f''(x)}{g''(x)}.$$

In fact, we can continue the process of differentiating the numerator and denominator until we reach a quotient whose limit can be calculated. This limit is the value of the original limit sought.

It may also happen, in evaluating

(52) $$\lim_{x \to a} \frac{f(x)}{g(x)},$$

where $f(a)$ and $g(a)$ are 0 and the limit is not obvious, that the limit

$$\lim_{x \to a} \frac{f'(x)}{g'(x)}$$

is infinite. Then we may consider

(53) $$\lim_{x \to a} \frac{g(x)}{f(x)},$$

and this leads us to considering

$$\lim_{x \to a} \frac{g'(x)}{f'(x)}.$$

This latter limit must be 0. Then the limit in (53) is 0, and because the expression in (52) is the reciprocal of that in (53), the limit in (52) must be infinity.

An example of this case is furnished by the problem of determing

$$\lim_{x \to 0} \frac{\sin x}{1 - \cos x}.$$

The numerator and denominator are 0 for x equal to 0. Hence we apply L'Hospital's rule and seek to determine

$$\lim_{x \to 0} \frac{\cos x}{\sin x}.$$

However, this fraction becomes infinite as x approaches 0. Hence

$$\lim_{x \to 0} \frac{\sin x}{1 - \cos x} = \infty.$$

In the types of indeterminate forms thus far considered, the indeterminacy arose because $f(x)$ and $g(x)$ are 0 for x equal to a finite number a. However, we might have the case of $f(x)$ and $g(x)$ becoming 0 as x *becomes infinite* and be interested in the limit of $f(x)/g(x)$ as x becomes infinite. L'Hospital's rule applies in this case, too. We introduce the change of variable $x = 1/z$. Then

$$\lim_{x \to \infty} \frac{f(x)}{g(x)} = \lim_{z \to 0} \frac{f(1/z)}{g(1/z)}.$$

Now we can apply L'Hospital's rule to the right side. We differentiate $f(1/z)$ with respect to z. To do this we differentiate $f(1/z)$ as though it were $f(u)$ with $u = 1/z$. Thus

$$\frac{df(1/z)}{dz} = f'(u) \frac{du}{dz} = f'(u)\left(-\frac{1}{z^2}\right).$$

The same applies to $g(1/z)$. So far, then, we have

$$\lim_{x \to \infty} \frac{f(x)}{g(x)} = \lim_{z \to 0} \frac{f(1/z)}{g(1/z)} = \lim_{z \to 0} \frac{f'(u)[-(1/z^2)]}{g'(u)[-(1/z^2)]} = \lim_{z \to 0} \frac{f'(u)}{g'(u)}.$$

Then

(54)
$$\lim_{x \to \infty} \frac{f(x)}{g(x)} = \lim_{z \to 0} \frac{f'(1/z)}{g'(1/z)} = \lim_{x \to \infty} \frac{f'(x)}{g'(x)}.$$

Thus L'Hospital's rule applies in exactly the same way when x approaches ∞ as when x approaches 0.

Exercises

1. Evaluate the following indeterminate forms:

(a) $\lim\limits_{x\to 2} \dfrac{x^2 - 4}{x^2 - 5x + 6}$.   *Ans.* -4.

(g) $\lim\limits_{x\to 0} \dfrac{\tan x - x}{x - \sin x}$.   *Ans.* 2.

(b) $\lim\limits_{x\to a} \dfrac{x - a}{x^3 - a^3}$.   *Ans.* $\dfrac{1}{3a^2}$.

(h) $\lim\limits_{x\to a} \dfrac{\sin x - \sin a}{x - a}$.

(c) $\lim\limits_{x\to n} \dfrac{\log(x/n)}{n - x}$.   *Ans.* $-\dfrac{1}{n}$.

(Can you state the answer here at once?)

(d) $\lim\limits_{x\to 3} \dfrac{x^2 - 6x + 9}{x^2 - 5x + 6}$.

(i) $\lim\limits_{x\to 5} \dfrac{2 - \sqrt{x - 1}}{x^2 - 25}$.   *Ans.* $-\dfrac{1}{40}$.

(e) $\lim\limits_{x\to 0} \dfrac{xe^x - x}{1 - \cos 2x}$.   *Ans.* $\dfrac{1}{2}$.

(j) $\lim\limits_{x\to 0} \dfrac{\tan x}{\tan 4x}$.   *Ans.* $\dfrac{1}{4}$.

(f) $\lim\limits_{x\to 0} \dfrac{e^x - e^{-x}}{\sin 2x}$.

2. To evaluate

$$\lim_{x\to 0} \frac{3x^2 - 1}{x - 1}$$

by L'Hospital's rule we differentiate numerator and denominator and obtain $6x/1$ and now substitute $x = 0$. However, if we look at the original function, we see at once that as x approaches 0 the function approaches 1. Why the discrepancy in the answers?

3. Let us consider

$$\lim_{x\to 0} \frac{x^4 \sin(1/x)}{x^3}.$$

We can, of course, divide through by x^3 and we then see that the function approaches 0 as x approaches 0. Suppose, however, that we evaluate the limit by L'Hospital's rule. This leads to

$$\lim_{x\to 0} -\frac{x^2 \cos(1/x)}{3x^2} = \lim_{x\to 0} -\frac{\cos(1/x)}{3}.$$

But this limit does not exist. What is wrong?

4. We showed in Chapter 11, formula (69), that if an object falls downward under the action of gravity and with air resistance proportional to the velocity, the velocity at any time t is given by the formula $v = (32/k)(1 - e^{-kt})$ where k is the proportionality constant. Show that as k approaches 0 the formula becomes $v = 32t$,—the formula that obtains when there is no air resistance.

5. In formula (71) of Chapter 11, we obtained the formula for the distance fallen by a dropped object in time t when gravity acts and the air resistance is proportional to the velocity. The distance y is given by $(32/k^2)(kt + e^{-kt} - 1)$,

where k is the proportionality constant. Show that as k approaches 0 the formula becomes $y = 16t^2$, which is the distance fallen by an object under the action of gravity but with no air resistance.

6. If an object is launched horizontally over some surface with an initial velocity of 100 ft/sec but the air resistance is proportional to the square of the velocity, then, as we found in Exercise 2 of Section 6, Chapter 11, the distance traveled in time t is given by $x = (1/k) \log (1 + 100kt)$ where k is the proportionality constant. Show that as k approaches 0 the formula for x approaches the one for the same motion but in a vacuum.

7. If an object is thrown downward with an initial velocity V in a medium whose resistance is proportional to the velocity v, the velocity is given by the formula $v = (32/k) - \{(32/k) - V\}e^{-kt}$ where k is the proportionality constant (See Exercise 9 in Section 6, Chapter 11). Show that as k approaches 0 the formula approaches $v = 32t + V$—the formula that holds when there is no air resistance.

Another class of indeterminate forms consists of those in which numerator and denominator are both *infinite* when x is some finite number a. Thus in

$$\log x/\cot x$$

the numerator and denominator are infinite for x equal to 0. These indeterminate forms are loosely described as ∞/∞ forms. We may however be interested in

$$\lim_{x \to 0} \frac{\log x}{\cot x}$$

and this can be evaluated by L'Hospital's rule. If $f(x)/g(x)$ is the quantity that approaches ∞/∞ as x approaches a, then $1/f(x)$ and $1/g(x)$ approach 0 as x approaches a. Now, it is correct algebra to state that

$$(55) \qquad \lim_{x \to a} \frac{f(x)}{g(x)} = \lim_{x \to a} \frac{\dfrac{1}{g(x)}}{\dfrac{1}{f(x)}}.$$

If we apply L'Hospital's rule (48) to the right side of (55), remembering that the numerator and denominator are $1/g(x)$ and $1/f(x)$ respectively, the rule tells us that

$$(56) \qquad \lim_{x \to a} \frac{\dfrac{1}{g(x)}}{\dfrac{1}{f(x)}} = \lim_{x \to a} \frac{\dfrac{-g'(x)}{g^2(x)}}{\dfrac{-f'(x)}{f^2(x)}} = \lim_{x \to a} \left\{ \frac{g' f^2}{f' g^2} \right\}.$$

We now use the theorem that the limit of a product is the product of the limits to write

$$(57) \qquad \lim_{x \to a} \left(\frac{g'}{f'} \cdot \frac{f^2}{g^2} \right) = \lim_{x \to a} \frac{g'}{f'} \cdot \lim_{x \to a} \frac{f^2}{g^2} = \lim_{x \to a} \frac{g'}{f'} \left(\lim_{x \to a} \frac{f}{g} \right)^2.$$

The steps (55), (56), and (57) provide a series of equalities which show that the first member of (55) equals the last member of (57); that is,

(58)
$$\lim_{x \to a} \frac{f(x)}{g(x)} = \lim_{x \to a} \frac{g'(x)}{f'(x)} \left(\lim_{x \to a} \frac{f(x)}{g(x)} \right)^2.$$

In (58) we see that the entire quantity on the left side is a factor of the right side. We divide through to obtain

$$1 = \lim_{x \to a} \frac{g'(x)}{f'(x)} \cdot \lim_{x \to a} \frac{f(x)}{g(x)}$$

Then

$$\lim_{x \to a} \frac{f(x)}{g(x)} = \frac{1}{\lim_{x \to a} \frac{g'(x)}{f'(x)}}.$$

Because the limit of a quotient is the quotient of the limits (provided the limit of the denominator is not 0),

(59)
$$\lim_{x \to a} \frac{f(x)}{g(x)} = \lim_{x \to a} \frac{1}{\frac{g'(x)}{f'(x)}} = \lim_{x \to a} \frac{f'(x)}{g'(x)}.$$

Thus we see that L'Hospital's rule also applies in this case where $f(x)$ and $g(x)$ become infinite as x approaches a.

We might note the conditions under which this result holds. Because we applied L'Hospital's rule to $1/f(x)$ and $1/g(x)$ to obtain (59), the most direct statement of the conditions is the following: If $f(x)$ and $g(x)$ both become infinite as x approaches a, if $1/f(x)$ and $1/g(x)$ are continuous is some interval $a \le x \le b$, and if the derivatives of $1/f(x)$ and $1/g(x)$ exist in $a < x < b$, then

(60)
$$\lim_{x \to a} \frac{f(x)}{g(x)} = \lim_{x \to a} \frac{f'(x)}{g'(x)}$$

when the right-hand limit exists.*

As an example of the use of (60) let us evaluate

$$\lim_{x \to 0} \frac{\log x}{\cot x}.$$

We see that as x approaches 0 both the numerator and denominator become infinite. Then we may apply (60). Thus

$$\lim_{x \to 0} \frac{\log x}{\cot x} = \lim_{x \to 0} \frac{1/x}{-\csc^2 x} = \lim_{x \to 0} -\frac{\sin^2 x}{x}.$$

---

* This result is correct also for the case when x becomes infinite. The proof is made in the same way as for (54).

Unfortunately, as x approaches 0 both $\sin^2 x$ and x approach 0. Hence we apply L'Hospital's rule for the case of a $0/0$ form. We have

$$\lim_{x \to 0} -\frac{\sin^2 x}{x} = \lim_{x \to 0} -\frac{2 \sin x \cos x}{1} = 0.$$

Our final result is

$$\lim_{x \to 0} \frac{\log x}{\cot x} = 0.$$

We may say loosely that $\log x$ becomes infinite more slowly than $\cot x$.

Exercises

1. Evaluate the following limits:

(*a*) $\displaystyle \lim_{x \to 0} \frac{\cot x}{\cot 2x}$. 　　　　　　　　　　　　　　　　　　　*Ans.* 2.

(*b*) $\displaystyle \lim_{x \to \infty} \frac{x^5}{e^x}$. 　　　　　　　　　　　　　　　　　　　　*Ans.* 0.

(*c*) $\displaystyle \lim_{x \to 0} \frac{\tan x}{\tan 3x}$.

(*d*) $\displaystyle \lim_{x \to \infty} \frac{x^n}{e^x}$. 　　　　　　　　　　　　　　　　　　　　*Ans.* 0.

(*e*) $\displaystyle \lim_{x \to \pi/2} \frac{\sec x + 1}{\tan x}$. 　　　　　　　　　　　　　　　　　　*Ans.* 1.

(*f*) $\displaystyle \lim_{x \to 0} \frac{\log \sin x}{\log \tan x}$.

(*g*) $\displaystyle \lim_{x \to \frac{1}{2}} \frac{\log (1 - 2x)}{\tan \pi x}$. 　　　　　　　　　　　　　　　　*Ans.* 0.

(*h*) $\displaystyle \lim_{x \to \infty} \frac{a_0 x^n + a_1 x^{n-1} + \cdots + a_n}{b_0 x^n + b_1 x^{n-1} + \cdots + b_n}$. 　　　　　*Ans.* $\dfrac{a_0}{b_0}$.

(*i*) $\displaystyle \lim_{x \to \infty} \frac{a_0 x^m + a_1 x^{m-1} + \cdots + a_m}{b_0 x^n + b_1 x^{n-1} + \cdots + b_n}$ for $m < n$. 　　*Ans.* 0.

2. Evaluate

$$\lim_{x \to \infty} \frac{x}{\sqrt{x^2 + 1}}.$$

Suggestion: Note that the application of L'Hospital's rule leads to the reciprocal of the given function. Hence the original function and its reciprocal must have the same limit (if any). But if $f(x)$ approaches l and if l is not 0, then $1/f(x)$ should approach $1/l$. What is l? 　　　　　　　　*Ans.* 1.

Indeterminate expressions may appear in a variety of ways. Thus one might encounter $x \log x$ which for $x = 0$ takes on the "value" $0 \cdot \infty$. Or one might be obliged to treat $\tan x - \sec x$ which for $x = \pi/2$ takes on the value $\infty - \infty$. Indeterminate forms of the class $0 \cdot \infty$ and $\infty - \infty$ can usually be recast by algebraic processes so as to take on the form $0/0$ or ∞/∞ and we may then seek the appropriate limit. Thus we may treat $x \log x$ as

$$\lim_{x \to 0} x \log x = \lim_{x \to 0} \frac{\log x}{1/x} = \lim_{x \to 0} \frac{1/x}{-1/x^2} = \lim_{x \to 0} (-x) = 0.$$

The passage from the second expression to the third was made in accordance with L'Hospital's rule for the case of ∞/∞.

Still another class of indeterminate forms arises in connection with powers. Thus suppose that we are obliged to determine $\lim_{x \to 0} x^x$. This function x^x takes on the value 0^0 for $x = 0$ and 0^0 is meaningless. However, $\lim_{x \to 0} x^x$ may nevertheless exist. To determine this limit we set

$$y = x^x$$

so that

$$\log y = x \log x.$$

We saw above that as x approaches 0, $x \log x$ approaches 0. Hence

(61)
$$\lim_{x \to 0} \log y = 0.$$

We think of y as $e^{f(x)}$, where $f(x)$ is some function of x, so that $\log y = f(x)$. Equation (61) says that $f(x)$ approaches 0. Then

$$\lim_{x \to 0} y = 1.$$

Among indeterminate forms that appear as powers, in addition to the case 0^0 just described, one encounters ∞^0 and 1^∞. The method of evaluating the limits the corresponding functions approach is illustrated by the treatment of x^x. The method is to take the logarithm of the power and evaluate this logarithm. Then the original limit sought is the antilogarithm of the limit for the logarithm. In fact, all three forms 0^0, ∞^0, and 1^∞ derive from the general form

(62)
$$[f(x)]^{g(x)}$$

where the expression may take on the values 0^0, ∞^0, or 1^∞ at, say, $x = a$. By taking the logarithm of (62) we have

(63)
$$\log y = g(x) \log f(x).$$

possible: $\dfrac{0}{0}; \dfrac{0}{\bar{0}}; \dfrac{\infty}{\infty}; 1^\infty; 0^\infty; \infty; \infty - \infty; \infty \cdot 0$

watch out for: $\dfrac{\infty}{0} = \infty$ $\quad$ $\dfrac{0}{\infty} = 0$ $\quad$ $\dfrac{c}{\infty} = 0$

If f and g take the respective values 0 and 0, then (63) gives the $0 \cdot \infty$ form. If f and g take the respective values ∞ and 0, then (63) gives the form $\infty \cdot 0$. And if f and g take the respective values 1 and ∞, then (63) gives the form $\infty \cdot 0$. All three cases then usually revert to the indeterminate form $\infty \cdot 0$, although in special cases log y may take a simple form (see Exercise 1w).

Exercises

1. Evaluate the following limits:

(a) $\lim\limits_{x \to 0} (\sqrt{x} \log x)$.   *Ans.* 0

(b) $\lim\limits_{t \to 0} (te^{-(1/t)})$.

(c) $\lim\limits_{x \to 0} \left(\csc^2 x - \dfrac{1}{x^2} \right)$.   *Ans.* $\frac{2}{3}$.

(d) $\lim\limits_{x \to \infty} \left(x \tan \dfrac{3}{x} \right)$.

(e) $\lim\limits_{t \to 1} \left(\dfrac{t}{t-1} - \dfrac{1}{\log t} \right)$.   *Ans.* $\frac{1}{2}$.

(f) $\lim\limits_{t \to \infty} (te^{-(1/t)})$.   *Ans.* ∞.

(g) $\lim\limits_{x \to 0} (x \log \tan x)$.

(h) $\lim\limits_{x \to \pi/2} (\tan 3x - \tan x)$.   *Ans.* ∞.

(i) $\lim\limits_{x \to 0} (\sin x)^x$.

(j) $\lim\limits_{x \to 0} x^{1/x}$ *Ans.* ∞.

(k) $\lim\limits_{x \to 0} (3 \sin x + \cos x)^{\cot x}$.

(l) $\lim\limits_{x \to 0} (e^x + 2x)^{1/x}$.   *Ans.* e^3.

(m) $\lim\limits_{x \to \pi/2} (\sec x)^{\cos x}$.

(n) $\lim\limits_{x \to 1} (x^{1/(1-x)})$.   *Ans.* e^{-1}.

(o) $\lim\limits_{x \to 2} \left(\dfrac{1}{x-2} \right)^{1/(x-2)}$

(p) $\lim\limits_{x \to 1} (x-1)^{1/(x-1)}$.

(q) $\lim\limits_{x \to \infty} [\log(1+x) - \log x]$.
          Ans. 0.

(r) $\lim\limits_{x \to 0} \sin x \log 2x$.

(s) $\lim\limits_{x \to 0} \left[\dfrac{1}{\sin x} - \dfrac{1}{x} \right]$.   *Ans.* ∞.

(t) $\lim\limits_{x \to \infty} (1+x)^{1/x}$ *Ans.* 1.

(u) $\lim\limits_{x \to 0} x \cot x$.

(v) $\lim\limits_{x \to \pi/2} (\sec x - \tan x)$.   *Ans.* 0.

(w) $\lim\limits_{x \to 0} x^{a/\log x}$.

2. Is an expression that takes the form ∞^∞ at some finite or infinite value of x determinate?   *Ans.* Yes.

3. Answer the same question as in Exercise 2 but for the form 0^∞.   *Ans.* Yes.

4. We know from formula (75) of Chapter 11 that the velocity of an object that is thrown up with a velocity of 1000 ft/sec in a medium whose resistance is proportional to the velocity is

$$ v = -\frac{32}{k} + \frac{32 + 1000k}{k} e^{-kt}. $$

Show that as k approaches 0, the formula for v approaches that for the vacuum case, namely, $v = 1000 - 32t$. *Suggestion:* As the expression for v now stands, when $k = 0$ we have an $\infty - \infty$ type of indeterminate form. Add the fractions.

5. Formula (77) of Chapter 11 states that the height above the ground of an object that is thrown up with an initial velocity of 1000 ft/sec in a medium whose resistance is proportional to the velocity is

$$y = -\frac{32t}{k} + \frac{32 + 1000k}{k^2}(1 - e^{-kt}).$$

Show that as k approaches 0, this formula approaches that for the vacuum case, namely, $y = -16t^2 + 1000t$. *Suggestion:* See the preceding exercise.

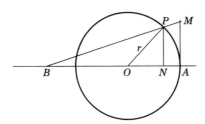

Figure 12-12

6. In Fig. 12-12, P is a point on a circle with center at O and radius r; $AM = $ arc AP and line MP meets OA at B. Show that the limiting position of B as P approaches A is given by $OB = 2r$. *Suggestion:* Use the similar triangles BNP and BAM.

CHAPTER THIRTEEN

Further Technique of Integration

1. Introduction. In the foregoing chapters we learned how to integrate a variety of functions. In almost all of these cases it was possible to integrate by reversing at once a known differentiation formula. The only exceptions were an occasional use of substitution of a new variable or change of variable. We shall not introduce any new functions in this introduction to the calculus, but we shall find in a variety of applications still to be explored that the familiar functions occur in combinations that do not obviously lend themselves to integration; yet there is a considerable number of techniques that enable us to find the integral in such cases. In this chapter we shall study the most important of these techniques. Our principal objective is to dispose, so to speak, of the purely technical problem of integration. The acquisition of this technique is not exciting or perhaps not even engrossing. The mathematician may be more interested in creating themes and solving significant problems, but he must also be somewhat of a technician.

2. Integration by Parts. Among general techniques perhaps the most important is the technique called integration by parts. The procedure stems from a formula for differentiation that we learned much earlier. If u and v are two functions of x, we know that

$$(1) \qquad \frac{d}{dx}(uv) = u\dot{v} + v\dot{u}.$$

Then

$$u\dot{v} = \frac{d}{dx}(uv) - v\dot{u}.$$

If we now indicate integration by using the integral sign and the differential notation, then

$$\int u\dot{v}\, dx = \int \frac{d}{dx}(uv)\, dx - \int v\dot{u}\, dx + C.$$

Of course, the integral of a differential gives the function itself, so that

$$(2) \qquad \int u\dot{v}\, dx = uv - \int v\dot{u}\, dx + C$$

or, because $dv = \dot{v}\,dx$ and $du = \dot{u}\,dx$,

(3)
$$\int u\,dv = uv - \int v\,du + C.$$

Formula (2) or (3) is the formula for integration by parts. At first sight it does not appear to be helpful, for the right-hand side, which presumably gives the answer to the integral on the left, itself contains an integral. However, the right-hand integral is often easier to evaluate than the left one and so the formula is useful. Let us consider some examples.

To evaluate
$$\int x \sin x\,dx$$

let us choose $u = x$ and $\dot{v} = \sin x$. It is helpful to arrange the work as follows:

$$u = x \qquad \dot{v} = \sin x$$
$$\dot{u} = 1 \qquad v = -\cos x.$$

Then following (2) we have

$$\int x \sin x\,dx = -x \cos x - \int (-\cos x) \cdot 1\,dx + C$$

or

(4)
$$\int x \sin x\,dx = -x \cos x + \sin x + C.$$

Thus we have obtained the answer readily.

From this example we see that the function chosen for $\dot{v}$ must itself be readily integrable. This choice does not guarantee that $\int v\dot{u}\,dx$ will itself be integrable. That is, the method does not always work. However, by choosing $\dot{v}$ to be as complicated as possible and yet integrable we often succeed in making the evaluation of $\int v\dot{u}\,dx$ possible.

As another example let us consider
$$\int \sec^3 x\,dx.$$

One might try to do integrations involving powers of trigonometric functions by using one or more of the identities, but in the present case integration by parts is the only direct scheme. We regard $\sec^3 x$ as $\sec x \cdot \sec^2 x$ and choose $\dot{v}$ to be $\sec^2 x$ because we know how to integrate this function. We first make the preliminary calculations. Thus

$$u = \sec x \qquad \dot{v} = \sec^2 x$$
$$\dot{u} = \sec x \tan x \qquad v = \tan x.$$

By formula (2)

$$\int \sec x \sec^2 x\,dx = \sec x \tan x - \int \tan x \tan x \sec x\,dx + C.$$

The right-hand integral does not seem manageable, and so presumably we did not gain by applying integration by parts. However, let us see what happens if we replace $\tan^2 x$ by $\sec^2 x - 1$. We obtain

$$\int \sec^3 x \, dx = \sec x \tan x - \int (\sec^2 x - 1) \sec x \, dx + C$$

or

$$\int \sec^3 x \, dx = \sec x \tan x - \int \sec^3 x \, dx + \int \sec x \, dx + C.$$

We can transpose the integral involving $\sec^3 x$ from the right side to the left and thus obtain

(5) $$2 \int \sec^3 x \, dx = \sec x \tan x + \int \sec x \, dx + C.$$

So far we have at least reduced our problem to finding $\int \sec x \, dx$. This is evaluated by a trick that was discovered by someone in the past. The trick is the following:

$$\int \sec x \, dx = \int \sec x \, \frac{\sec x + \tan x}{\sec x + \tan x} \, dx$$

or

(6) $$\int \sec x \, dx = \int \frac{\sec^2 x + \sec x \tan x}{\sec x + \tan x} \, dx.$$

Now, if we let

$$u = \sec x + \tan x = \tan x + \sec x,$$

we see that

$$\frac{du}{dx} = \sec^2 x + \sec x \tan x.$$

The integrand on the right side of (6) is of the form

$$\frac{1}{u} \frac{du}{dx} \, dx.$$

Then, by formula (30) of Chapter 11,

$$y = \log u$$

or

(7) $$\int \sec x \, dx = \log (\sec x + \tan x).$$

We substitute this result in (5) and divide by 2. The final result is

(8) $$\int \sec^3 x \, dx = \frac{\sec x \tan x}{2} + \frac{\log (\sec x + \tan x)}{2} + \frac{C}{2}.$$

Of course, $C/2$ can be replaced by a new constant.

This example is noteworthy not only for the result but for the peculiar feature that integration by parts leads to the same integral, namely $\int \sec^3 x \, dx$, with which we started; by transposing this term we managed to express the desired integral in terms of something that we could integrate.

Exercises

1. Evaluate the following integrals by using integration by parts:

(a) $\int x \cos x \, dx.$ *Ans.* $x \sin x + \cos x + C.$

(b) $\int x \log x \, dx.$

(c) $\int x e^x \, dx.$ *Ans.* $x e^x - e^x + C.$

(d) $\int x^2 e^x \, dx.$

(e) $\int e^x \sin x \, dx.$ *Ans.* $e^x \dfrac{\sin x}{2} - e^x \dfrac{\cos x}{2} + C.$

(f) $\int \log x \, dx.$

(g) $\int x e^{ax} \, dx.$ *Ans.* $\dfrac{x e^{ax}}{a} - \dfrac{e^{ax}}{a^2} + C.$

(h) $\int e^{ax} \sin nx \, dx.$

(i) $\int x \sin 2x \, dx.$ *Ans.* $-\dfrac{x \cos 2x}{2} + \dfrac{\sin 2x}{4} + C.$

(j) $\int x \sec^2 2x \, dx.$

(k) $\int x \sin^2 \dfrac{x}{2} \, dx.$ *Ans.* $\dfrac{x^2}{4} - \dfrac{x \sin x}{2} - \dfrac{\cos x}{2} + C.$

(l) $\int \sin x \cos 3x \, dx.$

(m) $\int \arcsin x \, dx.$ *Ans.* $x \arcsin x + \sqrt{1 - x^2} + C.$

(n) $\int \arctan x \, dx.$

(o) $\int \dfrac{x e^x}{(1 + x)^2} \, dx.$ *Ans.* $\dfrac{e^x}{1 + x} + C.$

(p) $\int x \cos^2 \dfrac{x}{2} \, dx.$ *Ans.* $\dfrac{x^2}{4} + \dfrac{x \sin x}{2} + \dfrac{\cos x}{2} + C.$

(q) $\int x^2 \cos x \, dx.$ *Ans.* $x^2 \sin x + 2x \cos x - 2 \sin x + C.$

2. Let us evaluate $\int (1/x)\, dx$ by parts. If we let $u = 1/x$ and $dv = 1dx$, we obtain $\int dx/x = 1 + \int dx/x$ or $1 = 0$. What is wrong?

3. (*a*) Let us try to evaluate $\int dx/(x \log x)$ by integration by parts. Let $u = 1/\log x$ and $\dot{v} = 1/x$. Then $\dot{u} = -(1/(\log x)^2)1/x$ and $v = \log x$. By the "parts" formula $\int dx/x \log x = 1 + \int dx/x \log x$. It follows that $1 = 0$. What is wrong?

(*b*) Evaluate $\int dx/x \log x$ by some other method.   *Ans.* $\log (\log x) + C$.

4. Evaluate $\int \sec x\, dx$ by making the substitution $\sec x = \cosh u$.
$$\textit{Ans. } \cosh^{-1} (\sec x) \text{ or } \sinh^{-1} (\tan x).$$

5. Evaluate $\int \csc x\, dx$ by making the substitution $\csc x = \cosh u$.
$$\textit{Ans. } -\sinh^{-1} (\cot x) \text{ or } -\cosh^{-1} (\csc x).$$

6. In formula (7) of the text we found that $\int \sec x\, dx = \log (\sec x + \tan x)$. Show that this result is the same as that obtained in Exercise 4.

3. *Reduction Formulas.* There is a technique of integration that is actually an application of integration by parts but whose effectiveness requires a little examination. Let us consider an example.

Suppose that we wish to evaluate

$$(9) \qquad\qquad \int \sin^5 x \cos^4 x\, dx.$$

This integral can be treated in various ways but let us use integration by parts. We should try to choose our u and $\dot{v}$ so that we can integrate $\dot{v}$. Let us therefore make the following choice:

$$u = \cos^3 x, \qquad\qquad \dot{v} = \sin^5 x \cos x.$$
Then
$$\dot{u} = -3 \cos^2 x \sin x, \qquad v = \frac{\sin^6 x}{6}.$$

Formula (2) for integration by parts now gives

$$(10) \qquad \int \sin^5 x \cos^4 x\, dx = \frac{\sin^6 x}{6} \cos^3 x + 3 \int \frac{\sin^7 x}{6} \cos^2 x\, dx.$$

This result may not be very gratifying but if we examine it closely we see that we have accomplished something. We started with $\sin^5 x \cos^4 x$ and we ended, apart from the term already integrated, with $\sin^7 x \cos^2 x$. We have reduced the exponent in the cosine term by 2. One more application of the same procedure will then yield $\cos^0 x$ or 1, so that the cosine term will be eliminated. We shall then have to integrate an expression of the form $\sin^m x$, which, as we shall see, can be done by using trigonometric identities.

In reducing the exponent of the $\cos x$ term in (10) we did increase the exponent of the $\sin x$ term, and this will lead to more work in integrating the ultimate $\sin^m x$. However, we can improve on (10). We note that

$$(11) \quad \sin^7 x \cos^2 x = \sin^5 x(1 - \cos^2 x) \cos^2 x = \sin^5 x \cos^2 x - \sin^5 x \cos^4 x.$$

If we substitute this result in the last term of (10), we see that we can bring the term involving $\sin^5 x \cos^4 x$ to the left side and combine it with the term already there. The result of this algebra is

$$(12) \qquad \int \sin^5 x \cos^4 x \, dx = \frac{\sin^6 x \cos^3 x}{9} + \frac{3}{9} \int \sin^5 x \cos^2 x \, dx.$$

This result (12) is better than (10) because we have reduced the integral on the left to that on the right in which the power of $\sin x$ *remains the same* and yet the power of $\cos x$ is still reduced by 2.

Both formulas (10) and (12) illustrate the major point of this section, namely, that a method of integration, integration by parts in the present case, may not in itself achieve the full result of finding the integral, but it may convert the given integral into one that is simpler. Formulas (10) and (12) are called *reduction formulas* because they reduce the given integral to a form in which some exponent is smaller and thus the resulting integral is easier to handle. Continued application of the formula will often eliminate one of the factors in the original integrand and produce a much simpler integrand. We can see this point more clearly if we first generalize (12). By using the same procedure as we used to obtain (12) we can prove that

$$(13) \qquad \int \sin^m x \cos^n x \, dx = \frac{\sin^{m+1} x \cos^{n-1}}{m + n} + \frac{n - 1}{m + n} \int \sin^m x \cos^{n-2} x \, dx$$

provided that $m + n \neq 0$. We see that continued application of this formula will either eliminate the $\cos^n x$ factor if n is a positive even integer or give only $\cos x$ on the right side if n is a positive odd integer. In the latter case we can certainly complete the integration by letting $u = \sin x$. In the former case we can resort to another simpler reduction formula (see Exercise 3) if necessary.

We have used the term reduction formula to mean that the exponent of some power is decreased. However, the term is also used in an extended sense. Suppose that we had started with

$$(14) \qquad \int \sin^5 x \cos^{-4} x \, dx,$$

wherein $\cos^{-4} x$ means $(\cos x)^{-4}$. If we were to reduce the power of the $\cos^{-4} x$ factor by 2 and end up with

$$\int \sin^5 x \cos^{-6} x \, dx,$$

we would be worse off than when we started. To simplify (14) we would want to increase the exponent of the $\cos^{-4} x$ factor. We can do this. Essentially we have but to use formula (13) in reverse. If we reverse this formula by solving for the last term, we obtain

(15) $\displaystyle\int \sin^m x \cos^{n-2} x \, dx$

$$= -\frac{\sin^{m+1} x \cos^{n-1} x}{n-1} + \frac{m+m}{n-1}\int \sin^m x \cos^n x \, dx$$

or if we replace $n - 2$ by p so that $n = p + 2$, we obtain

(16) $\displaystyle\int \sin^m x \cos^p x \, dx$

$$= -\frac{\sin^{m+1} x \cos^{p+1} x}{p+1} + \frac{m+p+2}{p+1}\int \sin^m x \cos^{p+2} x \, dx,$$

provided that $p + 1 \neq 0$. Thus we see that if p were -4, we could convert the left-hand integral to that on the right in which the exponent of the cos x factor would be -2, while the exponent of the sin x factor would remain the same.

Formula (16) is as much a reduction formula as is (13). The real point, then, about a reduction formula is not that it decreases the exponent of some factor in the original integrand. The formula may increase the exponent or decrease it, but it should change the given integral to another form that may be easier to handle, or continued application of the reduction formula may produce an integral that is easier to handle. There are many reduction formulas, some of which will be given later in a table of integrals. However, all of them are used for the same general purpose that we have just indicated.

Exercises

1. Show by generalizing on the example in the text that formula (13) is correct.

2. Establish the following reduction formulas:

(*a*) $\displaystyle\int \cos^n x \, dx = \cos^{n-1} x \sin x + (n-1)\int \cos^{n-2} x \sin^2 x \, dx$. *Suggestion:* Let $u = \cos^{n-1} x$.

(*b*) Convert the result in (*a*) to

$$\int \cos^n x \, dx = \frac{1}{n}\cos^{n-1} x \sin x + \frac{n-1}{n}\int \cos^{n-2} x \, dx.$$

3. Establish the following reduction formula:

$$\int \sin^n x \, dx = -\frac{1}{n}\sin^{n-1} x \cos x + \frac{n-1}{n}\int \sin^{n-2} x \, dx$$

by following the procedure in Exercise 2.

4. Evaluate the following:

(*a*) $\int \sin^6 x \, dx.$

$$\text{Ans. } -\tfrac{1}{6} \sin^5 x \cos x - \tfrac{5}{24} \sin^3 x \cos x - \tfrac{5}{16} \sin x \cos x + \tfrac{5}{16}x + C.$$

(*b*) $\int \cos^6 x \, dx.$

(*c*) $\int \sin^4 x \cos^2 x \, dx.$

$$\text{Ans. } \tfrac{1}{6} \sin^5 x \cos x - \tfrac{1}{24} \sin^3 x \cos x - \tfrac{1}{16} \sin x \cos x + \tfrac{1}{16}x + C.$$

(*d*) $\int \sin^4 x \cos^4 x \, dx.$

(*e*) $\int \sin^4 x \cos^{-2} x \, dx.*$

$$\text{Ans. } \sin^5 x \cos^{-1} x + \tfrac{5}{4} \sin^3 x \cos x + \tfrac{15}{8} \sin x \cos x - \tfrac{15}{8}x + C.$$

(*f*) $\int \sin^4 x \cos^{-1} x \, dx.$

(*g*) $\int \sin^{-4} x \, dx.$ *Suggestion:* Use the result of Exercise 3.

4. Integration by Partial Fractions. It is possible to integrate any function that is a quotient of two polynomials. As an example of such a quotient we have

$$\frac{3x^2 - 7x + 2}{x^3 + 5x^2 + 6x + 2}.$$

More generally, a polynomial or rational integral function of x is a function of the form

$$a_0 x^n + a_1 x^{n-1} + \cdots + a_{n-1} x + a_n,$$

wherein $a_0, a_1, \ldots, a_n$ are constants, and a quotient of two polynomials or a rational function of x is of the form

(17) $$\frac{a_0 x^n + a_1 x^{n-1} + \cdots + a_{n-1} x + a_n}{b_0 x^m + b_1 x^{m-1} + \cdots + b_{m-1} x + b_m}.$$

The terms rational integral function and rational function are suggested by the analogy with ordinary numbers; the polynomial is the analogue of the integer and the rational function is the analogue of the quotient of two integers or rational number.

To avoid getting lost in a lot of symbols, let us consider concrete examples of (17) instead of working with the general rational function. Suppose, then, that we have the problem of integrating

$$\frac{x^4 + 4x^3 + x^2 + 6}{x^2 + 2x + 1}.$$

* In exercises (*e*), (*f*), and (*g*) the exponent denotes a power and not the inverse function.

When, as in the present example, the degree of the numerator is equal to or greater than the degree of the denominator, the first useful step is to divide the denominator into the numerator. Let us see what happens when this is done.

The division process, which is entirely analogous to long division of ordinary numbers, is as follows:

$$x^2 + 2x + 1 \overline{)x^4 + 4x^3 + x^2 + 6} \qquad \begin{array}{c} x^2 + 2x - 4 \end{array}$$

$$
\begin{array}{r}
x^2 + 2x - 4 \\
x^2 + 2x + 1 \overline{)x^4 + 4x^3 + x^2 + 6} \\
x^4 + 2x^3 + x^2 \\
\hline
2x^3 + 0x^2 + 0x \\
2x^3 + 4x^2 + 2x \\
\hline
-4x^2 - 2x + 6 \\
-4x^2 - 8x - 4 \\
\hline
6x + 10.
\end{array}
$$

The result of the division process then is

(18) $$\frac{x^4 + 4x^3 + x^2 + 6}{x^2 + 2x + 1} = x^2 + 2x - 4 + \frac{6x + 10}{x^2 + 2x + 1}.$$

The advantage of performing the division is that the quotient, $x^2 + 2x - 4$ in the present case, consists of simple powers of x which can be integrated at once, and the remainder, $(6x + 10)/(x^2 + 2x + 1)$ in the present case, in which the degree of the numerator is less than the degree of the denominator, is simpler than the original fraction.

The rational functions that can occur as a remainder are of various types; we shall consider them in turn.

Case I. Suppose that the remainder is

(19) $$\frac{x^2 + 2x + 4}{x^3 - 2x^2 - 5x + 6}.$$

The first step is to attempt to express the denominator as a product of linear or first degree factors. To do this we call upon algebra. We learn there that if a is a root of a polynomial equated to 0 then $x - a$ is a factor of the polynomial. To each root there is a factor. This means that we should find the roots of

$$x^3 - 2x^2 - 5x + 6 = 0.$$

The process of finding the roots of a polynomial equation can be a lengthy one. To avoid getting lost in algebra, let us assume that we have found the roots. They are in the present case 1, -2, and 3. Then the factors of $x^3 - 2x^2 - 5x + 6$ are $x - 1$, $x + 2$, and $x - 3$; that is,

$$x^3 - 2x^2 - 5x + 6 = (x - 1)(x + 2)(x - 3).$$

We may now write (19) as

$$\frac{x^2 + 2x + 4}{(x - 1)(x + 2)(x - 3)}.$$

At this stage the method of partial fractions enters. We set

(20) $$\frac{x^2 + 2x + 4}{(x - 1)(x + 2)(-3)} = \frac{A}{x - 1} + \frac{B}{x + 2} + \frac{C}{x - 3}$$

where A, B, and C are constants that must be determined. The fractions on the right side of (20) are called the partial fractions into which the left side is decomposed. The reasonableness of (20) may be apparent from the fact that when we add the fractions on the right-hand side, the denominator of the sum is the product of the three separate denominators, and in the numerator we have A, B, and C each multiplied by a quadratic polynomial. Hence for some choice of A, B, and C the sums of the terms in the numerator might equal the numerator on the left side, namely $x^2 + 2x + 4$*. Our problem then is to find the A, B, and C for which (20) is a correct statement.

To determine A, B, and C let us add the fractions on the right. Then

(21) $$\frac{x^2 + 2x + 4}{(x - 1)(x + 2)(x - 3)}$$

$$= \frac{A(x + 2)(x - 3) + B(x - 1)(x - 3) + C(x - 1)(x + 2)}{(x - 1)(x + 2)(x - 3)}.$$

We are supposed to choose A, B, and C in (20) so that the left and right sides are identical, that is, so that they yield the same numbers for all values of x. Because we used correct algebra to obtain (21), the same must be true for it. Of course, (20) and (21) have no meaning for $x = 1$, $x = -2$, and $x = 3$. Now, because the denominators in (21) are equal, the numerators must be equal. Moreover, despite the fact that the fractions in (21) have no meaning for the three special values of x, the numerators are equal for *all* values of x. The reason is a theorem of algebra that we already had occasion to use in Section 7 of Chapter 11, namely, if two nth degree polynomials are equal for $n + 1$ or more values of x, they are equal for all values of x. The numerators in (21) are certainly equal for an infinite number of values of x and therefore the theorem applies. Thus the numerators in (21) are equal for all values of x; that is,

$$x^2 + 2x + 4 \equiv A(x + 2)(x - 3) + B(x - 1)(x - 3) + C(x - 1)(x + 2).$$

If we let $x = 1$, we see that

$$7 = -6A$$

---

* One can prove that the form assumed in (78) is correct. However, to avoid dependence on theorems of algebra we can, when we have determined A, B, and C, add the partial fractions and see that the sum is the given fraction.

or
$$A = -\tfrac{7}{6}.$$

If we let $x = -2$, then
$$4 = 15B$$

or
$$B = \tfrac{4}{15}.$$

If we let $x = 3$, then
$$19 = 10C$$

or
$$C = \tfrac{19}{10}.$$

With these values of A, B, and C we return to (20) and we have

(22) $\quad \dfrac{x^2 + 2x + 4}{(x - 1)(x + 2)(x - 3)} = -\dfrac{7}{6(x - 1)} + \dfrac{4}{15(x + 2)} + \dfrac{19}{10(x - 3)}.$

We are now ready to perform integration. That is, given the problem

$$\int \frac{x^2 + 2x + 4}{(x - 1)(x + 2)(x - 3)}\, dx,$$

we may in view of (22) replace this integral by

$$-\frac{7}{6} \int \frac{dx}{x - 1} + \frac{4}{15} \int \frac{dx}{x + 2} + \frac{19}{10} \int \frac{dx}{x - 3}.$$

Each of these integrals is readily evaluated in terms of logarithmic functions.

Exercises

1. Evaluate the following integrals:

(a) $\displaystyle \int \frac{dx}{(x - 3)(x + 2)}.$
   Ans. $\tfrac{1}{5} \log \dfrac{x - 3}{x + 2} + C.$

(b) $\displaystyle \int \frac{dx}{x(x - 3)(x + 2)}.$

(c) $\displaystyle \int \frac{dx}{x^2 - 5x + 6}.$
   Ans. $\log \dfrac{x - 3}{x - 2} + C.$

(d) $\displaystyle \int \frac{x + 2}{(x - 3)(x - 4)}\, dx.$
   Ans. $6 \log (x - 4) - 5 \log (x - 3) + C.$

(e) $\displaystyle \int \frac{x^2 + x + 1}{(x - 1)(x + 2)(x - 3)}\, dx.$
   Ans. $-\tfrac{1}{2} \log (x - 1) + \tfrac{1}{5} \log (x + 2) + \tfrac{13}{10} \log (x - 3) + C.$

(f) $\displaystyle \int \frac{x^2 + x}{x^3 + 7x^2 + 6x}\, dx.$

(g) $\displaystyle \int \frac{dx}{\cos x(1 + \cos x)}.$
   Ans. $\log (\sec x + \tan x) - \tan \dfrac{x}{2} + C.$

2. In the study of the growth of a population it is often assumed that the rate of growth is proportional to the existing population; then as we saw in Chapter 11, the population increases according to a simple exponential law. However, housing and food supply often set an upper limit to the population that a given region can support. The effect of these limitations is to impede the increase in population long before the upper limit is reached because as people find housing and food more difficult to acquire they either delay having children or decide not to have them. A reasonable assumption about the effect of these limitations is that the rate of increase in population is proportional to the existing population and to the difference between the upper limit, say L, and the existing population. This means in mathematical language that if P is the population at any time t, then $dP/dt = kP(L - P)$, where k is a constant. Find the formula for P as a function of t. The curve corresponding to this formula is called the logistic curve.

Ans. $P = LP_0/[P_0 + (L - P_0)e^{-kLt}]$.

3. When two substances, say, A and B mix to form a compound substance, the rate of mixing is proportional to the amount (number of atoms) present in the separate or as yet unmixed substances. This law of chemistry is called the law of mass action. Let a and b be the number of atoms of A and B present to start with and suppose that one atom of each combines to form the molecule of the mixed substance C. Find the formula giving the number x of molecules of the substance C at time t. *Suggestion:* If x molecules of C are formed, then $a - x$ is the number of unmixed atoms of A. The statement that the rate of mixing is proportional to the number of atoms of the as yet unmixed substances means in mathematical language that $dx/dt = k(a - x)(b - x)$. Assume that b and a are unequal and $b > a$.   *Ans.* $x = [abe^{(b-a)kt} - ab]/[be^{(b-a)kt} - a]$.

4. Show that at the inflection point of the logistic curve (Exercise 2) the population is $\frac{1}{2}$ the limiting population L.

5. To break up $(x^2 + 1)/(x^2 - 1)$ into partial fractions we assume that

$$\frac{x^2 + 1}{x^2 - 1} = \frac{A}{x - 1} + \frac{B}{x + 1}.$$

Then $x^2 + 1 = A(x + 1) + B(x - 1)$. By letting $x = 1$, we obtain $A = 1$ and by letting $x = -1$, we obtain $B = -1$. Then we have that

$$\frac{x^2 + 1}{x^2 - 1} = \frac{1}{x - 1} - \frac{1}{x + 1}.$$

But addition of the partial fractions does not give the left-hand side. What is wrong?

Case II. When the rational function to be integrated has a denominator that can be factored into linear factors some of which are repeated the partial fractions procedure we used in Case I still applies but with one modification. Let us suppose that the rational function is

(23)
$$\frac{x + 3}{(x - 2)(x - 3)^2}.$$

We might be inclined to try to reexpress this function in the form

(24) $$\frac{A}{x-2} + \frac{B}{(x-3)^2}$$

and then determine A and B. However, the form (24) is not correct. We can see that this will not do because if we add the fractions the numerator will surely contain a second degree term in x whereas the numerator in (23) does not. The proper way to break up (23) into a sum of partial fractions is to assume that

(25) $$\frac{x+3}{(x-2)(x-3)^2} = \frac{A}{x-2} + \frac{B}{x-3} + \frac{C}{(x-3)^2}.$$

This form takes care of the difficulty that (24) presented because when we add the fractions in (25) the numerator will contain two second degree terms in x, and these may offset each other for proper values of A and B and thus yield the first degree numerator on the left side.

The form on the right side of (25) is required for another reason. We are assuming that some sum of fractions will yield the left side of (25). This left side could be a sum of three terms such as we have in (25). If it is, we would be wrong to assume that it necessarily came from the more limited type of sum in (24). In other words, we should assume the most general form from which the sum on the left side of (25) might have come.

Now that we believe that we have the correct partial fractions in (25) the method of determining A, B, and C is the same as before. From (25), by adding the fractions on the right, we have

(26) $$\frac{x+3}{(x-2)(x-3)^2} = \frac{A(x-3)^2 + B(x-2)(x-3) + C(x-2)}{(x-2)(x-3)^2}.$$

Our argument for determining A, B, and C is the same as in Case I. The two fractions in (26) are to be identical for all values of x except $x = 2$ and $x = 3$, for which values the fractions are not defined. However, the numerators, which are polynomials, are to be equal for more than two values of x. We may regard the left numerator as $0x^2 + x + 3$, so that we have two second degree polynomials equal for more than two values of x. Then by the theorem of algebra cited in Case I the numerators must be equal for *all* values of x; that is,

(27) $$x + 3 \equiv A(x-3)^2 + B(x-2)(x-3) + C(x-2).$$

By letting $x = 2$ we see that

$$5 = A.$$

By letting $x = 3$ we see that

$$6 = C.$$

We now choose any other convenient value of x. Let us choose $x = 0$. Then

$$3 = 9A + 6B - 2C.$$

Because we know A and C, we have from this last equation that

$$B = -5.$$

We substitute the values of A, B, and C in (25) and obtain

(28) $$\frac{x+3}{(x-2)(x-3)^2} = \frac{5}{x-2} - \frac{5}{x-3} + \frac{6}{(x-3)^2}.$$

Thus, given the problem of evaluating

$$\int \frac{x+3}{(x-2)(x-3)^2},$$

we may in view of (28) replace this integral by

$$5\int \frac{dx}{x-2} - 5\int \frac{dx}{x-3} + 6\int \frac{dx}{(x-3)^2}.$$

Each of these integrals is readily evaluated.

Exercises

1. Evaluate the following integrals:

(a) $\displaystyle\int \frac{x}{(x-3)(x+1)^2}\,dx.$

  Ans. $\frac{3}{16}\log\dfrac{x-3}{x+1} - \dfrac{1}{4(x+1)} + C.$

(b) $\displaystyle\int \frac{3x+2}{x^2(x+1)}\,dx.$

(c) $\displaystyle\int \frac{x+1}{x(x-1)^3}\,dx.$

  Ans. $\log\dfrac{x-1}{x} + \dfrac{1}{x-1} - \dfrac{1}{(x-1)^2} + C.$

(d) $\displaystyle\int \frac{x+1}{(x-2)^2(x-3)^2}\,dx.$

Case III.   Given a rational function such as

(29) $$\frac{4}{x^3 - x^2 + 4x - 4}$$

our first thought would be to factor the denominator. It is at once apparent that 1 is a zero of the polynomial, that is, a root of $x^3 - x^2 + 4x - 4 = 0$, and therefore $x - 1$ is a factor. Then

(30) $$\frac{4}{x^3 - x^2 + 4x - 4} = \frac{4}{(x-1)(x^2 + 4)}.$$

We can now find the two linear factors of $x^2 + 4$. However, these factors, $x + 2i$ and $x - 2i$, involve complex numbers, and it is desirable in elementary

calculus to avoid such numbers because they involve a host of new considerations. Can we then keep the quadratic factor and break up (30) into a sum
of two fractions? And if so, can we integrate the separate fractions?

We can reexpress the right side of (30) as a sum of fractions, but because
one factor in the denominator is quadratic there is a new element in the
picture. We might be tempted to assume that

(31) $$\frac{4}{(x-1)(x^2+4)} = \frac{A}{x-1} + \frac{B}{x^2+4}.$$

However, we can see that if we add the two fractions, there will be an x^2-term
in the numerator no matter how we choose A and B, but there is no x^2-term
in the numerator on the left side of (31). The way to eliminate the x^2-term in
the sum of the two partial fractions is to assume that

(32) $$\frac{4}{(x-1)(x^2+4)} = \frac{A}{x-1} + \frac{Bx+C}{x^2+4}.$$

Let us add the fractions and see if we can determine A, B, and C. Addition
of the fractions gives

$$\frac{4}{(x-1)(x^2+4)} = \frac{A(x^2+4)+(Bx+C)(x-1)}{(x-1)(x^2+4)}.$$

Our argument is now the same as in Cases I and II. The numerators on the
two sides are polynomials which must be equal for all values of x. That is,

$$4 \equiv A(x^2+4) + (Bx+C)(x-1).$$

We choose convenient values of x to determine A, B, and C. When $x=1$,

$$4 = 5A$$

or

$$A = \tfrac{4}{5}.$$

When $x=0$,

$$4 = 4A - C.$$

Then

$$C = -\tfrac{4}{5}.$$

When $x=-1$,

$$4 = 5A + 2B - 2C.$$

Then

$$B = -\tfrac{4}{5}.$$

We now have from (32) that

(33) $$\frac{4}{(x-1)(x^2+4)} = \frac{4}{5(x-1)} + \frac{-4x-4}{5(x^2+4)}.$$

To evaluate

$$\int \frac{4}{(x-1)(x^2+4)}\,dx$$

we can instead, in view of (33), evaluate

$$\frac{4}{5}\int \frac{dx}{x-1} - \frac{4}{5}\int \frac{x+1}{x^2+4}\,dx.$$

The first integral can be handled at once. The second can be expressed as the sum

$$-\frac{4}{5}\int \frac{x}{x^2+4}\,dx - \frac{4}{5}\int \frac{1}{x^2+4}\,dx.$$

Both of these can be integrated by methods already available.

The evaluation of

$$\int \frac{x+1}{x^2+4}\,dx$$

can be done readily because the x-term is missing in the denominator. Let us consider a case in which the full quadratic expression occurs in the denominator. We shall evaluate

(34)
$$\int \frac{dx}{x^3+8}.$$

We see at once that -2 is a zero of x^3+8 so that

$$x^3+8 = (x+2)(x^2-2x+4).$$

However, the quadratic factor x^2-2x+4 does not have any real zeros because its discriminant, b^2-4ac, is -12. In accordance with the method we just examined, we set

$$\frac{1}{x^3+8} = \frac{A}{x+2} + \frac{Bx+C}{x^2-2x+4}.$$

We need not repeat the process of determining A, B, and C. The results are $A = \frac{1}{12}$, $B = -\frac{1}{12}$, $C = \frac{1}{3}$. Then

$$\frac{1}{x^3+8} = \frac{1}{12}\frac{1}{x+2} + \frac{-\frac{1}{12}x+\frac{1}{3}}{x^2-2x+4}.$$

In place of (34) we have

(35)
$$\frac{1}{12}\int \frac{dx}{x+2} + \int \frac{-\frac{1}{12}x+\frac{1}{3}}{x^2-2x+4}.$$

The first integral is readily evaluated. To handle the second integral, we note that we can integrate forms of the type

(36)
$$\frac{u}{u^2+a^2} \quad\text{and}\quad \frac{c}{u^2+a^2}$$

where c and a are constants. To put the second integral in (35) into the forms in (36), we complete the square* in the denominator; that is,

$$\int \frac{-\frac{1}{12}x+\frac{1}{3}}{x^2-2x+4}\,dx = \int \frac{-\frac{1}{12}x+\frac{1}{3}}{x^2-2x+1+3}\,dx.$$

---

* To complete the square in x^2+bx+c one adds $(b/2)^2$ and then subtracts it, thus $x^2+bx+c = x^2+bx+(b/2)^2+c-(b/2)^2 = (x+b/2)^2+c-(b/2)^2$.

We now use the method of substitution. That is, let

$$x - 1 = u \quad \text{so that} \quad x = u + 1.$$

Then

(37) $$\int \frac{-x + \frac{1}{12}\frac{1}{3}}{(x-1)^2 + 3}\, dx = \int \frac{-\frac{1}{12}u - \frac{1}{12} + \frac{1}{3}}{u^2 + 3}\, dx.$$

To integrate a function of u with respect to x, we must also have the du/dx following the function of u. However du/dx is 1. Hence we can write in place of the right side of (37)

$$\int \frac{-\frac{1}{12}u + \frac{1}{4}}{u^2 + 3}\, du,$$

and this can be reexpressed as

$$-\frac{1}{2 \cdot 12} \int \frac{2u}{u^2 + 3}\, du + \frac{1}{4} \int \frac{1}{u^2 + 3}\, du.$$

These integrals are known to us. They yield*

$$-\frac{1}{24} \log (u^2 + 3) + \frac{1}{4\sqrt{3}} \arctan \frac{u}{\sqrt{3}}$$

or in terms of x,

$$-\frac{1}{24} \log [(x-1)^2 + 3] + \frac{1}{4\sqrt{3}} \arctan \frac{x-1}{\sqrt{3}} + C.$$

Of course, the full answer to our original problem (34) must include the first integral in (35).

Exercises

1. Evaluate the following integrals:

(a) $\displaystyle \int \frac{dx}{x(x^2 + 4)}$ *Ans.* $\frac{1}{4} \log \dfrac{x}{\sqrt{x^2 + 4}} + C.$

(b) $\displaystyle \int \frac{x\, dx}{(x+1)(x^2+1)}.$

(c) $\displaystyle \int \frac{(x+1)^2}{x^3 + x}\, dx.$ *Ans.* $\log x + 2 \arctan x + C.$

(d) $\displaystyle \int \frac{x^2\, dx}{x^4 + 5x^2 + 4}.$

---

* We shall occasionally use arc tan x in place of $\tan^{-1} x$ partly to become familiar with this alternative notation and partly because $\tan^{-1} x$ sometimes occurs in connection with powers of $\tan x$ and there is danger of confusion.

(e) $\displaystyle\int \frac{dx}{(x-1)(x^2+4x+5)}$.

    Ans. $\frac{1}{10}\log(x-1) - \frac{1}{20}\log(x^2+4x+5) - \frac{3}{10}\arctan(x+2) + C$.

(f) $\displaystyle\int \frac{dx}{(x-1)^2(x^2+4x+5)}$.

(g) $\displaystyle\int \frac{dx}{x^3+1}$.

    Ans. $\frac{1}{3}\log(x+1) - \frac{1}{6}\log(x^2-x+1) + \dfrac{1}{\sqrt{3}}\arctan\dfrac{2x-1}{\sqrt{3}} + C$.

Case IV. There is one other situation that can arise in integrating rational functions. The denominator, as we know, is a polynomial of the form

$$b_0 x^m + b_1 x^{m-1} + \cdots + b_{m-1}x + b_m.$$

The linear factors with real coefficients of this polynomial correspond to the real zeros of the polynomial. After determining these linear factors, we may have one or more quadratic factors of which some are repeated. Or the denominator may already be in this form. Thus suppose that we have to integrate the rational function

(38)
$$\frac{5}{(x-1)(x^2+2x+4)^2}.$$

As we might expect from our discussion of the first three cases, the proper partial fractions for this given rational function are

$$\frac{A}{x-1} + \frac{Bx+C}{x^2+2x+4} + \frac{Dx+E}{(x^2+2x+4)^2}.$$

That is, just as in the case in which a linear factor occurs to a higher power than the first, we must allow for all powers of the quadratic factor up to and including the given one, and each partial fraction with this quadratic factor must have a linear numerator. The unknown coefficients A, B, C, and so forth are then determined in the usual way.

    From the standpoint of integration the only new problem is how to handle a term such as

$$\frac{Dx+E}{(x^2+2x+4)^2}.$$

We must complete the square in the parentheses and introduce $u = x - 1$ as in Case III. The expression then reduces to two terms of the form

$$\frac{u}{(u^2+a^2)^2} \quad \text{and} \quad \frac{c}{(u^2+a^2)^2}.$$

The former can be handled at once. The latter must be handled by a reduction formula that reads

$$\int \frac{du}{(u^2 + a^2)^n} = \frac{1}{2a^2(n-1)} \frac{u}{(u^2+a^2)^{n-1}} + \frac{2n-3}{2a^2(n-1)} \int \frac{du}{(u^2+a^2)^{n-1}}.$$

We did not prove this reduction formula, but its correctness can be established by differentiating both sides. We shall not carry out the details of integrating (38) because the procedure is clear.

There is just one more point to be noted in connection with the method of partial fractions. The denominator, we know, is a polynomial

$$(39) \qquad\qquad b_0 x^m + b_1 x^{m-1} + \cdots + b_{m-1} x + b_m$$

where the coefficients are, as usual, real numbers. The question one might raise is, do these four cases take care of all possible factors that may occur in treating polynomials? The answer is yes and results from some theorems of algebra. The zeros of the polynomial (39) are m in number and can be real and complex numbers. To each zero there is a linear factor. The complex zeros occur in conjugate pairs, that is, if $a + bi$ is a zero, then $a - bi$ must also be a zero. Then the corresponding factors are $x - (a + bi)$ and $x - (a - bi)$. The product of two such factors is $x^2 - 2ax + a^2 + b^2$; it is, in other words, a quadratic factor with *real* numbers as coefficients. To each real zero of the polynomial there is a real linear factor. Hence the polynomial must necessarily be factorable into a product of linear and quadratic factors with *real* coefficients.

Exercises

1. Evaluate the following integrals:

(a) $\displaystyle\int \frac{dx}{(x^2 + 1)^2}.$ *Ans.* $\dfrac{x}{2(x^2 + 1)} + \frac{1}{2}$ arc tan $x + C.$

(b) $\displaystyle\int \frac{2x\, dx}{(1 + x)(1 + x^2)^2}.$

5. Integration by Substitution and Change of Variable.   No matter how many formulas for integration are established, it is always necessary to keep in mind that a given integral may have to be reduced to a known formula by a substitution or a change of variable. There are unfortunately no rules to indicate what substitution or change of variable will reduce a given integral to a known formula. We shall, however, consider two classes of integrals that are of sufficient frequency to be worth noting.

The first of these classes deals with integrands involving $\sqrt{x^2 \pm a^2}$ or $\sqrt{a^2 - x^2}$. Let us consider as an example*

(40)
$$\int \sqrt{a^2 - x^2}\, dx.$$

The radical can be eliminated by a change of variable. Thus let

$$x = a \sin u.$$

To convert the entire integrand to a derivative with respect to u we must replace dx by $(dx/du)\, du$. But

$$\frac{dx}{du} = a \cos u.$$

Then (40) becomes

$$\int \sqrt{a^2 - a^2 \sin^2 u}\; a \cos u\, du$$

or

$$\int a^2 \cos^2 u\, du.$$

In the present case we come down to a simple trigonometric function, and by using the identity

$$\cos u = \sqrt{\frac{1 + \cos 2u}{2}}$$

we can carry out the integration and then replace u by arc sin (x/a) in order to return to a function of x.

One may have, to start with, a more complicated function involving $\sqrt{a^2 - x^2}$ or one of the other radicals mentioned earlier, and one of the changes of variable $x = a \sin u$, $x = a \tan u$, or $x = a \sec u$ will at least eliminate the radical. Whether the integration can then be completed depends, of course, on the original function.

The second class of integrands worth noting deals with trigonometric functions and in fact includes many of the trigonometric functions that arise from the change of variable just discussed. The integrands we have in mind are those that involve the trigonometric functions sin x and cos x rationally. The integrand

(41)
$$\int \frac{dx}{\sin x + \cos x}$$

is an example. The statement that the integrand involves sin x and cos x rationally means that if we replace sin x by s, say, and cos x by t, then the resulting expression is a rational function of the two variables s and t. A rational function in the two variables is a form that involves constants and

---

* See also Chapter 10, Section 5.

positive integral powers of s and t joined by the operations of addition, subtraction, multiplication, and division. Thus

$$\frac{3s^3t^2 + 2s^2t^2 - 4st + 5}{3s^2t^2 + 4s + 5t + 7}$$

is a rational function of s and t.

If we have a rational function of $\sin x$ and $\cos x$, the change of variable

(42) $x = 2 \arctan u$

will convert the rational function into a rational function of u. We can see this in the following way. Because

$$\sin \frac{x}{2} = \sqrt{\frac{1 - \cos x}{2}}$$

and

$$\cos \frac{x}{2} = \sqrt{\frac{1 + \cos x}{2}},$$

then

$$\tan^2 \frac{x}{2} = \frac{1 - \cos x}{1 + \cos x}$$

or, because, by (42), $u = \tan (x/2)$,

$$u^2 = \frac{1 - \cos x}{1 + \cos x}.$$

By solving for $\cos x$ we obtain

(43) $\cos x = \dfrac{1 - u^2}{1 + u^2}.$

Then, as we can see from Fig. 13-1 or by using the identity

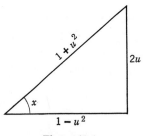

Figure 13-1

$$\sin x = \sqrt{1 - \cos^2 x},$$

we have

(44) $\sin x = \dfrac{2u}{1 + u^2}.$

Also, because

$$x = 2 \arctan u,$$

then

(45) $\dfrac{dx}{du} = \dfrac{2}{1 + u^2}.$

To see how this change of variable works out in practice let us consider the integral in (41), namely,

$$\int \frac{dx}{\sin x + \cos x}$$

The process is change of variable as given by (42). We know what sin x, cos x, and dx are by (43), (44), and (45). Then the integral becomes

$$\int \frac{1}{\dfrac{2u}{1+u^2} + \dfrac{1-u^2}{1+u^2}} \frac{2}{1+u^2}\, du$$

or

$$\int \frac{2}{1+2u-u^2}\, du.$$

This integral may be evaluated by completing the square in the denominator.

The class of integrands we have just discussed, namely, those that involve sin x and cos x rationally, includes those that involve the other four functions, tan x, cot x, sec x, and csc x, rationally, for each of these functions can be converted to sin x and cos x by rational expressions. For example, tan $x =$ sin x/cos x. Hence, if the given function involves tan x rationally, it will involve sin x and cos x rationally.

Exercises

1. Evaluate the following integrals:

(a) $\displaystyle\int \frac{d\theta}{5 + 4\cos\theta}.$ $\qquad$ *Ans.* $\dfrac{2}{3}\arctan\left(\dfrac{1}{3}\tan\dfrac{\theta}{2}\right) + C.$

(b) $\displaystyle\int \frac{dx}{1 + \sin x + \cos x}.$

(c) $\displaystyle\int \frac{dx}{\sin x + \tan x}.$ $\qquad$ *Ans.* $\dfrac{1}{2}\log\tan\dfrac{x}{2} - \dfrac{1}{4}\tan^2\dfrac{x}{2} + C.$

6. *The Use of Tables*. Let us suppose that we face the problem of integrating a given function and we do not recognize the integral by reversing a familiar differentiation formula. Nor do we find that the techniques of integration by parts, partial fractions, reduction formulas, substitution, and change of variable help us. What can we do? One answer would be to study more techniques or seek to discover a new one. However, the number of techniques and special tricks is quite extensive. It is neither wise nor efficient to spend months or years on what is really an incidental process or means to an end at the expense of the acquisition of more significant knowledge. Fortunately, the results of a large amount of work on integration have been collected in tables, and one utilizes these results. The situation here is entirely analogous to what we do with logarithmic or trigonometric values. We know in principle how these can be calculated* but we do not spend months in calculating these tables ourselves. They were calculated by expert mathematicians, and

* See Chapter 20.

we are satisfied to use the results. In the case of integral tables we have an additional advantage. We can always differentiate the given integral and check that it gives the derived function that we happen to be facing. The practical procedure, then, when facing an integral which one does not see how to handle immediately, is to look up the tables. Many of the results obtained in the last few sections are given there at once, and one need not use the processes we have been learning. Our purpose in going through many of these processes was to shed light on how so many integrals are obtained.*

A set of tables containing the forms that one is likely to encounter in the ordinary uses of the calculus is appended to this book. From this point on the student may use these tables. There are special collections of tables that contain many more forms than are given here, and one who goes much farther in mathematics may want to purchase such a set so as to have it on hand for immediate use.

There are a few points to be noted in the use of tables. First, because there are many forms, they are classified to help the user locate the right one as readily as possible. Thus one finds a class of forms involving $\sqrt{a + bu}$, another class involving $\sqrt{a^2 + u^2}$, and still another class involving $\sqrt{2au + u^2}$. Obviously, one looks among the forms of that class which includes the given integrand.

Secondly, the integrals in the table are deliberately written so as to involve the variable u instead of x. Thus instead of

(46)
$$\int x^n \, dx = \frac{x^{n+1}}{n + 1} + C$$

one finds

(47)
$$\int u^n \, du = \frac{u^{n+1}}{n + 1} + C.$$

The use of u instead of x is intended to suggest that u may be any function of x. Thus

$$\int (1 + x^2)^{1/2} 2x \, dx$$

comes under (47) if we let u be $(1 + x^2)$. The only point to be careful about is that if u is a function of x, the du in (47) is $(du/dx) \, dx$, and this factor *must be present* in the integrand if one is to use (47). This restriction is in accordance with what we learned about integration by substitution. On the other hand, if one has

$$\int x^{1/2} \, dx,$$

the form (47) surely covers it because one has merely to think of u as x.

* Now he tells us.

Exercises

1. Use the tables to perform the following integrations. Of course, a substitution of a new variable or a change of variable before using the table may be necessary.

(a) $\displaystyle\int \frac{dx}{x^2\sqrt{x-1}}$.

Ans. $\displaystyle\frac{\sqrt{x-1}}{x} + \arctan \sqrt{x-1} + C.$

(b) $\displaystyle\int \frac{dx}{1+x+x^2}$.

(c) $\displaystyle\int \frac{\sqrt{1-x}}{x}$.

Ans. $\displaystyle 2\sqrt{1-x} + \log \frac{\sqrt{1-x}-1}{\sqrt{1-x}+1} + C.$

(d) $\displaystyle\int \frac{\sqrt{10-x^2}}{x^4} \, dx.$

(e) $\displaystyle\int \frac{dx}{x^2\sqrt{1+3x}}$.

Ans. $\displaystyle -\frac{\sqrt{1+3x}}{x} - \tfrac{3}{2}\log \frac{\sqrt{1+3x}-1}{\sqrt{1+3x}+1} + C.$

(f) $\displaystyle\int \frac{dx}{x\sqrt{9+x^2}}$.

(g) $\displaystyle\int \frac{\sqrt{3x^2+5}}{x^2} \, dx.$ Ans. $\displaystyle -\frac{\sqrt{3x^2+5}}{x} + \sqrt{3}\log(\sqrt{3x^2+5} + x\sqrt{3}) + C.$

The Integral as the Limit of a Sequence of Sums

1. Introduction. We mentioned at the beginning of this book that one of the major classes of problems that led to the calculus was the determination of areas, volumes, and centers of gravity of a variety of figures. We have already shown how the calculus can be used in calculating some areas (see Section 5 of Chapter 5 and Section 8 of Chapter 6), but for reasons that will be apparent shortly we shall approach the problem anew.

The calculation of areas of figures bounded by *straight line segments* can be performed with the methods of Euclidean geometry. Thus the areas of triangles, rectangles, and parallelograms are readily found. More complicated rectilinear figures, that is, figures bounded by line segments, can at the very worst be broken up into triangles, and the area can then be obtained as the sum of areas of the triangles. It is in this way that, for example, the areas of regular polygons are calculated.

The first really difficult figure is the circular region. The Greeks solved the problem of finding its area by taking a very natural step. First, they approximated the area by inscribing a square (Fig. 14-1). Then they improved the approximation by inscribing the regular octagon, then the regular 16-sided polygon, and so on. Each new polygon is evidently a better approximation to the desired area. The Greeks then noted that the areas of these successive inscribed polygons approached more closely the area of the circle. They also used circumscribed regular polygons which, as the number of sides increased, also approached the area of a circle through larger values.* Euclid (300 B.C.), following Eudoxus (406–355 B.C.), then proved that the areas of any two circles are to each other as the squares of their respective radii. From this it follows that for any circle the area $A = kr^2$ where k is a constant and r is the radius. Archimedes (287–212 B.C.) then calculated the value of k, which is π, of course, by calculating the perimeters of inscribed and circumscribed regular polygons of more and more sides in a circle of diameter 1, and showed that π lies between $3\frac{1}{7}$ and $3\frac{10}{71}$.

---

* The Greeks did not use limits explicitly. They used an indirect method of proof known as the method of exhaustion. For simplicity we speak in this section of the Greeks using limits.

Figure 14-1

The next major result in the determination of areas was Archimedes' calculation of the area between an arc of a parabola and a chord, that is, the area bounded by the arc $BA'AA''C$ and the chord BC in Fig. 14-2. Because regular polygons are not inscribable in this area, Archimedes hit upon the idea of using triangles. His first approximation was the triangle ABC, the point A having been chosen as the one at which the tangent to the parabola is parallel to BC. His next approximation was obtained by adding to triangle ABC the triangle $AA''C$, which takes in area between the arc $AA''C$ and the chord AC, and the triangle $AA'B$, which takes in area between the arc $AA'B$ and the chord AB. To obtain his third approximation, he inscribed triangles in each of the four regions still not included—the region between arc $A'B$ and chord $A'B$ in one such region—and so the third approximation was the sum of triangles ABC, $AA'B$, $AA''C$, and the four new triangles. By observing the limit approached by these successive approximations, Archimedes showed that the area of the parabolic segment is $\frac{4}{3}$ of the area of triangle ABC.

A few other striking results about area were obtained by Archimedes. However, each problem that he tackled required a specially designed set of

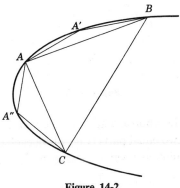

Figure 14-2

approximating figures. Moreover, the determination of the limit was a problem of considerable difficulty for the Greeks because they did not possess our algebra and analytic geometry. Algebra is, of course, useful in converting one expression into another whose limiting value may be more perspicuous, and analytic geometry enables us to put facts about curves into algebraic form.

From Greek times until the seventeenth century no progress was made in finding areas and volumes bounded in whole or in part by curved figures. However, in that century and certainly in Newton's work itself the method of finding areas that we learned in Chapter 5 became available and it would seem as if the problem were settled. While this method was being developed and applied, some mathematicians—Pascal, Fermat, and notably Leibniz—continued to pursue the Greek idea of approximating curvilinear areas by rectilinear figures and of coming closer and closer to the desired area by improving the rectilinear approximation. Let us examine next the manner in which they executed this scheme.

2. *Area as the Limit of a Sum.* Consider the area shown in Fig. 14-3, that is, the area bounded by the curve CD, by the vertical lines at $x = a$ and $x = b$, and by the x-axis. We can obtain an approximation to it by choosing the minimum y-value in (a, b) and multiplying it by $b - a$. In anticipation of future steps, we write $b - a$ as Δx and we denote the minimum y-value by m_1. Thus the first approximation is $m_1 \Delta x$. Geometrically, this approximation is the area of the rectangle shown in the figure. We write

$$\underline{S_1} = m_1 \Delta x.$$

The S refers to the sum that, as we shall see, enters into our process; the subscripts reminds us that we have the first approximation; the bar underneath is to indicate that we have used the minimum y-value in Δx.

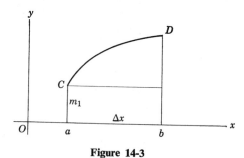

Figure 14-3

We can obtain a better approximation to the area in question if we divide the interval (a, b) into two equal parts (Fig. 14-4), each of which we denote by Δx, if we take the minimum y-value in each part, and then form the sum

$$\underline{S_2} = m_1 \Delta x + m_2 \Delta x.$$

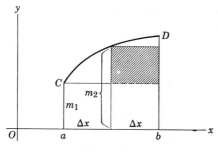

Figure 14-4

Geometrically, S_2 is the sum of two rectangles, and it is clear that S_2 is a better approximation to the area under the curve than S_1, because it includes the shaded area in Fig. 14-4, whereas S_1 did not include it.

We can now divide (a, b) into three equal parts and form S_3, then into four equal parts and form S_4, and so on. Let us try to be general. Suppose that we divide the interval (a, b) into n equal parts (Fig. 14-5) and denote each by Δx. In each part or subinterval Δx we choose the minimum y-value, which we denote by $m_1, m_2, \ldots, m_n$, respectively. We now form the sum

(1) $$S_n = m_1 \, \Delta x + m_2 \, \Delta x + \cdots + m_n \, \Delta x,$$

where the dots indicate the missing terms. Geometrically, S_n is a sum of n rectangles.

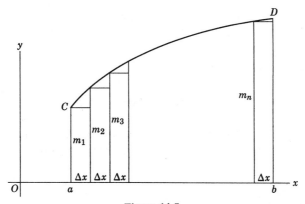

Figure 14-5

The important point to see now is that the larger we make n, which means that Δx becomes smaller and smaller, the closer does the sum S_n approach the area under the curve. Geometrically this statement is evident, because the smaller Δx is, the less the minimum y-value in any subinterval Δx can differ from the other y-values in that subinterval.

Now, the quantity n can be made larger and larger without bound. To each n there is a sum S_n, and therefore the quantity S_n varies with n. Hence we can speak of

$$\lim_{n \to \infty} S_n;$$

geometrically, this limit seems to be the exact area under the curve CD. If we denote this area by A, we can say that

(2) $$\lim_{n \to \infty} S_n = A.$$

The limit concept involved in (2) is in some respects different from the limit of, say, x^2 as x approaches 2 or of $1/x$ as x becomes infinite, but for the moment, let us not pursue the difference.

The approximations to the area A that we obtained in $S_1, S_2, \ldots, S_n$ were all less than A because in each Δx we chose the minimum y-value. We can obtain another sequence of approximations to A if we use the *maximum* y-value in each Δx. Because the considerations are the same as those we have just considered, let us jump at once to the nth approximation. We divide the interval (a, b) into n equal parts (Fig. 14-6) and, as before, denote the width of

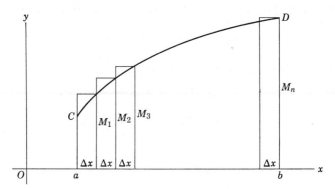

Figure 14-6

each part or subinterval by Δx. In each Δx we take the maximum y-value and denote them by $M_1, M_2, \ldots, M_n$. We now form the sum

(3) $$\overline{S_n} = M_1 \, \Delta x + M_2 \, \Delta x + \cdots + M_n \, \Delta x.$$

We use the notation $\overline{S_n}$ to remind ourselves that we have used the maximum y-value in each Δx. Each term in this sum is the area of a rectangle, and each rectangle is larger than that portion of the area under the curve which it approximates. Our argument now is that as n is taken larger, and as Δx becomes smaller accordingly, the corresponding sum $\overline{S_n}$ is a better approximation to the area under the curve, because in a smaller Δx the maximum y-value differs less from the other y-values in that Δx. Since n can increase without bound, we can at least speak about

$$\lim_{n \to \infty} \overline{S}_n,$$

and on geometric grounds it appears that

(4) $$\lim_{n \to \infty} \overline{S}_n = A.$$

   This scheme of approximating a given area by a sum of rectangles is entirely analogous to the Greek scheme of approaching the area of a circle by regular polygons. Each sum of rectangles that approaches the area from below is analogous to an inscribed regular polygon. Each sum of rectangles that approaches the area from above is analogous to a circumscribed regular polygon. Moreover, just as the area of the circle lies between the increasing areas of the set of inscribed regular polygons and the decreasing areas of the circumscribed regular polygons, so the area under the curve lies between the increasing areas of the sums of rectangles that approximate the area from below and the decreasing areas of the sums of the rectangles that approximate the area from above.

   Before we develop further our new approach to area, let us see how it works out in a particular case. Let us find the area (Fig. 14-7) under the straight line $y = 2x$ and between $x = 1$, $x = 5$, and the x-axis. We want to calculate

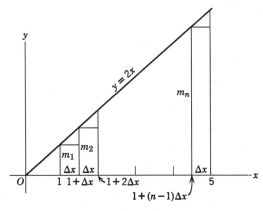

Figure 14-7

the limit called for in (2). Hence we must first find $\underline{S}_n$, which is defined in (1). We break up the interval from $x = 1$ to $x = 5$ into n equal parts, each of width Δx. In each subinterval we choose the smallest y-value. In the first subinterval this is the y-value at $x = 1$. Then, because $y = 2x$,

$$m_1 = 2 \cdot 1.$$

In the second subinterval the smallest y-value is the left-hand y-value. The corresponding x-value is $1 + \Delta x$; hence

$$m_2 = 2(1 + \Delta x).$$

In the third subinterval the smallest y-value is again the left-hand y-value and the corresponding x-value is $1 + 2\Delta x$. Hence

$$m_3 = 2(1 + 2\Delta x).$$

We see that the same procedure applies to each subinterval. Let us therefore note only the last one. The smallest y-value is the left-hand y-value and the corresponding x-value is $1 + (n - 1)\,\Delta x$. Then

$$m_n = 2[1 + (n - 1)\,\Delta x].$$

The sum $\underline{S_n}$ in this example is

(5) $$\underline{S_n} = 2\Delta x + 2(1 + \Delta x)\,\Delta x + 2(1 + 2\Delta x)\,\Delta x$$

$$+ \cdots + 2[1 + (n - 1)\,\Delta x]\,\Delta x$$

or

(6) $$\underline{S_n} = 2\Delta x + 2\Delta x + 2(\Delta x)^2 + 2\Delta x + 2 \cdot 2(\Delta x)^2$$

$$+ \cdots + 2\Delta x + 2(n - 1)(\Delta x)^2.$$

We would like to find the number approached by $\underline{S_n}$ as n becomes infinite. First, let us rearrange the terms. We see that the quantity $2\Delta x$ occurs in each term. Because there are n-terms, these amount to $2n\,\Delta x$. In addition, we have the quantities

$$2(\Delta x)^2 + 2 \cdot 2(\Delta x)^2 + \cdots + 2(n - 1)(\Delta x)^2$$

or

$$2(\Delta x)^2[1 + 2 + \cdots + (n - 1)].$$

The quantity in the brackets is the sum of an arithmetic progression of $n - 1$ terms. The formula for such a sum is

$$s = \frac{n}{2}(a + l)$$

where n is the number of terms, a is the first term, and l is the last term. In our case

$$s = \frac{n - 1}{2}(1 + n - 1) = \frac{(n - 1)n}{2}.$$

Hence

(7) $$\underline{S_n} = 2n\,\Delta x + 2(\Delta x)^2 \frac{(n - 1)n}{2}.$$

We know that as n becomes infinite, Δx approaches 0 because we divided the interval from $x = 1$ to $x = 5$ into n equal parts each of width Δx, so that

(8) $$\Delta x = \frac{5 - 1}{n}.$$

If we try to use the facts that n becomes infinite and Δx approaches 0 in (7), we do not see clearly what number S_n approaches. Let us substitute the value of Δx given by (8) in (7). Then

$$\underline{S_n} = 2n\,\frac{4}{n} + 2\left(\frac{4}{n}\right)^2 \frac{(n-1)n}{2} = 8 + 16\,\frac{(n-1)n}{n^2}$$

or

$$\underline{S_n} = 8 + 16 - \frac{16}{n}.$$

It is now clear that as n becomes infinite, $16/n$ approaches 0 and $\underline{S_n}$ approaches 24. That is,

$$(9) \qquad\qquad \lim_{n\to\infty} \underline{S_n} = 24.$$

We have found that the area under $y = 2x$ between $x = 1$ and $x = 5$ is 24. In the present case the figure is a trapezoid whose bases are the ordinates at $x = 1$ and $x = 5$, that is, 2 and 10, and whose altitude is 4. Because the area of a trapezoid is one half the altitude times the sum of the bases, we see that the area as given by plane geometry agrees with the result obtained by the calculus method.

Let us consider next a more difficult example. We shall evaluate the area (Fig. 14-8) under the parabola $y = x^2$ and lying between $x = 0$ and $x = 5$ by

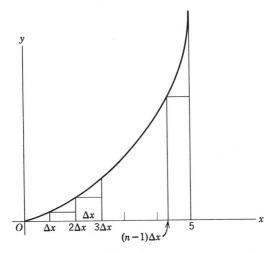

Figure 14-8

using (1) and (2). We divide the interval from 0 to 5 into n equal parts, each of width Δx. In each subinterval the smallest y-value is the left-hand value. The abscissas at the left-hand end points of the subintervals are

$$0,\ \Delta x,\ 2\Delta x,\ 3\Delta x \ldots (n-1)\,\Delta x.$$

Because $y = x^2$, the ordinates at these abscissas are

$$0^2, (\Delta x)^2, (2\Delta x)^2, \ldots, \{(n-1)\,\Delta x\}^2.$$

These successive y-values are, of course, the $m_1, m_2, m_3, \ldots, m_n$ of (1). Then, in accordance with (1),

$$S_n = 0^2 \cdot \Delta x + (\Delta x)^2\,\Delta x + (2\Delta x)^2\,\Delta x + \cdots + \{(n-1)\,\Delta x\}^2\,\Delta x$$

or

(10) $$S_n = (\Delta x)^3[1^2 + 2^2 + 3^2 + \cdots + (n-1)^2].$$

To simplify this result, let us accept for the moment that the sum of the squares of the first n integers is given by the formula*

(11) $$s = \frac{n^3}{3} + \frac{n^2}{2} + \frac{n}{6}.$$

Because our expression (10) calls for the sum of the squares of the first $(n-1)$ integers, we could substitute $n-1$ for n in (11) or we can obtain the result faster by noting that we want $s - n^2$, which is

$$\frac{n^3}{3} - \frac{n^2}{2} + \frac{n}{6}.$$

We substitute this value for the quantity in brackets in (10) and obtain

$$S_n = (\Delta x)^3\left(\frac{n^3}{3} - \frac{n^2}{2} + \frac{n}{6}\right).$$

As S_n now stands, it is difficult to determine the limit as n becomes infinite because Δx approaches 0. However, we divided the interval from $x = 0$ to $x = 5$ into n parts so that

$$\Delta x = \frac{5}{n}.$$

Then

$$S_n = \left(\frac{5}{n}\right)^3\left(\frac{n^3}{3} - \frac{n^2}{2} + \frac{n}{6}\right) = 125\left(\frac{1}{3} - \frac{1}{2n} + \frac{1}{6n^2}\right).$$

We now see that

$$\lim_{n \to \infty} S_n = \tfrac{125}{3}.$$

This number is the area under the parabola $y = x^2$ between $x = 0$ and $x = 5$.

Before we do more with the above method of finding areas, we should become a little more familiar with it through use.

Exercises

1. Find the area under the line $y = 3x$ between $x = 1$ and $x = 5$ by the method employed in the text.   *Ans.* 36.

---

* The proof is given in the Appendix to this chapter.

2. Find the area of Exercise 1 but use the largest y-value in each subinterval in place of the smallest y-value.
3. Find the area under the parabola $y = x^2$ from $x = 0$ to $x = 5$ by using the largest y-value in each subinterval. *Ans.* $\frac{125}{3}$.
4. Find the area under the curve $y = x^2$ from $x = 1$ to $x = 5$. *Ans.* $\frac{124}{3}$.
5. Compute approximately the area under $y = x^2$ from $x = 0$ to $x = 5$ by using 10 subintervals Δx to fill out the interval $(0, 5)$ and by using the largest y-value in each subinterval.
6. Compute approximately the area under the curve $y = 1/(1 + x^2)$ for the interval $0 \le x \le 1$. Use $n = 10$ and the smallest y-value in each subinterval. *Ans.* 0.75.

3. The Definite Integral. The method of finding areas that we examined in Section 2 introduces several new concepts into the calculus, and we should obtain a clearer understanding of them before considering whether we can do anything more significant with the method.

There is, first, a new limit concept. Each approximation to the area under a curve is a sum of rectangles. We have denoted these sums, when the minimum y-value is used in each Δx, by

$$\underline{S_1}, \underline{S_2}, \underline{S_3}, \ldots, \underline{S_n}, \ldots$$

This set of successive sums is called an *infinite sequence.* More generally, an infinite sequence is a set of numbers or functions such that there is a first member, a second member, and in fact a member corresponding to each positive integer n. Thus the set is unending. What is of interest in sequences is the number which the members of the sequence approach as one considers more and more members or terms of the sequence. That is, we are concerned with the *limit* toward which the members tend. We denote the fact that we are interested in what the successive members approach by speaking first of all of n becoming infinite. We denote the number which the members approach by the notation

$$\lim_{n \to \infty} \underline{S_n}.$$

If we consider any infinite sequence, we need not use the bar underneath, and we can write it as

$$S_1, S_2, S_3, \ldots, S_n, \ldots$$

Thus if the sequence consists of the numbers

$$1, \frac{1}{2}, \frac{1}{3}, \ldots, \frac{1}{n}, \ldots,$$

then $S_1 = 1$, $S_2 = \frac{1}{2}$, $S_3 = \frac{1}{3}, \ldots, S_n = 1/n$. It is evident in this case that

$$\lim_{n \to \infty} S_n = 0$$

because as n gets larger and larger, the quantity $1/n$ comes closer and closer to 0. If $n = 10^6$, $1/n = 0.000,001$; if $n = 10^9$, $1/n = 0.000,000,001$; and so on.

If the sequence consists of the numbers

$$1, 1\frac{1}{2}, 1\frac{1}{3}, 1\frac{1}{4}, \ldots, 1\frac{1}{n}, \ldots,$$

it is evident that the limit is 1 because the additional quantity $1/n$ in the nth term approaches 0.

Not every sequence has a limit. Thus the members of the sequence

$$1, 4, 9, \ldots, n^2, \ldots$$

become larger and larger and increase beyond bound. They do not approach a definite number. We sometimes say that the nth term becomes infinite, but this means only that the successive terms increase and become larger than any number that one may name.

A sequence may not have a limit or, one says, may fail to converge even if the terms do not become infinite. For example, consider the sequence

$$1, 2, \tfrac{1}{2}, 1\tfrac{1}{2}, \tfrac{1}{4}, 1\tfrac{1}{4}, \tfrac{1}{8}, 1\tfrac{1}{8}, \ldots.$$

Here the odd-numbered terms approach 0 and the even-numbered terms approach 1. Because *all* the terms do not come closer and closer to one fixed number, the sequence does not have a limit. Yet the terms of the entire sequence are bounded; that is, they all are less than a fixed number, for example, 3.

It is desirable to distinguish between a sequence and a function. The function $y = x^2$ takes on values for *all* values of x in some domain. If, for example we were interested in this function over the domain $x = 3$ to $x = 5$, the possible values of x would be the whole numbers, fractions, and irrational numbers between 3 and 5. On the other hand, if we have a sequence whose nth term is, say, n^2, then only the values of n^2 for $n = 1$, $n = 2$, $n = 3$, and so on are of interest. One can regard n as a variable and n^2 as a function, but only the values of n^2 for positive integral values of n matter.

The difference between a function and a sequence insofar as the values that x can take on in the former case and n in the latter is reflected in the corresponding limit concepts. For example,

$$\lim_{x \to 2} x^2$$

is the number that x^2 approaches as x takes on *all* values closer and closer to 2. On the other hand, when one considers, for example,

$$\lim_{n \to \infty} \frac{1}{n^2},$$

he is interested in the number that $1/n^2$ approaches as n takes on larger and larger positive integral values.

We shall say more about sequences in connection with the work on infinite series. At the present time some acquaintance with the notions of infinite sequence and limit of a sequence is sufficient, and we may return to the subject of the area under a curve.

Exercises

1. Write the first 5 terms of the sequence whose nth term is the following:

(a) $\dfrac{n}{3}$.

(b) n^2.

(c) $\dfrac{n + 1}{n + 2}$.

(d) $\dfrac{n + 3}{\sqrt{n}}$.

2. Write the nth term of the following sequences:

(a) $3, 2\frac{1}{2}, 2\frac{1}{3}, 2\frac{1}{4}, \ldots$.
     Ans. $2 + (1/n)$.

(b) $\frac{1}{2}, \frac{1}{4}, \frac{1}{8}, \frac{1}{16}, \ldots$.
   Ans. $1/2^n$.

(c) $2\frac{1}{2}, 2\frac{1}{4}, 2\frac{1}{8}, 2\frac{1}{16}, \ldots$.

(d) $1, -\frac{1}{2}, \frac{1}{3}, -\frac{1}{4}, \frac{1}{5}, \ldots$.

(e) $\dfrac{1}{1 \cdot 2}, \dfrac{1}{2 \cdot 3}, \dfrac{1}{3 \cdot 4}, \dfrac{1}{4 \cdot 5}, \ldots$.

(f) $1, \frac{1}{2}, \frac{1}{6}, \frac{1}{24}, \frac{1}{120}, \ldots$.
     Ans. $1/n!$.

3. Determine by inspection the limit, if there is one, of each of the following sequences. The symbol s_n denotes the nth term of the sequence.

(a) $s_n = \dfrac{1}{\sqrt{n}}$.
   Ans. 0.

(b) $s_n = \dfrac{n}{n + 1}$.
   Ans. 1.

(c) $s_n = \dfrac{1/n}{1/(n + 1)}$.
   Ans. 1.

(d) $s_n = (-1)^n \dfrac{n - 1}{n + 1}$.
     Ans. None.

(e) $s_n = \sqrt{n}$.

(f) $s_n = (-1)^n \dfrac{1}{n!}$.

(g) $s_n = 1^n$.

(h) $s_n = \dfrac{n^2 + 3n}{n + 2}$.
   Ans. None.

(i) $s_n = \dfrac{2(n - 1)}{n^2 - 1}$.

(j) $s_n = 5 + \dfrac{1}{n} + \dfrac{6}{n^2}$.

When we discussed previously approximating the area under a curve by rectangles, we decided that in each subinterval Δx we would choose the smallest y-value or the largest y-value. With either choice the successive sums obtained by utilizing narrower and narrower rectangles approach the area under the curve. If, however, we should select in each subinterval *any*

y-value (Fig. 14-9), then the sum of the rectangular areas should likewise approach the area under the curve. This fact is rather easy to establish. Suppose that we have subdivided the interval (a, b) into equal subintervals Δx. As before, we denote by m_i the smallest y-value in the ith subinterval and by M_i, the largest y-value. Now let y_i denote any y-value in the ith

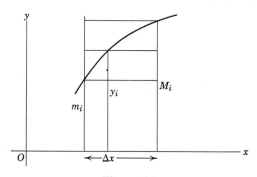

Figure 14-9

subinterval. Thereby we obtain three different sequences of sums whose nth terms are

$$\underline{S_n} = m_1\,\Delta x + m_2\,\Delta x + \cdots + m_n\,\Delta x,$$

$$S_n^* = y_1\,\Delta x + y_2\,\Delta x + \cdots + y_n\,\Delta x,$$

$$\overline{S_n} = M_1\,\Delta x + M_2\,\Delta x + \cdots + M_n\,\Delta x.$$

From the fact that

$$m_i \leq y_i \leq M_i$$

we have that

$$\underline{S_n} < S_n^* < \overline{S_n}.$$

Now, when n becomes infinite, both $\underline{S_n}$ and $\overline{S_n}$ approach the area under the curve. Because S_n^* lies between the other two, it must approach the same limit. Hence, if we should find it convenient to choose some y-value in each subinterval Δx other than the minimum or maximum one, we may do so.

We may take another liberty with respect to the construction of the sequence of approximating sums. We introduced this concept by starting with subdivisions of the interval (a, b) into equal parts of width Δx. However, our main concern is to have the sum of the rectangles that we form come closer, as the number of rectangles increases, to the area under the curve. The way to attain this end is to make each rectangle narrower and narrower, even though in any one subdivision the rectangles are not of equal width. That the essential point is the narrowness of each rectangle is easily seen. Why is each rectangle only an approximation to a portion of the area under the curve? An examination of Fig. 14-9 or of any of the foregoing figures in this chapter shows that the y_i we choose in any subinterval Δx is inexact only because the y-values that correspond to the x-values in Δx vary and the y_i we choose may differ from the others. However, if Δx is small, the y-values corresponding to the x-values in Δx cannot differ very much from the y_i we choose, and the smaller Δx is, the less these y-values can differ from y_i. Hence what matters in forming the sequence of sums of rectangles is not that the Δx's be equal in each subdivision of (a, b) but that the Δx's approach 0 in size as n, the number of subintervals, increases. This requirement is usually stated thus: the maximum Δx in the nth subdivision must approach 0 as n becomes infinite. For if the maximum Δx approaches 0, so must each of the others.

If we do choose unequal subintervals to fill out the interval (a, b), we cannot denote the width of each subinterval by Δx. In place of this we use Δx_1, Δx_2, and so on for the successive widths (Fig. 14-10). If we let y_1 be the y-value corresponding to any x-value in Δx_1, let y_2 be the y-value corresponding to any x-value in Δx_2, and so on, the nth term of the sequences of approximating sums is

$$S_n = y_1 \Delta x_1 + y_2 \Delta x_2 + \cdots + y_n \Delta x_n$$

and the area is given by

$$\lim_{n \to \infty} S_n,$$

provided that the maximum or largest Δx in S_n approaches 0 as n becomes infinite.

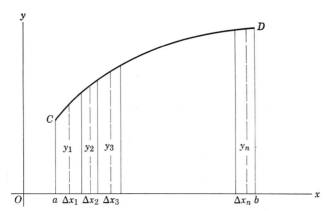

Figure 14-10

We see, then, that we can form many different kinds of sequences, each of which approaches the area under a curve or, we may say, has the area under the curve as its limit. If we are given a particular curve and are to find the area between that curve and the x-axis and between two vertical lines at $x = a$ and $x = b$, we could choose anyone of the sequence $\{S_n\}$ of approximating sums—by $\{S_n\}$ we denote the entire sequence, whereas S_n denotes the *n*th term itself—and then seek

$$\lim_{n\to\infty} S_n.$$

There is another notation for this limit which is very helpful in keeping before us the factors that determine the area. If $y = f(x)$ is the equation of the curve, then we write for the limit

(13) $$\int_a^b y \, dx \quad \text{or} \quad \int_a^b f(x) \, dx.$$

That is, no matter which of the approximating sequences we may use,

$$\lim_{n\to\infty} S_n = \int_a^b y \, dx \quad \text{or} \quad \lim_{n\to\infty} S_n = \int_a^b f(x) \, dx.$$

The notation (13) must not be taken too literally. The symbol $\int$ is an elongated S, introduced by Leibniz, to remind one that he is dealing with the limit of a sequence of sums. The symbols a and b are the left- and right-hand end values of the x-domain over which the area is being calculated. The $y \, dx$ or $f(x) \, dx$ is a reminder that we took rectangles of height y_i and width Δx_i. If one is dealing with the specific function $y = x^2$ and wishes to indicate that function instead of y or $f(x)$, he can write

(14) $$\int_a^b x^2 \, dx.$$

Clearly the notation (13) or (14) is more informative than

$$\lim_{n\to\infty} S_n.$$

The quantity (13) is called the *definite integral*. The use of the word integral is not justified by what we have said so far, for integrals in the past have arisen through antidifferentiation. The connection between definite integrals and antidifferentiation remains to be discussed. The word "definite," however, is intended to convey the fact that the symbol (13) stands for a number, whereas ordinary integrals, or indefinite integrals as they are often called, are functions.

Exercises

1. Describe the area represented by the following:

(a) $\displaystyle\int_1^3 x^2 \, dx.$ (c) $\displaystyle\int_0^\pi \sin x \, dx.$

(b) $\displaystyle\int_0^5 x^3 \, dx.$ (d) $\displaystyle\int_{-1}^4 x^2 \, dx.$

2. Our discussion of the definite integral has been confined to functions whose *y*-values are positive. Suppose, however, that the function has the behavior shown in Fig. 14-11. Could we define the definite integral for this function over the interval (a, b)? What area would the integral represent?

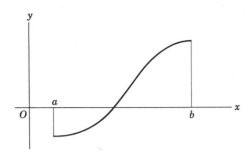

Figure 14-11

3. The definite integral is (*a*) a sum, (*b*) a sequence of sums, (*c*) a limit of a sequence of sums, or (*d*) a limit of many sequences of sums. Which of the alternative answers is most appropriate?

4. Express the area under $y = \sin x$ between $x = 0$ and $x = \pi$ as a definite integral.

5. The following definite integrals are, of course, numbers. State whether they are positive numbers or negative numbers.

(*a*) $\displaystyle\int_1^3 x^2 \, dx$.

(*d*) $\displaystyle\int_0^2 -x \, dx$.

(*b*) $\displaystyle\int_1^3 x^3 \, dx$.

(*e*) $\displaystyle\int_0^{2\pi} x^2 \sin^2 x \, dx$.

(*c*) $\displaystyle\int_0^2 -x^2 \, dx$.

6. Evaluate $\displaystyle\int_0^1 e^x \, dx$ by applying the definition of the definite integral. *Suggestion:* You will need the formula for the sum of a geometric progression. Also recall that $\lim\limits_{h \to 0} \dfrac{e^h - 1}{h} = \dfrac{d}{dx} (e^x)$ at $x = 0$.   *Ans. $e - 1$.*

4. The Evaluation of Definite Integrals.   Thus far in this chapter we have followed the Greek method of finding areas bounded in whole or in part by curves. Although we have improved on the Greeks by using sums of rectangles as the approximating figures and by using the equation of the curve and algebra to calculate the limit approached by the sequence of sums of rectangles, there is some question as to whether we have gained very much. The few examples we have studied which show how to find an area by finding the limit of a sequence of sums also show that the process is more cumbersome than the method of antidifferentiation. Indeed, if the equation of the curve should be complicated, the summation technique might not be practical at all for the actual calculation. It would seem, then, that we have gained nothing by our new approach to curvilinear areas. About the best we can say at the present time is that the concept of the definite integral has offered a new point of view: the quantity area can now be regarded as a limit of a sequence of sums of rectangles.

Although we have not, so far at least, gained much by introducing the definite integral, let us suppose that we do decide to approach areas in this way and raise a question. Is there an easy way of evaluating definite integrals?

We do have the knowledge to answer this question affirmatively. The definite integral, although it is a limit of a sequence of sums of rectangles, does represent an area. However, we learned rather early in our work (see Chapter 5, Section 5) that areas can be evaluated by antidifferentiation. If the curve CD (Fig. 14-12) is given by y as a function of x and if $A(x)$ is the

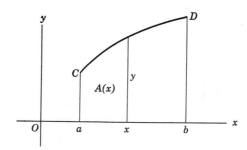

Figure 14-12

variable area under the curve between the ordinates at $x = a$ and $x = x$, then we proved that

$$(15) \qquad \frac{dA(x)}{dx} = y$$

where y is the ordinate at x. We may also write (15) in differential notation so that

$$dA(x) = y\,dx$$

or

$$A(x) = \int y\,dx.$$

Next we found the integral itself which gave us A as a function of x. We then substituted b in this function, substituted a, and subtracted the second result from the first.

Thus, if we have to find the area under $y = x^3$, say from $x = 1$ to $x = 5$, we write

$$\frac{dA(x)}{dx} = x^3$$

or

$$A(x) = \int x^3 \, dx$$

or

(16)
$$A(x) = \frac{x^4}{4}.$$

We do not bother to write the constant of integration because it does not affect the answer. We now substitute 5 for x in (16), which gives $\frac{625}{4}$. We substitute 1 for x and obtain $\frac{1}{4}$. We subtract the second result from the first and find that the area in question is $\frac{624}{4}$ or 156.

This area is what we represent also by the definite integral

$$\int_1^5 x^3 \, dx.$$

Hence

$$\int_1^5 x^3 \, dx = 156.$$

The result—that the definite integral, which is a limit of sequences of sums of rectangles, is evaluated essentially by antidifferentiation—is fundamental. It is, in fact, called the *fundamental theorem of the calculus*. We signalize it by stating it separately as a theorem:

Theorem: The definite integral, $\int_a^b y \, dx,$ *which is a limit of sequences of sums of rectangles, is evaluated by finding the indefinite integral of the function y of x and by subtracting the result of substituting a in this integral from the result of substituting b in this integral.*

We have stated a theorem, but what have we done about its proof? We have given only some limited geometrical evidence. The definite integral was introduced to represent an area and, because we already knew that areas can be evaluated by antidifferentiation, we concluded that definite integrals can be evaluated by antidifferentiation. This reliance upon geometrical evidence, although intuitively quite sound and even convincing, is from a strict logical standpoint inadequate. However, we rest our argument on the geometric evidence for the present time and use antidifferentiation and the substitution of the end values of the x-interval as the method of evaluating definite integrals.

We can also see now that the differential notation, for example, $A = \int y \, dx$, anticipates the symbol used for the definite integral. Historically the differential notation was introduced by Leibniz for the reason given in Chapter 13, Section 1. When he came to the subject of areas, he thought that when Δx was sufficiently small, $y \, \Delta x$ was the correct value of the element of area under the curve, and for such small Δx he wrote dx. Then the entire area for him was just a sum of elements $y\, dx$. Newton, on the other hand, worked entirely with derivatives and integrals obtained by antidifferentiation.

The definite integral, or the integral as the limit of sequences of sums, is a concept independent of the derivative, and it has been customary in the literature to think of the calculus as consisting of two parts: the differential calculus, concerned with differentiation and antidifferentiation, and the integral calculus, concerned with the definite integral and its ramifications. However, the fundamental theorem shows us that there is only one calculus.

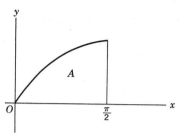

Figure 14-13

The definite integral will prove to be a most important concept for tackling problems and is indeed something new, but the effective evaluation of definite integrals reduces to antidifferentiation.

To be certain that we understand the use of the fundamental theorem, let us consider one more example. Suppose that we wish to find the area (Fig. 14-13) under the curve $y = \sin x$ from $x = 0$ to $x = \pi/2$. We know that we can express this area as a limit of a sequence of sums of rectangles, and this limit is denoted by

$$A = \int_0^{\pi/2} \sin x\, dx.$$

According to the fundamental theorem, we can proceed as follows. We seek first the indefinite integral

$$A(x) = \int \sin x\, dx.$$

Then

$$A(x) = -\cos x.$$

We now substitute specific values for x; that is, we substitute $\pi/2$ for x, then 0 for x, and subtract the second result from the first. This procedure is often indicated by the notation

$$A = -\cos x \Big|_0^{\pi/2}.$$

Then

$$A = -\cos \frac{\pi}{2} - (-\cos 0) = 0 - (-1) = 1.$$

Exercises

1. Given that $S_n = x_1{}^3\, \Delta x_1 + x_2{}^3\, \Delta x_2 + \cdots + x_n{}^3\, \Delta x_n$ where $\Delta x_1, \Delta x_2, \ldots, \Delta x_n$ fill out the interval $(0, 1)$ and x_i is a value of x in Δx_i, show that, provided the maximum Δx_i of any subdivision of $(0, 1)$ approaches 0 as n becomes infinite, $\lim\limits_{n \to \infty} S_n = \tfrac{1}{4}$. *Suggestion:* Use the fundamental theorem.

2. Let $S_n = y_1 \Delta x_1 + y_2 \Delta x_2 + \cdots + y_n \Delta x_n$, where the Δx_i fill out the x-interval from $x = 1$ to $x = 5$ and y_i is a value of $y = 3x^2$ in Δx_i. If the maximum Δx_i approaches 0 as n becomes infinite, evaluate $\lim\limits_{n \to \infty} S_n$. *Ans.* 124.

3. Let $S_n = 3x_1{}^2 \Delta x_1 + 3x_2{}^2 \Delta x_2 + \cdots + 3x_n{}^2 \Delta x_n$, where the Δx_i fill out the x-interval from $x = -2$ to $x = 6$ and x_i is any value of x in Δx_i. Evaluate $\lim\limits_{n \to \infty} S_n$ with the understanding that the maximum Δx_i approaches 0 as n becomes infinite.

4. Let $S_n = \sin x_1 \Delta x_1 + \sin x_2 \Delta x_2 + \cdots + \sin x_n \Delta x_n$, where the Δx_i fill out the x-interval from $-\pi/2$ to $\pi/2$ and x_i is any value of x in Δx_i. Evaluate $\lim\limits_{n \to \infty} S_n$ on the condition that the maximum Δx_i approaches 0 as n becomes infinite.

5. Let $S_n = 2x_1{}^2 \Delta x + 2x_2{}^2 \Delta x + \cdots + 2x_n{}^2 \Delta x$, where the Δx are equal subintervals that fill out the x-interval from $x = 3$ to $x = 6$ and x_i is a value of x in the ith subinterval Δx. If $\Delta x = (6 - 3)/n$, evaluate $\lim\limits_{n \to \infty} S_n$. *Ans.* 189.

6. Let $S_n = x_1 \sqrt{x_1{}^2 - 2} \, \Delta x_1 + x_2 \sqrt{x_2{}^2 - 2} \, \Delta x_2 + \cdots + x_n \sqrt{x_n{}^2 - 2} \, \Delta x_n$, where the Δx_i fill out the x-interval from $x = 2$ to $x = 10$ and x_i is any value of x in Δx_i. Assuming that the maximum Δx_i approaches 0 as n becomes infinite, evaluate $\lim\limits_{n \to \infty} S_n$.

7. Compute the following:

(a) $\displaystyle\int_1^3 x^2 \, dx$.   *Ans.* $\frac{26}{3}$.

(b) $\displaystyle\int_0^1 e^x x \, dx$.   *Ans.* $\dfrac{\cdot - 1}{2}$.

(c) $\displaystyle\int_0^1 \frac{1}{\sqrt{1 - x^2}} \, dx$.

(d) $\displaystyle\int_{\pi/2}^\pi \sin x \, dx$.   *Ans.* 1.

(e) $\displaystyle\int_0^{\pi/2} \cos x \, dx$.

(f) $\displaystyle\int_0^{\pi/2} \sin^2 x \, dx$.   *Ans.* $\dfrac{\pi}{4}$.

(g) $\displaystyle\int_0^1 y \, dx$, where $y = x^3$.   *Ans.* $\frac{1}{4}$.

(h) $\displaystyle\int_{-2}^3 \cos x \, dx$.

5. Some Simple Properties of the Definite Integral.

There are a few simple properties of the definite integral that are frequently used. The definition of the definite integral

$$(17) \qquad \int_a^b y \, dx$$

assumes that the upper end value b is larger than the lower end value a. There is, however, no objection to considering the definite integral

$$(18) \qquad \int_b^a y \, dx$$

where, with $a < b$, the upper end value is smaller than the lower one. We can, in fact, take over everything that applied to (17) with one exception. Previously, when we used equal subintervals in the interval (a, b), we took

Δx to be $(b - a)/n$. For the sake of consistency we agree in the case of (18) that

$$\Delta x = \frac{a - b}{n}.$$

When $a < b$—the case that we are now discussing—Δx is negative. Moreover, even if we choose unequal subintervals in the interval (a, b), we take them to be negative. The choice of y-values in each subinterval can be the same for both (17) and (18). Hence the effect of our choice of sign for Δx is to make each S_n that we form for (18) the negative of the corresponding S_n for (17). However, if the sequence

$$\frac{1}{2}, \frac{3}{4}, \frac{7}{8}, \ldots, \frac{n - 1}{n}, \ldots$$

approaches 1, the sequence

$$-\frac{1}{2}, -\frac{3}{4}, -\frac{7}{8}, \ldots, -\frac{n - 1}{n}, \ldots$$

approaches -1. Hence

(19)
$$\int_b^a y \, dx = -\int_a^b y \, dx.$$

We can consider the same fact from the standpoint of antidifferentiation. The left-hand integral calls for finding the indefinite integral of the function represented by y and then subtracting the result of substituting b in this indefinite integral from the result of substituting a. The right-hand integral calls for the same indefinite integral and then subtracting the result of substituting a from the result of substituting b. Then the final numbers will be the negatives of each other.

The second property to which we wish to call attention is the following. Given y as some function of x we can, of course, now speak of the definite integral.

$$\int_a^b y \, dx.$$

Suppose that c is some value of x between a and b. Then we may also introduce

$$\int_a^c y \, dx \quad \text{and} \quad \int_c^b y \, dx.$$

If we remember that each definite integral represents an area (Fig. 14-14), it certainly seems clear that

(20)
$$\int_a^b y \, dx = \int_a^c y \, dx + \int_c^b y \, dx.$$

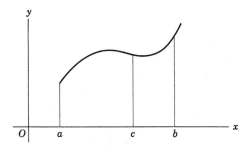

Figure 14-14

Let us look at this result from the standpoint of antidifferentiation. To evaluate the left side, we first find the indefinite integral of the function represented by y. Suppose that we use function notation and let this indefinite integral be represented by $F(x)$. Then the left side calls for

$$(21) \qquad \int_a^b y \, dx = F(x) \Big|_a^b = F(b) - F(a).$$

Because the same y or the same function appears in the integrands on the right side of (20), the indefinite integral in each case will be $F(x)$. Then

$$\int_a^c y \, dx = F(x) \Big|_a^c = F(c) - F(a)$$

and

$$\int_c^b y \, dx = F(x) \Big|_c^b = (Fb) - F(c).$$

Therefore,

$$(22) \quad \int_a^c y \, dx + \int_c^b y \, dx = F(b) - F(c) + F(c) - F(a) = F(b) - F(a).$$

Thus the results in (21) and (22) agree.

The third property that we wish to consider may be introduced by an example. Suppose that we wish to evaluate

$$\int_1^4 y \, dx$$

where $y = 5x - x^2$. The function $y = 5x - x^2$ is a single function, and the definite integral represents the area shown in Fig. 14-15. However, when we

Figure 14-15

come to evaluate

$$\int_1^4 (5x - x^2)\, dx,$$

we first evaluate the indefinite integral

$$\int (5x - x^2)\, dx;$$

we do this by evaluating

$$\int 5x\, dx - \int x^2\, dx$$

and then substituting the end values 1 and 4 in each integral. That is, resorting to antidifferentiation means evaluating

$$\int_1^4 (5x - x^2)\, dx$$

by evaluating

$$\int_1^4 5x\, dx - \int_1^4 x^2\, dx.$$

Geometrically (Fig. 14-16) the latter expression is the area between $y = 5x$ and $y = x^2$ and between the lines $x = 1$ and $x = 4$.

This example illustrates two facts. The first is that if u and v are any two functions of x, then

$$\int_a^b (u \pm v)\, dx = \int_a^b u\, dx \pm \int_a^b v\, dx.$$

Furthermore, the definite integral can also represent the area between two curves, as in Fig. 14-16.

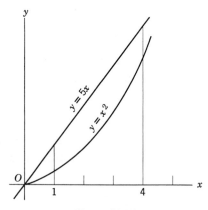

Figure 14-16

Exercises

1. Prove with the aid of the fundamental theorem that

$$\int_a^b cy\, dx = c \int_a^b y\, dx.$$

2. Evaluate the following:

(a) $\displaystyle\int_5^3 x^2 \, dx.$

(b) $\displaystyle\int_5^{-2} x^2 \, dx.$ *Ans.* $-\frac{133}{3}.$

3. Evaluate $\displaystyle\int_1^4 (x^2 + x^3) \, dx.$ *Ans.* $84\frac{3}{4}.$

4. Express the area under the curve of $y = 9 - x^2$ between $x = 0$ and $x = 1$ as a definite integral and then calculate it.   *Ans.* $8\frac{2}{3}.$

5. Express the area between $y = x^3 + 9$, $y = x^2$, $x = 1$, and $x = 5$ as a definite integral and then evaluate it.   *Ans.* $150\frac{2}{3}.$

6. Find the geometrical area bounded by $y = \sin x$, the x-axis, $x = 0$, and $x = 3\pi/2$.

7. The function $y = e^{-x^2}$ is immensely useful in the theory of probability; its graph is shown in Fig. 14-17. If we consider the area under the curve from $x = 0$ to $x = t$, the area is a function of t, say $F(t)$, and $F(t) = \displaystyle\int_0^t e^{-x^2} \, dx.$ Using geometric evidence, show that the following hold:

(a) $F(2)$ is positive.

(b) $F(-2) = -F(2).$

(c) $F(3) > F(2).$

(d) $F(t)$ is an increasing function for positive t.

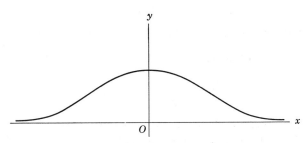

Figure 14-17

8. In Chapter 10 we defined the inverse function $x = g(y)$ of $y = f(x)$. Let us write the inverse function with the notation $y = g(x)$. By appealing to geometric evidence, show that the following hold true:

(a) $\displaystyle\int_0^1 x^n \, dx + \int_0^1 x^{1/n} \, dx = 1$ for n a positive integer.

(b) $\displaystyle\int_1^e \log x \, dx + \int_0^1 e^x \, dx = e.$

9. Show that the area under $y = x^a$, $a \neq -1$, and between $x = c$ and $x = d$ equals $1/a$ times the area bounded by $y = x^a$, the y-axis, $y = c^a$, and $y = d^a$.

APPENDIX

The Sum of the Squares
of the First n Integers

We wish to prove that

$$S = 1^2 + 2^2 + 3^2 + \cdots + n^2 = \frac{n^3}{3} + \frac{n^2}{2} + \frac{n}{6}.$$

Proof: One method of proof depends on a trick. We have the identity

$$n^3 - (n-1)^3 = 3n^2 - 3n + 1.$$

By replacing n by $n-1$, we have

$$(n-1)^3 - (n-2)^3 = 3(n-1)^2 - 3(n-1) + 1.$$

Similarly,

$$(n-2)^3 - (n-3)^3 = 3(n-2)^2 - 3(n-2) + 1$$
$$\cdots\cdots\cdots\cdots\cdots\cdots\cdots\cdots\cdots\cdots\cdots\cdots\cdots$$
$$3^3 - 2^3 = 3 \cdot 3^2 - 3 \cdot 3 + 1$$
$$2^3 - 1^3 = 3 \cdot 2^2 - 3 \cdot 2 + 1$$
$$1^3 - 0^3 = 3 \cdot 2^2 - 3 \cdot 1 + 1$$

If we now add the left sides and then the right sides, we have

$$n^3 = 3(1^2 + 2^2 + \cdots + n^2) - 3(1 + 2 + \cdots n) + n$$

$$= 3S - 3\frac{n}{2}(n+1) + n.$$

If we solve this equation for S, we obtain the result above.

The proof can also be made by mathematical induction.

CHAPTER FIFTEEN

Some Geometric Uses
of the Definite Integral

1. Introduction. If the concept of the definite integral amounted to no more than another way of viewing area, it would not be very significant. To calculate areas even after expressing them as definite integrals we still resort to antidifferentiation, and therefore might just as well base the entire approach to areas on antidifferentiation and dispense with definite integrals.

Actually, the definite integral is a very powerful and general concept. The derivative and definite integral are, in fact, the two basic concepts of the calculus (and they are related, as we have seen, by the fundamental theorem). We shall see that the definite integral is the tool for casting any number of physical problems into mathematical form. The experience of mathematicians with the definite integral is very similar to that with the derivative. The derivative was introduced to represent velocity and acceleration, but proved to be enormously useful in representing any number of instantaneous rates of change. The definite integral likewise proves to be useful in an extraordinary variety of situations, and we shall consider some of them in the next two chapters. Of these a few could still be done by first obtaining a rate of change and then applying antidifferentiation; nevertheless we shall employ the definite integral in order to practice its use.

2. Volumes of Solids: The Cylindrical Element. To know the volumes of solids—such as cans, tanks for oil and water, granaries, and the earth—is obviously useful if somewhat mundane. Some of these problems, such as finding the volume of granaries, are among the oldest to which mathematics was applied. With the calculus that we have thus far developed we cannot find the volumes of all solids. We can, however, find the volumes that are formed by revolving a curve around an axis. For example, the sphere can be generated by revolving a semicircle around a diameter. The solids enclosed by revolving a curve about an axis are called solids of revolution.

To illustrate the method of finding volumes of figures of revolution by means of the definite integral, let us try to find the volume of the hemisphere (Fig. 15-1) formed by revolving the quarter-circle ABC about the x-axis.

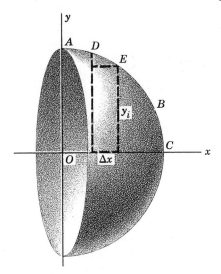

Figure 15-1

The problem of finding volumes bounded by curved surfaces presents essentially the same difficulty as that of finding areas bounded by curves. We have no direct method of finding such volumes, and therefore we seek to approximate them by simpler figures whose volume we do know and then improve the approximation. Guided somewhat by success in the area problem, one might introduce the rectangle shown in Fig. 15-1 as an approximation to the area under arc *DE* and consider rotating the entire rectangle around the *x*-axis. Figure 15-2 shows the figure generated by the rectangle. This figure is a circular cylinder standing on its side. The radius of the cylinder is what we have already denoted by y_i and its height is Δx. To calculate the volume of this cylinder, we take over from Euclidean geometry the formula for the volume of the circular cylinder. The volume of a cylinder is the area of the base times the altitude, and so in our case it is $\pi y_i^2 \, \Delta x$.

Figure 15-2

We now have the basis for an approximation to the desired volume. We divide the interval OC of Fig. 15-1 into n equal subintervals, each of width Δx. We erect the ordinates at the end points of these subintervals, and in each subinterval we choose the minimum y-value of the curve ABC. Thus the subinterval Δx and the y_i shown in Fig. 15-1 is one of the many subintervals and corresponding y_i's in the interval OC. If we now imagine rotating each of these rectangles about OC, each generating a cylinder, then the sum of the volumes of these cylinders is an approximation to the volume of the hemisphere. In symbols this sum is

(1) $$S_n = \pi y_1{}^2\,\Delta x + \pi y_2{}^2\,\Delta x + \cdots + \pi y_n{}^2\,\Delta x.$$

As n becomes larger, Δx becomes smaller, and the sum of the rectangles becomes a better approximation to the area under the curve ABC. Then the sum S_n becomes a better approximation to the volume of the hemisphere. The larger n is, the better the approximation. Hence the volume we want is

(2) $$\lim_{n \to \infty} S_n.$$

This limit is a definite integral of exactly the same kind as that considered in the Chapter 14. There we considered S_n of the form

(3) $$S_n = y_1\,\Delta x + y_2\,\Delta x + \cdots + y_n\,\Delta x.$$

If we use y_i to denote any one of the y-values in (3), we may say that the y_i in (3) are analogous to the $\pi y_i{}^2$ in (1). The y_i in (3) are the function values of some function of x; but the $\pi y_i{}^2$ in (1) are also the function values of some function of x, namely, the function πy^2 where y itself represents the ordinates of arc ABC in Fig. 15-1. In fact, we could interpret (1) as the approximation to an area—the area under the curve whose equation is given by the function $Y = \pi y^2$. This area would then be given by the limit in (2) or by

(4) $$\int_a^b \pi y^2\,dx.$$

Whether we think of (1) and therefore of (2) as representing a volume generated by revolving arc ABC about the x-axis or as an area under the curve $Y = \pi y^2$, the quantity that we obtain in (4) is the same. The letters a and b in (4) represent, of course, the x-values of the end points O and C of the interval filled out by the Δx. Thus we can evaluate (4) by using the fundamental theorem of the calculus.

Let us evaluate (4) for a specific case. Suppose that the radius of the quarter-circle ABC in Fig. 15-1 is 5. Then $a = 0$ and $b = 5$. Moreover, the equation of the circle with center at the origin and radius 5 is

$$x^2 + y^2 = 25.$$

Hence the equation of the arc ABC is given by

$$y = \sqrt{25 - x^2}.$$

Then the volume V that we are seeking, given by (4), is

(5) $$V = \int_0^5 \pi(25 - x^2)\, dx.$$

To evaluate the definite integral (5) we use the fundamental theorem. We first find the antiderivative of $\pi(25 - x^2)$, that is, we seek

$$V(x) = \int \pi(25 - x^2)\, dx.$$

We use the notation $V(x)$ to indicate the *function* given by the indefinite integral. In integrating, the constant π can be ignored for the moment. The antiderivative of the difference $25 - x^2$ is $25x - x^3/3$. Hence we want

$$V = \pi\left(25x - \frac{x^3}{3}\right)\Big|_0^5.$$

The result is $(2\pi/3)125$. Then, the volume of the full sphere is $(4\pi/3)125$; this agrees with the formula, which we usually learn without proof, that the volume of a sphere of radius r is $4\pi r^3/3$.

Exercises

1. If the portion of the line $y = x/3$ lying in the first quadrant is rotated around the x-axis, a cone is generated. Find the volume of the cone extending from $x = 0$ to $x = 5$.   *Ans.* $125\pi/27$.
2. The upper half of the parabola $y^2 = 16x$ is rotated around the x-axis. Find the volume of the solid generated by the arc lying between $x = 3$ and $x = 5$.
3. A segment of a sphere is the volume cut out by two parallel planes. Suppose that the two planes are perpendicular to the x-axis of Fig. 15-1 and pass through $x = 2$ and $x = 4$. Find the volume of the segment of the sphere that the planes cut out.   *Ans.* $94\pi/3$.
4. The upper half of the ellipse $3x^2 + 6y^2 = 48$ is rotated around the x-axis. The surface it generates is a special kind of ellipsoid called a prolate spheroid and has the shape of a football. Find the volume of this spheroid.
5. If the upper half of the ellipse $6x^2 + 3y^2 = 48$ is rotated around the x-axis, the surface it generates is another kind of ellipsoid called an oblate spheroid. Find the volume of this spheroid.   *Ans.* $128\sqrt{2}\pi/3$.
6. The area bounded above by the line $y = 3$, below by the line $y = 0$, on the left by the y-axis, and on the right by an arc of the hyperbola $9x^2 - 16y^2 = 144$ is rotated around the x-axis. Find the volume of the solid generated.
                                              Ans. $24\pi(2\sqrt{2} - 1)$.

3. *Volumes of Solids: The Shell Game.* In Section 2 we found volumes of solids of revolution by approximating the volumes by cylinders and then letting the heights Δx of these cylinders approach 0. It is not necessary to restrict the approximating figures to cylinders. We can use any other solid provided that we know the volume of this solid and that, as we increase the number of these solids, the sum of their volumes comes closer and closer to the volume we are seeking. Let us consider an example.

Suppose that we want to find the volume generated by revolving an ellipse around its minor axis; the resulting figure is a special kind of ellipsoid called an oblate spheroid. Let the equation of the ellipse be

(6)
$$\frac{x^2}{9} + \frac{y^2}{4} = 1.$$

In Fig. 15-3 we show the part of the ellipse that lies in the first quadrant. The semiminor axis is the length OB. If we obtain the volume of the solid enclosed by revolving arc BCA and segment OA around OB and then double the result, we shall have the desired volume. We know that rectangles of width Δx, such as the one shown, can be used to approximate the area under BCA, and therefore if we revolve all these rectangles about the line OB, we shall have a set of volumes whose sum approximates to the desired volume. We can then let the number of rectangles increase and thus improve our approximation more and more.

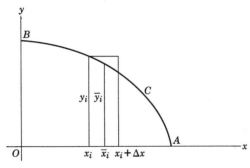

Figure 15-3

Let us see what volume any one rectangle generates when it is revolved around the line OB. Figure 15-4 shows the figure generated. It is called a cylindrical shell. We shall find the volume of this shell and then consider summing these volumes to find the volume of the oblate spheroid.

The volume of the shell is the area of its base times its height. The area of the base is the area of the outer circle (Fig. 15-5) of radius $x_i + \Delta x$ minus the area of the inner circle of radius x_i. Thus the area of the base is

$$\pi(x_i + \Delta x)^2 - \pi x_i^2.$$

We can obtain a somewhat simpler expression. By factoring we obtain

$$\pi(x_i + \Delta x + x_i)(x_i + \Delta x - x_i).$$

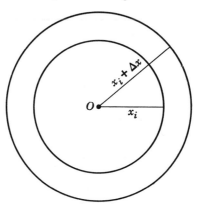

Figure 15-4

We replace the quantity in the first parentheses by twice the arithmetic mean of $x_i + \Delta x$ and x_i, namely,

$$2\bar{x}_i = 2\,\frac{x_i + \Delta x + x_i}{2}.$$

The area of the base then is

$$2\pi\bar{x}_i \, \Delta x.$$

In other words, the area of the base is the area of the mean circumference $2\pi x_i$ times the width of the base. The volume of the shell then is

(7) $$2\pi\bar{x}_i y_i \, \Delta x,$$

where y_i is the height of the cylinder in Fig. 15-4.

Figure 15-5

We now sum the volumes of the cylindrical shells, each a result of revolving a rectangle under the curve BCA of Fig. 15-3, about the line OB. This sum is

(8) $$S_n = 2\pi\bar{x}_1 y_1 \, \Delta x + 2\pi\bar{x}_2 y_2 \, \Delta x + \cdots + 2\pi\bar{x}_n y_n \, \Delta x.$$

We let the number of rectangles increase, and consequently Δx approaches 0. What limit does S_n approach? Compare this S_n with the S_n of the form

(9) $$S_n = y_1 \, \Delta x + y_2 \, \Delta x + \cdots + y_n \, \Delta x$$

considered in Chapter 14. The y_i in (9) are the y-values of some function of x; in particular, y_i is a y-value that belongs to some x-value in the typical or ith subinterval Δx. Now (8) is *almost* of the same form. We can say that the typical $2\pi \bar{x}_i y_i$ is the function value of some function of x, the function being $2\pi xy$ where y itself represents the equation of arc BCA in Fig. 15-3. This statement is not quite correct. The $\bar{x}_i$ does indeed belong to some x-value in the ith subinterval Δx, but the y_i is the y-value of *another* x-value in the ith subinterval Δx. However, we learned in Chapter 14 that in setting up the S_n which leads to a definite integral we may choose *any* function value in each Δx. Let us therefore replace y_i in $2\pi \bar{x}_i y_i$ by $\bar{y}_i$ where $\bar{y}_i$ is the y-value at $\bar{x}_i$ (see Fig. 15-3). Then $2\pi \bar{x}_i \bar{y}_i$ is the function value of the function $2\pi xy$ in the ith subinterval Δx, and now

(10) $$S_n = 2\pi \bar{x}_1 \bar{y}_1 \, \Delta x + 2\pi \bar{x}_2 \bar{y}_2 \, \Delta x + \cdots + 2\pi \bar{x}_n \bar{y}_n \, \Delta x$$

is exactly like (9), with the $2\pi \bar{x}_i \bar{y}_i$ in (10) corresponding to the y_i in (9). The choice of $\bar{y}_i$ in (10) in place of y_i in (8) means geometrically that instead of the rectangle $y_i \, \Delta x$ in Fig. 15-3 we use the rectangle $\bar{y}_i \, \Delta x$ to generate the cylindrical shell.

What limit, then, does the S_n of (10) approach as n becomes infinite? Because the function whose values are represented in (10) is $2\pi xy$, the limit is the definite integral

(11) $$V = \int_0^3 2\pi xy \, dx.$$

The end values 0 and 3 are the abscissas of O and A in Fig. 15-3.

The evaluation of (11) is straightforward. The process, which we have already used several times, is to find, first, the antiderivative of the function that appears under the integral sign in (11). The function for which y stands is given by (6) and is

$$y = \tfrac{1}{3}\sqrt{36 - 4x^2}.$$

Hence

$$2\pi xy = \frac{2\pi}{3} \sqrt{36 - 4x^2}\, x.$$

We must now calculate the indefinite integral, which we denote by $V(x)$ namely,

$$V(x) = \int \frac{2\pi}{3} \sqrt{36 - 4x^2}\, x \, dx.$$

It seems likely in view of the presence of the x^2 inside the radical and the x outside that the substitution

$$u = 36 - 4x^2$$

will reduce the integral to a familiar form. With this value of u,

$$\frac{du}{dx} = -8x.$$

To have the proper du/dx following the radical, we may write $V(x)$ in the form

(12) $$V(x) = \int -\frac{\pi}{12} \sqrt{36 - 4x^2}(-8x)\, dx.$$

The constant $-\pi/12$ can be ignored for the moment. This fact is sometimes indicated by writing

$$V(x) = -\frac{\pi}{12} \int \sqrt{36 - 4x^2}(-8x)\, dx,$$

so that our attention can be concentrated on what follows the integral sign or what is called the integrand. In terms of u,

$$V(x) = -\frac{\pi}{12} \int u^{1/2} \frac{du}{dx}\, dx.$$

Now by the inverse of the generalized power rule (see (48) of Chapter 7)),

$$V(u) = -\frac{\pi}{12} \cdot \frac{2}{3} u^{3/2} = -\frac{\pi}{18} u^{3/2},$$

so that

$$V(x) = -\frac{\pi}{18} (36 - 4x^2)^{3/2}.$$

Then

$$V = -\frac{\pi}{18} (36 - 4x^2)^{3/2} \Big|_0^3.$$

Substitution of 3 for x and then of 0 for x and subtraction of the second result from the first gives

(13) $$V = 0 - \left(-\frac{\pi}{18} \cdot 216 \right) = 12\pi.$$

The volume of the entire oblate spheroid is 24π.

We built up the volume of the oblate spheroid by using cylindrical shells as the fundamental element, that is, as the approximating element. We can use other approximating elements, provided that as the number of elements is increased (while each approaches 0 in size) the sum of these elements approximates more and more closely the desired volume. For example, let us consider the problem of obtaining the volume of a sphere. This time we shall use *spherical shells.*

Figure 15-6 shows a cross section of the sphere of radius a. We regard this sphere as consisting of shells such as the

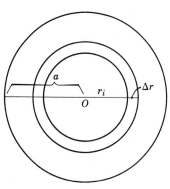

Figure 15-6

one whose cross section is shown in the interior of the figure. The volume of the sphere is exactly the sum of these shells. If we knew the volume of each shell, we could obtain the volume of the sphere merely by adding the sums of the shells. That is, whether we break up the volume of the sphere into five, ten, or fifty shells, the sum of their volumes is the volume of the sphere. However, we do not know the volume of a shell unless we use the formula for the volume of the sphere, and this is what we are trying to find. However, let us suppose that the formula for the area of the surface of a sphere is available to us. We shall denote by r_i the radius of the inner surface of the typical or ith shell. A good approximation to the volume of a shell would be the area of the surface of the inner sphere namely, $4\pi r_i^2$, multiplied by Δr. This product,

$$4\pi r_i^2 \, \Delta r,$$

is only an approximation because the inner surface is too small.

Now let us break up the interval from $r = 0$ to $r = a$ into n equal subintervals Δr; each Δr fixes the width of a spherical shell just as in Fig. 15-6. Then the sum

(14) $$S_n = 4\pi r_1^2 \, \Delta r + 4\pi r_2^2 \, \Delta r + \cdots + 4\pi r_n^2 \, \Delta r$$

is an approximation to the volume of the sphere. As n increases, which implies that Δr approaches 0, each term becomes a better approximation to the volume of the corresponding shell because the inner surface $4\pi r_i^2$ is more nearly correct as an average surface for that shell. Moreover, for each n the sum of the shells fills out the volume of the sphere. Thus the larger n is, the more nearly does the sum (14) represent the volume of the sphere. Then the volume V of the sphere should be

$$V = \lim_{n \to \infty} S_n.$$

This limit is expressed in the notation

(15) $$V = \int_0^a 4\pi r^2 \, dr.$$

The definite integral (15) is easily evaluated. We consider first

$$V(r) = \int 4\pi r^2 \, dr = 4\pi \int r^2 \, dr = 4\pi \frac{r^3}{3}.$$

Then

(16) $$V = 4\pi \frac{r^3}{3} \Big|_0^a = 4\pi \frac{a^3}{3}.$$

The result, of course, is not the important thing here. The main point of this example is that we can employ spherical shells to fill out the volume of a sphere and, by using an approximate expression for the volume of each shell, still obtain the correct volume by a limiting process.

Exercise

1. Consider the curve $y = 9 - x^2$. First, find the volume of the solid of revolution generated by revolving the arc of the curve between $x = 0$ and $x = 3$ around the x-axis. Then find the volume of the solid of revolution generated by revolving the same arc about the y-axis.   *Ans.* $684\pi/5$; $81\pi/2$.

2. Consider the area lying between an arc of $y = (12 - x^3)/8$, the y-axis, and the line $y = 2$. What is the volume of the solid of revolution generated by revolving this area around the y-axis?

3. Find the volume of the torus (doughnut) generated by revolving a circle of radius a about a line in the plane of the circle and distant $b > a$ from the center of the circle (Fig. 15-7).   *Ans.* $2\pi^2 a^2 b$.

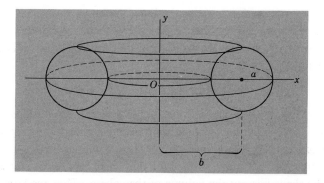

Figure 15-7

4. Find the volume generated by revolving the area lying under $y = \sin x$ from $x = 0$ to $x = \pi$ about the y-axis.

5. A hole 6 inches long (Fig. 15-8) is drilled through the center of a solid sphere of radius b so that the segments of the sphere at the top and bottom of the cylinder are also removed. The resulting figure, incidentally, is that of many napkin bands and wedding rings. What is the volume of the remaining material.

   Ans. 36π cu in. Is the answer remarkable in any respect?

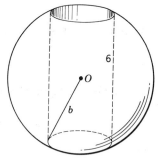

Figure 15-8

6. Derive the integral for the mass of the earth on the assumption that the mass per unit volume, that is, the density ρ, varies from the center to any point r units from the center in accordance with the formula $\rho = f(r)$.

7. Suppose that in a sphere of radius R the mass per unit volume, that is, the density, at any point is the square of the distance from the center. Find the mass of the sphere.   *Ans.* $\frac{4}{5}\pi R^5$.

8. Find the volume of an apple. *Suggestion:* Our first task is to represent the apple algebraically. Suppose that we take the circle (Fig. 15-9) with center $(b, 0)$, radius a, and $a > b$. The equation of this circle is $(x - b)^2 + y^2 = a^2$. Consider the arc from $x = 0$ to $x = a + b$ and rotate the area bounded by this arc, the y-axis, and the x-axis around the y-axis. This volume generated is half the volume of the apple.

Ans. $4\pi ab\{(\pi/4) + \frac{1}{2}\text{ arc sin }(b/a) + \frac{1}{4} - \frac{1}{4}(b^2/a^2)\} + (4\pi/3a)(a^2 + b^2)^{3/2}$.

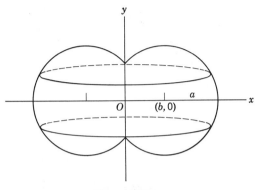

Figure 15-9

4. *Lengths of Arcs of Curves.* Another major problem that is most readily tackled with the help of the definite integral, that is, as a limit of a sequence of sums, is the calculation of lengths of curves. In practice this problem is very important. If a suspension bridge is to be built and if its main cable is to be a parabolic arc, one would like to know in advance exactly how long this arc is to be.

In Euclidean geometry one commonly works with the lengths of straight lines. This notion of length presents no fundamental conceptual difficulties. When a particular segment of a line has been chosen as the unit of length, the length of any other given segment is the number of times that the unit length can be laid off on the given segment. Of course, this number may not be an integer; it may be a fraction or even an irrational number.

However, the problem of determining the length of a curve cannot be approached in this way. The reason is that curves (except the circle) change shape from one place to another along the curve, and so it is impossible to find a unit of length whose shape will fit all along the curve. In fact, even if a unit of length could be found to fit all curves, the problem of relating that unit to the unit for line segments would still remain, because whatever notion of curve length we might adopt, we should still want to know its relation to the unit for straight line lengths. For example, if a cable of a bridge is to be built and its length is calculated by some means to be 500 units of "curve length," we would still want to know what these 500 units mean in terms of inches, feet, or yards used for straight line lengths in order to fabricate the proper amount of wire.

The effective approach to curvilinear length, that is, lengths of arcs, is to build it up on the basis of straight line lengths. The intuitive idea behind what we shall do is that a very small arc should not differ much from a line segment and the smaller the arc the less it will differ. Let AB (Fig. 15-10) be an arc of some curve C. We choose points $P_0, P_1, P_2, P_3, \ldots$ with $P_0 = A$ and $P_n = B$, so that the arc is subdivided into subarcs $P_0P_1, P_1P_2, \ldots, P_{n-1}P_n$.

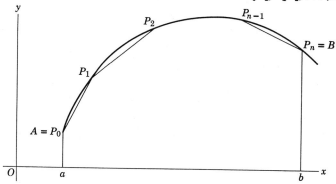

Figure 15-10

We now introduce the chords $P_0P_1, P_1P_2, \ldots, P_{n-1}P_n$. These chords are approximations to the lengths of the respective arcs in which they are inscribed. Then the sum

(17) $$S_n = P_0P_1 + P_1P_2 + \cdots + P_{n-1}P_n$$

is an approximation to the arc length AB.

We can improve this approximation by taking more points of subdivision, which means, of course, that n above will be larger and the various subarcs smaller. Thus, as Fig. 15-11 shows, if CD is a subarc that is approximated by the chord CD, then by choosing an additional point E, subdividing arc DC into arcs CE and ED, and introducing the new chords CE and ED, the sum $CE + ED$ thereby obtained is a better approximation to the length of arc CD than chord CD is. Intuitively it seems clear that we can approach the length of arc AB more and more closely as we let n, the number of points of subdivision, become larger and larger and, of course, let all chords become smaller and smaller, so that they approximate more closely the subarcs in

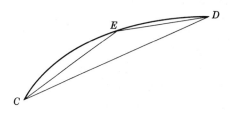

Figure 15-11

which they are inscribed. The reasonable conclusion is that s, the length of arc AB, can be obtained by

(18) $$s = \lim_{n \to \infty} S_n = \lim_{n \to \infty} P_0 P_1 + P_1 P_2 + \cdots + P_{n-1} P_n$$

with the understanding that the maximum chord length must approach 0 as n becomes infinite.

Of course, there are any number of choices for the points $P_1, P_2, \ldots, P_{n-1}$. Also, as we introduce new points of subdivision so as to increase n, we can make any number of choices, but if we make certain that the maximum chord approaches 0 as the number of subdivisions is increased, we are sure on intuitive grounds that the limit as expressed in (18) will still be the very same length of arc that we wish to calculate.

Thus far we have described in geometrical form the way in which we can obtain the arc length AB. However, this approach does not help us to calculate the length. The calculation requires the use of analysis. We suppose that the curve is placed in some coordinate system and that we know the equation $y = f(x)$ of the curve. Let us consider (Fig. 15-12) one subarc

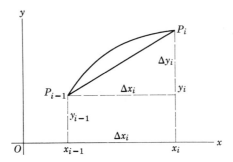

Figure 15-12

$P_{i-1} P_i$ and its approximating chord $P_{i-1} P_i$. Corresponding to the chord $P_{i-1} P_i$ there is the subinterval on the x-axis determined by the abscissas of P_{i-1} and P_i. We call this subinterval Δx_i. We must say Δx_i here rather than Δx because our choice of the P_i on the arc does not necessarily result in equal subintervals Δx. The difference in the ordinates of P_i and P_{i-1} is the actual increment in y that corresponds to the increment Δx_i in x and therefore is Δy_i. By the Pythagorean theorem

$$(P_{i-1} P_i)^2 = (\Delta x_i)^2 + (\Delta y_i)^2 = \left(1 + \frac{(\Delta y_i)}{(\Delta x_i)^2}\right)(\Delta x_i)^2$$

or*

(19) $$P_{i-1} P_i = \sqrt{1 + \left(\frac{\Delta y_i}{\Delta x_i}\right)^2}\, \Delta x_i.$$

* We choose the positive root. However, we shall have occasion to say more about signs later.

When the proper indices are used, such an expression holds for each of the chords. We may now reexpress (18) in the form

$$(20) \quad s = \lim_{n \to \infty} \left\{ \sqrt{1 + \left(\frac{\Delta y_1}{\Delta x_1}\right)^2} \, \Delta x_1 + \sqrt{1 + \left(\frac{\Delta y_2}{\Delta x_2}\right)^2} \, \Delta x_2 + \cdots + \right.$$
$$\left. + \sqrt{1 + \left(\frac{\Delta y_n}{\Delta x_n}\right)^2} \, \Delta x_n \right\}.$$

Unfortunately, the limit called for in (20) apparently is not of the kind that leads to a definite integral. The limit that we have studied is of the form

$$(21) \qquad \lim_{n \to \infty} (y_1 \, \Delta x_1 + y_2 \, \Delta x_2 + \cdots + y_n \, \Delta x_n)$$

where y_i is the y-value of some function of x and taken anywhere in the subinterval Δx_i. However, we can recast (20) so that it takes the form (21). In Section 3 of Chapter 12 we considered the law of the mean which states that if $f(x)$ is any function of x and if a and b are any two values of x, then

$$f(b) - f(a) = f'(\bar{x})(b - a)$$

where $\bar{x}$ is some value of x between a and b. Now suppose that a is x_{i-1} and b is x_i. Then $b - a$ is Δx_i and $f(b) - f(a)$ is Δy_i. We can, therefore, state that

$$\Delta y_i = f'(\bar{x}) \, \Delta x_i$$

where $\bar{x}_i$ is some value of x between x_{i-1} and x_i. Consequently,

$$\frac{\Delta y_i}{\Delta x_i} = f'(\bar{x}_i).$$

For convenience of notation, we write $\dot{y}_i$ for $f'(\bar{x}_i)$ so that

$$(22) \qquad \frac{\Delta y_i}{\Delta x_i} = \dot{y}_i.$$

We may apply the law of the mean to each of the quotients in (20), and then this expression becomes

$$(23) \quad s = \lim_{n \to \infty} \left\{ \sqrt{1 + \dot{y}_1^2} \, \Delta x_1 + \sqrt{1 + \dot{y}_2^2} \, \Delta x_2 + \cdots + \sqrt{1 + \dot{y}_n^2} \, \Delta x_n \right\}.$$

Do we now have a limit of the form in (21)? We recall that the derived function of a function is itself a function of x and therefore $\sqrt{1 + \dot{y}^2}$ is also a function of x. Each term of (23) is a value of the function $\sqrt{1 + \dot{y}^2}$ taken at some value of x in the subinterval Δx_i and then multiplied by Δx_i. Hence (23) is of the form (21). Then the limit called for in (23) is representable as

$$(24) \qquad\qquad s = \int_a^b \sqrt{1 + \dot{y}^2} \, dx$$

where a and b are the end values of the x-interval that the Δx_i's fill out (see Fig. 15-10). Thus (24) gives us arc length expressed as a definite integral.

Formula (24) is the basic formula for arc length. There are several points about it to be noted. First, there is the matter of sign. In step (19) we chose the positive square root, and as a consequence formula (24) gives a positive arc length. However, it is often convenient to introduce both a positive and a negative arc length. If in Fig. 15-10 the arc length is taken to be positive in the direction from A to B, we should want formula (24) to give us a positive result. If, on the other hand, we choose the direction from B to A as positive, we should want formula (24) to give us a negative result. In this case we should use

$$(25) \qquad\qquad s = \int_a^b - \sqrt{1 + \dot{y}^2}\, dx.$$

Secondly, several relations involving arc length prove to be useful in applications. They are readily derived from (24) [or (25)]. To evaluate (24) we use the fundamental theorem of the calculus, that is, we first evaluate the indefinite integral

$$s(x) = \int \sqrt{1 + \dot{y}^2}\, dx.$$

This statement is equivalent to the statement

$$(26) \qquad\qquad \frac{ds}{dx} = \sqrt{1 + \dot{y}^2}.$$

Here s is arc length measured from some point on the curve. Which point we choose as the origin for arc length does not matter because if the origin

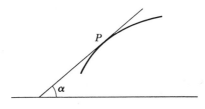

Figure 15-13

is shifted, the arc length changes by a constant and the derivative is not affected. However, because ds/dx is positive, the arc length must increase with x.

Furthermore, if we introduce the tangent to the curve (Fig. 15-13) at point P, we can make the following assertions. Let α be the inclination of the tangent line; then

$$\dot{y} = \tan \alpha.$$

Consequently, from (26) we have

(27) $$\frac{ds}{dx} = \sqrt{1 + \tan^2 \alpha} = \begin{cases} \sec \alpha & \text{for} \quad 0 \leq \alpha < (\pi/2), \\ -\sec \alpha & \text{for} \quad (\pi/2) < \alpha \leq \pi. \end{cases}$$

By the theorem on inverse functions

(28) $$\frac{dx}{ds} = \begin{cases} \cos \alpha & \text{for} \quad 0 \leq \alpha \leq (\pi/2), \\ -\cos \alpha & \text{for} \quad (\pi/2) \leq \alpha \leq \pi; \end{cases}$$

this relation is often useful.

Finally, the use of (24) to evaluate arc lengths often leads to difficult integrations. However, we know that a curve can be represented by x as a function of y as well as by y as a function of x. Thus the arc AB in Fig. 15-14

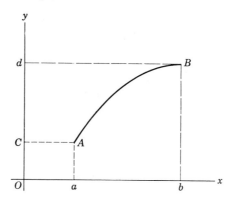

Figure 15-14

might be part of the parabola $y = \sqrt{4x}$; then it can also be represented by $x = y^2/4$. By treating y as the independent variable and x as the dependent variable, we can go through a proof very much like the one we used to derive (24) and obtain

(29) $$s = \pm \int_c^d \sqrt{1 + \dot{x}^2} \, dy.$$

Sometimes this integral is more readily evaluated than (24).

From (29) we have, by the use of the fundamental theorem,

(30) $$\frac{ds}{dy} = \pm \sqrt{1 + \dot{x}^2}.$$

Also, if we again introduce the angle of inclination α of the tangent line at any point P of the curve, then

$$\dot{x} = \frac{1}{\dot{y}} = \cot \alpha.$$

From (30)

(31) $$\frac{ds}{dy} = \pm \sqrt{1 + \cot^2 \alpha} = \pm \csc \alpha$$

and

(32)
$$\frac{dy}{ds} = \pm\sin\alpha.$$

The proper signs in (29) to (32) must be chosen on the basis of whether s is increasing with y and the value of α. Compare (27) and (28).

Equations (27), (28), (31), and (32) are easily remembered by a mnemonic device. We form the triangle shown in Fig. 15-15. Then from this triangle we can read off whatever relation happens to be useful. Thus from the triangle we see that

$$\frac{dx}{ds} = \cos\alpha.$$

The proper signs are not indicated by this triangle but can always be determined in a specific case.

Figure 15-15

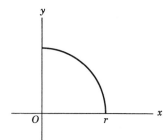

Figure 15-16

Let us use (24) to find the circumference of the circle $x^2 + y^2 = r^2$. It is, of course, sufficient to find the length of arc in the first quadrant (Fig. 15-16) and multiply by 4.

Because

$$y = \sqrt{r^2 - x^2},$$

$$\dot{y} = \frac{-x}{\sqrt{r^2 - x^2}}.$$

Then

$$\sqrt{1 + \dot{y}^2} = \sqrt{1 + \frac{x^2}{r^2 - x^2}} = \frac{r}{\sqrt{r^2 - x^2}}.$$

By (24)

(33)
$$s = \int_0^r \frac{r}{\sqrt{r^2 - x^2}}\, dx.$$

We now call upon the fundamental theorem and first evaluate the indefinite integral

(34)
$$s(x) = \int \frac{r}{\sqrt{r^2 - x^2}}\, dx.$$

The integration of this expression is no problem. If we first take the r^2 out of the radical, we obtain

(35)
$$s(x) = \int \frac{1}{\sqrt{1 - \dfrac{x^2}{r^2}}} \, dx.$$

This form suggests formula (28) of Chapter 10, namely,

(36) $\qquad$ if $\dfrac{dy}{dx} = \dfrac{1}{\sqrt{1 - u^2}} \dfrac{du}{dx}$ then $y = \sin^{-1} u.$

If we let $u = x/r$ in (35) and then multiply and divide by r, we have

$$s(x) = \int \frac{r}{\sqrt{1 - u^2}} \frac{1}{r} \, dx$$

where $1/r$ is du/dx. Then by (36)

$$s(u) = r \sin^{-1} u$$

and

$$s(x) = r \sin^{-1} \frac{x}{r}.$$

In view of (33) we want

(37)
$$s = r \sin^{-1} \frac{x}{r} \Big|_0^r = \frac{\pi r}{2}.$$

This is the length of one quarter of the circle.

As we have already noted, the calculation of lengths of arcs often presents difficulties because formula (24) involves an awkward integrand. The quantity $\sqrt{1 + \dot{y}^2}$, largely because of the square root, is a function for which the antiderivative is not easily found or cannot be found at all. The classic example is that of finding the length of arc of an ellipse. If we start with the equation

(38)
$$\frac{x^2}{a^2} + \frac{y^2}{b^2} = 1$$

and follow the procedure used above for the circle, we obtain

(39)
$$s = \int_0^a \sqrt{1 + \frac{b^2}{a^2} \frac{x^2}{a^2 - x^2}} \, dx.$$

To obtain a simpler form for the radicand, one might replace b^2 by $a^2 - c^2$, then replace c/a by the eccentricity e, and simplify. The result is

$$s = \int_0^a \sqrt{\frac{a^2 - e^2 x^2}{a^2 - x^2}} \, dx.$$

One might now try the often helpful change of variable

$$x = s \sin \theta$$

and obtain

(40) $$s = \int_0^{\pi/2} a\sqrt{1 - e^2 \sin^2 \theta} \, d\theta.$$

However, this integral cannot be evaluated in terms of elementary functions, that is, the algebraic, trigonometric, exponential, and logarithmic functions that we have already studied. The integral (40) is called an elliptic integral. The theory of elliptic integrals·belongs to a higher branch of analysis than the calculus. We shall say something about the approximate evaluation of (40) in a later chapter.

Exercises

1. Find the arc lengths along the following curves:

(a) $y = x^{3/2}$ from $x = 0$ to $x = 4$.   *Ans.* $\frac{8}{27}(10\sqrt{10} - 1)$.

(b) $y = \frac{1}{2}(e^x + e^{-x})$ from $x = -1$ to $x = 1$.

(c) $y^3 = x^2$ from the point $(0, 0)$ to the point $(8, 4)$.   *Ans.* 9.07.

(d) $y = \dfrac{x^3}{6} + \dfrac{1}{2x}$ from $x = 1$ to $x = 3$.

(e) $y = \log \sec x$ from $x = 0$ to $x = \pi/3$.   *Ans.* $\log(2 + \sqrt{3})$.

2. A bridge has been designed so that its main cable is to be an arc of a parabola whose equation is $y = x^2/16$. Find the length of the cable from the vertex to $x = 12$. *Suggestion:* You may use the integral formula

$$\int \sqrt{x^2 + a^2} \, dx = (x/2)\sqrt{x^2 + a^2} + (a^2/2) \log(x + \sqrt{x^2 + a^2}) + C.$$

Ans. $3\sqrt{13} + 4 \log \dfrac{3 + \sqrt{13}}{2}$.

3. Evaluate the integral in (33) of the text by making the change of variable $x = r \sin \theta$.

5. Curvature. That a curve curves can be inferred without too much difficulty, but the answer to the question of how much a curve curves is by no means obvious, and this answer is sorely needed in a number of physical phenomena. Let us see why. According to Newton's first law of motion any object in motion will, if no force acts on it, continue to move in the direction in which it is headed. Thus, if some object moves along a curve and is at, say, point P (Fig. 15-17), it will, if no force acts on it, move in the direction in which it is headed, and this means along the tangent to the curve

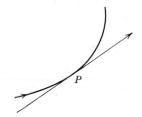

Figure 15-17

at *P*. For example, an automobile or a train traveling in a curve will shoot off in a straight line if no force is provided to keep it on the curve. In practice this force is provided by sloping or banking the road. Likewise, an object whirled at the end of a string will shoot off along a tangent to its path the instant the hand, which provides the restraining force, lets go of the string. It may be intuitively apparent that the sharper the curve, the more force must be provided to keep the object moving along that curve. To know, then, how much force must be provided, one must know how sharply the curve turns or how sharply it changes direction. In mathematical language we say that one must know the curvature of the curve.

To calculate the curvature we must first formulate a quantitative definition of what we mean by curvature, and this will be our immediate goal. It is intuitively acceptable that a straight line has no curvature. Hence we shall say that at every point a straight line has zero curvature. A circle does have curvature at each point, and the curvature is certainly the same at all points. What should we take as the measure of curvature? The clue to an answer may come from considering two circles, one large and one small (Fig. 15-18).

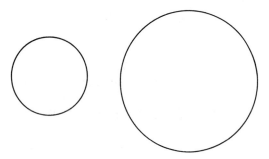

Figure 15-18

An object moving along either of the two circles and going once around changes its direction by 360°, but the one moving along the larger circle changes direction less per unit of distance traveled than the one moving along the smaller circle. That is, the curvature of the larger circle is less at any point than that of the smaller one. The larger the circle, the greater is its radius. Hence a possible measure of the curvature would be the reciprocal of the radius, that is, $1/R$, if R denotes the radius. This definition is recommended by the fact that as R increases, $1/R$ decreases. Moreover, the larger R gets, the closer does an arc of a circle approximate a straight line, and the quantity $1/R$ does approach 0 as R becomes larger and larger. We seem, then, to have a satisfactory definition of the curvature of a circle, namely, the curvature of a circle of radius R is $1/R$ at each point.

What should we adopt as a measure of curvature for an arbitrary curve? Our intuitive notion of curvature is how rapidly a curve changes direction

The direction of a curve at a point P is the direction of the tangent (Fig. 15-19), and this direction can be measured by the angle of inclination ϕ. Then the rapidity of change of direction is really a matter of how much ϕ changes from point to point along the curve or rather how much ϕ changes compared to distance moved along the curve. What this suggests is that the curvature of a curve at any point be taken to be the rate of change of ϕ with respect to arc length.

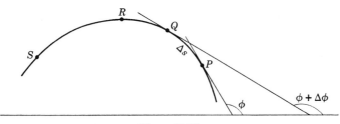

Figure 15-19

Suppose that an object moves from P to Q along a curve (Fig. 15-19). During this motion the change in direction is $\Delta\phi$ and the distance moved is Δs. Then the average change in direction per unit of distance is $\Delta\phi/\Delta s$. The curvature at P should be the limit of this average as Δs approaches 0; that is, the curvature at P is $d\phi/ds$. Thus we arrive at the following definition:

Definition: The curvature of a curve at any point is $d\phi/ds$ where ϕ is the inclination of the tangent and s is the arc length measured from some fixed point.

To this definition we shall add one proviso on the values to be used for ϕ. As point P of Fig. 15-19 approaches R, ϕ approaches 180°. But as the point S approaches R, ϕ approaches 0°. At R, then, ϕ changes abruptly from 0° to 180°. Certainly, we do not want this change in ϕ to enter into our measure of curvature. What we can do is change the range of ϕ-values for the purpose of measuring curvature. At points from R to the right, where ϕ varies from $+180°$ to smaller values we replace this range by the range from 0 to $-90°$. Thus a ϕ-value of 150° will be replaced by the ϕ-value of $-30°$. In fact, the new entire range of ϕ values, namely from 90° to $-90°$, is the principal branch of the inverse tangent function. In calculations we use the corresponding radian measure.

We now have a definition of curvature but no clear way of calculating it at any given point of a given curve. Because curves are represented by formulas of the form $y = f(x)$, we shall seek to express $d\phi/ds$ in terms of $f(x)$ and its derivatives. About the inclination ϕ we know that

$$\tan \phi = \dot{y}$$

so that (under the new or old range of ϕ-values)

$$\phi = \tan^{-1} \dot{y}.$$

Then

$$\frac{d\phi}{ds} = \frac{d}{ds}(\tan^{-1}\dot{y}).$$

Now $\dot{y}$ is a function of x. Hence it would seem wise to use the chain rule and write

$$\frac{d\phi}{ds} = \frac{d}{dx}(\tan^{-1}\dot{y})\frac{dx}{ds}.$$

To perform the first differentiation on the right, the chain rule is again needed; that is,

$$\frac{d\phi}{ds} = \frac{d}{d\dot{y}}(\tan^{-1}\dot{y})\frac{d\dot{y}}{dx}\cdot\frac{dx}{ds}.$$

Now we call upon the theorem for differentiating the inverse tangent function and use formula (26) for dx/ds. These give

(41) $$\frac{d\phi}{ds} = \frac{1}{1+\dot{y}^2}\cdot\ddot{y}\cdot\frac{1}{\sqrt{1+\dot{y}^2}} = \frac{\ddot{y}}{(1+\dot{y}^2)^{3/2}}.$$

This expression for the curvature is satisfactory because it calls for $\dot{y}$ and $\ddot{y}$, both of which are readily calculated from the given function $y = f(x)$.

The curvature of a curve is often denoted by the single letter K so that

(42) $$K = \frac{d\phi}{ds} = \frac{\ddot{y}}{(1+\dot{y}^2)^{3/2}}.$$

Because at a given point on a curve $\ddot{y}$ may be positive or negative, the curvature may have either sign. Most often we are interested only in the amount of curvature and use $|K|$.

It is also useful to speak of the radius of curvature of a curve at a given point, and this is defined to be $1/|K|$. Given a curve, we can construct a circle (Fig. 15-20) which passes through point P of the given curve and which has as its center the point along the normal to P at a distance $1/|K|$ from P, and on the concave side of the curve. This circle will have the tangent to the curve at P as its tangent because the radius of the circle lies along the normal to the curve at P. Because the radius of the circle is $1/|K|$, the curvature of the circle by our definition of curvature for circles is $|K|$. Thus this circle has

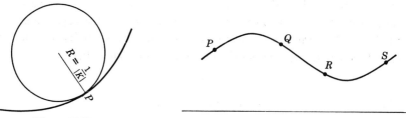

Figure 15-20   Figure 15-21

the same curvature as the curve itself at *P*. For this reason the circle is called the *circle of curvature* of the curve at *P*.

Sometimes the sign of the curvature does matter. To fix the sign of *K* or $d\phi/ds$ we must agree on the signs of ϕ and *s*. The sign of ϕ is fixed by an earlier agreement and ϕ can have any value from $-\pi/2$ to $\pi/2$. However, the sign of *s* is not fixed. It is convenient to take *s* as increasing with increasing *x* so that *s* increases as a point moves along the curve (Fig. 15-21) from *P* to *Q* to *R*. At point *P*, ϕ is decreasing; that is, as a point moves through *P* in the direction of increasing *x*-values, the values of ϕ decrease; but *s* increases. Hence $d\phi/ds$ is negative (or, in exceptional cases, zero). The slope $\dot{y}$ of the curve at *P* is also decreasing, and so the derivative $\ddot{y}$ of the slope is negative (or, in exceptional cases, zero). Then, if we take the positive square root in (42), as we should because ds/dx is positive (see (26)), the expression on the right side of formula (42) is also negative. Formula (42) is thus correct as it stands because both $d\phi/ds$ and the expression to the right are negative. Likewise, an examination of the facts at a point such as *Q* on the curve will show that the curvature is negative and formula (42) is correct as to signs. At points such as *R* and *S*, ϕ is increasing, and therefore $d\phi/ds$ should be positive. But $\ddot{y}$ is also positive at *R* and *S*, and formula (42) again gives the correct sign.

Exercises

1. Show geometrically that the general definition of curvature does yield 0 for the curvature of any straight line.
2. Show geometrically that the general definition of curvature yields $1/R$ for a circle of radius *R*.
3. Show that formula (42) yields 0 for the curvature of a straight line.
4. Show that formula (42) yields $1/R$ for the curvature of a circle of radius *R*.
5. What is the curvature at a point of inflection of a curve?
6. Find the radius of curvature of the following curves at the lowest point:
   - (*a*) $ay = x^2$.   *Ans. a/2.*
   - (*b*) $bay = bx^2 + x$.
   - (*c*) $y = \sqrt{a^2 + x^2} - a$.   *Ans. a.*
   - (*d*) $y = b\left(1 - \cos\dfrac{x}{a}\right)$.   *Ans. a^2/b.*
   - (*e*) $\dfrac{x^2}{a^2} + \dfrac{y^2}{b^2} = 1$.

7. Suppose that the ellipse in part (*e*) of Exercise 6 is a circle, that is, $a = b$. What should the radius of curvature be for this circle and does the answer to part (*e*) yield this expected value?
8. Prove that the radius of curvature at one end of the major axis of an ellipse is equal to one half of the latus rectum.

6. *Areas of Surfaces of Revolution.* If an arc of a parabola, an ellipse, or some other curve is revolved around an axis, a surface is generated. Thus a semicircle revolved about its diameter generates the surface of a sphere, and if an arc of a parabola starting from the vertex is rotated around the axis of the parabola, a portion of a paraboloidal surface or of a paraboloid is generated. The areas of such surfaces must often be computed. For example, paraboloidal surfaces are used as antennas for radio systems of various sorts and paraboloidal mirrors are used in searchlights. Before building such devices one usually wants to know the surface area, for this determines the cost and the weight.

To be specific, let us consider (Fig. 15-22) the upper arc of the parabola $y^2 = 8x$ between $x = 0$ and $x = 6$ and let us suppose that this arc is revolved all the way around the x-axis and generates a portion of a paraboloid. We seek the area of this paraboloidal surface. As was the case for plane areas, volumes, and lengths of arcs, we have no simple formula for this surface area and we have to obtain it by using the technique of approximating it by rectilinear figures and then improving the approximation.

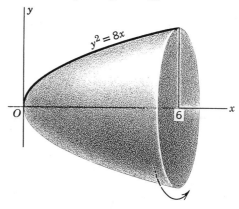

Figure 15-22

A possible approximating figure is obtained by first dividing the x-interval between $x = 0$ and $x = 6$ into n subintervals Δx_i and erecting y-values at the points of subdivision. Figure 15-23 shows one subinterval Δx_i and the y-values erected at its end points. The chord PQ is an approximation to the arc PQ. If chord PQ is revolved about the x-axis, it generates a surface. This surface is an approximation to the surface generated by the arc PQ. We might then sum all the surfaces generated by the chords that approximate the entire arc and then let the number of chords become infinite (while each approaches 0 in length). Because as we know from our study of arc length, the sum of the chords approaches the arc length, the surface area generated by the sum of the chords should approach the surface area generated by the arc.

Figure 15-23

We shall calculate first the surface area generated by a chord such as PQ. The chord PQ generates the surface of a frustrum of a cone or a truncated cone. Figure 15-24 shows the surface generated by PQ when in the position shown in Fig. 15-23. The area that we seek is the area of the lateral surface of this truncated cone. If we slit the frustrum along PQ, say, we can flatten

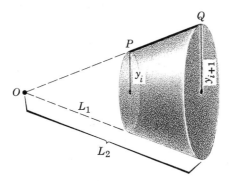

Figure 15-24

it out and it becomes the area $PP'Q'Q$ in Fig. 15-25. From Fig. 15-24 we see that

$$PP' = 2\pi y_i.$$

But Fig. 15-25 shows that PP' is also an arc of the circle whose radius is L_1. If α is the central angle of the circle, the length of this arc is $(\alpha/2\pi)2\pi L_1$ or αL_1. Hence

(43) $$2\pi y_i = \alpha L_1.$$

Likewise

(44) $$2\pi y_{i+1} = \alpha L_2,$$

where L_2 is the length OQ of Fig. 15-25. The area $PP'Q'Q$ is the difference in the area of two circular sectors. Because the formula for the area of a

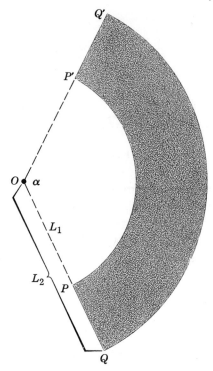

Figure 15-25

circular sector is $\alpha r^2/2$ where r is the radius and α is the central angle, the
area $PP'Q'Q$ is

$$\frac{\alpha}{2} L_2{}^2 - \frac{\alpha}{2} L_1{}^2$$

or

$$\frac{\alpha}{2} (L_2{}^2 - L_1{}^2)$$

or

$$\tfrac{1}{2}(\alpha L_2 + \alpha L_1)(L_2 - L_1).$$

We now use (43) and (44) for the values of αL_2 and αL_1 and we note that
$L_2 - L_1$ is PQ. Then

$$\text{area } PP'Q'Q = \pi(y_{i+1} + y_i)(PQ) = 2\pi\left(\frac{y_{i+1} + y_i}{2}\right)(PQ).$$

If we replace $(y_{i+1} + y_i)/2$ by the mean y-value, $\bar{y}_i$ say, our final result is

(45) $$\text{area } PP'Q'Q = 2\pi\bar{y}_i(PQ).*$$

---

* Had we wished to assume the formula for the lateral surface of a frustrum of a cone,
namely, $A = \tfrac{1}{2}(r_1 + r_2)\, l$ where r_1 and r_2 are the radii of the bases and l is the slant height,
we could have proceeded at once to this result.

Hence the surface area generated by PQ is

$$2\pi\bar{y}_i(PQ)$$

or (see Fig. 15-23)

$$2\pi\bar{y}_i\sqrt{(\Delta x_i)^2 + (\Delta y_i)^2}.$$

This expression can be changed to

$$2\pi\bar{y}_i\sqrt{1 + \left(\frac{\Delta y_i}{\Delta x_i}\right)^2}\,\Delta x_i.$$

We encountered this radical in our derivation of the formula for arc length and we found there that by using the law of the mean we could replace $\Delta y_i/\Delta x_i$ by $\dot{y}$ evaluated at some value of x between x_i and x_{i+1}. Let us denote the proper value of $\dot{y}$ by $\dot{y}_i$. Then our expression for the surface area generated by PQ is

$$2\pi\bar{y}_i\sqrt{1 + \dot{y}_i^2}\,\Delta x.$$

The surface area generated by the n chords of which PQ is typical is then

(46) $\qquad S_n = 2\pi\bar{y}_1\sqrt{1 + \dot{y}_1^2}\,\Delta x_1 + 2\pi\bar{y}_2\sqrt{1 + \dot{y}_2^2}\,\Delta x_2 + \cdots$

$$+ 2\pi\bar{y}_n\sqrt{1 + \dot{y}_n^2}\,\Delta x_n.$$

The quantity $\bar{y}_1\sqrt{1 + \dot{y}_1^2}$ is the value of a function of x, namely, $y\sqrt{1 + \dot{y}^2}$, taken at some value* of x in Δx_1. Likewise, each of the other terms on the right side of (46) is a value of the same function taken at a value of x within the respective subinterval Δx_i. Hence we have the typical summation that leads, as the number n of subintervals becomes infinite while the maximum Δx approaches 0, to a definite integral. If we denote the desired surface areas by S, then

(47) $\qquad S = \displaystyle\int_a^b 2\pi y\sqrt{1 + \dot{y}^2}\,dx$

where a and b are the end values of the x-interval that the Δx_i fill out.

To apply (47) to the problem of the surface area generated by the arc of

$$y = \sqrt{8}x^{1/2}$$

that extends from $x = 0$ to $x = 6$, we first calculate $\dot{y}$. This is

$$\dot{y} = \tfrac{1}{2}\sqrt{8}x^{-1/2}.$$

Then by (47)

$$S = \int_0^6 2\pi\sqrt{8}\,x^{1/2}\sqrt{1 + 2x^{-1}}.$$

---

* There is strictly an extra point to be considered here. The value $\bar{y}_1$ and the value $\dot{y}_1$ are not necessarily taken at the same value of x. However, both are taken at values of x within the same Δx_1. Because we intend to let all the Δx_i approach 0, these two different values of x will come closer and closer. We shall consider this point more carefully in Section 7.

In accordance with the fundamental theorem, we first evaluate

$$S(x) = 2\pi\sqrt{8}\int x^{\frac{1}{2}}\sqrt{1 + 2x^{-1}}\,dx.$$

Putting the factor $x^{\frac{1}{2}}$ inside the radical yields

$$S(x) = 2\pi\sqrt{8}\int \sqrt{x + 2}\,dx,$$

and integrating gives

$$S(x) = 2\pi\sqrt{8}\,\frac{(x + 2)^{\frac{3}{2}}}{\frac{3}{2}} = \tfrac{4}{3}\pi\sqrt{8}(x + 2)^{\frac{3}{2}}.$$

Then

$$S = \tfrac{4}{3}\pi\sqrt{8}(x + 2)^{\frac{3}{2}}\Big|_0^6 = \tfrac{4}{3}\pi\,64 - \tfrac{4}{3}\pi\,8 = \tfrac{4}{3}\pi \cdot 56.$$

What we have done for the parabolic arc applies, of course, to any arc lying in the upper half plane.

We have shown that if an arc of a curve is revolved around the x-axis and the arc extends from $x = a$ to $x = b$, the surface area generated is given by

(48)
$$S = 2\pi\int_a^b y\sqrt{1 + \dot{y}^2}\,dx.$$

This formula is sometimes written in another form. In our work on arc length we showed that

$$\frac{ds}{dx} = \sqrt{1 + \dot{y}^2},$$

and this means that in differential form

$$ds = \sqrt{1 + \dot{y}^2}\,dx.$$

Hence one can write (48) in the form

(49)
$$S = 2\pi\int_a^b y\,ds.$$

Formula (49) has a certain mnemonic value. It suggests that we take little pieces of arc ds; then $2\pi y\,ds$ is the surface area generated by revolving the arc ds about the x-axis and the integral sign means loosely that we are summing these elements of surface area.

Exercises

1. Calculate the surface area of a zone on a sphere of radius a. *Suggestion:* A zone is generated by revolving an arc CD of the circle of radius a about the x-axis (Fig. 15-26). *Ans.* $2\pi a(d - c)$.

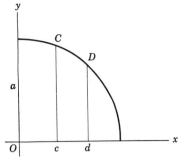

Figure 15-26

2. Find the surface area generated by revolving the following arcs about the x-axis:

(*a*) The arc of $y = 2\sqrt{x}$ from $x = 0$ to $x = 8$.   *Ans.* $208\pi/3$.

(*b*) The arc of $y = \frac{1}{3}x^3$ from $x = 0$ to $x = 2$.

(*c*) The arc of $y = \frac{1}{2}(e^x + e^{-x})$ from $x = -1$ to $x = 1$.

Ans. $\pi(e^2 + 4 - e^{-2})/2$.

(*d*) The arc of $y = \sin x$ from $x = 0$ to $x = \pi$. *Suggestion:* To integrate, let

$u = \cos x$.   *Ans.* $\pi\left(2\sqrt{2} + \log \dfrac{\sqrt{2} + 1}{\sqrt{2} - 1}\right)$.

3. Suppose that an arc whose end points have the ordinates $y = c$ and $y = d$ is revolved about the y-axis. Write a formula for the area of the surface generated.

4. Find the area of the surface generated by revolving each of the following about the y-axis:

(*a*) The arc of $x = y^3$ running from $y = 0$ to $y = 3$. *Ans.* $\pi[(730)^{3/2} - 1]/27$.

(*b*) The arc of $y^2 = x^3$ from $x = 0$ to $x = 8$.   *Ans.* 131.2

(*c*) The arc of $y = \frac{1}{4}x^2$ from $y = 0$ to $y = 4$.

7. Remarks on Approximating Figures.

Our procedure for finding areas under curves, the volumes of figures of revolution, arc lengths, and areas of surfaces of revolution has depended on finding the proper simple figures that approximate the desired quantity and then letting the approximating figures decrease in size while the number of them increases. The sum, then, of the areas, lengths, or volumes of the approximating figures approaches the desired quantity. Thus we used rectangles to get at areas under curves, cylinders and cylindrical shells to get at volumes of revolution, chords to approximate arc lengths, and truncated cones to approximate areas of surfaces of revolution. The choice of the approximating figure was determined entirely by visual evidence, which seemed to assure us that the sum of these approximating figures would approach more and more closely the quantity that we sought. We have, of course, relied on visual and intuitive evidence in many instances and we shall continue to do so. Yet one must be critical and, in the absence of a strict proof, try to check intuitive arguments as much as possible. This is especially true of the choice of approximating elements in obtaining areas, volumes, and similar quantities.

Let us reconsider one or two of the derivations that we have made. When we sought the area under a curve in Chapter 14, we used as an approximating element (Fig. 15-27) the rectangle of width Δx and of height m_i, where m_i is the minimum y-value in Δx. Our sum S_n was

(50)
$$\underline{S_n} = m_1 \, \Delta x + m_2 \, \Delta x + \cdots + m_n \, \Delta x.$$

We then found the limit of $\underline{S_n}$ as n becomes infinite. Although we were, and no doubt still are, reasonably confident that the choice of approximating

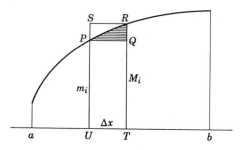

Figure 15-27

element was correct, nevertheless some area is, in fact, neglected. Thus the shaded area, PQR in Fig. 15-27 is not included in the ith rectangle, and the sum of all these neglected n areas may still approach a nonzero quantity even though the rectangles are made narrower and narrower and their number becomes infinite. We might think that we really disposed of this possible difficulty when we formed the sum

(51)
$$\overline{S_n} = M_1 \, \Delta x + M_2 \, \Delta x + \cdots + M_n \, \Delta x,$$

where M_i is the maximum y-value in each Δx, and concluded that this sum too approaches the area under the curve. But this choice of $M_i \, \Delta x$ as the approximating element includes the area PSR of Fig. 15-27 which is not part of the area that we seek. There is the possibility that the sum of these n additional areas, one in each rectangle $M_i \, \Delta x$, might approach a nonzero quantity even though the rectangles are made narrower and narrower and their number becomes infinite.

We can reassure ourselves that either choice of approximating element, $m_i \, \Delta x$ or $M_i \, \Delta x$, is correct by the following consideration. If we can show that the difference between $\underline{S_n}$ and $\overline{S_n}$ approaches 0 as n becomes infinite, then, because the true area lies between them, either sum must approach the true area. However,

(52) $$\overline{S_n} - \underline{S_n} = (M_1 - m_1) \, \Delta x + (M_2 - m_2) \, \Delta x + \cdots + (M_n - m_n) \, \Delta x.$$

Suppose that we replace the various differences $M_i - m_i$ by the maximum one, say $M_j - m_j$. There are n such differences. Hence

$$\overline{S_n} - \underline{S_n} \le (M_j - m_j)n \, \Delta x.$$

However, $n \, \Delta x$ is $b - a$ because the $n \, \Delta x$'s fill out the interval $b - a$. Then

(53) $$\overline{S_n} - \underline{S_n} \le (M_j - m_j)(b - a).$$

Now, as n increases the difference between the maximum and minimum y-value in any Δx surely approaches 0, because we are dealing with continuous functions that change gradually as x changes and the smaller the change in x, that is, the smaller Δx, the smaller the change in y-values (see Section 2 of Chapter 6). Hence the quantity (53) approaches 0 as n becomes infinite.

In other words, not only the sum of the shaded areas (see Fig. 15-27) but also the sum (52) of the rectangles $PQRS$, one for each Δx, approaches 0 as n becomes infinite; thus the approximating rectangles that we took, namely the $m_i \, \Delta x$, do give the proper approximation to the area under the curve.

What we have just pointed out about the choice of approximating element in connection with area under a curve may seem to elaborate the obvious. Perhaps so, but then there is at least no mental strain involved. Let us reconsider next our method of determining arc length. In this task we choose as our approximating element the chord PQ of Fig. 15-28. Why did we not choose a simpler element, namely, the horizontal segment PR? This latter choice would seem as reasonable as the choice of rectangle $PRTS$ in finding area.

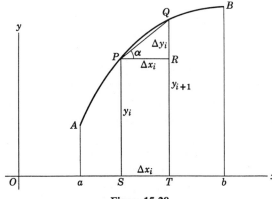

Figure 15-28

However, we can see almost at once that the choice of PR as the approximating element for arc length will not do. For PR equals Δx_i and the sum of the $n \, \Delta x_i$'s, one for each of the elements into which arc AB is divided, is

$$S_n = \Delta x_1 + \Delta x_2 + \cdots + \Delta x_n = b - a.$$

As n becomes larger and the Δx_i become smaller, the sum will still be $b - a$, and so the limit of the sequence of approximations will be $b - a$. This quantity, the horizontal distance from $x = a$ to $x = b$, is not of course, the arc length AB.

Let us confirm analytically that the *difference* between the proper approximating element PQ and the improper one PR is significant. We know from our work on arc length [see (19) and (22)] that

$$PQ = \sqrt{1 + \dot{y}_i^2}\, \Delta x_i$$

where $\dot{y}_i$ is the derivative at some value of x in Δx_i. On the other hand, PR is Δx_i. Then

$$PQ - PR = \sqrt{1 + \dot{y}_i^2}\, \Delta x_i - \Delta x_i$$

$$= (\sqrt{1 + \dot{y}_i^2} - 1)\, \Delta x_i.$$

Then, because there is one such difference for each approximating element, the sum of the differences is

$$(54) \quad (\sqrt{1 + \dot{y}_1^2} - 1)\, \Delta x_1 + (\sqrt{1 + \dot{y}_2^2} - 1)\, \Delta x_2 + \cdots$$

$$+ (\sqrt{1 + \dot{y}_n^2} - 1)\, \Delta x_n.$$

As n becomes infinite and the maximum Δx approaches 0, this sum, which is precisely the kind of sum that we set up as a typical S_n, approaches

$$\int_a^b (\sqrt{1 + \dot{y}^2} - 1)\, dx.$$

This integral is not 0 (except in trivial cases). Hence we see analytically that the difference between the approximating element PQ and the possible element PR is significant.

Now let us compare (52) and (54). Both represent the sum of the differences between two possible choices of approximating elements. In (52) the two choices are the rectangles $M_i\, \Delta x$ and $m_i\, \Delta x$ of Fig. 15-27. In (54) the two choices are PQ and PR of Fig. 15-28. One sum, (52), does approach 0 as n becomes infinite, but the other, (54), does not. How could we characterize them? We note in (52) that the *coefficient* of each Δx approaches 0 as Δx does. However, in (54) the *coefficient* of each Δx does *not* approach 0 as Δx does. In fact, because $\dot{y}_i$ is the slope of the curve AB at some value of x in Δx_i and this slope is generally not 0, $\sqrt{1 + \dot{y}_i^2} - 1$ is not 0 no matter how small Δx_i is.

Several points can be learned from the foregoing discussion. First, there are correct and incorrect approximating elements. Second, if there is some doubt as to whether we have a correct approximating element, we may be able to settle it by going through a proof similar to the ones we went through to show that $m_i \, \Delta x$ is a correct approximating element in the case of area and that the element PR or Δx_i is not a correct approximating element in the case of arc length. Third, we have a criterion as to whether the difference between two approximating elements is significant: if the difference in the approximating elements, apart from the factor Δx, does approach 0 as Δx does, then the difference is not significant.

Let us make use of this criterion. First, we shall consider a point that we slid over when we determined the appropriate approximating element for the area of surfaces of revolution. We found [see (46)] that the element is

$$(55) \qquad\qquad 2\pi \bar{y}_i \sqrt{1 + \dot{y}_i^2} \, \Delta x_i.$$

We then said that this quantity is the value of a function of x, namely, $2\pi y \sqrt{1 + \dot{y}^2}$, times Δx_i taken at some value of x in the ith subinterval Δx_i. But, as we pointed out in a footnote, this last statement is not strictly correct because $\bar{y}_i$ was determined as an average of y_i and y_{i+1}, whereas $\dot{y}_i$ was obtained by applying the mean value theorem to $\Delta y_i / \Delta x_i$. Hence $\bar{y}_i$ and $\dot{y}_i$ are not values of y and $\dot{y}$, respectively, at the *same* value of x in Δx. Yet to apply the concept of the definite integral we should have chosen $\bar{y}_i$ and $\dot{y}_i$ at the same value of x. Let us consider the two elements

$$2\pi \bar{y}_i \sqrt{1 + \dot{y}_i^2} \, \Delta x_i \quad \text{and} \quad 2\pi \bar{y}_i \sqrt{1 + \bar{\dot{y}}_i^2} \, \Delta x_i$$

where the latter, apart from Δx_i, is the value of $2\pi y \sqrt{1 + \dot{y}^2}$ taken at the same value of x as $\bar{y}_i$ is taken. The difference of these two elements is

$$2\pi \, \Delta x_i (\bar{y}_i \sqrt{1 + \dot{y}_i^2} - \bar{y}_i \sqrt{1 + \bar{\dot{y}}_i^2}).$$

As Δx_i approaches 0, $\dot{y}_i$ will approach $\bar{\dot{y}}_i$ because both are values of $\dot{y}$ in the same Δx_i. Hence the quantity in parentheses will approach 0 as Δx_i approaches 0. By our criterion the element (55) can be used as a correct approximating element for surface area.

Our criterion also leads to a helpful principle in the choice of approximating element which is very much worth noting. This principle is really a theorem, but we shall not give a strict proof. Suppose that u is any function of x. Then Δu is the increment in u when Δx is the increment in x and du is the differential of u corresponding to this same Δx. The principle asserts that if Δu is the correct approximating element for the limit of a sequence of sums, then so is du. For

$$\Delta u - du = \frac{\Delta u}{\Delta x} \Delta x - \dot{u}(x) \, \Delta x$$

$$= \left(\frac{\Delta u}{\Delta x} - \dot{u}(x) \right) \Delta x.$$

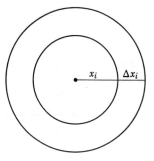

Figure 15-29

As Δx approaches 0, the quotient $\Delta u/\Delta x$ approaches $\dot{u}(x)$. Hence the *coefficient* of Δx approaches 0 as Δx does. Suppose now that we had to form a sum S_n of approximating elements and the suitable element was Δu where u is some function of x. What we have just learned is that du would do as well. Moreover, du may be simpler than Δu or easier to obtain.

Let us see how we can use this principle. In finding volumes of revolution by the cylindrical shell method (see Fig. 15-4) we had to find the volume of a typical shell. This is the area of the base times the height. Now, the base is a circular disc (Fig. 15-29), and the area of the base is

$$\Delta A = \pi(x_i + \Delta x_i)^2 - \pi x_i^2.$$

We are dealing here with the function

$$A = \pi x^2$$

and ΔA is the true increment when x has the value x_i and Δx is Δx_i. The differential dA at this value of x is

$$dA = 2\pi x_i \, \Delta x_i.$$

According to our principle, we could use dA in place of ΔA, and had we done so in our work in Section 3, we could have saved a few steps.

We did use the principle without signalizing it when in Section 3 we found the volume of a sphere by using spherical shells. If r_i is the radius of the inner sphere of the shell and $r_i + \Delta r_i$ is the radius of the outer sphere, the true volume of the shell is

$$\Delta V = \frac{4\pi}{3}(r_i + \Delta r_i)^3 - \frac{4\pi}{3}r_i^3.$$

Here we are dealing with the function

$$V = \frac{4\pi}{3}r^3,$$

and the differential dV of this function at $r = r_i$ is

$$dV = 4\pi r_i^2 \, \Delta r_i;$$

this is precisely the approximating element we used in (14).*

We shall use differential elements in place of the actual increments in many of our subsequent applications of the definite integral.

---

* Of course, since we were finding the volume of a sphere in that problem, we could not have used the exact ΔV without reasoning in a circle. However, the principle that we are explaining is still correct.

Exercises

1. To find the area under a curve (Fig. 15-30) we could use as our approximating element the trapezoid *PQST* in place of the rectangle *PRST*. Show that the area obtained will be the same in either case. *Suggestion:* The difference between the trapezoid and the rectangle is the triangle *PQR* whose area is $\Delta y_i \, \Delta x/2$.

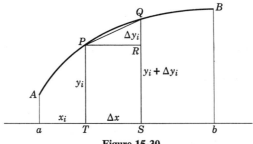

Figure 15-30

2. Suppose that to find the area of the surface of revolution generated by revolving arc *AB* about the *x*-axis (Fig. 15-30) we used the lateral area of the cylindrical element generated by *PRST* in place of the area of the truncated cone that is generated by revolving *PQST* about the *x*-axis. The argument for using the cylinder in place of the truncated cone is that the volume of the cylinder gives the correct result when the cylindrical element is used to find the volume of revolution generated by revolving *AB* about the *x*-axis, and so its surface area should be a good approximating element in finding the surface area generated by *AB*. Show that the cylinder will not do. *Suggestion:* First demonstrate that we can take $2\pi f(x_i) \sqrt{1 + [f'(x_i)]^2} \, \Delta x_i$ to be the element in finding the surface area and compare this with the cylindrical element.

3. Consider a right circular cone with radius *r* and altitude *h* (Fig. 15-31). To find the lateral surface, let us divide the altitude into *n* equal segments of length h/n. Now introduce the circular sections made by planes parallel to the base and through the points of subdivision. We now use cylinders as approximating elements. The upper base of each cylinder is one of the sections, and the altitude of each cylinder is h/n. In all we have $n - 1$ circular cylinders. The radius of the lowest cylinder is $r(1 - (1/n))$, the radius of the next higher cylinder is $r(1 - (2/n))$, etc. Then

$$S_{n-1} = 2\pi r\left(1 - \frac{1}{n}\right)\frac{h}{n} + 2\pi r\left(1 - \frac{2}{n}\right)\frac{h}{n} + \cdots + 2\pi r\left(1 - \frac{n-1}{n}\right)\frac{h}{n}$$

$$= 2\pi r\frac{h}{n}\left(1 - \frac{1}{n} + 1 - \frac{2}{n} + \cdots + 1 - \frac{n-1}{n}\right)$$

$$= 2\pi r\frac{h}{n}\left[n - 1 - \frac{1}{n}\frac{n(n-1)}{2}\right] = \pi r h\left(1 - \frac{1}{n}\right).$$

Then

$$\lim_{n \to \infty} S_{n-1} = \pi r h.$$

Is the result correct and, if not, what is wrong with the argument?

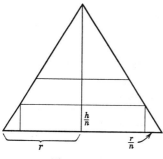

Figure 15-31   Figure 15-32

4. Let ABC be an arbitrary right triangle (Fig. 15-32). To obtain the length of the hypotenuse we might, just to experiment with the method of finding arc length, proceed in the following way. We divide the hypotenuse into n equal parts CD_1, $D_1D_2, \ldots$ Through each point of subdivision we draw the perpendiculars such as D_1C_1, $D_2C_2, \ldots$, and through C, D_1, $D_2, \ldots$ we draw the horizontal lines CC_1, $D_1C_2, \ldots$ The sum of the segments CC_1, C_1D_1, D_1C_2, $C_2D_2, \ldots$ is an approximation to the length CB. By increasing the number of subintervals on CB and obtaining a new series of "steps," we obtain a new sum that intuitively seems closer to the length of ACB. This process can be continued, and the limit of the sequence of sums should be the length CB. The merit of this approach is that we apparently do not need to use the Pythagorean theorem, because the sum of the horizontal segments CC_1, $C_1C_2, \ldots$ is b and the sum of the vertical segments, C_1D_1, $C_2D_2, \ldots$ is h. Hence we know that the first sum obtained as an approximation to the length of BC is $b + h$.

(a) What are the values of the successive approximations and what is $\lim\limits_{n \to \infty} S_n$ where S_n is the nth approximation?

(b) Does the method work?

(c) What is wrong with the method?

(d) Do the points of the segments CC_1, C_1D_1, D_1C_2 approach the points of CB as the successive approximations are formed?

5. Let $S_n = (2y_1 - y_1')\,\Delta x_1 + (2y_2 - y_2')\,\Delta x_2 + \cdots + (2y_n - y_n')\,\Delta x_n$, where y_i and y_i' are values of $y = 3x^2$ corresponding to different values of x in Δx_i. The Δx_i fill out the interval from $x = 1$ to $x = 4$. Find $\lim\limits_{n \to \infty} S_n$ with the understanding, of course, that as n becomes infinite the maximum Δx approaches 0.

6. (a) In view of (26), we can define the differential of arc ds to be $ds = \sqrt{1 + \dot{y}^2}\,dx$. Show by a figure what ds is geometrically and distinguish it from Δs and from $\sqrt{(\Delta x)^2 + (\Delta y)^2}$.

(b) Could one use ds in place of $\sqrt{(\Delta x)^2 + (\Delta y)^2}$ in a summation leading to a definite integral?

CHAPTER SIXTEEN

Some Physical Applications of the Definite Integral

1. Introduction. The calculation of areas, volumes, lengths of curves, and other geometrical quantities is a very useful task but hardly a very inspiring one. The fact that the volume of a certain figure is 36 cubic inches does not change much, if at all, one's outlook on the world. Indeed, the geometric quantities are often details in significant problems. More exciting and more profound knowledge comes from the study of physical phenomena because this knowledge not only satisfies man's curiosity about the way the physical world functions but has also enabled him to take advantage of nature's behavior. In this chapter we shall consider some physical applications of the definite integral. Of these the calculation of the gravitational force exerted by various bodies is fundamental in physical science, because this force governs basic motions on and near the earth and in the heavens. In particular, we shall establish Newton's famous theorem that every sphere attracts an object as though the mass of the sphere were concentrated at the center.

The remark made at the beginning of Chapter 15 about the applications treated there applies here also. We could do many of the problems by first calculating the appropriate rate of change and then merely reverse differentiation. However, the summation concept, that is the definite integral, is often the more natural approach and sometimes the only practical one, and so we shall seek to acquire facility with it.

2. The Calculation of Work. In Chapter 6 we had occasion to introduce and utilize the concept of work done by some force on an object. At that time we were able to approach the concept through antidifferentiation; that is, we calculated $\dot{W}$, the derivative of work with respect to distance moved, and by antidifferentiation we obtained W. Let us now examine similar problems but approached through the notion of summation and the definite integral. It would be helpful to review Section 10 of Chapter 6 before proceeding.

Let us calculate the work done in raising an object from the surface of the earth to a height of 100 miles above the surface (Fig. 16-1). To do this work, one must exert a force that opposes the force of gravity. The magnitude of this force is

(1)
$$F = \frac{GMm}{r^2}$$

where M is the mass of the earth, m is the mass of the object being raised, and r is the distance, positive in the upward direction, from the center of the earth (we are still using without proof the fact that earth's force acts as though its mass were concentrated at the center). The force of gravity is directed downward, but the force that must be exerted to counteract the gravitational pull must be directed upward, and therefore we

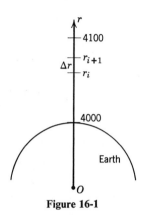

Figure 16-1

shall use (1) with the positive sign to represent the upward force. Because this force varies with distance from the center of the earth, we cannot just multiply the force to be exerted by the distance over which it is exerted to calculate the work done. In accordance with the summation technique, we divide the interval from $r = 4000$ (we shall use miles for the moment) to $r = 4100$ into n equal subintervals Δr. Thus the ith subinterval runs from r_i to r_{i+1}. Of course, the force that must be exerted even to move the object over the distance Δr is not constant, and so there is some question about how to express even the small elements of work whose sum might yield the total work done.

To see more clearly how we might approach the quantity—total work done—let us look at the graph of the function (1) considered over the interval 4000 to 4100. Let F_i be the value of F at r_i. The work done in lifting the object through the typical element Δr, that is, from r_i to r_{i+1}, is less than the rectangle $F_i \Delta r$ in Fig. 16-2 because F decreases in Δr and more than the rectangle $F_{i+1} \Delta r$ because F_{i+1} is too small. In fact, the work done in lifting the object the distance Δr is precisely the area under the arc PQ of the curve.

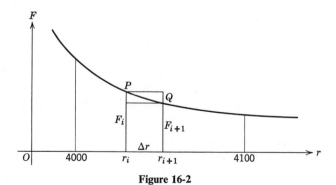

Figure 16-2

We shall, therefore, set up a sum

(2) $$S_n = F_1 \, \Delta r + F_2 \, \Delta r + \cdots + F_n \, \Delta r$$

that will approximate the work done and then let the number of subintervals Δr become infinite. This sum is precisely of the form

(3) $$y_1 \, \Delta x + y_2 \, \Delta x + \cdots + y_n \, \Delta x$$

that we considered in our first investigation of the definite integral. We found there that it does not matter which value of y we take in each subinterval Δx insofar as the limit of such sums is concerned. Hence to form the sum (2) we can take any value of F in each Δr. Let us, then, take the value at the left-hand end point of each subinterval Δr. Thus we take

$$F_i = \frac{GMm}{r_i^{\,2}}$$

for the ith subinterval Δr. Then our approximating sum is

(4) $$S_n = \frac{GMm}{r_1^{\,2}} \, \Delta r + \frac{GMm}{r_2^{\,2}} \, \Delta r + \cdots + \frac{GMm}{r_n^{\,2}} \, \Delta r.$$

As the number n of subintervals that fill out the interval from $r = 4000$ to $r = 4100$ becomes infinite while, of course, each Δr approaches 0, the sum S_n in (4) approaches as its limit the definite integral

(5) $$W = \int_{4000}^{4100} \frac{GMm}{r^2} \, dr,$$

where W is the amount of work we are seeking to calculate. To evaluate (5), we calculate the antiderivative

(6) $$W(r) = \int \frac{GMm}{r^2} \, dr.$$

Then

(7) $$W(r) = -\frac{GMm}{r}$$

and

$$W = -\frac{GMm}{r} \Bigg|_{4000}^{4100}$$

or

(8) $$W = -\frac{GMm}{4100} + \frac{GMm}{4000}.$$

To obtain a numerical answer we must, of course, substitute the numerical values of G, M, and m. As for G and M, we can use the fact established in formula (60) of Chapter 6, namely,

$$GM = 32(4000 \cdot 5280)^2.$$

The value of m is, of course, the mass of the object that is being raised and is therefore some number of pounds. The denominators in (8) must be expressed in feet because the units we are using are in the foot-pound-second system. Then the value of W is in the unit of foot-poundals. As in all calculations of work, the result tells us what work must be supplied by some mechanical, electrical, or chemical agency.

We calculated this same quantity—work—in Section 10 of Chapter 6; let us compare those calculations with what we have just done. In Chapter 6 we found that

(9) $$\Delta W = \bar{F}\Delta r = -\frac{GMm}{\bar{r}^2}\Delta r$$

where $\bar{F}$ was some average value of F in the subinterval Δr and $\bar{r}$ was the value of r that gave the value $\bar{F}$. We then formed $\Delta W/\Delta r$, took the limit of this quantity as Δr approaches 0, and obtained $\dot{W}$ or dW/dr. $\dot{W}$ proved to be

$$\dot{W} = -\frac{GMm}{r^2}.$$

Then in differential notation and with the use of integral sign

$$W = \int -\frac{GMm}{r^2}\,dr.$$

Except for the sign, this result is the same as in (6). The difference in sign comes in merely because in Chapter 6 we calculated the work done by gravity in pulling an object downward, whereas here we treated the problem of the work done in raising an object. We should note, too, that the use of an average value of F in (9) would be equivalent to taking the average value of F in each subinterval Δr of Fig. 16-2 in place of the left-hand end point. Then the sum (4) would have contained average values of F in each Δr in place of values at the left-hand end points. However, we know from our work on the definite integral that any value of F in each Δr would give the same limit (5). We see, then, that insofar as this work problem is concerned either approach—that of Chapter 6 using antidifferentiation or the present one using the definite integral—gives the same result.

Exercises

1. Calculate the work done in lifting an object whose mass is 1000 pounds from the surface of the earth to a height of 300 miles.   *Ans.* $4.72 \cdot 10^7$ ft-pdl.

2. Calculate the work done in lifting an object whose mass is 1000 pounds from a height of 300 miles to a height of 600 miles. Before you calculate the work, decide whether the result should be less than that in Exercise 1 or more.

3. Suppose that an object of mass m is pushed up a hill (Fig. 16-3). If the hill is on the surface of the earth, we may take the magnitude F of the force of gravity to be constant and equal to $32m$. However, the force that must be applied along

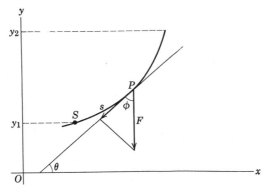

Figure 16-3

the hill at any point P is the negative of the component of F down the hill. This component is $F \cos \phi = F \sin \theta$. Then the work done is

$$\int_{s_1}^{s_2} - F \sin \theta \, ds$$

where s_1 and s_2 are the values of the arc length measured from some point S on the hill. However, $\sin \theta = dy/ds$. Then the work done is

$$\int_{s_1}^{s_2} F \frac{dy}{ds} \, ds.$$

But by a change of variable this integral equals

$$\int_{y_1}^{y_2} F \, dy.$$

What conclusion do you draw as to the work done?

4. Suppose that the hill in Exercise 3 were the path that an airplane took in climbing from the surface of the earth to a height of 20 miles. Then it may be desirable to take into account that the magnitude F of the gravitational force is not constant but is GMm/r^2 where m is the mass of the airplane and r is, of course, the distance from the center of the earth to any point on the variable path. Would the argument and conclusion of Exercise 3 still apply?

5. Suppose that a rocket is to be lifted from the surface of the earth to a height of 300 miles. Initially the rocket with its fuel may have a mass of 2000 pounds. However, as the rocket goes up, its fuel, which is a considerable part of the mass, burns up gradually. Then the mass of the rocket varies with altitude. Suppose that the variable mass is given by the formula $m = 2000 \, R^3/r^3$ where R

is the radius of the earth and r is the distance from the center of the earth. Set up the definite integral which represents the work done in raising the rocket.

6. Express as an integral the work done by gravity in emptying a full cylindrical reservoir 3 feet in radius and 12 feet high by causing the water to flow through a hole in the bottom. Water weighs 62.5 lb/cu ft.

7. A conical reservoir with vertex at the lower end is 12 feet deep. The top of the reservoir is a circle 8 feet in diameter and it is filled to within 4 feet of the top with liquid weighing 80 lb/cu ft. Calculate the work necessary to pump all the liquid over the top of the reservoir.   *Ans.* 81,920π/9 ft-lb.

3. Velocity and Time of Motion Along Curves.

A problem of some interest in itself and important in studies of motion is the calculation of the velocity acquired and the time required by an object that slides along a curve. The force that causes the motion is gravity and if the motion takes place near the surface of the earth, we may use the fact that the acceleration caused by gravity is 32 ft/sec². For example, suppose that a particle of mass m starts from rest at A (Fig. 16-4) and slides down a smooth curve whose equation is known to us. Let us try to calculate the velocity of the particle and the time elapsed when it reaches point B on the curve.

Figure 16-4

Let us consider first what happens at any point P along the path. The force that drives the particle *along the curve* is the component of gravity along the curve. This component is $32m \cos \phi$ or $32m \sin \alpha$. Then, by Newton's second law of motion, the acceleration a along the curve is

(10) $a = 32 \sin \alpha.$

If we let v be the velocity of the particle along the curve, then

$$\frac{dv}{dt} = 32 \sin \alpha.$$

Now, α is a function of s. Hence we are not in a position to integrate. But by formula (32) of Chapter 15,

$$\sin \alpha = -\frac{dy}{ds} \, ;$$

the minus sign enters because y decreases as s increases if s is measured from A toward B.

Then

(11)
$$\frac{dv}{dt} = -32\frac{dy}{ds}.$$

This equation also contains too many variables to permit a direct integration. However, we can use an old device involving dv/dt. By the chain rule,

$$\frac{dv}{dt} = \frac{dv}{ds}\frac{ds}{dt} = \frac{dv}{ds}v.$$

Thus

$$v\frac{dv}{ds} = -32\frac{dy}{ds}.$$

We can now apply the chain rule in reverse to argue that the integral with respect to s of $v\, dv/ds$ is $v^2/2$ and the integral of $-32\, dy/ds$ is $-32y$. Then

(12)
$$\frac{v^2}{2} = -32y + C.$$

Because $v = 0$ when $y = y_0$, for the object starts from rest there, $C = +32y_0$. The result then is

$$\frac{v^2}{2} = 32y_0 - 32y$$

or

(13)
$$v = 8\sqrt{y_0 - y}.$$

We take the positive square root because we chose the acceleration to be positive in (10) and (11) (dy/ds is itself negative), and therefore v increases from 0 as t increases or as y decreases.

We have the rather surprising result that the velocity at any point P whose ordinate is y depends on the difference in the ordinates at A and at P. Thus, if an object slides along any curve under the acceleration provided by gravity, it is not the distance traveled along the curve but the *vertical* distance traveled which determines its velocity. If the object had traveled along a straight line from A to P, its velocity at P would still have been that given by (13).

Now let us calculate the time required by the object to slide from A to P. The quantity v in (13) is velocity along the curve. Hence

(14)
$$\frac{ds}{dt} = 8\sqrt{y_0 - y}.$$

Because we would prefer to calculate the time in terms of the position or coordinates of P, let us make t the dependent variable. That is,

(15)
$$\frac{dt}{ds} = \frac{1}{8\sqrt{y_0 - y}}.$$

This equation contains too many variables to be integrated. Let us see if we can eliminate s. By the chain rule

$$\frac{dt}{ds} = \frac{dt}{dy}\frac{dy}{ds},$$

and by the theorem on inverse functions

$$(16) \qquad \frac{dt}{ds} = \frac{\dfrac{dt}{dy}}{\dfrac{ds}{dy}}.$$

Then, if we use (16) in (15), we obtain

$$(17) \qquad \frac{dt}{dy} = \frac{\dfrac{ds}{dy}}{8\sqrt{y_0 - y}}.$$

If we knew s as a function of y, this equation would be tractable. In fact, we do know s as a function of y. We call on one of our results in connection with arc length, namely (30) of Chapter 15, which states that

$$\frac{ds}{dy} = \pm\sqrt{\left(\frac{dx}{dy}\right)^2 + 1}.$$

This fact, substituted in (17), gives

$$(18) \qquad \frac{dt}{dy} = \frac{\pm\sqrt{\left(\dfrac{dx}{dy}\right)^2 + 1}}{8\sqrt{y_0 - y}},$$

and therefore

$$(19) \qquad t = \int_{y_0}^{y} \frac{\pm\sqrt{\left(\dfrac{dx}{dy}\right)^2 + 1}}{8\sqrt{y_0 - y}}\, dy.$$

This expression for t is acceptable because, if the equation of the curve is expressed as $x = f(y)$, the right side is entirely a function of y. We use the minus sign when y decreases as s increases, as is the case of Fig. 16-4. This result, because it involves dx/dy, shows that the time of travel does depend on the particular curve along which the particle slides.

To illustrate the application of the result, let us calculate the time required for an object to slide along the curve $y = -x$ (Fig. 16-5) from $y = -2$ to $y = -5$ if the object starts from rest at some value y_0 of y, a condition presupposed in the derivation of (19). In view of (19), we shall calculate the time required to travel from $y = -2$ to $y = -5$ by calculating the time

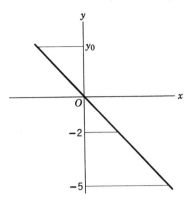

Figure 16-5

required to travel from $y = y_0$ to $y = -5$ and then subtract the time required to travel from $y = y_0$ to $y = -2$. That is, the desired time T, say, is given by

$$T = \int_{y_0}^{-5} \frac{-\sqrt{\left(\frac{dx}{dy}\right)^2 + 1}}{8\sqrt{y_0 - y}}\, dy - \int_{y_0}^{-2} \frac{-\sqrt{\left(\frac{dx}{dy}\right)^2 + 1}}{8\sqrt{y_0 - y}}\, dy.$$

By a basic property of definite integrals [see (20) of Chapter 14],

$$T = \int_{-2}^{-5} \frac{-\sqrt{\left(\frac{dx}{dy}\right)^2 + 1}}{8\sqrt{y_0 - y}}\, dy.$$

Because in our case $x = -y$,

$$\sqrt{\left(\frac{dx}{dy}\right)^2 + 1} = \sqrt{2},$$

and we have

$$T = \int_{-2}^{-5} \frac{-\sqrt{2}}{8\sqrt{y_0 - y}}\, dy.$$

This integration is readily performed by inverting the generalized power rule. Then

$$T = \frac{\sqrt{2}}{8} 2(y_0 - y)^{\frac{1}{2}} \Big|_{-2}^{-5} = \frac{\sqrt{2}}{4} (\sqrt{y_0 + 5} - \sqrt{y_0 + 2}).$$

One of the interesting and historically significant questions involving motion along curves is that of finding the curve joining two given points, such as A and B of Fig. 16-4, for which the time that an object requires to slide along it from A to B is least. We shall return to the subject of motion along curves and to this particular question when we discuss parametric equations.

Exercises

1. Calculate the time required for an object which slides along the line $y = -x + 2$ and which starts from rest at $y = 10$ to travel from $y = 0$ to $y = -5$.

Ans. 0.26 sec.

2. Suppose that the y-axis is chosen positive in the downward direction (Fig. 16-6) and a particle slides down a curve starting from rest at $y_0 = 0$, that is, from the x-axis. Show that the expression for the time of fall from $y = a$ to $y = b$ is

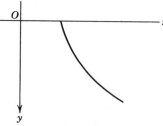

Figure 16-6

$$t = \int_a^b \frac{\sqrt{1 + \left(\dfrac{dx}{dy}\right)^2}}{8\sqrt{y}}\, dy.$$

3. Suppose that a particle slides down the curve of $y = (x^2/4) + 1$ (Fig. 16-7) but starts at $y = 1$ with a velocity due to a free fall from the x-axis. The y-axis is directed downward. Show that the time required to slide from $y = 1$ to $y = 10$ is $\frac{1}{4}(\sqrt{10 - 1} - \sqrt{1 - 1})$ or $\frac{3}{4}$.

Figure 16-7

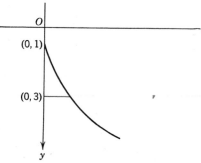

Figure 16-8

4. Suppose that a particle slides down the curve (Fig. 16-8) of $x^2 = \frac{4}{9}(y - 1)^3$ from $y = 3$ to $y = 10$ but starting at $y = 3$ with a velocity that the particle acquires in falling directly down from the x-axis. The y-axis is directed downward. Calculate the time of slide.

Ans. $\frac{7}{8}$.

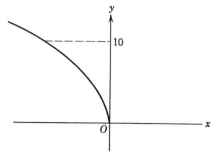

Figure 16-9

5. A particle slides down the curve (Fig. 16-9) of $x^2 = \frac{4}{9}y^3$ from $y = 10$ to $y = 0$ starting from rest at $y = 10$. Calculate the time required for the slide. *Suggestion:* to carry out the integration, let $y_0 - y = u^2$.   *Ans.* $\frac{1}{8}(\sqrt{10} + 11 \sin^{-1}\sqrt{\frac{10}{11}})$.

4. The Hanging Chain. A physical problem of historical and current importance in the design of cables for bridges and of telephone or electric cables hung between two poles is that of determining the shape assumed by a cable suspended from two points A and B (Fig. 16-10). This problem was first solved by John Bernoulli about 1700. The cable is supposed to be made of inelastic material, which means that it will not stretch or contract when suspended, and it is supposed to be perfectly flexible so that it will not resist bending at any point and as a consequence will assume a smooth shape.

Figure 16-10

We could approach this problem in practically the same way in which we approached the problem of the cable that supports a uniform horizontal load (Section 5 of Chapter 4). However, we shall use this opportunity to learn a slightly different method. At point P of the cable the weight of the portion from A to P exerts a pull or tension and the portion BP of the cable exerts an equal and opposing pull. Let us denote the magnitude of the tension by T and consider the direction to be that which BP exerts at P. The argument that we gave in Chapter 4 when discussing the parabolic cable to show that the direction of this tension is tangential to the cable at P applies here also.

If θ is the angle that the tangent at P makes with the horizontal, then the horizontal and vertical components of the tension are T_x, which is $T\cos\theta$, and T_y, which is $T\sin\theta$, respectively. Let us now consider what the changes in the horizontal and vertical components are if we move from point P to a nearby point Q of the cable.

We may speak of the arc length s of the cable measured from any point on it, say, L, to P. Then the arc length from L to Q is some quantity $s + \Delta s$. We shall consider first the change in T_x as a function of s. As we move from

P to Q, the only new force which is introduced and which might change the value of T_x is the weight of the arc PQ of the cable. If the cable has a weight of w pounds per foot of length, the weight of the arc PQ is $w \Delta s$. This weight is directed straight down and thus has no effect on the horizontal force. That is, the horizontal component T_x is not altered in passing from P to Q.* Hence

$$(20) \qquad\qquad T_x = C$$

where C is a constant. This result applies in particular at point L of Fig. 16-10, where the entire tension T is horizontal (because the tension is tangential to the curve). Let us denote the tension at L by T_0 so that, aside from direction,

$$(21) \qquad\qquad T_x = T_0.$$

Now let us consider the change in the vertical component T_y introduced by passing from P to Q. T_y itself is the vertical tension that BP exerts at P. At Q the vertical tension exerted by BQ must offset the additional weight of PQ, namely $w \Delta s$. Hence, if we regard T_y as a function of s, the increase in T_y from P to Q is given by

$$\Delta T_y = w \Delta s$$

or

$$(22) \qquad\qquad \frac{\Delta T_y}{\Delta s} = w.$$

If we let Δs approach 0, we obtain

$$(23) \qquad\qquad \frac{dT_y}{ds} = w.$$

We now assume that the cable is uniform; that is, w, its weight per unit foot of length, does not change from point to point along the cable. Hence we may integrate (23) at once with respect to s and write

$$(24) \qquad\qquad T_y = ws + D,$$

where D is a constant of integration. To evaluate D, we note that at L, $s = 0$ and $T_y = 0$, the latter because the tension at L is entirely horizontal. Then $D = 0$ and

$$(25) \qquad\qquad T_y = ws.$$

If we now divide (25) by (21), we obtain

$$\frac{T_y}{T_x} = \frac{ws}{T_0}.$$

---

* The horizontal force all along the arc $LPQB$ is produced by the pull of the arc AL at L, which forces the cable to take a curved form rather than hang straight down.

However, $T_y = T \sin \theta$ and $T_x = T \cos \theta$, so that the quotient is $\sin \theta / \cos \theta$. But this is the slope of the curve at P. Then

(26)
$$\dot{y} = \frac{ws}{T_0} = \frac{s}{c},$$

where $c = T_0/w$.

This is what we might call the differential equation of the cable, that is, an equation which the derived function of the equation of the curve satisfies. However, the left side is dy/dx and the right side is a function of s. We need, therefore, some relation between s and x or s and y which might help us to obtain an equation involving only two variables. What we do know which relates s and x? We know from our work on arc length that

(27)
$$\frac{ds}{dx} = \sqrt{1 + \dot{y}^2}.$$

If we now substitute (26) into (27), we see that

$$\frac{ds}{dx} = \sqrt{1 + \frac{s^2}{c^2}}.$$

This equation does involve just two variables s and x. Because the right side is a function of the dependent variable, we use the theorem on inverse functions to write

$$\frac{dx}{ds} = \frac{1}{\sqrt{1 + \dfrac{s^2}{c^2}}}.$$

Hence

$$x = \int \frac{1}{\sqrt{1 + \dfrac{s^2}{c^2}}} \, ds.$$

To integrate, we note that the integrand is close to formula 38 in the Table of Integrals.* To make our integrand fit this formula we merely make the substitution $u = s/c$ or the change of variable

$$s = cu.$$

Then

$$x = \int \frac{1}{\sqrt{1 + u^2}} \, c \, du$$

and

$$x = c \log \left(u + \sqrt{1 + u^2} \right) + C.$$

* We can perform the integration by letting $s = cu$ and then letting $u = \tan \theta$. We then have to integrate $\sec \theta$, which we did in (17) of Chapter 13.

Because we chose to measure arc length from L of Fig. 16-10, $s = 0$ there and so is u. If we also choose our y-axis to go through L, then $x = 0$ when $s = 0$. Hence $C = 0$ and

$$x = c \log (u + \sqrt{1 + u^2})$$

or

(28)
$$x = c \log \left(\frac{s}{c} + \sqrt{1 + \frac{s^2}{c^2}}\right).$$

We now have a relation between x and s but, to obtain y as a function of x by means of (26), we need s as a function of x. Let us therefore solve (28) for s in terms of x. First, we have

$$e^{x/c} = \frac{s}{c} + \sqrt{1 + \frac{s^2}{c^2}}.$$

If we now write z for s/c,

$$e^{x/c} = z + \sqrt{1 + z^2}.$$

By subtraction

$$e^{x/c} - z = \sqrt{1 + z^2},$$

and by squaring both sides and simplifying

$$e^{2x/c} - 2e^{x/c}z = 1.$$

Then

$$z = \frac{e^{2x/c} - 1}{2e^{x/c}} = \frac{e^{x/c} - e^{-x/c}}{2},$$

and by the meaning of z

(29)
$$s = c\,\frac{e^{x/c} - e^{-x/c}}{2}.$$

If we now use this relation in (26), we have

$$\dot{y} = \frac{e^{x/c} - e^{-x/c}}{2}.$$

Each term on the right side is almost immediately integrable, and we obtain

(30)
$$y = c\,\frac{e^{x/c} + e^{-x/c}}{2} + D.$$

If we take y to be c when $x = 0$, then $D = 0$ and

(31)
$$y = c\,\frac{e^{x/c} + e^{-x/c}}{2}.$$

This relation between y and x gives the equation of the cable.

We may recall that we introduced the hyperbolic functions sinh x and cosh x in Chapter 11. In terms of these functions,

(32)
$$y = c \cosh \frac{x}{c}$$

and

(33)
$$s = c \sinh \frac{x}{c}.$$

A curve whose equation is given by (31) or (32) is called a catenary. The lowest point, point L in Fig. 16-10, is called the *vertex*, and the line coinciding with the x-axis is called the *directrix*.

We have the equation of the catenary, but it contains one constant which is unknown; this is c which equals T_0/w. This constant should be determinable from some given conditions. Specifying w, the weight per unit length, would not be enough. We might also have to specify the positions of the end points A and B. Even this does not seem to be sufficient because we could hang ropes of different lengths between two fixed points A and B. However, to require w, the positions of A and B, and the length in order to determine the one constant c seems to call for too much information.

Let us see if we can resolve this difficulty. First of all we cannot specify A and B by giving them coordinates at will. We have fixed the axes so that the lowest point has coordinates $(0, c)$. Hence any choice of coordinates for A and B must be consistent with this fact.* Moreover, the curve of equation (32) is symmetric with respect to the y-axis. Hence if one point, say B to the right of the y-axis, is specified, another point A symmetrically placed to the left must also be on the curve.

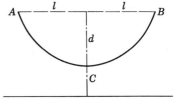

Figure 16-11

Then specifying B certainly means specifying the distance apart of A and B or the quantity $2l$ in Fig. 16-11. Now we can hang different ropes from A and B. Suppose that we also specify the sag d. The two quantities l and d fix c, because point B now has coordinates $(l, c + d)$. Then from (31)

$$c + d = c \frac{e^{l/c} + e^{-l/c}}{2}$$

or

(34)
$$c \left(\frac{e^{l/c} + e^{-l/c}}{2} - 1 \right) = d.$$

---

* If we had not fixed the constants of integration in steps (28) and (31), we would not have fixed the positions of the axes and thus we would have had two more constants in (31). Under this procedure we would be able to choose the coordinates of A and B.

This equation contains the one unknown c. It is not possible to calculate c by any ordinary algebraic method, but we could show that there is one and only one positive solution for c*. Hence fixing the width $2l$ and the sag d fixes c. Then the length of the catenary is also fixed. This follows from (29) because the x-coordinate of B is l, and because x and c in (29) are now fixed, so is the arc length s.

So far we have not specified w, the weight per unit length of cable, and yet the catenary is unique. How can this be? The weight w enters into the equation of the catenary through the value of c which is T_0/w. Since c is fixed by the width and sag, the ratio T_0/w is fixed. Hence, if w is changed, it must be that T_0 also changes. This is physically reasonable because the pull exerted by the arc AL at L in Fig. 16-10 must change if the weight of the cable changes. Since changing w does not change c, the shape of the cable is independent of the weight per unit length provided, of course, that it is the same all along the cable. Then if we hang a light rope or a heavy rope from the same two fixed points and if the sag or the length is the same for both ropes their curves will be identical.

The derivation of (31), the equation of the cable, presupposed that the weight of the cable per unit foot is constant all along the cable. Let us now see what we can do when we let the weight of the cable vary from point to point. Let us denote by $w(s)$ the function that gives the weight per unit foot at point s. Then (21) and (23) still hold, but (24) must be changed to read

$$(35) \qquad\qquad T_y = \int w(s)\, ds + D.$$

If we divide this equation by (21) and use the fact that T_y/T_x is $\dot{y}$, we obtain

$$(36) \qquad\qquad \dot{y} = \frac{1}{T_0} \int w(s)\, ds + D'$$

where D' is D/T_0. If the function $w(s)$ is given, we can calculate $\int w(s)\, ds$. The quantity D' can now be fixed by letting s be 0 at $\dot{y} = 0$. We may

---

* To see that there is one and only one positive solution for c, let $x = l/c$ in (34). Then

$$e^x + e^{-x} - 2 - \frac{2d}{l} x = 0.$$

Let

$$f(x) = e^x + e^{-x} - 2 - \frac{2d}{l} x.$$

We see, first, that $f(0) = 0$. Hence the curve of $y = f(x)$ starts at the origin. As x increases from the value 0, $f'(x)$ or $e^x - e^{-x} - 2d/l$ is negative for small values of x. Hence $f(x)$ decreases and the curve is in the fourth quadrant. Next, $f''(x) = e^x + e^{-x}$; this is positive for all x. The curve is therefore always concave upward, and therefore if it crosses the positive x-axis, it continues upward and does not cross it again. However, for large x, $e^x + e^{-x}$ is larger than $-2 - (2d/l)x$, and therefore $f(x)$ is positive. Because $f(x)$ is negative for small x, the curve must cross the positive x-axis.

proceed as we did in the case where $w(s)$ is a constant and seek to obtain s as a function of x through

$$\frac{ds}{dx} = \sqrt{1 + \dot{y}^2}$$

but $\dot{y}$ is now given by (36). If the integration can be performed and s is obtained as a function of x, we can substitute this value of s in (36) and attempt to obtain y as a function of x.

We can also solve another kind of problem. Suppose that we wish to distribute weight along the cable so that the cable hangs in a given shape; that is, we presume that we know the equation of the cable and we wish to find $w(s)$. To solve this problem, we differentiate (36) with respect to x. On the left side differentiation with respect to x produces $\ddot{y}$. On the right side to differentiate with respect to x we use the chain rule and differentiate with respect to s and multiply by ds/dx. The derivative of $\int w(s)\, ds$ with respect to s must be $w(s)$ because the integral is that function whose derivative is $w(s)$. Thus our result is

(37)
$$\ddot{y} = \frac{1}{T_0} w(s) \frac{ds}{dx}.$$

Because we presume that we know the equation of the curve, we can calculate $\ddot{y}$ and ds/dx. Hence we can find $w(s)$, that is, the variation of weight along the curve that produces the particular shape of the hanging cable. Of course, the shape of the cable need no longer be a catenary. It is often called a non-uniform catenary.

The theory presented in this section is useful under more general conditions than those so far described. In the derivations of (31) and (36), we attributed the weight to the cable. However, the weight $w(s)$ might be the load on the cable, that is, the load of the bridge itself, if the cable's weight is negligible, or the combined weight of cable and load. In the case of the theory leading to (31), this load would have to be proportional to the arc length of the cable; that is, the load would have to be the same for each unit of length of the cable. In the case of (36), the load could vary along the cable or the combined weight of load and cable could vary along the cable, and the function $w(s)$ would have to represent the variation of the total weight with arc length.

Exercises

1. Show that we can determine the value of c in (31) by specifying the width and arc length of the cable. Is the sag then also determined?

2. Calculate the tension T at any point on the catenary (31). *Suggestion:* By (21) and (25) $T^2 = T_0^2 + w^2 s^2 = w^2 c^2 + w^2 s^2 = w^2 c^2 (1 + s^2/c^2)$. Now use (29). *Ans.* $T = wy$. Thus the tension at any point is the weight of a length of cable equal to the y-value at that point.

3. Suppose that one end of rope is attached to A (Fig. 16-12); the rope hangs between A and B; at B it is run over the peg and extends to C on the directrix of the catenary. Show that the rope will not slip in either direction at B. *Suggestion:* See Exercise 2. You may also use the physical fact that the tension at B due to the weight of BC is offset by the tension at B due to the weight of LB.

Figure 16-12   Figure 16-13

4. Two smooth pegs are at the same level and $2a$ feet apart (Fig. 16-13). Show that the shortest rope which can be hung over them and which will not slip at A or B is of length $2ea$. *Suggestion:* The length of rope is used partly to fill out the arc ALB of the catenary and partly to make the lengths BC and AD. We learn from Exercise 3 that the lengths BC and AD must reach to the directrix if the rope is not to slip at A or B. Hence we wish to minimize the sum of arc ALB and $2h$ or $2LB + 2h$. The quantity e is the base of the natural logarithms.

5. Show that the relation $y^2 - c^2 = s^2$ holds at any point on the catenary. Note that with this result, given the arc length and sag, we can calculate c readily.

6. On each catenary $y = c \cosh (x/c)$ there is a point (x_0, y_0) at which the tangent passes through the origin. Show that x_0 is determined by the equation $x_0/c = \coth (x_0/c)$.

7. Find the law of variation of the mass of a string suspended from two points and acted on by gravity, so that it hangs in the form of a semicircle (Fig. 16-14) with a horizontal diameter. *Suggestion:* Take the semicircle to be part of $x^2 + y^2 = 2ay$ and use (37).   *Ans.* $w(s) = aT_0/(a^2 - x^2)$.

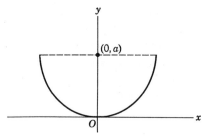

Figure 16-14

8. The derivation given in (36) for a cable whose load varies with arc length applies also to a cable whose load varies with horizontal distance from, say, the lowest point. Thus (21) remains $T_x = T_0$ and (35) becomes $T_y = \int w(x)\, dx + D$. Then (36) is $\dot{y} = (1/T_0)\int w(x)\, dx + D'$. Given that the load per horizontal foot is $w(x) = ax^2 + b$, find the equation of the cable.

Ans. $y = (ax^4 + 6bx^2)/12T_0$.

9. Suppose that the mass Δm of the element Δs of a cable is proportional to the projection Δx of Δs on the x-axis. Show that the curve of the hanging cable is a parabola.

10. A heavy chain is suspended at its two extremities and forms an arc of the parabola $y = x^2/4p$. Show that the weight per horizontal foot is constant. *Suggestion:* Use (37).

11. Calculate the area under the arc of the catenary $y = c(e^{x/c} + e^{-x/c})/2$ from $x = 0$ to $x = d$. Then show that this area is the area of a rectangle whose base has the length of the arc and whose altitude is c.   *Ans.* $c^2 \sinh(d/c)$.

12. Show that the slope of the catenary at any point is the arc length from the vertex to that point divided by c.

13. Prove that the radius of curvature at any point of a catenary is y^2/c.

14. A cable is hung from two points at the same height and 30 feet apart. The length of the cable is 50 feet and the weight per unit foot is 5 pounds. Write an equation for the tension T_0 at the lowest point.
   $$\text{\textit{Ans.} } 250 = T_0(e^{75/T_0} - e^{-75/T_0}).$$

15. A cable hangs from two points at the same height and 100 feet apart. The slope of the cable at the right-hand point of support is $\frac{3}{4}$. Find the sag of the cable. It will be necessary to use the e-table.   *Ans.* Approx. 18 ft

5. Gravitational Attraction of Rods. The calculation of the gravitational attraction exerted by bodies of various shapes is important, because this force causes or enters into an enormous variety of motions including, of course, the motions of the planets about the sun. The problem itself needs some clarification. The usual statement of the law of gravitation is that any two objects attract each other with a force whose magnitude F is given by the formula

(38)
$$F = G\frac{Mm}{r^2},$$

where G is a constant, M and m are the masses of the two objects, and r is the distance between them. As we pointed out in Section 10 of Chapter 6, this statement is somewhat loose. Strictly speaking, the law of gravitation applies to particles, that is, to masses that can be regarded as located each at one point, and then r is the distance between these points. Of course, physically no mass is concentrated at a mathematical point. However, if two masses are very far apart compared to their sizes, as are, for example, the earth and sun, then each mass can be regarded as concentrated at one point. But if we consider the attraction of the earth on a mass which is 10 or 100 miles above the surface of the earth, then, even if the mass is small enough to be regarded as concentrated at one point, the earth cannot be. All that the law of gravitation tells us in this case is that each particle of the earth attracts the small mass according to the law of gravitation but we do not know the force exerted by the whole earth on the small mass. In particular, we would not know what the quantity r should be because each particle of the earth is at a different distance from the small mass.

In other words, to calculate the gravitational force which an extended body such as the earth exerts on a nearby small mass, we must somehow sum up the forces exerted by the separate particles of the earth each at its own distance from the small mass. This summation process requires the calculus.

Our concern in the next few sections will be to calculate the gravitational force exerted by extended bodies of various shapes on other objects. Of course, we are most interested in the attraction exerted by the earth, but to become better acquainted with the calculation of gravitational force we shall start with simple bodies. It is also worth noting that unlike electric charges attract each other in accordance with the same mathematical law as masses do. Hence the mathematical work that we shall undertake is important also for the study of electricity.

Let us begin with a relatively simple problem. Suppose that we have a rod 6 feet long and of mass 18 pounds which is uniformly distributed. The rod is so thin that we think of it as extending in one dimension only. Three feet from one end of the rod (Fig. 16-15) and along the line of the rod is a small object of mass 2 pounds which we shall regard as located at one point. What gravitational force does the rod exert on the 2-pound mass? The difficulty clearly lies in the fact that the rod is an extended body and the various parts of it are at different distances from the 2-pound mass. How should we handle the fact that the mass of the rod is distributed over a 6-foot length?

Figure 16-15

One might guess that the mass of the rod can be regarded as concentrated at its center, so that the quantity r to be used in (38) is the distance from the center to the 2-pound mass, a distance of 6 feet. This guess is plausible. Each portion of the rod to the left of the center should attract the 2-pound mass with less force than that same mass placed at the center. However, to each such portion to the left there is one equally far to the right which should attract with more force, and therefore the two portions, symmetrically placed with respect to the center, should produce the same total force as when both are regarded as the center. If we regard the entire mass of the rod as concentrated at the center, the distance between the rod and the 2-pound mass is 6 feet and the force of attraction is

(39) $$F = \frac{G \cdot 18 \cdot 2}{6^2} = G \text{ poundals.}$$

The quantity G is, of course, a definite number, but its value is not important at the moment.

Let us now see whether our plausible argument is really sound. Let us introduce an r-axis with origin at one end of the rod (Fig. 16-16), so that the rod extends from $r = 0$ to $r = 6$ and the 2-pound mass is located at $r = 9$. We next break up the interval from 0 to 6 into n equal subintervals Δr. Because the rod has a mass of 3 lb/ft, each Δr has a mass of $3\Delta r$. We now choose a point r_1 in the first subinterval Δr, r_2 in the second subinterval Δr, and generally r_i in the ith subinterval Δr. This choice of r_i in each subinterval can be the one at which the mass of that subinterval is concentrated for the purpose of determining the gravitational attraction exerted by the mass $3\Delta r$. Actually, we know from our work on the definite integral that it does not matter which r_i we choose.

Figure 16-16

Then the gravitational attraction of the ith subinterval on the 2-pound mass is

$$G \frac{3\Delta r \cdot 2}{(9 - r_i)^2}.$$

The sum of the attractions exerted by all the subintervals is

$$S_n = G \frac{3\Delta r \cdot 2}{(9 - r_1)^2} + G \frac{3\Delta r \cdot 2}{(9 - r_2)^2} + \cdots + G \frac{3\Delta r \cdot 2}{(9 - r_n)^2}.$$

We rewrite this as

$$(40) \quad S_n = G \frac{6}{(9 - r_1)^2} \Delta r + G \frac{6}{(9 - r_2)^2} \Delta r + \cdots + G \frac{6}{(9 - r_n)^2} \Delta r.$$

We can now see that we have a function of r, namely,

$$G \frac{6}{(9 - r)^2},$$

which is taken at some value r_1 in the first Δr and multiplied by Δr, taken at some value r_2 in the second Δr_2 and multiplied by Δr_2, and so on. As the subintervals Δr are made smaller while the number of subintervals is increased so as to always fill out the interval from 0 to 6, the sum S_n approaches the definite integral

$$(41) \quad F = \int_0^6 G \frac{6}{(9 - r)^2} \, dr.$$

This integral is readily evaluated. By the fundamental theorem of the calculus, we first evaluate the indefinite integral

$$(42) \quad F(r) = 6G \int \frac{1}{(9 - r)^2} \, dr.$$

If we make the substitution
$$u = 9 - r,$$

we see that we need -1 in the numerator of the integrand to have the proper du/dr. We can of course multiply the integrand by -1 and multiply by -1 outside the integral sign and not change the value of the integral. By integrating we find that

$$F(r) = -6G \frac{-1}{(9 - r)} = \frac{6G}{9 - r}.$$

The quantity F is then

(43) $$F = \frac{6G}{9 - r} \Big|_0^6 = 2G - \tfrac{2}{3}G = \tfrac{4}{3}G \text{ poundals.}$$

The result in (43) does not agree with (39); if we have not made any mistake in calculating (43), it must be that the plausible argument which led to (39) is wrong. What might be wrong with it? In this argument we supposed that portions of the rod symmetrically placed with respect to the center should exert the same force as if both were placed at the center. Suppose that we consider the two portions, one extending from $r = 1$ to $r = 2$ and the other from $r = 4$ to $r = 5$. According to the argument that the mass of any rod may be regarded, for the sake of calculating its gravitational attraction, as concentrated at its center, the mass of the first portion can be taken at $r = 1\tfrac{1}{2}$ and the mass of the second at $r = 4\tfrac{1}{2}$. Then the sum of the attractions of the two masses on the 2-pound mass is

(44) $$G \frac{3 \cdot 2}{(9 - 1\tfrac{1}{2})^2} + G \frac{3 \cdot 2}{(9 - 4\tfrac{1}{2})^2} = \frac{24G}{225} + \frac{24G}{81} = \frac{11}{27} G \text{ approximately.}$$

If these two portions were placed at the center of the rod, the sum of their attractions would be

(45) $$2G \frac{3 \cdot 2}{(9 - 3)^2} = \frac{12G}{36} = \frac{1}{3} G.$$

If we compare (44) and (45), we see that it is not correct to regard portions of the rod symmetrically located with respect to the center as equivalent to the same two portions located at the center. Functions that vary inversely as the square of r, as F does, cannot be treated in this way.

The correct answer, then, to the gravitational attraction exerted by the entire rod is given by (43). We might ask, at what point could the mass of the rod be concentrated so that it would exert the same gravitational force as the extended rod? Let us denote by $\bar{r}$ the point at which the mass might be concentrated. Then the force of attraction of the entire mass of the rod on the 2-pound mass would be

$$G \frac{18 \cdot 2}{(9 - \bar{r})^2}$$

and this, according to (43) must equal $4G/3$. The equation

$$\frac{36G}{(9-\bar{r})^2} = \frac{4G}{3}$$

leads to

(46) $$\bar{r} = 3.8 \text{ feet.}$$

In other words, the mass could be regarded as concentrated at the point which is 3.8 feet from the left-hand end point. Concentrating it at the center where $r = 3$ would produce too small a force of attraction, as the result (39) shows.

Exercises

1. Find the gravitational force that a rod of uniformly distributed mass M and of length l exerts on a particle of mass m which lies in the line of the rod and h units from one end. *Ans. $GMm/h(h + l)$.*

2. Find the gravitational force that a rod of uniformly distributed mass M and of length $2l$ exerts on a particle of mass m situated on the perpendicular bisector of the rod and h units from it.

3. Find the gravitational force that a semicircular wire of uniformly distributed mass M and of radius a exerts on a particle of mass m located at the center.
   Ans. $2GmM/\pi a^2$.

4. Show that the result in Exercise 3 implies that the wire attracts the particle as if the mass of the wire were located on the radius which bisects the semicircle and at a distance of $a\sqrt{\pi/2}$ from the center.

5. Find the gravitational force that a circular wire of uniformly distributed mass M and of radius a exerts on a particle of mass m located on a line perpendicular to the plane of the wire and passing through its center. The particle is h units from the center. *Ans. $GMmh/(a^2 + h^2)^{3/2}$.*

6. (a) Consider a thin rod of uniform mass M per unit foot of length and occupying the length AB (Fig. 16-17). Let a unit mass be placed at a point P which is p units above point Q on the line determined by AB. Show that the horizontal and vertical components of the attraction that the rod exerts at P are $(2GM/p) \sin \frac{1}{2}(\alpha + \beta) \sin \frac{1}{2}(\alpha - \beta)$ and $(2GM/p) \sin \frac{1}{2}(\alpha - \beta) \cos \frac{1}{2}(\alpha + \beta)$, respectively, where α is the angle QPA and β the angle QPB.

   (b) Show that the resultant attraction has the magnitude $(2GM/p) \sin \frac{1}{2}(\alpha - \beta)$ or $(2GM/p) \sin \frac{1}{2}APB$ and acts along the bisector of angle APB.

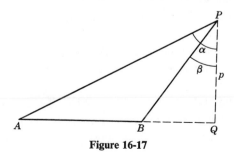

Figure 16-17

7. Prove that the attraction of a thin uniform (open-ended) cylindrical shell (Fig. 16-18) of radius a and length l on a unit mass located at a point on the axis of the shell b units from one end and $l - b$ units from the other ($b < l/2$) is

$$\frac{GM}{l}\left[\frac{1}{\sqrt{a^2 + b^2}} - \frac{1}{\sqrt{a^2 + (l - b)^2}}\right]$$

Figure 16-18

where M is the mass of the entire shell.

Suggestion: Use the result of Exercise 5 and regard the shell as a collection of circular wires, each of rectangular cross section. If M is the mass of the shell $(M/l)\,dh$ is the mass of a wire with thickness dh.

8. Having found in Exercise 7 the attraction of a uniform circularly cylindrical shell on a particle of unit mass on the axis of the shell, suppose that the particle is displaced a small distance, say x, from the center of the axis along the axis. Show that if $2l$ is the length of the cylindrical shell, a is the radius, and M is its mass, the particle will perform small oscillations about the center with a period of $2\pi(GM)^{-\frac{1}{2}}(l^2 + a^2)^{\frac{3}{4}}$. *Suggestion:* After changing notation slightly in the result of Exercise 7, assume that x is small and approximate the force on the particle by dropping all terms in x^2 and higher powers of x. It will be necessary also to expand the radicals by the use of binomial theorem for fractional exponents.

9. Find the attraction that a uniform circular wire of mass M and radius a exerts on a thin uniform rod of mass m and length $2l$ lying along the axis of the wire with its middle point at a distance $x < l$ from the center of the wire. *Suggestion:* Use the result of Exercise 5.

$$\textit{Ans.}\quad \frac{GMm}{2l}\left\{\frac{1}{\sqrt{(l - x)^2 + a^2}} - \frac{1}{\sqrt{(l + x)^2 + a^2}}\right\}.$$

10. Carrying on from Exercise 9, suppose that the wire is held fixed but the rod is released from rest when its center is at a small distance x from the center of the wire. Show that the rod will oscillate along the axis of the wire with a period of $2\pi(GM)^{-\frac{1}{2}}(a^2 + l^2)^{\frac{3}{4}}$. *Suggestion:* Use the result of Exercise 9 and approximate it by neglecting all powers of x higher than the first. As in Exercise 8, it will be necessary to use the binomial theorems for fractional exponents.

6. The Gravitational Attraction of a Disk.

Let us consider next a slightly more complicated problem in gravitational attraction. Suppose that a particle of mass m is located at point P which is h feet above the center O of a thin circular disk (Fig. 16-19) of radius a. Suppose, too, that the mass of the disk is M pounds per unit volume. What gravitational force does the disk exert on the mass m at P?

Before we undertake to solve this problem, let us note one or two facts about handling the mass of the disk. Physically, the disk has some thickness which we denote by t. Because the mass per unit volume is M, the mass of

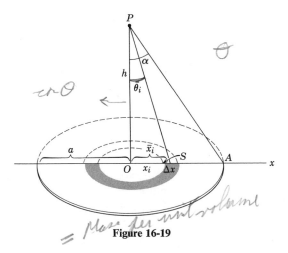

Figure 16-19

the entire disk is $\pi a^2 t M$. Then the mass of unit area and thickness t of the disk is Mt. Some books speak of a very thin disk as infinitely thin or of zero thickness and call it a lamina. They then introduce a mass $\bar{M}$ per unit area. This $\bar{M}$ is our Mt.

It is rather apparent from considerations of symmetry that there will be no horizontal force acting on m because, although any one little piece of the disk pulls the mass m both downward and horizontally, to each such piece there is another one symmetrically located with respect to the center which will also pull m downward but in the opposite direction horizontally and with the same horizontal force as that exerted by the first piece. Hence the horizontal components offset each other. There is, then, only a downward force acting along PO. Thus our problem is, what is the downward force exerted on m? Does the entire mass of the disk act as though it were concentrated at O? This does not seem reasonable, because the downward component of the force exerted by a piece of the disk far from the center is not as large as if this piece were at the center.

It would be natural to break up the disk into little squares (of thickness t), compute the downward attraction of each square, sum these attractions, and then let the squares become smaller while their number increases. However, we do not know how to obtain the limit of a sum whose elements are the areas of little squares.* There is a simpler approach. Suppose that we regard the disk as consisting of a series of successive rings each of width Δx. Figure 16-19 shows one such ring whose inner boundary has radius x_i. Consider this ring as consisting of little pieces of area ΔS and of mass $Mt\,\Delta S$. Each mass $Mt\,\Delta S$ in this ring pulls the mass m toward it. However, the downward component of the force is the same no matter where the mass $Mt\,\Delta S$ is in the

* It is possible to carry out such a plan once we know the theory of double integrals. See Chapter 23, Section 5, Exercise 15.

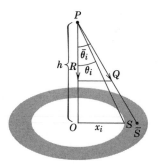

Figure 16-20

ring, for suppose PQ is the force (Fig. 16-20) exerted by the element of mass in the ring. The direction of PQ is that of $P\bar{S}$ where $\bar{S}$ is some point in the element of mass. The downward component of PQ is PR or $PQ \cos \bar{\theta}_i$, where $\bar{\theta}_i$ is the angle between $P\bar{S}$ and PO. Now, $\bar{\theta}_i$ is the same for every element of mass in the ring and the magnitude of PQ is the same for every element of mass in the ring. Hence the entire ring exerts a downward component which is determined by the entire mass in the ring multiplied by $\cos \bar{\theta}_i$.

Let us find the algebraic expression for this downward component. The mass in the ring is

$$Mt[\pi(x_i + \Delta x)^2 - \pi x_i^2]$$

or

$$2Mt\pi x_i \, \Delta x + Mt\pi(\Delta x)^2.$$

The downward component of the force exerted by this mass on the mass m is

$$F_i = GmMt \frac{2\pi x_i \, \Delta x + \pi(\Delta x)^2}{(P\bar{S})^2} \cos \bar{\theta}_i.$$

The sum of all these elements of force, one for each ring, is an approximation to the downward force exerted by the entire disk.

We intend, of course, to sum all these F_i and then to let Δx approach 0 so that the number n of the rings will become infinite. The limit of this sequence of sums as n becomes infinite is some definite integral. Before trying to express this definite integral, let us note that the term involving $(\Delta x)^2$ can be dropped, for, as we pointed out in Section 7 of Chapter 15, if the *coefficient* of Δx in the elements that we are summing approaches 0 as Δx does, these terms do not contribute to the limit. In the present case this coefficient is

$$GMmt \frac{\pi \cos \bar{\theta}_i}{(P\bar{S})^2} \Delta x,$$

and this does approach 0 when Δx does. Hence the element F_i that we need to consider is

(47) $$F_i = GMmt \frac{2\pi x_i \cos \bar{\theta}_i}{(P\bar{S})^2} \Delta x.$$

The quantities $\cos \bar{\theta}_i$ and $P\bar{S}$ in (47) are not strictly functions of x_i but of the x-value of some point $\bar{S}$ in ΔS. However, as we pointed out in Section 7 of Chapter 15 in connection with the discussion of surface area, if we replace $\bar{\theta}_i$ by θ_i and $P\bar{S}$ by PS, where θ_i and PS are determined by x_i (Fig. 16-20), we do not change the value of the limit. For the difference, namely,

$$GMmt2\pi x_i\left(\frac{\cos\bar\theta_i}{(P\bar S)^2} - \frac{\cos\theta_i}{(PS)^2}\right),$$

approaches 0 as Δx does, because $\cos\bar\theta_i$ approaches $\cos\theta_i$ and $P\bar S$ approaches PS when Δx approaches 0. Then the ith element of force that we need to consider is

(48) $$F_i = GMmt2\pi x_i\frac{\cos\theta_i}{(PS)^2}\Delta x.$$

Because, as is evident from Fig. 16-19,

$$PS = h\sec\theta_i,$$

(49) $$F_i = 2GmMt\pi\frac{x_i\cos\theta_i}{h^2\sec^2\theta_i}\Delta x.$$

Now $\cos\theta_i$ and $\sec\theta_i$ are functions of h, which is a constant, and x_i. Hence F_i is entirely determined by x_i and is the value of the function

$$2\pi GMmt\,\frac{x\cos\theta}{h^2\sec^2\theta}$$

taken at some value x_i in the ith subinterval Δx and multiplied by Δx. Then the limit of the sequence of the sums of F_i as Δx approaches 0 is

(50) $$F = \frac{2\pi GMmt}{h^2}\int_0^a\frac{x\cos\theta}{\sec^2\theta}\,dx.$$

To carry out the integration, we could express $\cos\theta$ and $\sec\theta$ as functions of h and x and then integrate the resulting function of x. However, we can work with θ as the independent variable. We see from Fig. 16-20 that

$$x = h\tan\theta.$$

Let us make this change of variable in (50). Then we must replace dx by

$$dx = \frac{dx}{d\theta}\,d\theta = h\sec^2\theta\,d\theta.$$

We must then also change the end values of the interval of integration. When $x = 0$, $\theta = 0$ and when $x = a$, θ is some value α (see Fig. 16-19) such that $a = h\tan\alpha$. Then (50) becomes

$$F = 2\pi GMmt\int_0^\alpha\sin\theta\,d\theta$$

or

(51) $$F = 2\pi GmMt(1 - \cos\alpha).$$

To see how this force of attraction of the entire disk depends on the radius a of the disk and the height h of the mass m above the center of the disk, let us

use the fact that

$$\cos \alpha = \frac{h}{\sqrt{a^2 + h^2}}.$$

Then

(52) $$F = 2\pi G m M t \left(1 - \frac{h}{\sqrt{a^2 + h^2}}\right).$$

Exercises

1. Suppose that we had assumed that the gravitational attraction exerted by the disk could be computed by regarding the mass of the disk as concentrated at its center. What expression for the gravitational force would we have obtained?
   Ans. $\pi G M m t \, (a^2/h^2)$.

2. Compute the gravitational force exerted on a mass of 2 pounds located 5 feet above the center of a circular disk of radius 10 feet and of mass 3 pounds per unit of area. *Suggestion: Mt = 3.*   *Ans.* $12\pi G[1 - (1/5\sqrt{5})]$.

3. Convert the expression (50) for F to a function of x and then integrate.

4. Obtain a formula for the gravitational attraction exerted by a circular annulus (a circular ring) of thickness t, of inner radius 3 feet and outer radius 5 feet, and of mass M per unit volume on a mass m located 10 feet above the center of the annulus.   *Ans.* $20\pi G M m t[(1/\sqrt{125}) - (1/\sqrt{109})]$.

5. Suppose that the distance h of the mass m of the text becomes larger and larger. On the basis of physical arguments, what would you expect the gravitational attraction of the disk on the mass to become. Establish your conclusion by using (52).

6. A frustum of a right circular cone bounded by planes at right angles to its axis of height h, and of mass M per unit volume, may be regarded as a pile of disks each of whose radii subtends the same angle α at the vertex of the cone. Using the result (51) in the text for the disk, calculate the attractive force that the frustum exerts on a mass m at the vertex. *Suggestion:* Because M is the mass per unit volume, Mdh is the mass per unit area of a disk of thickness dh.
   Ans. $2\pi G M m h(1 - \cos \alpha)$.

7. Calculate the attraction that a solid circular cylinder (Fig. 16-21) of height h, radius a, and mass M per unit volume exerts on a mass m located at O on the axis of the cylinder c units from the nearer end. *Suggestion:* Regard the cylinder as a sum of disks and use formula (52) of the text for the attraction of each disk.
   Ans. $2\pi G M m\{h - \sqrt{(h + c)^2 + a^2} + \sqrt{c^2 + a^2}\}$.

Figure 16-21

8. Prove that if the mass per unit volume of a circular disk of radius a at any point x units from the center is λx, the attraction at a point on the axis h units above the center is

$$2\pi G\lambda h\left(\log\frac{\sqrt{a^2+h^2}+a}{h}-\frac{a}{\sqrt{a^2+h^2}}\right).$$

Suggestion: Use the method of the text to set up the appropriate integral for the attraction.

7.   The Gravitational Attraction of Spheres.   The most interesting case of gravitational attraction is, of course, the attraction exerted by the earth. We shall take the earth to be a solid sphere of mass M per unit volume and calculate the force that the sphere exerts on a mass m. To start with, we shall suppose that the mass m is external to the sphere and that it is small enough for us to regard its mass as concentrated at one point.

The natural mathematical approach would be to approximate the sphere by a sum of small cubes, to calculate the sum of the gravitational forces exerted by each of the small cubes on the external mass, and then to calculate the limit of this sum as the size of the cubes is decreased while the number of cubes is increased to fill out the sphere. This approach, although a correct one, would lead to a kind of integral that we cannot handle.* We did, however, approach the volume of a sphere as the limit of a sum of thin spherical shells, and so perhaps we can calculate the gravitational attraction exerted by a shell's mass and then sum them to obtain the attraction exerted by the entire sphere.

The calculation of the gravitational attraction that a *thin* spherical shell exerts poses a problem in itself. Suppose that an object of mass m is located at point P (Fig. 16-22) which is D units from the center O of the shell. The shell has a thickness that we shall denote by t. The parts of the shell are all at

Figure 16-22

* The integral that results from summing elements involving the small cubes is called a triple integral. See Chapter 23, Section 6.

different distances from P, and so we cannot apply the law of gravitation at once to the shell and the mass m. We can, however, regard the shell as composed of small zones. Thus the circles QR and Q_1R_1 bound a zone on the outer sphere of the shell, and if we take this zone to have the thickness t of the shell, we may regard the shell as composed of a number of such zones. If we could calculate the gravitational attraction that the mass of the zone exerts on the mass m, we could sum the attractions of all the zones that make up the shell to obtain the attraction exerted by the entire shell.

Let us consider, then, the attraction exerted by any one zone on the mass m. We think of the zone (Fig. 16-23) as made up of equal little pieces such as U_1UTT_1, each of which pulls the mass m. However, we note that the line OP is the axis of symmetry for each zone. In view of this symmetry, the pulls exerted by any two diametrically opposite pieces of the zone, for example, a piece at QQ_1 and a piece at RR_1, in any direction except PO will offset each other so that the zone pulls the mass m along PO. What we should seek, then, is the component along PO that each piece of the zone exerts. These components can all be added to obtain the attraction caused by the zone because they are in the same direction.

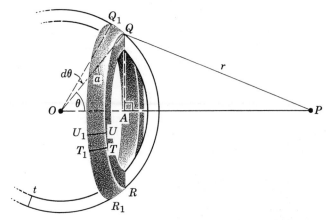

Figure 16-23

The little pieces of any one zone all make about the same angle with PO, namely the angle OPQ, and each piece is the same distance r from the mass m. Hence the component along PO of the force that each piece of the zone exerts is the same. If we let ΔV be the volume of each piece of the zone, then $M \, \Delta V$ is then mass of the piece. The force exerted by this piece along PO is

$$\frac{G \, \Delta V M m}{r^2} \cos \sphericalangle OPQ.$$

The sum of all these components is

(53) $V\dfrac{GMm}{r^2} \cos \sphericalangle OPQ$

where V is the volume of the zone. This volume is approximately t times the area of the zone. The area is approximately the circumference of the circle QR multiplied by the arc length QQ_1.* This area is

(54) $$2\pi \cdot QA \cdot a\, d\theta = 2\pi a \sin\theta \cdot a\, d\theta$$

where θ is the angle shown in Fig. 16-23. Then the component along PO of the force exerted by the entire zone is, from (53) and (54),

$$t \cdot 2\pi a \sin\theta \cdot a\, d\theta \, \frac{GMm}{r^2} \cos \measuredangle OPQ$$

or, if we denote this component by f,

(55) $$f = \frac{GMmt2\pi a^2 \sin\theta\, d\theta}{r^2} \cos \measuredangle OPQ.$$

Before we reformulate this expression, let us note that we made several approximations. We chose the angle OPQ to represent the angle that the line from each piece of the zone to P makes with OP; to find the surface area of the zone, we used the differential element $2\pi a^2 \sin\theta\, d\theta$; and we chose the length PQ to represent the distance of each piece of the zone from P. Will these approximations affect our result? Well, all of these approximations would be eliminated if instead of Q we chose some representative or average point in each piece of the zone. However, we intend to sum the contributions of the various zones that make up the shell and then let the number of zones become infinite; for this purpose any point Q in the zone will do, just as any choice of y_i in Δx_i will do for the limit of the sum $y_1\, \Delta x_1 + y_2\, \Delta x_2 + \cdots + y_n\, \Delta x_n$.

Let us now find an expression for $\cos \measuredangle OPQ$ in (55). We have from Fig. 16-23 that

$$\cos \measuredangle OPQ = \frac{AP}{PQ} = \frac{OP - OA}{PQ} = \frac{D - a\cos\theta}{r},$$

where D is the distance from the center of the sphere to the mass m at P. Then

(56) $$f = \frac{GmMt \cdot 2\pi a^2 \sin\theta\, d\theta}{r^2} \cdot \frac{D - a\cos\theta}{r}.$$

The sum of the forces f exerted by all the zones would be an approximation to that exerted by the whole shell. However, (56) contains two variables θ and r, and we must eliminate one of these to obtain the integrand of our ultimate definite integral. Fortunately, the law of cosines applied to triangle

---

* The area of a zone, according to the formula for the area of a surface of revolution is $S = \int 2\pi y\, ds$. Then $dS = 2\pi y\, ds$. This is an expression for the differential element of surface, which, as we saw in Section 7 of Chapter 15, can be used in place of the actual increment of surface for the purpose of a summation leading to a definite integral. For the present application, y is QA which equals $a\sin\theta$ and $ds = QQ_1 = a\, d\theta$.

OPQ furnishes

(57) $$r^2 = a^2 + D^2 - 2aD \cos \theta.$$

This equation defines r as a function of θ. By differentiating this implicit function with respect to θ, we obtain (in differential form)

$$r \, dr = aD \sin \theta \, d\theta.$$

The use of this relation to replace $a \sin \theta \, d\theta$ in (56) yields

(58) $$f = \frac{GmMt2\pi ar \, dr}{Dr^2} \cdot \frac{D - a \cos \theta}{r}.$$

To eliminate the remaining term in θ, we again use (57). From it we have that

$$r^2 + D^2 - a^2 = 2D^2 - 2aD \cos \theta$$

or

$$\frac{r^2 + D^2 - a^2}{2D} = D - a \cos \theta.$$

If we use this result in (58), we have

(59) $$f = \frac{GmMt\pi a}{D^2} \cdot \frac{r^2 + D^2 - a^2}{r^2} \, dr.$$

The quantity f is the attractive force along PO which is due to the single zone formed by QRR_1Q_1. To obtain the attractive force due to the entire shell, we must first sum all elements of the form (59), one for each zone, and then let the number of zones become infinite while the width dr or Δr of each zone approaches 0.* We can see from (59) what the integrand of our definite integral will be. However, we must also know the domain of r-values that our summation covers so as to know the end values of the definite integral. If we visualize the various zones that fill out the spherical shell in Fig. 16-22, we see that r will range from the value PT for the nearest zone to P to PT' for the farthest zone from P. Then r ranges from $D - a$ to $D + a$.†

Then our definite integral for the attractive force of the entire shell is

(60) $$F = \int_{D-a}^{D+a} \frac{GmMt\pi a}{D^2}\left(1 + \frac{D^2 - a^2}{r^2}\right) dr.$$

This integral is readily evaluated. It is, first of all, the sum

$$\frac{GmMt\pi a}{D^2} \int_{D-a}^{D+a} 1 \cdot dr + \frac{GmMt\pi a}{D^2} (D^2 - a^2) \int_{D-a}^{D+a} \frac{1}{r^2} \, dr.$$

---

* Δr is geometrically $Q_1P - QP$. dr is the differential of r corresponding to the change $d\theta$ in θ. Hence dr is not exactly the same as Δr but can replace Δr for purposes of a summation leading to a definite integral.
† Strictly r ranges from $D - a$ to $\sqrt{D^2 + a^2}$ and from $\sqrt{D^2 + a^2}$ to $D + a$. However, the sum of the two integrals with these pairs of end values and the same integrands is given by (60).

The results of the integration are

$$\frac{GmMt\pi a}{D^2}[(D+a)-(D-a)] + \frac{GmMt\pi a}{D^2}(D^2-a^2)\left[\frac{-1}{D+a}+\frac{1}{D-a}\right].$$

By factoring $D^2 - a^2$ and by other simple algebraic steps, we obtain

(61) $\qquad \dfrac{GmMt\pi a}{D^2}[(D+a)-(D-a)-(D-a)+(D+a)].$

Then

(62) $$F = \frac{GmMt4\pi a^2}{D^2}.$$

We can interpret this result rather readily. Because the area of a sphere of radius a is $4\pi a^2$ and because the mass per unit volume of the sphere is M, the quantity $Mt4\pi a^2$ is the mass of the shell. The quantity m is the mass at P, and D is the distance from the center of the shell to P. Then the quantity (62) is exactly what one would obtain by regarding the mass of the shell as concentrated at the center of the shell and by applying the law of gravitation to the two masses m and $Mt4\pi a^2$ separated by the distance D. In other words, *a spherical shell acts, insofar as its gravitational attraction on an external mass is concerned, as though the mass of the shell were concentrated at the center.*

The result that we have just proved must be applied with care. The derivation of (62) is not quite exact, because we used the outer sphere of the shell as the basic one and merely multiplied by the thickness t to take the volume into account. Of course, the volume of the shell is not exactly the area of the outer sphere times the thickness. This means, then, that (62) is not quite justified for a shell of actual thickness, but (62) is a better and better approximation as the thickness approaches 0. Mathematicians idealize the shell by regarding it as a sphere of zero thickness but with mass M per unit *area*. For this idealized shell, the italicized statement is exact. However, we shall soon see that even the gravitational attraction of a thick shell may be computed as if the mass of the entire shell were concentrated at the center.

We are now able to consider the gravitational force that a solid sphere of radius R exerts on an external particle (point mass) of mass m. We shall regard the sphere as a sum of n spherical shells (Fig. 16-24). However, in place of the notation t for the thickness of each shell we shall use the quantity Δx or dx. (They are the same when x is the independent variable.)

The mass of a typical shell whose inner surface has radius x is the volume times the mass M per unit volume, that is

(63) $\qquad\qquad\qquad\qquad 4\pi x^2\, dx \cdot M.$

This expression is not quite correct, because the volume of a shell is not just the area of the inner surface times the thickness. However, the smaller the

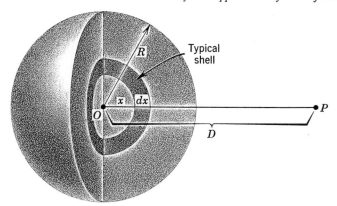

Figure 16-24

thickness of the shell, the more accurate (63) will be. In fact, (63) is the differential element of mass and, because we intend to approximate the mass of the sphere by a sum of the masses of a finite number of shells and then let the thickness of each shell approach 0, the use of the differential element of mass is justified in view of what we discussed in Section 7 of Chapter 15.

We did show that the gravitational attraction of a thin shell may be computed by regarding the mass of the shell as concentrated at its center. Hence the force that the typical shell exerts on the particle of mass m is

(64)
$$\frac{GMm4\pi x^2\,dx}{D^2},$$

where D is the distance OP, that is, the distance from the center to the location of the particle.

To obtain the gravitational force exerted by the solid sphere, we sum the forces exerted by the n concentric shells into which the sphere is divided and let the number of shells increase while the width of each shell approaches 0. Such a limit of a sequence of sums is a definite integral. To write down the definite integral, we need only the additional knowledge that x varies from O to R. If we let F be the force exerted by the solid sphere, then

$$F = \int_0^R \frac{GMm4\pi x^2\,dx}{D^2}$$

or

(65) $$F = \frac{GMm4\pi}{D^2}\int_0^R x^2\,dx = \frac{GMm4\pi}{D^2}\frac{R^3}{3} = \frac{Gm}{D^2}\left(\frac{4\pi R^3 M}{3}\right).$$

This result has a very simple physical interpretation. The quantity $4\pi R^3 M/3$ is the mass of the entire sphere. Because D is the distance from the center of the sphere to the particle at P, we see that the whole sphere acts on the external particle as though the sphere's mass were concentrated at the center. The usual law of gravitation applies to the two masses with the distance between them the distance from the center of the sphere to P. We have used this fact in earlier chapters.

The calculation of the attraction exerted by a solid sphere on an external particle is a major result of science and is enormously useful in applications in which the earth is the attracting body. The question also arises, how does the earth act on a particle inside? Suppose, for example, that a deep tunnel were dug in the earth and a particle were placed inside the tunnel. Would the earth attract this particle as though the entire mass of the earth were concentrated at its center and inversely as the square of the distance from the center of the earth to the particle? The answer is surprising.

To consider the attraction of a solid sphere on an external particle, we first had to consider the attraction of a thin shell on an external particle. Apparently, we should now consider the attraction of a thin shell on an internal particle. Let us replace Fig. 16-22 by Fig. 16-25 in which the particle of mass m is

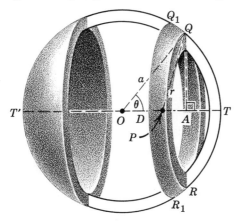

Figure 16-25

located at point P inside the shell. No matter where P is inside the shell, we can take the line OP as an axis and divide the shell into zones that are symmetric about this axis. We now repeat the derivation of (60). There are, however, two essential differences. One is a matter of signs. In the case where P is external to the shell, the angle OPQ is acute for each zone of the shell. However, in the case where P is internal, we can see from Fig. 16-25 and 16-26 that angle OPQ is obtuse for some zones and acute for others. Thus for a zone that lies to the right of P, angle OPQ is obtuse, while for a zone that lies to the left of P (Fig. 16-26), angle OPQ is acute. However, (56) is correct for both cases because θ also changes from acute to obtuse. Hence the integrand in (60) is still correct. However, the end values of the interval of integration must be changed. In the present case r varies from PT, which is

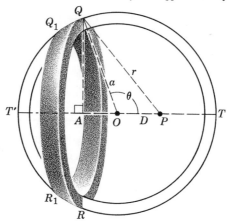

Figure 16-26

$a - D$, to PT', which is $a + D$. Hence in place of (60) we have

(66) $$F = \int_{a-D}^{a+D} \frac{GMmt\pi a}{D^2}\left(1 + \frac{D^2 - a^2}{r^2}\right) dr.$$

Then in place of (61) we have

(67) $F = \dfrac{GMmt\pi a}{D^2}\left[(a + D) - (a - D) + (a - D) - (a + D)\right] = 0.$

Thus we have the surprising result that a thin spherical shell exerts no attractive force on any point mass or particle inside the shell. Of course, the remark we made about (62) also applies here; so far our result is approximate in that we took the volume of the shell to be the surface area of the outer sphere multiplied by the thickness, which is only approximately correct. However, we shall now see that the result is exact even for shells of any thickness.

Consider the shell of thickness $R - h$ (Fig. 16-27). We may regard it as a sum of n shells each of thickness Δx where x ranges from h to R. Now let

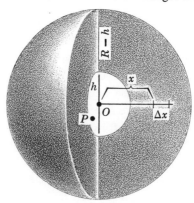

Figure 16-27

us apply (67) to each shell of thickness Δx. We have but to replace t in (67) by Δx to use the result there. However, (67) tells us that the force exerted by a thin shell on a particle P interior to it is 0. This statement, as we have already observed, is not quite correct. The force is approximately 0 for a thin shell, and the approximation becomes better when the shell is thinner. Hence an approximation to the force for each shell of thickness Δx (and mass M per unit volume) is $0 \cdot \Delta x$.* The sum of the forces due to n shells is then $n \cdot 0 \cdot \Delta x$. As Δx approaches 0, the approximation to the force exerted by each shell and therefore by the sum of the n shells is better and the limit as n becomes infinite, which gives the exact force, is 0. Hence we see that even a shell of finite (as opposed to zero) thickness exerts no force on a particle interior to it.

We can now consider the attraction that a solid sphere exerts on a particle of mass m inside the sphere. Figure 16-28 represents a solid sphere of radius R with a particle of mass m at point P which is h units from the center of the sphere. Point P is internal to the spherical shell whose inner radius is h and whose outer radius is R, and P is also external to the solid sphere whose radius is h. This statement is not quite correct because P is *on* the inner surface of the shell and *on* the surface of the solid sphere of radius h. However, let us take the statement as the basis for action at the moment, and we shall see shortly how we correct for the inaccuracy.

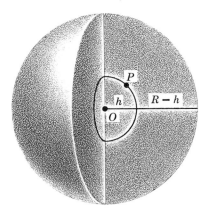

Figure 16-28

Because the particle at P is inside the shell, the shell exerts no force on it. As for the force exerted on the particle at P by the solid sphere of radius h, this is, by (65),

$$(68) \qquad\qquad F = \frac{Gm}{h^2}\left(4\pi \frac{h^3}{3} M\right).$$

* We may state the argument as follows. The exact force exerted by a shell of thickness Δx is of the form $f \Delta x$, where f replaces the coefficient of t in (67). But f approaches 0 as Δx does. Hence $f - 0$ approaches 0 as Δx does. By Section 7 of Chapter 15 we may replace f by 0 for the purpose of a summation leading to an integral.

Hence the action of the entire sphere is equivalent to that of a sphere of radius h and, as (68) shows, the mass of this sphere may be regarded as concentrated at the center.

If one is interested in the variation of F with the distance of the particle from the center, then we have at once from (68) that

(69)
$$F = GMm \frac{4\pi}{3} h.$$

In this form our result states that the attraction of the entire sphere varies with the distance h of the particle from the center. Thus the action of a sphere on a particle inside is quite different from the action on a particle outside. The distance from the center of the sphere to the particle, the quantity h, is still the distance to be taken between the two masses, but the dependence of the force F on that distance is no longer inversely as the square of the distance.

The result (69) can be put in a slightly different form. If we multiply numerator and denominator on the right side of (69) by R^3, we have

$$F = GmM \frac{4\pi}{3} R^3 \cdot \frac{1}{R^3} h.$$

Because M is the mass per unit volume, the quantity $M4\pi R^3/3$ is the mass of the *entire* sphere. If we denote this mass by $\bar{M}$, then

(70)
$$F = \frac{Gm\bar{M}}{R^3} h.$$

Thus the product $Gm\bar{M}$ enters here as in the law of gravitation for particles. However, the factor R^3 in the denominator is new here and, of course, so is the factor h.

There is one detail to be taken care of. Point P is not strictly internal to the shell of thickness $R - h$ nor is it strictly external to the solid sphere of radius h. Suppose, however, that we introduce the shell of thickness $2e$ and that this shell is devoid of matter (Fig. 16-29). Then the outer shell is of thickness $R - h - e$ and the inner solid sphere has radius $h - e$. Point P is now truly internal to the shell of thickness $R - h - e$, and this shell exerts no attractive force on the particle at P. The solid sphere of radius $h - e$ does exert, in view of (69) the force

(71)
$$GMm \frac{4\pi}{3} (h - e).$$

Now suppose that we let e approach 0. Then the outer shell continues to exert no force on the particle at P, and the inner solid sphere a force which, in view of (71), approaches (69). The limit as e approaches 0 of the force exerted by the outer shell is 0, and the limit of the force exerted by the inner solid sphere

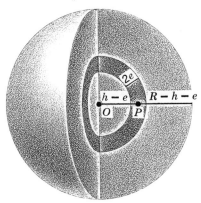

Figure 16-29

is (69). However, in this limiting situation we have the case of the full sphere of radius R with shell of thickness $R - h$ and inner solid sphere of radius h. Thus, considering P in Fig. 16-28 to be internal to the shell and external to the solid sphere of radius, h is seen to be justified.

The several results that we have just obtained on the attraction of hollow and solid spheres on particles within and without were first demonstrated by Newton in his *Mathematical Principles of Natural Philosophy (Philosophiae Naturalis Principia Mathematica)* the first edition of which appeared in 1687. Our results are given in his Propositions 70 to 74 of Book I of the third edition. Newton started this sequence of theorems with the proof that a hollow sphere exerts no force on a particle located inside. His proof is worth noting, although it is loose by modern standards. He considers the particle of unit mass at P inside a hollow sphere and considers the mass of the hollow sphere to be uniformly distributed over the surface. He then introduces the two cones shown in Fig. 16-30. These two cones have equal vertex angles at P. Consider the attraction exerted on P by the mass along base A and the mass along base

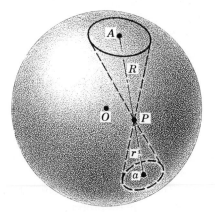

Figure 16-30

a. If the areas A and a are small, it is approximately correct to regard them as spherical caps on spheres of radii R and r, respectively. Because these caps correspond to equal vertex angles at P, the areas are to each other as R^2 to r^2. Since the masses M and m of A and a are proportional to the areas A and a,

$$\frac{M}{m} = \frac{A}{a} = \frac{R^2}{r^2} .$$

However, the force F with which M attracts the unit mass at P is

$$F = \frac{GM \cdot 1}{R^2} ,$$

and the force f with which m attracts the unit mass at P is

$$f = \frac{Gm \cdot 1}{r^2} .$$

In view of the fact that

$$\frac{M}{m} = \frac{R^2}{r^2} ,$$

we see that $F = f$. Hence the two caps exert equal and oppositely directed forces on the mass at P. However, the entire surface can be divided into pairs of cones with vertices at P such as the two shown, and in each pair the result will be the same. Then the force exerted by the entire shell at P will be 0.

Newton then derived the result on the force exerted by a hollow sphere on an external particle. His proof, modified somewhat by Maclaurin, is essentially the one with which we started.

The calculation of the gravitational force exerted by the earth is not really disposed of by all of the above theory, for the earth is not a sphere but an oblate spheroid, that is, one type of ellipsoid. For some astronomical calculations the earth may indeed be taken to be spherical but, for example, to calculate the moon's motion the ellipsoidal shape must be taken into account. However, the subject of the gravitational force exerted by ellipsoids extends far beyond the elements of the calculus. This latter problem engaged the best mathematicians of the eighteenth century.

Exercises

1. Find the attractive force that a thin hemispherical shell of radius a and mass M per unit volume exerts on an external particle P of mass m and D units from the center of the shell. The shell is the right half of the spherical shell in Fig. 16-22. *Suggestion:* Use (60) with the proper end values of the integral, namely $D - a$ and $\sqrt{D^2 + a^2}$.

2. Find the attractive force that a thin hemispherical shell of radius a and mass M per unit volume exerts on an internal particle of mass m located at the center of the shell. *Suggestion:* Do not apply (66) directly because the integrand is infinite since $D = 0$. Use the method of the text with P, of course, at the center O. See Fig. 16-31.

    Ans. $GmMt\pi$. Also, $GmMt\pi = GmMt\pi 2a^2/2a^2$. But $Mt2\pi a^2$ = mass $\bar{M}$ of shell. Hence the answer can be written also as $Gm\bar{M}/2a^2$.

Figure 16-31

3. Find the attractive force that a solid hemisphere of mass M per unit volume and radius R exerts on a particle of mass m located at the center. *Suggestion:* Use the result of Exercise 2; that is, regard the solid hemisphere as a limit of a sum of shells.

    Ans. $\pi GMmR$ or $3Gm\bar{M}/2R^2$ where $\bar{M}$ is the mass of the solid hemisphere.

4. Using the result of Exercise 3, show that the mass of the hemisphere could be regarded as concentrated at the distance h (Fig. 16-32) above the mass m, h being $R\sqrt{6}/3$.

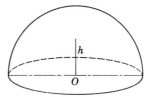

Figure 16-32

5. What modification would you make in the proof of (65) to obtain the gravitational attraction that a spherical shell of inner radius b and outer radius a exerts on an external point mass which is D units from the center?

6. Prove that a solid sphere of radius R, whose mass per unit volume, that it, its density, varies with distance r from the center, attracts an external particle of mass m and D units from the center as if the total mass of the sphere were concentrated at the center. *Suggestion:* Let $\rho(r)$ be the density of the earth and use (64).

$$\text{*Ans.* } \frac{Gm}{D^2} \int_0^R \rho(r)\, 4\pi r^2\, dr.$$

7. In view of the result of Exercise 6, the attractive force that the earth, whose density varies as $\rho(r)$, exerts on a 1-pound mass at the surface is $G\bar{M}/R^2$ where $\bar{M}$ is the total mass of the earth. Now let $\bar{\rho}$ be the mean density of the earth. Then $\bar{M} = 4\pi R^3\bar{\rho}/3$. We know that the attractive force of the earth on a 1-pound mass at the surface is 32 poundals. Hence calculate the mean density of the earth. The quantity G in the foot-poundal-second system is $1.07 \cdot 10^{-9}$.

    Ans. 340 lb/cu ft.

8. Give a verbal proof of the fact that two spheres attract each other as though both were particles concentrated at their respective centers. *Suggestion:* Start by considering the attraction that one sphere exerts on any small element of the second sphere.

9. Calculate the work done by the gravitational force of the earth (of radius R) in moving a particle of mass m from the surface *into* the earth to a distance

R_1 from the center. Assume that the mass of the earth is uniform throughout and is M lb/cu ft. *Suggestion:* Use (69).   *Ans.* $W = Gm\frac{4}{3}\pi M \left(\dfrac{R^2}{2} - \dfrac{R_1{}^2}{2} \right).$

10. Suppose that $\rho(r)$ is the density of the earth at any point r units from the center. What gravitational force does the earth exert on a unit mass inside the earth h units from the center?   *Ans.* $\dfrac{GM}{h^2} \displaystyle\int_0^h 4\pi\rho(r)r^2 \, dr.$

11. Suppose that the earth's density varies directly with the depth below the surface. Show that the attraction of the earth is greatest at a depth equal to $\frac{1}{3}$ of the radius and that the value there is $\frac{4}{3}$ of the value at the surface.

12. The amount of heat in a homogeneous solid mass m at temperature T is given in suitable units by cmT where c is the specific heat of the material.
    (a) Set up an integral for the total heat in a wire of length a and constant cross section s if the density ρ and the temperature T vary with the distance x from one end but c is a constant.
    (b) Do the same as asked in (a) but this time treat c as a function of t.
    (c) Under the same general conditions stated at the outset set up an integral for the heat in a solid spherical ball when ρ and T depend only on the distance from the center and c is a constant.

13. The centripetal force at the origin acting on a point mass revolving about the origin at a distance r and with angular velocity ω is $mr\omega^2$. Suppose that a thin rod of length l, uniform cross section s, and variable density ρ rotates at the constant rate of 10 rps around one of its end points. Set up an integral for the total centripetal force acting on the rod. *Suggestion:* If the notion of centripetal force is not familiar, see Chapter 18, Section 8.

Ans. $400\pi^2 s \displaystyle\int_0^l r\rho(r) \, dr.$

Polar Coordinates

1. The Polar Coordinate System. Given a curve, say the circle, we know that we can set up a rectangular coordinate system and express the equation of the curve in the form $x^2 + y^2 = r^2$. If we then wish to study analytically any properties of the curve, we use the relation between x and y given by this equation. Thus the tangent to the curve at any point or the area of some region inside the curve can be found by applying the methods of the calculus to the equation.

The scheme of locating points by their distances from two mutually perpendicular lines, the x- and y-axes, is clearly a useful one. However, it is also reasonable when, for example, one is aiming a gun to think in terms of distance from an origin, which would be taken at the location of the gun, and of direction measured from some base line. This scheme for locating points in terms of the distance from an origin and the direction as measured from some base line is known as the *polar coordinate* system. Once one recognizes that there can be alternative coordinate systems, the question arises whether one can represent curves in that system and perhaps use that representation more effectively than the representation in rectangular coordinates.

Let us look into the polar coordinate scheme for representing points and curves and then see what the calculus can do for us in the study of geometrical and physical problems when polar coordinates are utilized.

We start with a point O (Fig. 17-1) called the *pole* and choose the half line or *ray* that starts at O and runs horizontally to the right. This ray is called the *initial ray* or *polar axis*. Now let P be a definite point. We imagine a rotation of the initial ray about O until the ray passes through point P. Suppose that a counterclockwise rotation of $30°$ or $\pi/6$ radians brings the polar axis onto the ray through P. Let us suppose also that the length OP is 5 units. The two numbers 5 and $30°$, usually written $(5, 30°)$ or $(5, \pi/6)$ are the polar coordinates of point P. The two coordinates locate the position of P with reference to the pole and the polar axis. Thus, just as in the rectangular coordinate system, two coordinates are required to fix the position of a point in a plane.

A few more conventions are needed to complete the definition of polar coordinates. Suppose that point P lies as shown in Fig. 17-2. If the distance

Figure 17-1   Figure 17-2

of *P* from *O* along the ray *OP* is 5, this number is still the first of the two polar coordinates of *P*. However, there is some question about what angle the ray *OP* makes with the polar axis. We can imagine the polar axis rotated counterclockwise until it falls on *OP*. Then the angle might be, say, 330°. On the other hand, we can imagine the polar axis rotated clockwise until it falls on *OP*. Then the angle is −30° because we regard angles obtained by a clockwise rotation as negative. Hence the polar coordinates of point *P* can be given in two ways, namely, (5, 330°) or (5, −30°). The polar coordinate system thus differs from the rectangular coordinate system in that more than one set of coordinates may describe the same point.

The choices of coordinates to describe one and the same point are even more numerous than we have thus far indicated. Suppose that the polar axis in Fig. 17-2 rotates counterclockwise through 360° about the point *O* and then rotates through 330 additional degrees before coinciding with *OP*. Then the angle between the initial ray and *OP* is 690° and the coordinates of *P* can be taken to be (5, 690°). Or the polar axis may rotate clockwise about *O* through 360° and then through 30 additional degrees before coinciding with *OP*. In this case the angle between the polar axis and *OP* is −390° and another set of polar coordinates for *P* is (5, −390°). In fact, because the size of an angle between two rays emanating from a point is determined by the amount of rotation that one ray goes through to coincide with the second ray and because any multiple of 360° can be added to the rotation, the size of the angle is not unique, at least to the extent that any multiple of 360° can be included.

There is an additional arbitrariness in the choice of polar coordinates. Let us consider point *P* of Fig. 17-3. We could imagine the polar axis rotated

Figure 17-3

through 150° until it reaches the ray OQ. Now, instead of proceeding out from O along this ray, we can proceed from O away from Q or, as one says, backward along the ray OQ until we reach point P. To denote the fact that point P is reached by proceeding backward along the ray OQ, we use negative numbers. If the distance OP is 5, we denote the first coordinate of P by -5 and the two coordinates of P are $(-5, 150°)$. Here, too, any other positive or negative angle that locates the ray OQ, for example, $-210°$, can be used in place of 150°. These coordinates $(-5, 150°)$ and the other possible choices described above all denote the same point P. The pole O itself has 0 as its first coordinate; its second coordinate can be any angle.

We have seen so far that any point in the plane can be located by two co-ordinates, the first being the distance from a fixed point, the pole. If this distance is positive, the second coordinate is an angle that the ray from the pole to the point makes with the polar axis. This angle can be a positive one or a negative one. If the distance is negative, the angle is one made with the polar axis by the ray from the pole in the opposite direction from the point, as in Fig. 17-3. The two coordinates that locate the point in this polar co-ordinate system are generally denoted by ρ (rho) and θ (theta), although many books use r and θ. These coordinates are always written in the order (ρ, θ). We see that ρ can be any number positive, negative, or zero, and that θ, likewise, can be any number, positive, negative, or zero. The line segment OP from O, the pole, to a point P is called the *radius vector* to P, and the angle θ that together with ρ locates P is called the *vectorial angle*.

Exercises

1. Plot the following points on a polar coordinate system:

   (*a*) $(5, 0)$.
   (*b*) $(5, 30°)$.
   (*c*) $(5, \pi/6)$.
   (*d*) $(5, -\pi/6)$.
   (*e*) $(3, 390°)$.
   (*f*) $(3, -390°)$.
   (*g*) $(-3, 30°)$.
   (*h*) $(1, -\pi/4)$.
   (*i*) $(-3, -\pi/4)$.

2. For each point of Exercise 1 give one other set of polar coordinates with positive ρ-value and one other set with negative ρ-value.

2. The Polar Coordinate Equations of Curves.
The reason for using polar coordinates is, as already suggested, that the equations of many curves are more simply represented in polar coordinates. Let us examine the equations of a few common curves.

In the rectangular coordinate system the simplest equations of curves are $x = $ constant, which represents a line parallel to the y-axis, and $y = $ constant, which represents a line parallel to the x-axis. Let us see first what the ana-logues of such equations represent in the polar coordinate system. Suppose

that we consider the equation

(1) $$\theta = 30°.$$

Where are the points for which $\theta = 30°$? If we consider points with positive ρ-value, the angle made by the ray from O to any such point must make a 30° angle with the initial ray. Hence all such points must lie on the same *ray*, namely OP in Fig. 17-4. However, points on the ray OQ, which is the prolongation backward of OP, are also described by $\theta = 30°$, although the ρ-values of points on OQ are negative. Hence $\theta = 30°$ represents all the points on the line QOP. Moreover, there are no other points for which $\theta = 30°$ because any such point must have a positive, zero, or negative ρ-value, and we have already taken these into account. Thus $\theta = 30°$ represents the entire line that passes through the pole and makes a counterclockwise angle of 30° with the polar axis.

Figure 17-4

Now let us consider the curve represented by

(2) $$\rho = 5.$$

Where are all the points whose distances from the pole are 5? The answer is the circle of radius 5 (Fig. 17-5). Conversely, if a point lies on the circle of radius 5 with center at the pole O, then for this point $\rho = 5$.

The rectangular coordinate equation of a circle of radius 5 and center at the origin is, of course, $x^2 + y^2 = 25$. We see, then, that for the circle, the polar coordinate equation is very much simpler. This fact does not imply, however, that the polar coordinate equation is always preferable when working with the circle.

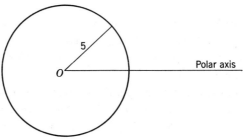

Figure 17-5

Let us now start with a curve and ask for its polar coordinate equation. Suppose that we take the straight line which is perpendicular to the polar axis and 5 units from the pole (Fig. 17-6). To obtain the equation of the line, we follow the reasoning used also in working with rectangular coordinates. We ask, what condition must all points on this line satisfy? Let P, then, be any point on the line. The polar coordinates of P, namely ρ and θ, are indicated in the diagram. We see from the diagram that

(3) $$\rho \cos \theta = 5.$$

Because this equation holds for the coordinates of the typical point P, this equation presumably is the polar coordinate equation of the line. This answer may be correct, but we must do a little more checking. Let us consider a point such as P'. Is it true for the coordinates of P' that $\rho \cos \theta = 5$? Because the θ-coordinate of P' can be the negative angle shown in the figure, and because $\cos \theta$ is positive for θ between 0 and $-90°$, it is true that the coordinates (ρ, θ) of P' satisfy this equation.

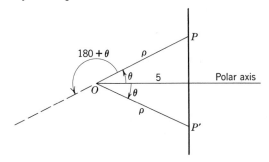

Figure 17-6

Strictly speaking, we have not finished showing that the coordinates of any point on the line satisfy the equation $\rho \cos \theta = 5$, because there are many other choices of coordinates for any point on the line. Consider again the point P. For a positive ρ-value not only θ but $\theta \pm 2\pi$, $\theta \pm 4\pi$, and so on, all serve as the proper angle for P. However, the cosine of all these angles equals $\cos \theta$. Hence for positive ρ any θ-value which belongs to P will, together with ρ, satisfy the equation. If a negative ρ-value is used to represent P, the corresponding angle is $180 + \theta$. However, $\cos (180 + \theta) = -\cos \theta$, and therefore $\rho \cos (180 + \theta) = 5$, because both factors are negative.*

---

* In the polar coordinate system we do *not* require that every possible choice of coordinates for a point must satisfy the equation. Thus consider the equation $\rho = \sin (\theta/2)$. The coordinates $(-\frac{1}{2}, \pi/3)$ do not satisfy the equation, but the coordinates $(-\frac{1}{2}, 7\pi/3)$, which represent the same point, do satisfy the equation. Hence the point lies on the curve represented by the equation. In other words, a curve and equation correspond if some pair or pairs of coordinates of any point on the curve satisfy the equation and if, whenever any pair of coordinates satisfies the equation, the corresponding point lies on the curve.

We have shown that given any point on the line, its coordinates satisfy the equation $\rho \cos \theta = 5$. We must also show that given a ρ and θ such that $\rho \cos \theta = 5$, the ρ and θ belong to a point on the line PP' of Fig. 17-6. We may dispose of this task by noting that if a point is not on the line PP' then for the ρ and θ of such a point $\rho \cos \theta < 5$ or $\rho \cos \theta > 5$. Hence if $\rho \cos \theta = 5$, the point must lie on the line PP'.

To consider another example of finding the polar equation of a curve, let us find the equation of the circle of radius a whose center lies on the polar axis and which passes through the pole (Fig. 17-7). Let P be any point on the

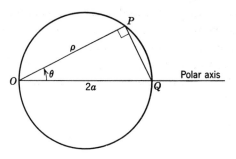

Figure 17-7

upper half of the circle. We know from Euclidean geometry that OPQ is a right angle because it is inscribed in a semicircle. Then we have at once that

(4) $$\rho = 2a \cos \theta.$$

This conclusion holds also when P is on the lower half of the circle because there we can take the coordinate of P to be a positive ρ-value and an acute negative value for θ. Because at least one choice of coordinates for each point on the circle satisfies equation (4), this is the equation of the circle. Conversely, if a point P has coordinates ρ and θ which satisfy (4), P must lie

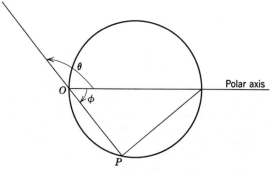

Figure 17-8

on the circle. For then $\cos \theta = \rho/2a$. If ρ is positive, θ must be an acute angle (we may ignore any multiple of $360°$) and ρ and $2a$ must be the adjacent side and hypotenuse of a right triangle with right angle at P. By a theorem of Euclidean geometry, the vertices of all right triangles with hypotenuse $2a$ must be on the circle with diameter $2a$. Then P must lie on the circle. If ρ is negative, for example -5, θ can be between $90°$ and $270°$. Suppose that θ is obtuse (Fig. 17-8). Then ϕ, the supplement of θ, is acute and the magnitude of OP is 5. The argument that we gave for ρ positive and θ acute now applies to ϕ and the magnitude of OP, and thus P lies on the circle. There are other possibilities for the values of ρ and θ, but they lead in each case to the conclusion that point P whose coordinates ρ and θ satisfy (4) must lie on the circle.

Exercises

1. What is the curve corresponding to $\theta = 30°$ and ρ positive?

2. What is the equation of a line parallel to the initial ray and 3 units above the pole?   *Ans.* $3 = \rho \sin \theta$.

3. What is the equation of a line parallel to the initial ray and 3 units below the pole?

4. Give another equation for the line represented by $\theta = 30°$

5. Describe the curve whose equation is the following:

(*a*) $\rho = 10 \cos \theta$.   (*e*) $\rho = 4/\cos \theta$.

(*b*) $\rho = 10 \sin \theta$.   (*f*) $\rho^2 = \sin^2 \theta$.

(*c*) $\rho = -10 \cos \theta$.   (*g*) $\rho \cos \theta = -4$.

(*d*) $\rho = -10 \sin \theta$.   (*h*) $\rho \sin \theta = 1$.

3. The Polar Coordinate Equations of the Conic Sections. Next to the straight line and circle the conic sections are the most useful curves. We shall now see what their equations become in polar coordinates.

Most often the conic sections—that is, parabola, ellipse, and hyperbola—are defined by a property peculiar to each one separately (see Chapters 4 and 7). Thus the ellipse is often defined as the set of all points such that the sum of the distances of any one from two fixed points is the same constant. However, all three conic sections can be defined by one common property, called the focus-directrix property. Under this definition, a conic section is the set of all points for which the ratio of the distance from a fixed point and from a fixed line is constant. This means that we start with a fixed line d (Fig. 17-9), called the directrix, and a fixed point F, called the focus. Then we consider all points P for which the ratio of the distance PF and the distance PD from P to the line d is a given constant. This set of points is a conic section. If the constant, denoted by e and called the eccentricity, is less than 1, the conic section is called an ellipse; if equal to 1, it is called a parabola; and if greater than 1, it is called a hyperbola.

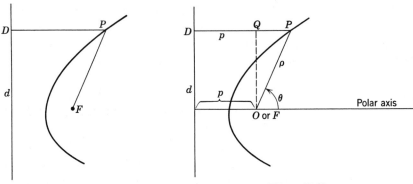

Figure 17-9   **Figure 17-10**

This definition is somewhat familar in that it happens to be the one used commonly for the parabola. However, one can show that it applies to all the conic sections by using it to find the equation of the curve in rectangular coordinates. This equation proves to be of the second degree in x and y, and we have proved (Appendix to Chapter 7) that any equation of the second degree in x and y must represent one of the conic sections. We shall not pursue the application of the focus-directrix definition in rectangular coordinates (see Exercise 15), but we shall apply it in the polar coordinate system.

We do have the possibility of choosing the pole and polar axis so as to make the resulting equation as simple as possible. Suppose that the focus F lies to the right of the directrix d. Experience shows that if we choose the point F as the pole and choose the polar axis perpendicular to the directrix d and pointing to the right, so that it points away from the directrix, then the equation is simple. With this choice (Fig. 17-10) let P be any point on a conic section and let (ρ, θ) be its coordinates. We wish to express in these coordinates the geometric condition

(5)
$$\frac{PF}{PD} = e$$

where e is a fixed constant.

The length PF is the ρ-value of P. The length $PD = PQ + QD$, where Q is the foot of the perpendicular from F to PD. Now $PQ = \rho \cos \theta$. The quantity QD is the distance from the focus F to the directrix d. This distance is, of course, fixed for any one curve because the focus and directrix are given. Let us denote it by p. Then

$$PD = \rho \cos \theta + p.$$

With these values of PF and PD we have from (5)

$$\frac{\rho}{\rho \cos \theta + p} = e.$$

If we solve this equation for ρ, we have that

(6)
$$\rho = \frac{ep}{1 - e \cos \theta}.$$

We do not know how the curve of the equation lies in relation to the pole and polar axis, but we can determine this in somewhat the same manner as one does for equations in rectangular coordinates. Suppose, for example, $e = 1$ and $p = 6$. Then (6) becomes

(7)
$$\rho = \frac{6}{1 - \cos \theta}.$$

We can now make a table of values for θ and ρ and thereby locate a few points. Thus

θ	30°	60°	90°	120°	180°
ρ	46	12	6	4	3

We could continue the table for values of θ larger than 180°, but we know that we can cover the range from 180° to 360° just as well by covering the range from $-180°$ through $-90°$ to 0°. Since $\cos(-\theta) = \cos \theta$, we should get the same ρ-values as θ ranges from 0° to $-180°$ as when it ranges from 0° to 180°. What this means geometrically is that the curve is symmetric with respect to the polar axis. The curve lies as shown in Fig. 17-10 and is a parabola.

We assumed in the derivation of (6) that the focus lies to the right of the directrix. However, it might equally well lie to the left (Fig. 17-11). If we again choose the pole to be the focus and choose the polar axis perpendicular to the directrix and pointing to the right, so that this time it points from the focus toward the directrix, the equation of the conic section is slightly altered.

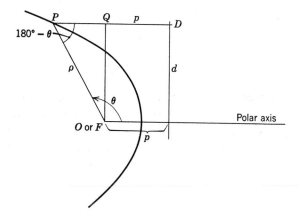

Figure 17-11

We again start with the definition

$$\frac{PF}{PD} = e.$$

PF is again ρ. Also $PD = PQ + QD$. But now $PQ = \rho \cos (180 - \theta) = -\rho \cos \theta$. Hence *PD* is $p - \rho \cos \theta$. Then

$$\frac{\rho}{p - \rho \cos \theta} = e$$

or, by solving for ρ,

(8) $$\rho = \frac{ep}{1 + e \cos \theta} \, .$$

A parabola has just one focus and one directrix. However, the ellipse and hyperbola have two foci (Fig. 17-12) and, as one might guess from the symmetry of these curves, each has a directrix associated with it. We may choose either pair of focus and directrix to write the equation of the curve and our result will be (6) or (8). To be more explicit, if in the case of the ellipse, say, we choose the directrix *d* and the focus *F* and the polar axis is, as always, directed from *F* to the right, then the facts are as in Fig. 17-10 and (6) will result. If we choose *F'* and *d'* (for the ellipse) and the polar axis is directed from *F'* to the right, then the facts are as in Fig. 17-11 and (8) will result. No matter which focus and directrix we pick, the other focus and directrix exist and may play a role. With the choice of *F* and *d* for the ellipse, the other focus is to the right of *F*. With the choice of *F'* and *d'*, the other focus is to the left of *F'*.

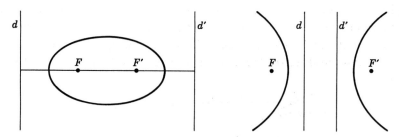

Figure 17-12

We may find it convenient at times to use the polar coordinate equation of a conic section when the focus lies below or above the directrix, the pole is chosen to be the focus, and the polar axis is chosen *parallel* to the directrix and pointing to the right as usual. If the focus lies below the direction (Fig. 17-13), the equation of the conic section is readily found, by the method above, to be

(9) $$\rho = \frac{ep}{1 + e \sin \theta}$$

Figure 17-13

If the focus lies above the directrix (Fig. 17-14), the equation of the conic section is found to be

(10)
$$\rho = \frac{ep}{1 - e \sin \theta}.$$

To plot a curve whose equation falls under one of the forms (6), (8), (9), or (10) we can advance the work considerably if we first determine which form is involved and what e and p are for the curve in question. Thus suppose that we are given the equation

(11)
$$\rho = \frac{10}{3 + 4 \sin \theta}.$$

This equation may be reduced to the form (9) if we divide numerator and denominator on the right side of (11) by 3. We obtain

(12)
$$\rho = \frac{\frac{10}{3}}{1 + \frac{4}{3} \sin \theta}.$$

If we now compare (12) and (9), we see that $e = \frac{4}{3}$ and $ep = \frac{10}{3}$. Then $p = \frac{5}{2}$. We know now from the fact that $e = \frac{4}{3}$ that the curve is a hyperbola. We also know that the directrix is $\frac{5}{2}$ units above the pole. To obtain a better picture of the curve, we would have to make a table of (ρ, θ)-values belonging to (12) and plot the corresponding points.

Figure 17-14

Exercises

1. What is the equation of the directrix in Fig. 17-10?   *Ans.* $\rho \cos \theta = -p$.

2. Sketch the curve whose equation is the following:

(a) $\rho = \dfrac{10}{5 - \cos \theta}$.

(b) $\rho = \dfrac{4}{1 + \cos \theta}$.

(c) $\rho = \dfrac{5}{3 + 2 \sin \theta}$.

(d) $\rho = \dfrac{4}{1 - 3 \cos \theta}$.

3. Find the equation of the ellipse with the following properties:
   (*a*) Eccentricity $\frac{2}{3}$ and directrix $\rho \cos \theta = -6$.   *Ans.* $\rho = 12/(3 - 2 \cos \theta)$.
   (*b*) Eccentricity $\frac{2}{3}$ and directrix $\rho \cos \theta = 6$.

4. Derive (9) under the conditions stated in the text.

5. Sketch the ellipse $\rho = 6/(2 - \cos \theta)$ and by relying on the sketch find the maximum and the minimum values of ρ.   *Ans.* Max. $= 6$, min. $= 2$.

6. In view of the results of Exercise 5, find the length of the major axis of the ellipse.

7. Sketch the ellipse $\rho = 6/(2 + \cos \theta)$ and answer the same questions as in Exercises 5 and 6.

8. Find the coordinates of the center of the ellipse $\rho = 6/(2 - \cos \theta)$.

9. Find the latus rectum of the ellipse $\rho = ep/(1 - e \cos \theta)$; that is, find the width of the ellipse at the focus.   *Ans. 2ep.*

10. Find the latus rectum of the parabola $\rho = p/(1 - \cos \theta)$; that is, find the width of the parabola at the focus.   *Ans. 2p.*

11. Show that the center C of the ellipse $\rho = ep/(1 + e \cos \theta)$ has the coordinates $[e^2p/(1 - e^2), -\pi]$.

12. Find the semimajor axis of the ellipse $\rho = ep/(1 - e \cos \theta)$. In coordinate geometry this quantity is usually denoted by a.   *Ans.* $a = ep/(1 - e^2)$.

13. According to Exercise 9 the latus rectum of the ellipse $\rho = ep/(1 - e \cos \theta)$ is $2ep$. In terms of the semimajor axis a and the semiminor axis b, the latus rectum of an ellipse is $2b^2/a$. The value of a was found in Exercise 12. Hence find the value of b in terms of e and p.   *Ans.* $b^2 = e^2p^2/(1 - e^2)$.

14. Suppose that the polar axis is chosen so that it makes the angle α with the line from the focus perpendicular to the directrix (Fig. 17-15). Write the equation of the conic section (here pictured as an ellipse).

$$Ans. \; \rho = ep/[1 + e \cos (\theta + \alpha)].$$

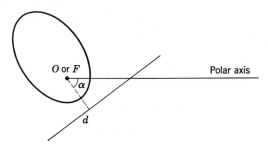

O or F   Polar axis

α

d

Figure 17-15

15. Show by use of rectangular coordinates that the focus-directrix definition of the ellipse agrees with the definition usually given in terms of the sum of the distance from two fixed points. That is, show that the focus-directrix definition leads to a second degree equation in x and y and so must be at least one of the conic sections. If you know how to translate axes, you can show that the section is an ellipse. *Suggestion:* Choose rectangular axes as shown in Fig. 17-16.

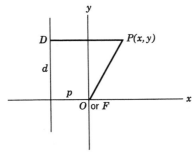

Figure 17-16

16. Show that if a chord of an ellipse is divided by a focus into two parts of lengths r_1 and r_2, then $(1/r_1) + (1/r_2) = 2/ep$.

17. The following equations do not necessarily represent conic sections. Obtain the curves of the equations by making a table of (ρ, θ)-values and plotting the corresponding points. The names of some of these curves are indicated.

(*a*) $\rho = 5 \sin 2\theta$ (four-leaved rose).

(*b*) $r = \theta$ (Archimedean spiral).

(*c*) $\rho = 5(1 + \cos \theta)$ (cardioid).

(*d*) $\rho = 3 (1 + \sin \theta)$.

(*e*) $\rho = 3 (1 - \sin \theta)$ (cardioid).

(*f*) $\rho = 5 - 3 \cos \theta$ (limacon).

(*g*) $\rho = a \sec \theta \pm b, b < a$
       (conchoid of Nicomedes)

(*h*) $\rho = 5(1 - \cos \theta)$ (cardioid).

(*i*) $\rho = 5 \cos 3\theta$ (three-leaved rose).

(*j*) $\rho = a \cos 2\theta$.

(*k*) $\rho^2 = a^2 \sin 2\theta$ (lemniscate).

(*l*) $\rho^2 = a^2 \cos 2\theta$ (lemniscate).

4. ***The Relation Between Rectangular and Polar Coordinates.*** We could pursue the subject of the polar coordinate equations of various curves and learn how to sketch quickly a variety of curves whose equations are given in polar coordinates. But we shall acquire some of this knowledge as we work with curves. There is, however, one more matter concerning the use of polar coordinates which should be taken up now. Suppose that a curve is given to us through the rectangular coordinate equation and that we wish to see if the polar coordinate equation of the curve is simpler for some purpose we may have in mind. We must know, then, how to obtain the polar coordinate equation from the rectangular one. Conversely, we might have the polar coordinate equation of a curve and might wish to find its rectangular coordinate equation. What we need, then, is a way to transform an equation from one coordinate system to the other.

A relation between rectangular and polar coordinates can be established, if we first agree on how the axes and origin of the rectangular system are to be fixed with respect to the pole and polar axis of the polar system. The most convenient correlation between the two coordinate systems is to have the origin at the pole and the positive half of the x-axis coinciding with the polar axis. Figures 17-17*a* and 17-17*b* presuppose this arrangement. Point O is the origin of the rectangular system and the role of the polar system. If we

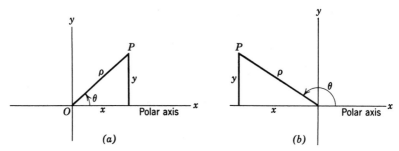

Figure 17-17

now consider a point P in the first quadrant, it is at once apparent that

(13) $x = \rho \cos \theta$ and $y = \rho \sin \theta.$

Fortunately, the relations in (13) hold also when point P is in any of the four quadrants. Figure (17-17b) shows that this is so when P is in the second quadrant, because $\cos \theta$, by its very definition for second quadrant angles, is x/ρ and $\sin \theta$ likewise is y/ρ.

Equations (13) are useful in transforming from rectangular coordinates to polar coordinates. To transform from polar to rectangular coordinates, we have from Figs. 17-17a and b that

(14) $\rho = \sqrt{x^2 + y^2}$, $\sin \theta = \dfrac{y}{\sqrt{x^2 + y^2}}$, $\cos \theta = \dfrac{x}{\sqrt{x^2 + y^2}}$.

These equations also yield unique ρ- and θ-values for a given x and y provided that we take ρ to be positive and $0 \leq \theta < 360°$. We have seen, however, that negative ρ-values may also be used to describe points in polar coordinates; in fact, the same point can be described by a positive ρ-value and a θ-value or by a negative ρ-value and another θ-value which may differ, for example, by 180° from the first one. If we do use

(15) $\rho = -\sqrt{x^2 + y^2}$,

we must also use

(16) $\sin \theta = \dfrac{y}{-\sqrt{x^2 + y^2}}$ and $\cos \theta = \dfrac{x}{-\sqrt{x^2 + y^2}}$.

Most often the use of positive ρ-values and therefore equations (14) suffice to transform from polar to rectangular coordinates.

Now let us see how the equations (13) to (16) can be used to transform the equation of a curve from one coordinate system to another. Consider the straight line $\theta = 30°$. To change this to rectangular coordinates, we can state first that $\tan \theta = \sqrt{3}/3$ and then, by the latter two equations in (14), $y/x = \sqrt{3}/3$ or $y = \sqrt{3}x/3$.*

* Strictly speaking, $\theta = 30°$ represents the entire straight line only if we include positive and negative ρ-values. If we restrict ourselves to positive ρ-values, we must use $\theta = 30°$ and $\theta = 210°$ to describe the entire line. However, in both cases $\tan \theta = \sqrt{3}/3$.

As a second illustration let us consider the circle with center at (a, O) and radius a. The rectangular coordinate equation of this circle is

$$(x - a)^2 + y^2 = a^2 \quad \text{or} \quad x^2 + y^2 - 2ax = 0.$$

If we use equations (13), we obtain $\rho^2 - 2a\rho \cos \theta = 0$ or $\rho = 2a \cos \theta$, which is the equation (4) obtained earlier in this chapter.

Exercises

1. Find the rectangular coordinate equations of the following:
   (a) $\rho = 5 \cos \theta$.   *Ans.* $x^2 + y^2 - 5x = 0$.
   (b) $\rho \cos \theta = 5$.
   (c) $\rho^2 = a^2 \cos 2\theta$.   *Ans.* $x^4 + y^4 + x^2(y^2 - a^2) + y^2(x^2 + a^2) = 0$.
   (d) $\rho = -4 \cos \theta$.
   (e) $\rho \sin \theta = -4$.   *Ans.* $y = -4$.
   (f) $\rho = 5$.
   (g) $\rho = 5 \sin 3\theta$.

   (h) $\rho = \dfrac{2}{1 - \cos \theta}$.   *Ans.* $y^2 = 4(x + 2)$.

   (i) $\rho = \dfrac{6}{2 - \cos \theta}$.

   (j) $\rho = \dfrac{6}{2 + \cos \theta}$.   *Ans.* $\dfrac{(x + 2)^2}{16} + \dfrac{y^2}{12} = 1$.

2. Find the polar coordinate equations of the following:
   (a) $x^2 + y^2 = 36$.   *Ans.* $\rho = 6$.   (e) $(x - 2)^2 + (y - 3)^2 = 13$.
   (b) $x = 5$.   *Ans.* $\rho = 4 \cos \theta + 6 \sin \theta$.
   (c) $x + 2y = 7$.   (f) $(x^2 + y^2)^2 = a^2(x^2 - y^2)$.
        Ans. $\rho(\cos \theta + 2 \sin \theta) = 7$.   (g) $(x^2 + y^2)^3 = 4a^2x^2y^2$.
   (d) $x^2 + y^2 - 8y = 0$.   *Ans.* $\rho = a \sin 2\theta$.
                                (h) $y^2 = 4x + 4$.

3. Change the equation $(x^2/a^2) + (y^2/b^2) = 1$ of the ellipse to polar coordinates. Does the result come under one of the standard forms of section 3? If not, why not?

4. Suppose that a point P has the polar coordinates (ρ, θ) in a polar coordinate system and a new polar system is introduced whose pole coincides with the pole of the first system but whose polar axis makes the positive angle α with the polar axis of the first system. Let (ρ', θ') be the coordinates of P with respect to the second system. What equations relate (ρ', θ') and (ρ, θ)?
                    Ans. $\rho' = \rho, \theta' = \theta - \alpha$.

5. The Derivative of a Polar Coordinate Function. Let us now see how the calculus serves when functions are expressed in polar coordinates. Given a relation between ρ and θ, say $\rho = 4 \sin \theta$, we can, of course, ask for the instantaneous rate of change of ρ with respect to θ. The values of ρ and θ are numbers, just as the values of y and x are in any of the functions considered earlier, and therefore the concept of the derivative applies at once. That is,

$$
(17) \qquad\qquad \dot{\rho} = \frac{d\rho}{d\theta} = \lim_{\Delta\theta\to 0} \frac{\Delta\rho}{\Delta\theta}.
$$

Physically, this meaning of the derivative depends entirely on what ρ and θ mean physically. If θ should represent time values and ρ distance along some straight line, then $\dot{\rho}$ is instantaneous velocity. In fact, the derivative and its physical meaning are independent of any choice of a coordinate system for plotting ρ and θ and therefore of the curve representing the function. Even in the case of, say, $s = -16t^2 + 128t$, the physical meaning deals with straight-line motion and the derivative represents velocity; however, the curve, if we choose to plot the function in rectangular coordinates, is a parabola.

The *geometrical* meaning of the derivative is different in the polar coordinate representation from that in the rectangular coordinate system. Let us see why. To obtain the derivative we start with some value θ_0 and the corresponding ρ-value, ρ_0. The θ_0 and ρ_0 are the coordinates of a point, P in Fig. 17-18. We now change the value of θ to $\theta_0 + \Delta\theta$ and, because ρ is a function of θ, ρ changes to some value $\rho_0 + \Delta\rho$. These values, $(\theta_0 + \Delta\theta, \rho_0 + \Delta\rho)$, are the coordinates of point Q in the figure. Of course, P and Q lie on the curve representing the function. If we draw the circle whose center is the pole 0 and whose radius is OP, the circle cuts OQ in P', say. Then $P'Q = \Delta\rho$. The angle POQ is $\Delta\theta$. To obtain a geometrical meaning for the derivative $\dot{\rho}$, we should find one for $\Delta\rho/\Delta\theta$ and then see what the latter becomes as $\Delta\theta$ approaches 0. However *geometrically* $\Delta\rho$ is a length and $\Delta\theta$ is an angle, and there seems to be no significant meaning for the ratio of these two quantities. Certainly, we cannot obtain the geometrical meaning for $\dot{\rho}$ that we obtained for $\dot{y}$ in rectangular coordinates, that is, $\dot{\rho}$ is *not* the slope of the curve at point P.

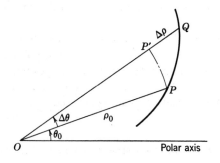

Figure 17-18

Before we answer the question of what the geometrical meaning of $\dot{\rho}$ may be, we would like to point out that some other results that we established when dealing with y as a function of x do hold for functions relating ρ and θ. Thus we gave conditions under which we can find relative maxima and minima of y. These conditions involved $\dot{y}$ and $\ddot{y}$. This theory does apply to ρ as a function of θ. To be clear about this point, we must distinguish two approaches that we made to the theory of maxima and minima. In Chapter 8, Section 2, we gave geometrical arguments to show that if $\dot{y} = 0$ at some value a of x and if $\dot{y}$ changes from positive to negative as x changes from values less than a to values greater than a, then y has a relative maximum at $x = a$. The geometrical arguments do *not* carry over to ρ as a function of θ because we cannot interpret $\dot{\rho}$ as a slope. However, in Sections 3 and 4 of that chapter we gave *analytical* arguments for the very same conclusions about relative maxima and minima. These analytical arguments, which do not rely upon pictures, do apply to ρ as a function of θ. The arguments should be reviewed at this time to see that they do apply also to ρ as a function of θ.

Thus we can conclude that ρ has a relative maximum at $\theta = \theta_0$ if $\dot{\rho} = 0$ at $\theta = \theta_0$ and if $\dot{\rho}$ is positive for values of θ near but less than θ_0 and if $\dot{\rho}$ is negative for values of θ near but greater than θ_0. All of the results and tests for relative maxima and minima carry over to ρ as a function of θ.

Exercises

1. Find $\dot{\rho}$ for the function $\rho = ep/(1 - e\cos\theta)$.

Ans. $\dot{\rho} = -e^2 p\sin\theta/(1 - e\cos\theta)^2$.

2. (*a*) For the ellipse $\rho = ep/(1 - e\cos\theta)$ with e between 0 and 1, find the minimum value of ρ and the maximum value of ρ.

Ans. Min. $= ep/(1 + e)$, Max. $= ep/(1 - e)$.

    (*b*) Show geometrically where the minimum and maximum ρ-values lie on the ellipse and show the focus from which ρ is measured.

3. For the ellipse in Exercise 2 show that ρ decreases as θ varies from 0 to π.

4. In view of the result in Exercise 2, find the length of the major axis of the ellipse in question.

Ans. $2ep/(1 - e^2)$

5. For the parabola $\rho = p/(1 - \cos\theta)$ show that ρ has the minimum value $p/2$ at $\theta = \pi$.

6. For the parabola $\rho = p/(1 - \cos\theta)$ show that ρ decreases as θ increases from 0 to π.

7. If y is a function of x and x is the inverse function of y, we know that $dy/dx = 1/(dx/dy)$. What is the analogous statement for ρ as a function of θ and does the analogous statement hold?

Let us return to the question of whether we can find some geometrical meaning for $\dot{\rho}$. We shall experiment a bit. We start again with a curve

(Fig. 17-19) that represents ρ as a function of θ and on which lie the points P and Q with coordinates (ρ_0, θ_0) and $(\rho_0 + \Delta\rho, \theta_0 + \Delta\theta)$, respectively. We draw the circle with center O and radius OP and thus obtain the point P' on OQ. The arc PP' has the length $\rho_0 \Delta\theta$ and QP' has the length $\Delta\rho$.

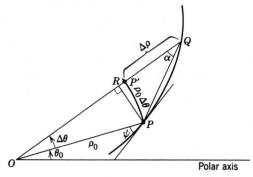

Figure 17-19

Even though PP' is an arc, let us speak of the triangle PQP'. This is a right triangle because the arc of a circle meets a radius at right angles. Then, for the angle α, which is the angle between the radius vector to Q and the secant PQ, we may say that

(18)
$$\cot \alpha = \frac{\Delta\rho}{\rho_0 \Delta\theta} = \frac{1}{\rho_0} \frac{\Delta\rho}{\Delta\theta}.$$

We now have an expression involving $\Delta\rho/\Delta\theta$ which is approximately correct and may become more accurate as $\Delta\theta$ approaches 0. As $\Delta\theta$ approaches 0, the secant PQ approaches the tangent at P and the radius vector OQ approaches OP. Hence α approaches the angle ψ, the angle between the radius vector to P and the tangent at P. Moreover, as $\Delta\theta$ approaches 0, the right side of (18) approaches $\dot\rho/\rho_0$, with $\dot\rho$ denoting the derivative at (θ_0, ρ_0). Hence, if the approximation that we made is reasonable in the sense that it yields the same limit as the exact quantity would, we have shown that

(19)
$$\cot \psi = \frac{\dot\rho}{\rho_0},$$

where ψ is the angle between the radius vector to P and the tangent at P. This result may be valuable because it tells us the angle which the tangent to the curve at P makes with the radius vector to P.

The result (19) was obtained by making an approximation; namely, we regarded arc PP' as part of a right triangle. Hence the result may or may not be correct. Let us see if we can establish it by a sounder argument. To obtain a right triangle containing α (Fig. 17-19), let us drop the perpendicular

PR from *P* onto *OQ*. If we use triangle *PRQ*, we can say that

(20)
$$\cot \alpha = \frac{RQ}{PR}.$$

However,

$$RQ = OQ - OR = \rho_0 + \Delta\rho - \rho_0 \cos \Delta\theta$$

and

$$PR = \rho_0 \sin \Delta\theta.$$

If we substitute these results in (20), we have

$$\cot \alpha = \frac{\rho_0 + \Delta\rho - \rho_0 \cos \Delta\theta}{\rho_0 \sin \Delta\theta}$$

or

$$\cot \alpha = \frac{\rho_0(1 - \cos \Delta\theta) + \Delta\rho}{\rho_0 \sin \Delta\theta}.$$

Let us see if we can obtain the limit (19) from this expression for cot α. We divide numerator and denominator by Δθ. Then

(21)
$$\cot \alpha = \frac{\rho_0 \dfrac{(1 - \cos \Delta\theta)}{\Delta\theta} + \dfrac{\Delta\rho}{\Delta\theta}}{\rho_0 \dfrac{\sin \Delta\theta}{\Delta\theta}}.$$

Let us now consider what happens as Δθ approaches 0. We proved in Chapter 9, Section 3 that

$$\lim_{\Delta\theta \to 0} \frac{1 - \cos \Delta\theta}{\Delta\theta} = 0 \quad \text{and} \quad \lim_{\Delta\theta \to 0} \frac{\sin \Delta\theta}{\Delta\theta} = 1.$$

Moreover, we do know from our earlier discussion that α approaches ψ as Δθ approaches *P*. Hence (21) yields

(22)
$$\cot \psi = \frac{\dot{\rho}}{\rho_0}.$$

Because this is true at any point *P* on the curve, we may drop the subscript and write

$$\cot \psi = \frac{\dot{\rho}}{\rho}$$

or

(23)
$$\tan \psi = \frac{\rho}{\dot{\rho}}.$$

Thus we have obtained a geometrical interpretation of the derivative $\dot{\rho}$

coupled with ρ as the tangent of the angle between the radius vector and the tangent line at a point P on the curve.

A few points should be noted in connection with (23). The first is that there are two angles between the radius vector and the tangent, one being the supplement of the other (Figs. 17-20*a* and 17-20*b*). We shall see that the angle that formula (23) gives is the counterclockwise angle from the radius OP to the tangent at P. We suppose that we use positive ρ-values; moreover, if ρ increases as θ does, then $\dot{\rho}$ is positive (or 0 in exceptional cases). Thus the right side of (23) is positive and ψ must be acute. This is the case in Fig. 17-20*a*. If ρ decreases as θ increases, then $\dot{\rho}$ is negative (or 0 in exceptional cases), and so tan ψ is negative and ψ must be obtuse. As Fig. 17-20*b* shows, ψ is obtuse in this case.

Figure 17-20

The second point to note about (23) is that although the proof does not hold for a point P at which $\rho = 0$, because triangle OPQ of Fig. 17-19 does not exist in this case, the result does hold. For one can regard the radius vector (Fig. 17-21) at point O as the limiting vector of the radius vector OQ as Q approaches 0. But the tangent at O is also the limiting position of OQ as Q approaches 0. Hence one can regard the radius vector and the tangent as having the same direction at O, and therefore the angle ψ between them is 0. This is what (23) gives when $\rho = 0$.

Figure 17-21

Our efforts to find a geometrical meaning for $\dot{\rho}$ have led to formula (23), which gives the angle between the radius vector and the tangent. However, one may want the slope of the tangent because, as we know from earlier applications, this slope is an important quantity. In Fig. 17-22*a* we see that ϕ is the angle of inclination of the tangent with respect to the polar axis and that $\phi = \theta + \psi$. Then the slope of the tangent line is

(24) $$\tan \phi = \tan (\theta + \psi).$$

However, the relation $\phi = \theta + \psi$ does not always hold, as Figs. 17-22*b* and

Polar axis

(*a*)

Polar axis

(*b*)

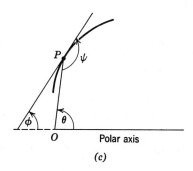

Polar axis

(*c*)

Figure 17-22

17-22*c* show. In these figures $\theta = \phi + \pi - \psi$, and so $\phi = \theta + \psi - \pi$.
But (24) holds in these cases also. Still other geometrical configurations do
obtain, because θ can be arbitrarily large. However, (24) does hold in all
cases.

This last statement is true even when the curve passes through the pole.
Here $\psi = 0$, as we pointed out in connection with Fig. 17-21, and so $\phi = \theta$.
The value of θ at point O is that value (or values) for which $\rho = 0$, that is,
it is the value (or values) of θ which, when substituted in the polar coordinate
equation of the curve, yields $\rho = 0$.

Because (24) holds for the various possible relations among ϕ, θ, and ψ,
we now have a method of finding the slope of a curve whose equation is given

in polar coordinates. We have from (24), in view of a trigonometric identity,
that

(25) $$\tan \phi = \frac{\tan \theta + \tan \psi}{1 - \tan \theta \tan \psi}.$$

If, therefore, we wish to find the slope of a curve at a given point whose
θ-value is known, we know $\tan \theta$ and by using (23) we have $\tan \psi$. Formula
(25) then gives the slope.

Exercises

1. Find the slope of $\rho = 10 \cos \theta$ at $\theta = 30°$.   *Ans.* $-\sqrt{3}/3$.

2. The curve $\rho = ce^{a\theta}$ is called an equiangular spiral (or logarithmic spiral), because
the angle between the radius vector and the tangent is the same at all points on
the curve. Prove this fact.

3. Prove the converse of the statement in Exercise 2.

4. Find the angle between the radius vector and the tangent for the curve $\rho = a(1 - \cos \theta)$ at $(a, \pi/2)$. Also find the angle of inclination of this tangent. Sketch
the curve to see the correct relation among ψ, θ, and ϕ.

Ans. $\psi = \pi/4$; $\phi = 3\pi/4$.

5. Find the angle between the radius vector and the tangent at the point indicated
for each of the following curves:

(*a*) $\rho = 10$ at $(10, \pi/2)$.   *Ans.* $\pi/2$.

(*b*) $\rho = a \sin \theta$ at $(a/2, \pi/6)$.

(*d*) $\rho = \dfrac{6}{2 + \sin \theta}$ at $(2, \pi/2)$.

(*c*) $\rho = \dfrac{6}{1 - \cos \theta}$ at $(4, 2\pi/3)$.

Ans. $5\pi/6$.

6. Prove the reflection property for the parabola (cf. Chapter 4, Section 4); that is,
prove that for the curve $\rho = p/(1 - \cos \theta)$ the radius vector OP (or FP) and the
horizontal line PD make equal angles with the tangent at P, P being any point on
the curve (Fig. 17-23).

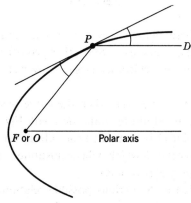

Figure 17-23

7. Given the ellipse $\rho = ep/(1 - e \cos \theta)$ with $0 < e < 1$, what would you expect ψ to be at the end points of the major axis? Calculate ψ.

8. Show for any $\rho = f(\theta)$ that ψ is $\pi/2$ at a maximum or minimum value of ρ.

9. Show that the length d of the perpendicular from the pole to a tangent of $\rho = f(\theta)$ at a point P is given by $\rho^2/\sqrt{\rho^2 + \dot\rho^2}$, where ρ and $\dot\rho$ are the values at P.

6. *Areas in Polar Coordinates.* One of the advantages of the polar coordinate representation of curves is that it may be used to find the areas of some regions far more easily than if the same area were described in terms of rectangular coordinates. The shape of areas that are most readily handled in polar coordinates is exemplified by that of OPQ in Fig. 17-24; this region is bounded by the radii vectors OP and OQ and by the arc PQ of some curve.

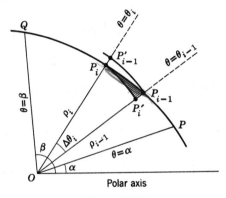

Figure 17-24

The procedure for setting up an integral that yields the area OPQ is very much like that used for areas in rectangular coordinates. The independent variable here is θ and the domain over which it extends is from α to β; that is, $\theta = \alpha$ is the equation of OP and $\theta = \beta$ is the equation of OQ. We divide the domain $\alpha \leq \theta \leq \beta$ into n subintervals, which we may as well take to be equal. The values of θ that are selected to subdivide the domain are $\theta_0 = \alpha$, $\theta_1, \theta_2 \cdots \theta_n = \beta$. A typical subinterval $\Delta\theta_i$, which is determined by the end values $\theta = \theta_{i-1}$ and $\theta = \theta_i$, is shown in Fig. 17-24. The equations $\theta = \theta_{i-1}$ and $\theta = \theta_i$ are also the equations of the radii vectors which along with the arc $P_{i-1}P_i$ bound the ith subregion ΔA_i into which the area OPQ is subdivided.

If we could find a suitable expression for the area of these subregions, then by summing them we would have the area of the entire region OPQ. Unfortunately, we do not have an exact expression for the area of any one of these subregions. If, however, we draw a circle with OP_i as radius and let P_i' be the point at which the circle cuts OP_{i-1}, we have the circular sector OP_iP_i', which is an approximation to ΔA_i. The approximation fails to include the shaded area in ΔA_i. Such circular sectors are analogous to the

Figure 17-25

rectangles that we used to approximate the area under a curve when rectangular coordinates were involved.

The area of a circular sector (Fig. 17-25) of a circle of radius r and central angle θ (in radians) is given by

(26) $\tfrac{1}{2}r^2\theta,$

for the area of the entire circle is πr^2 and the area of the sector is to the area of the entire circle as θ is to 2π, if θ is expressed in radians. Then the area of the sector is

$$\frac{\theta}{2\pi} \cdot \pi r^2 = \tfrac{1}{2}r^2\theta.$$

If we apply (26) to express the area of the circular sector OP_iP_i' we obtain

(27) $\tfrac{1}{2}(OP_i)^2 \, \Delta\theta_i$ or $\tfrac{1}{2}\rho_i{}^2 \, \Delta\theta_i$

where ρ_i is the ρ-value of OP_i. Then the sum of the n approximating subregions is

(28) $S_n = \tfrac{1}{2}\rho_1{}^2 \, \Delta\theta_1 + \tfrac{1}{2}\rho_2{}^2 \, \Delta\theta_2 + \cdots + \tfrac{1}{2}\rho_n{}^2 \, \Delta\theta_n.$

It is intuitively clear that as $\Delta\theta$ approaches 0, the area of the circular sector OP_iP_i' approaches the area ΔA_i of the ith subregion. Hence what we want is

$$\lim_{n \to \infty} S_n.$$

We know from our work on the definite integral that this limit is given by

(29) $A = \displaystyle\int_\alpha^\beta \tfrac{1}{2}\rho^2 \, d\theta$

where ρ is the function of θ which describes the curve PQ. Thus we have in (29) a formula for the area OPQ.

Before we apply formula (29), we might satisfy ourselves that we were wise to use the circular sector OP_iP_i' as the approximation to the subregion ΔA_i. We did point out in Chapter 15, Section 7, that failure to use a proper approximating element can lead to the wrong result. We can assure ourselves of the correctness of our choice in several ways. Instead of using the sector OP_iP_i' we might use the sector $OP_{i-1}P_{i-1}'$ (Fig. 17-24) determined by the radius vector OP_{i-1}. The area of this sector is

(30) $\tfrac{1}{2}\rho_{i-1}^2 \, \Delta\theta_i$

where ρ_{i-1} is the length of OP_{i-1}. This circular sector is larger than the area ΔA_i because ρ_{i-1} is the largest value of ρ in $\Delta\theta_i$, whereas in (27) ρ_i is the smallest ρ-value in $\Delta\theta_i$. In our study of the definite integral we found that either choice will lead to the same definite integral. Because the true area lies between what we obtain by using the smallest ρ-value in each subinterval and the largest ρ-value and because both choices lead to the same definite integral, namely (29), the true area must also be given by this definite integral.

Alternatively, we could have argued that between ρ_i, which is too small, and ρ_{i-1}, which is too large, there must be some value $\bar{\rho}_i$ which, if chosen as the radius of a circular sector, would give us exactly the area ΔA_i. Then the sum

$$S_n = \tfrac{1}{2}\bar{\rho}_1{}^2 \,\Delta\theta_2 + \tfrac{1}{2}\bar{\rho}_2{}^2 \,\Delta\theta_2 + \cdots + \tfrac{1}{2}\bar{\rho}_n{}^2 \,\Delta\theta_n$$

would be correct, although of course we would not know how large $\bar{\rho}_i$ is. However, this sum also leads to the definite integral (29) because any choice of a ρ-value in each $\Delta\theta_i$ leads to the same integral.

Let us now apply (29) and let us consider, first, finding the area of the circle $\rho = 10 \cos \theta$ shown in Fig. 17-26. To use formula (29), we must know the end values of the domain of θ-values which belong to the area in question. The upper half of this curve is described as θ varies from 0 to $\pi/2$. The lower half can be obtained by letting θ run from $\pi/2$ to π while ρ takes on negative values. Alternatively, the lower half of the curve is described by letting θ vary from $-\pi/2$ to 0, while ρ takes on positive values. Hence we can use either of the two integrals,

$$\int_0^\pi \tfrac{1}{2}(10 \cos \theta)^2 \, d\theta \quad \text{or} \quad \int_{-\pi/2}^{\pi/2} \tfrac{1}{2}(10 \cos \theta)^2 \, d\theta.$$

To evaluate either of these we, of course, use antidifferentiation. Both lead to the correct result, namely 25π, for the radius of the circle is 5.

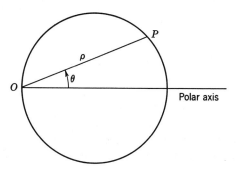

Figure 17-26

As a second example let us consider the curve whose equation is $\rho^2 = 4 \sin 2\theta$. This curve (Fig. 17-27) is called a lemniscate. Our problem is to find the area within the two loops. Actually, the two loops contain the same area; hence we shall find the area within the upper loop. We must determine the range of θ-values which belong to points on this loop. These points are

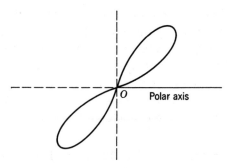

Figure 17-27

obtained as θ varies from 0 to $\pi/2$. Hence the area of this loop is

$$\tfrac{1}{2}\int_0^{\pi/2} 4\sin 2\theta \; d\theta.$$

This area is readily obtained and proves to be 2. Hence the area of both loops is 4.

Exercises

1. Find the area enclosed by the cardioid $\rho = a(1 - \sin\theta)$. The curve of this equation is shown in Fig. 17-28.   *Ans.* $3\pi a^2/2$.

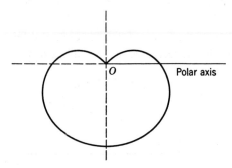

Figure 17-28

2. Find the area bounded by one loop of the lemniscate $\rho^2 = a\cos 2\theta$.

3. Find the area between the parabola $\rho = 8/(1 - \cos\theta)$ and its latus rectum.
                                                                         Ans. 128/3.

4. Find the area between the parabola $\rho = 8/(1 + \cos\theta)$ and the vertical line through the pole.   *Ans.* 128/3.

5. The curve $\rho = a\theta$ is called the spiral of Archimedes. Graph the curve and then find the area swept out by the radius vector in the following number of revolutions:

   (*a*) One revolution.   *Ans.* $4\pi^3 a^2/3$.

   (*b*) Two revolutions.

Archimedes (287–212B.C.) actually calculated these areas by using the Greek method of exhaustion and the same approximating elements that we used.

6. Find the area swept out by the radius vector of the equiangular spiral $\rho = ce^\theta$ in (*a*) one revolution, (*b*) two revolutions.

7. Find the area between the two circles $\rho = 2a \cos \theta$ and $\rho = a$.

Ans. $(a^2/2)[(5\pi/3) - \sqrt{3}]$.

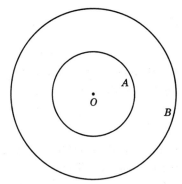

8. Criticize the following argument. Suppose that A and B are two concentric circular areas (Fig. 17-29) and that the radius of B is twice the radius of A. The area of A is the sum of its radii and the same is true of B. Because the radii of B are twice as long as the radii of A, the area of B is twice the area of A.

Figure 17-29

7. Arc Length in Polar Coordinates. Just as it may be more convenient to use polar coordinates to find some areas bounded entirely or in part by curves, so it is to find arc lengths of some curves. Our first task is to find the proper expression for arc length in the polar coordinate representation. Suppose that we have the arc $APQB$ of a curve (Fig. 17-30) and that we wish to find the length of this arc.

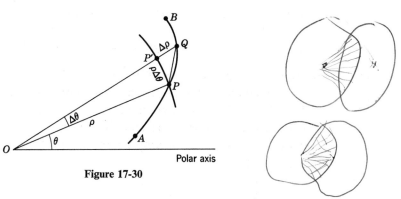

Figure 17-30

Our method of obtaining arc length is to find the sum of inscribed chords and then let the number of these chords become infinite while each approaches zero in size (Chapter 15, Section 4). Let PQ in Fig. 17-30 be a typical chord. We should now try to find an expression for it in terms of ρ and θ. Suppose that, as in our treatment of area, we draw a circle with OP as radius. This circle cuts OQ in P'. Now the figure $PP'Q$ is almost a right triangle. Certainly, the arc PP' cuts the radius OP' at right angles but, of course, the arc PP' is not a line segment. Nevertheless, let us suppose for a moment that it is; for small $\Delta\theta$, the arc PP' and the chord PP' will not differ very much. Then we can apply the Pythagorean theorem to triangle $PP'Q$ and assert that

$$PQ^2 = (\rho\,\Delta\theta)^2 + (\Delta\rho)^2$$

or

(31)
$$PQ = \sqrt{\rho^2 + \frac{\Delta\rho^2}{\Delta\theta}}\,\Delta\theta.$$

We may now apply the same theorem that we used in the treatment of arc length in rectangular coordinates, namely, the theorem of the mean. According to this theorem

$$\frac{\Delta\rho}{\Delta\theta} = \dot\rho_i$$

where $\dot\rho_i$ is the derivative of ρ as a function of θ taken at some value of θ in the interval $\Delta\theta$. Then

(32)
$$PQ = \sqrt{\rho^2 + \dot\rho_i^2}\,\Delta\theta.$$

We now have an expression for the chord PQ. According to our method of obtaining arc length, we form a sum S_n of such chords and then let $\Delta\theta$ approach 0 so that each chord approaches 0 in length while the number of chords required to fill out the arc from A to B becomes infinite. The arc length from A to B is given by

$$\lim_{n\to\infty} S_n;$$

this limit is expressed by a definite integral, namely,

(33)
$$\text{arc length } AB = \int_\alpha^\beta \sqrt{\rho^2 + \dot\rho^2}\,d\theta$$

where α and β are the values of θ at A and B, respectively.

The derivation of (33) was based on an approximation; we took triangle QPP' in Fig. 17-30 to be a right triangle even though PP' is an arc of a circle. Let us now see if a more accurate approach will yield the same result. Suppose that (Fig. 17-31) we drop a perpendicular from P onto OQ and now

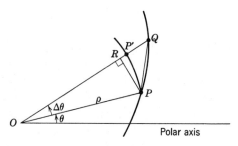

Figure 17-31

actually have a right triangle PQR. Then

(34) $$\overline{PQ}^2 = \overline{PR}^2 + \overline{QR}^2.$$

We see from the figure that

$$PR = \rho \sin \Delta\theta$$

and

$$QR = QO - RO = \rho + \Delta\rho - \rho \cos \Delta\theta.$$

If we substitute these values in (34), we obtain

$$\overline{PQ}^2 = \rho^2 \sin {}^2 \Delta\theta + \{(\rho + \Delta\rho) - \rho \cos \Delta\theta)\}^2.$$

Then, by expanding the binomial in which $\rho + \Delta\rho$ is treated as a single term,

$$\overline{PQ}^2 = \rho^2 \sin^2 \Delta\theta + (\rho + \Delta\rho)^2 - 2\rho(\rho + \Delta\rho) \cos \Delta\theta + \rho^2 \cos^2 \Delta\theta.$$

The first and last terms on the right side amount to just ρ^2. Hence, after further squaring and multiplying, we obtain

$$\overline{PQ}^2 = \rho^2 + \rho^2 + 2\rho\,\Delta\rho + (\Delta\rho)^2 - 2\rho^2 \cos \Delta\theta - 2\rho\,\Delta\rho \cos \Delta\theta$$

or

$$\overline{PQ}^2 = 2\rho^2(1 - \cos \Delta\theta) + 2\rho\,\Delta\rho(1 - \cos \Delta\theta) + (\Delta\rho)^2$$

or

(35) $\quad PQ = \{2\rho^2(1 - \cos \Delta\theta) + 2\rho\,\Delta\rho(1 - \cos \Delta\theta) + (\Delta\rho)^2\}^{\frac{1}{2}}.$

We would like to put this result for the element of arc in the form of a function of θ times $\Delta\theta$ so that we could see what the sum of the elements and the limit of this sum should be; that is, we should look for something of the form (32) and, in fact, we hope to show that (32) is correct. Let us multiply the right side of (35) by $\Delta\theta$ and divide inside the square root by $(\Delta\theta)^2$. Then

(36) $\quad PQ = \left\{ 2\rho^2 \dfrac{(1 - \cos \Delta\theta)}{(\Delta\theta)^2} + 2\rho \dfrac{\Delta\rho}{\Delta\theta} \dfrac{(1 - \cos \Delta\theta)}{\Delta\theta} + \left(\dfrac{\Delta\rho}{\Delta\theta}\right)^2 \right\}^{\frac{1}{2}} \Delta\theta.$

The use of the mean value theorem enables us to replace the third term on the right by $\dot\rho_i^2$, as we did in obtaining (32). As for the second term on the right, the factor $\Delta\rho/\Delta\theta$ may likewise be replaced by $\dot\rho_i$. However, the fraction $(1 - \cos \Delta\theta)/\Delta\theta$ approaches 0 as $\Delta\theta$ does, and so the whole term does. We found in Chapter 15, Section 7, that we can neglect in a summation process any term which (apart from $\Delta\theta$) approaches 0. Hence we shall ignore this second term. There remains the term

$$2\rho^2 \frac{(1 - \cos \Delta\theta)}{(\Delta\theta)^2}.$$

If the denominator were $\Delta\theta$, this term too would approach 0 when $\Delta\theta$ does and we could ignore it. However, the denominator is $(\Delta\theta)^2$. Let us use the trigonometric identity

$$1 - \cos\theta = 2\sin^2\frac{\theta}{2}.$$

Then

$$2\rho^2\frac{(1-\cos\Delta\theta)}{(\Delta\theta)^2} = \frac{4\rho^2\sin^2\dfrac{\Delta\theta}{2}}{(\Delta\theta)^2} = \rho^2\frac{\sin^2\dfrac{\Delta\theta}{2}}{\left(\dfrac{\Delta\theta}{2}\right)^2}$$

$$= \rho^2\frac{\sin\dfrac{\Delta\theta}{2}}{\dfrac{\Delta\theta}{2}}\frac{\sin\dfrac{\Delta\theta}{2}}{\dfrac{\Delta\theta}{2}}.$$

We may replace this term by ρ^2 because the difference

$$\rho^2 - \rho^2\frac{\sin\dfrac{\Delta\theta}{2}}{\dfrac{\Delta\theta}{2}}\frac{\sin\dfrac{\Delta\theta}{2}}{\dfrac{\Delta\theta}{2}}$$

approaches 0 as $\Delta\theta$ approaches 0, and we found in Chapter 15, Section 7, that if a term of the summation (apart from the factor $\Delta\theta$ itself) approaches 0, it does not contribute to the limit of the sum.

The substance, then, of our consideration of three terms on the right side of (36) is that we may replace this right side by

(37) $PQ = \sqrt{\rho^2 + \dot\rho_i^{\,2}}\,\Delta\theta.$

We see that we are at the same point as (32), and thus (33) is correct.*

Exercises

1. Find by use of (33) the following:

   (a) The circumference of the circle $\rho = a$.
   (b) The circumference of the circle $\rho = 2a\sin\theta$.   *Ans.* $2\pi a$.
   (c) The length of arc of the parabola $\rho = p/(1-\cos\theta)$ from $\theta = \pi/6$ to π.
   (d) The length of arc of $\rho = e^{a\theta}$ from $\theta = 0$ to $\theta = 2\pi$.

   Ans. $\sqrt{1 + a^2}(e^{2\pi a} - 1)/a$.

   (e) The length of arc of $\rho = a\theta^2$ from $\theta = 0$ to $\theta = \pi$.

---

* There is still a point to be disposed of. In both (32) and (37) ρ and $\dot\rho_i$ are not taken at the same value of θ in the interval $\Delta\theta$. However, we know from the discussion in Chapter 15, Section 7 that this fact does not matter.

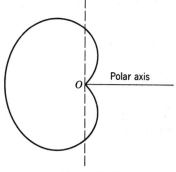

2. Find the length of the cardiod $\rho = a(1 - \cos\theta)$. See Fig. 17-32.

Ans. 8a.

Figure 17-32

3. Show that the length of arc of the equiangular spiral $\rho = ce^{a\theta}$ between any two values of θ is proportional to the increase in the radius vector between those two values of θ.

4. Show that at any point P of a curve whose equation is expressed in polar coordinates, $ds/d\theta = \rho^2/d$ where d is the perpendicular distance from the pole to the tangent at P.

5. Find the length of the complete curve $\rho = a\sin^3(\theta/3)$.   *Ans. $3\pi a/2$.*

8. *Curvature in Polar Coordinates.* In Section 5 of Chapter 15 we introduced the notion of the curvature of a curve and we found a formula for that curvature when the curve is expressed in a rectangular coordinate equation. Let us now derive the formula for curvature when the curve is represented by a polar coordinate equation.

If s is the arc length measured from some fixed point on a curve (Fig. 17-33) to any point P and if ϕ is the angle of inclination of the tangent to the

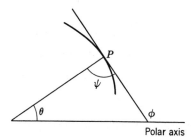

Figure 17-33

curve at P then, by definition (Chapter 15, Section 5), the curvature

(38)
$$K = \frac{d\phi}{ds}.$$

We should then start with some expression for ϕ and calculate $d\theta/ds$. We did find in Section 5 that*

$$\phi = \theta + \psi,$$

---

* The point made in Chapter 15 on the domain of ϕ-values applies here too. However, the change from the domain 180° to 90° to the domain 0° to −90° does not affect the result (39).

or where this relation does not hold, that

$$\phi = \theta + \psi - \pi.$$

In either case

(39) $$K = \frac{d\phi}{ds} = \frac{d\theta}{ds} + \frac{d\psi}{ds}.$$

To calculate $d\theta/ds$ we need but to recall that the indefinite integral for arc length is

$$s = \int \sqrt{\rho^2 + \dot{\rho}^2} \, d\theta$$

so that

$$\frac{ds}{d\theta} = \sqrt{\rho^2 + \dot{\rho}^2},$$

and by the theorem on inverse functions

(40) $$\frac{d\theta}{ds} = \frac{1}{\sqrt{\rho^2 + \dot{\rho}^2}}.$$

We have one of the two quantities that we need in (39). To calculate the second quantity, we first ask ourselves, what formula do we know for ψ? We do know that

$$\tan \psi = \frac{\rho}{\dot{\rho}}$$

or

(41) $$\psi = \tan^{-1} \frac{\rho}{\dot{\rho}}.$$

This formula really gives us ψ as a function of θ because ρ and $\dot{\rho}$ are functions of θ. However, the chain rule chains tells us that

(42) $$\frac{d\psi}{ds} = \frac{d\psi}{d\theta} \frac{d\theta}{ds}.$$

In view of (40), all we need now is $d\psi/d\theta$. From (41) we have

$$\frac{d\psi}{d\theta} = \frac{1}{1 + \left(\frac{\rho}{\dot{\rho}}\right)^2} \frac{d}{d\theta}\left(\frac{\rho}{\dot{\rho}}\right)$$

$$= \frac{\dot{\rho}^2}{\dot{\rho}^2 + \rho^2} \frac{\dot{\rho}^2 - \rho\ddot{\rho}}{\dot{\rho}^2},$$

so that

(43) $$\frac{d\psi}{d\theta} = \frac{\dot{\rho}^2 - \rho\ddot{\rho}}{\dot{\rho}^2 + \rho^2}.$$

Now, by (42) and (40),

$$(44) \qquad \frac{d\psi}{ds} = \frac{\dot{\rho}^2 - \rho\ddot{\rho}}{(\dot{\rho}^2 + \rho^2)^{\frac{3}{2}}} \, .$$

We have but to use (40) and (44) in (39). Thus

$$K = \frac{d\phi}{ds} = \frac{1}{(\rho^2 + \dot{\rho}^2)^{\frac{1}{2}}} + \frac{\dot{\rho}^2 - \rho\ddot{\rho}}{(\dot{\rho}^2 + \rho^2)^{\frac{3}{2}}}$$

or by adding fractions

$$K = \frac{\rho^2 + 2\dot{\rho}^2 - \rho\ddot{\rho}}{(\rho^2 + \dot{\rho}^2)^{\frac{3}{2}}} \, .$$

This quantity can be positive or negative, but we are usually interested in its magnitude, and so we shall not bother with the matter of signs.

Exercises

1. Find the curvature of the following:

   (*a*) The circle $\rho = a$.

   (*b*) The circle $\rho = a \sin \theta$.   *Ans.* $2/a$.

   (*c*) The equiangular spiral $\rho = ce^{a\theta}$.   *Ans.* $1/c\sqrt{1 + a^2}e^{a\theta}$.

   (*d*) The parabola $\rho = p/(1 - \cos \theta)$.

   (*e*) The spiral of Archimedes $\rho = a\theta$.   *Ans.* $(\theta^2 + 2)/a\sqrt{\theta^2 + 1}$.

   (*f*) The lemniscate $\rho^2 = 4 \sin 2\theta$.

2. Use the result of 1(*d*) to show that the curvature of a parabola is a maximum at its vertex.

3. Use the result of 1(*c*) to show that the radius of curvature at any point of the equiangular spiral is proportional to ρ.

4. Show that the curvature of the cardioid $\rho = a(1 - \cos \theta)$ is $3/4a \sin (\theta/2)$.

5. Show that the curvature of the ellipse $\rho = ep/(1 - e \cos \theta)$ with $0 < e < 1$ is a maximum at either end of the major axis.

Tables

TABLE I *Degrees to Radians*

°	Radians	′	Radians	″	Radians
1	0.01745 33	1	0.00029 09	1	0.00000 48
2	0.03490 66	2	0.00058 18	2	0.00000 97
3	0.05235 99	3	0.00087 27	3	0.00001 45
4	0.06981 32	4	0.00116 36	4	0.00001 94
5	0.08726 65	5	0.00145 44	5	0.00002 42
6	0.10471 98	6	0.00174 53	6	0.00002 91
7	0.12217 30	7	0.00203 62	7	0.00003 39
8	0.13962 63	8	0.00232 71	8	0.00003 88
9	0.15707 96	9	0.00261 80	9	0.00004 36
10	0.17453 29	10	0.00290 89	10	0.00004 85
20	0.34906 59	20	0.00581 78	20	0.00009 70
30	0.52359 88	30	0.00872 66	30	0.00014 54
40	0.69813 17	40	0.01163 55	40	0.00019 39
50	0.87266 46	50	0.01454 44	50	0.00024 24
60	1.04719 76	60	0.01745 33	60	0.00029 09
70	1.22173 05				
80	1.39626 34				
90	1.57079 63				

TABLE II *Radians to Degrees*

Radians	1.0	0.1	0.01	0.001	0.0001
1	57°17′44″.8	5°43′46″.5	0°34′22″.6	0° 3′26″.3	0°0′20″.6
2	114°35′29″.6	11°27′33″.0	1° 8′45″.3	0° 6′52″.5	0°0′41″.3
3	171°53′14″.4	17°11′19″.4	1°43′07″.9	0°10′18″.8	0°1′01″.9
4	229°10′59″.2	22°55′05″.9	2°17′30″.6	0°13′45″.1	0°1′22″.5
5	286°28′44″.0	28°38′52″.4	2°51′53″.2	0°17′11″.3	0°1′43″.1
6	343°46′28″.8	34°22′38″.9	3°26′15″.9	0°20′37″.6	0°2′03″.8
7	401° 4′13″.6	40° 6′25″.4	4° 0′38″.5	0°24′03″.9	0°2′24″.4
8	458°21′58″.4	45°50′11″.8	4°35′01″.2	0°27′30″.1	0°2′45″.0
9	515°39′43″.3	51°33′58″.3	5° 9′23″.8	0°30′56″.4	0°3′05″.6

TABLE III *Natural Trigonometric Functions*

Degrees	Radians	Sin	Cos	Tan	Cot	Sec	Csc		
0°00′	.0000	.0000	1.0000	.0000	—	1.000	—	1.5708	90°00′
10	.0029	.0029	1.0000	.0029	343.8	1.000	343.8	1.5679	50
20	.0058	.0058	1.0000	.0058	171.9	1.000	171.9	1.5650	40
30	.0087	.0087	1.0000	.0087	114.6	1.000	114.6	1.5621	30
40	.0116	.0116	.9999	.0116	85.94	1.000	85.95	1.5592	20
50	.0145	.0145	.9999	.0145	68.75	1.000	68.76	1.5563	10
1°00′	.0175	.0175	.9998	.0175	57.29	1.000	57.30	1.5533	89°00′
10	.0204	.0204	.9998	.0204	49.10	1.000	49.11	1.5504	50
20	.0233	.0233	.9997	.0233	42.96	1.000	42.98	1.5475	40
30	.0262	.0262	.9997	.0262	38.19	1.000	38.20	1.5446	30
40	.0291	.0291	.9996	.0291	34.37	1.000	34.38	1.5417	20
50	.0320	.0320	.9995	.0320	31.24	1.001	31.26	1.5388	10
2°00′	.0349	.0349	.9994	.0349	28.64	1.001	28.65	1.5359	88°00′
10	.0378	.0378	.9993	.0378	26.43	1.001	26.45	1.5330	50
20	.0407	.0407	.9992	.0407	24.54	1.001	24.56	1.5301	40
30	.0436	.0436	.9990	.0437	22.90	1.001	22.93	1.5272	30
40	.0465	.0465	.9989	.0466	21.47	1.001	21.49	1.5243	20
50	.0495	.0494	.9988	.0495	20.21	1.001	20.23	1.5213	10
3°00′	.0524	.0523	.9986	.0524	19.08	1.001	19.11	1.5184	87°00′
10	.0553	.0552	.9985	.0553	18.07	1.002	18.10	1.5155	50
20	.0582	.0581	.9983	.0582	17.17	1.002	17.20	1.5126	40
30	.0611	.0610	.9981	.0612	16.35	1.002	16.38	1.5097	30
40	.0640	.0640	.9980	.0641	15.60	1.002	15.64	1.5068	20
50	.0669	.0669	.9978	.0670	14.92	1.002	14.96	1.5039	10
4°00′	.0698	.0698	.9976	.0699	14.30	1.002	14.34	1.5010	86°00′
10	.0727	.0727	.9974	.0729	13.73	1.003	13.76	1.4981	50
20	.0756	.0756	.9971	.0758	13.20	1.003	13.23	1.4952	40
30	.0785	.0785	.9969	.0787	12.71	1.003	12.75	1.4923	30
40	.0814	.0814	.9967	.0816	12.25	1.003	12.29	1.4893	20
50	.0844	.0843	.9964	.0846	11.83	1.004	11.87	1.4864	10
5°00′	.0873	.0872	.9962	.0875	11.43	1.004	11.47	1.4835	85°00′
10	.0902	.0901	.9959	.0904	11.06	1.004	11.10	1.4806	50
20	.0931	.0929	.9957	.0934	10.71	1.004	10.76	1.4777	40
30	.0960	.0958	.9954	.0963	10.39	1.005	10.43	1.4748	30
40	.0989	.0987	.9951	.0992	10.08	1.005	10.13	1.4719	20
50	.1018	.1016	.9948	.1022	9.788	1.005	9.839	1.4690	10
6°00′	.1047	.1045	.9945	.1051	9.514	1.006	9.567	1.4661	84°00′
10	.1076	.1074	.9942	.1080	9.255	1.006	9.309	1.4632	50
20	.1105	.1103	.9939	.1110	9.010	1.006	9.065	1.4603	40
30	.1134	.1132	.9936	.1139	8.777	1.006	8.834	1.4573	30
40	.1164	.1161	.9932	.1169	8.556	1.007	8.614	1.4544	20
50	.1193	.1190	.9929	.1198	8.345	1.007	8.405	1.4515	10
7°00′	.1222	.1219	.9925	.1228	8.144	1.008	8.206	1.4486	83°00′
10	.1251	.1248	.9922	.1257	7.953	1.008	8.016	1.4457	50
20	.1280	.1276	.9918	.1287	7.770	1.008	7.834	1.4428	40
30	.1309	.1305	.9914	.1317	7.596	1.009	7.661	1.4399	30
40	.1338	.1334	.9911	.1346	7.429	1.009	7.496	1.4370	20
50	.1367	.1363	.9907	.1376	7.269	1.009	7.337	1.4341	10
8°00′	.1396	.1392	.9903	.1405	7.115	1.010	7.185	1.4312	82°00′
10	.1425	.1421	.9899	.1435	6.968	1.010	7.040	1.4283	50
		Cos	Sin	Cot	Tan	Csc	Sec	Radians	Degrees

TABLE **III** (*Continued*)

Degrees	Radians	Sin	Cos	Tan	Cot	Sec	Csc		
20	.1454	.1449	.9894	.1465	6.827	1.011	6.900	1.4254	40
30	.1484	.1478	.9890	.1495	6.691	1.011	6.765	1.4224	30
40	.1513	.1507	.9886	.1524	6.561	1.012	6.636	1.4195	20
50	.1542	.1536	.9881	.1554	6.435	1.012	6.512	1.4166	10
9°00′	.1571	.1564	.9877	.1584	6.314	1.012	6.392	1.4137	81°00′
10	.1600	.1593	.9872	.1614	6.197	1.013	6.277	1.4108	50
20	.1629	.1622	.9868	.1644	6.084	1.013	6.166	1.4079	40
30	.1658	.1650	.9863	.1673	5.976	1.014	6.059	1.4050	30
40	.1687	.1679	.9858	.1703	5.871	1.014	5.955	1.4021	20
50	.1716	.1708	.9853	.1733	5.769	1.015	5.855	1.3992	10
10°00′	.1745	.1736	.9848	.1763	5.671	1.015	5.759	1.3963	80°00′
10	.1774	.1765	.9843	.1793	5.576	1.016	5.665	1.3934	50
20	.1804	.1794	.9838	.1823	5.485	1.016	5.575	1.3904	40
30	.1833	.1822	.9833	.1853	5.396	1.017	5.487	1.3875	30
40	.1862	.1851	.9827	.1883	5.309	1.018	5.403	1.3846	20
50	.1891	.1880	.9822	.1914	5.226	1.018	5.320	1.3817	10
11°00′	.1920	.1908	.9816	.1944	5.145	1.019	5.241	1.3788	79°00′
10	.1949	.1937	.9811	.1974	5.066	1.019	5.164	1.3759	50
20	.1978	.1965	.9805	.2004	4.989	1.020	5.089	1.3730	40
30	.2007	.1994	.9799	.2035	4.915	1.020	5.016	1.3701	30
40	.2036	.2022	.9793	.2065	4.843	1.021	4.945	1.3672	20
50	.2065	.2051	.9787	.2095	4.773	1.022	4.876	1.3643	10
12°00′	.2094	.2079	.9781	.2126	4.705	1.022	4.810	1.3614	78°00′
10	.2123	.2108	.9775	.2156	4.638	1.023	4.745	1.3584	50
20	.2153	.2136	.9769	.2186	4.574	1.024	4.682	1.3555	40
30	.2182	.2164	.9763	.2217	4.511	1.024	4.620	1.3526	30
40	.2211	.2193	.9757	.2247	4.449	1.025	4.560	1.3497	20
50	.2240	.2221	.9750	.2278	4.390	1.026	4.502	1.3468	10
13°00′	.2269	.2250	.9744	.2309	4.331	1.026	4.445	1.3439	77°00′
10	.2298	.2278	.9737	.2339	4.275	1.027	4.390	1.3410	50
20	.2327	.2306	.9730	.2370	4.219	1.028	4.336	1.3381	40
30	.2356	.2334	.9724	.2401	4.165	1.028	4.284	1.3352	30
40	.2385	.2363	.9717	.2432	4.113	1.029	4.232	1.3323	20
50	.2414	.2391	.9710	.2462	4.061	1.030	4.182	1.3294	10
14°00′	.2443	.2419	.9703	.2493	4.011	1.031	4.134	1.3265	76°00′
10	.2473	.2447	.9696	.2524	3.962	1.031	4.086	1.3235	50
20	.2502	.2476	.9689	.2555	3.914	1.032	4.039	1.3206	40
30	.2531	.2504	.9681	.2586	3.867	1.033	3.994	1.3177	30
40	.2560	.2532	.9674	.2617	3.821	1.034	3.950	1.3148	20
50	.2589	.2560	.9667	.2648	3.776	1.034	3.906	1.3119	10
15°00′	.2618	.2588	.9659	.2679	3.732	1.035	3.864	1.3090	75°00′
10	.2647	.2616	.9652	.2711	3.689	1.036	3.822	1.3061	50
20	.2676	.2644	.9644	.2742	3.647	1.037	3.782	1.3032	40
30	.2705	.2672	.9636	.2773	3.606	1.038	3.742	1.3003	30
40	.2734	.2700	.9628	.2805	3.566	1.039	3.703	1.2974	20
50	.2763	.2728	.9621	.2836	3.526	1.039	3.665	1.2945	10
16°00′	.2793	.2756	.9613	.2867	3.487	1.040	3.628	1.2915	74°00′
10	.2822	.2784	.9605	.2899	3.450	1.041	3.592	1.2886	50
20	.2851	.2812	.9596	.2931	3.412	1.042	3.556	1.2857	40
30	.2880	.2840	.9588	.2962	3.376	1.043	3.521	1.2828	30
		Cos	Sin	Cot	Tan	Csc	Sec	Radians	Degrees

TABLE III   (*Continued*)

Degrees	Radians	Sin	Cos	Tan	Cot	Sec	Csc		
40	.2909	.2868	.9580	.2994	3.340	1.044	3.487	1.2799	20
50	.2938	.2896	.9572	.3026	3.305	1.045	3.453	1.2770	10
17°00′	.2967	.2924	.9563	.3057	3.271	1.046	3.420	1.2741	73°00′
10	.2996	.2952	.9555	.3089	3.237	1.047	3.388	1.2712	50
20	.3025	.2979	.9546	.3121	3.204	1.048	3.356	1.2683	40
30	.3054	.3007	.9537	.3153	3.172	1.049	3.326	1.2654	30
40	.3083	.3035	.9528	.3185	3.140	1.049	3.295	1.2625	20
50	.3113	.3062	.9520	.3217	3.108	1.050	3.265	1.2595	10
18°00′	.3142	.3090	.9511	.3249	3.078	1.051	3.236	1.2566	72°00′
10	.3171	.3118	.9502	.3281	3.047	1.052	3.207	1.2537	50
20	.3200	.3145	.9492	.3314	3.018	1.053	3.179	1.2508	40
30	.3229	.3173	.9483	.3346	2.989	1.054	3.152	1.2479	30
40	.3258	.3201	.9474	.3378	2.960	1.056	3.124	1.2450	20
50	.3287	.3228	.9465	.3411	2.932	1.057	3.098	1.2421	10
19°00′	.3316	.3256	.9455	.3443	2.904	1.058	3.072	1.2392	71°00′
10	.3345	.3283	.9446	.3476	2.877	1.059	3.046	1.2363	50
20	.3374	.3311	.9436	.3508	2.850	1.060	3.021	1.2334	40
30	.3403	.3338	.9426	.3541	2.824	1.061	2.996	1.2305	30
40	.3432	.3365	.9417	.3574	2.798	1.062	2.971	1.2275	20
50	.3462	.3393	.9407	.3607	2.773	1.063	2.947	1.2246	10
20°00′	.3491	.3420	.9397	.3640	2.747	1.064	2.924	1.2217	70°00′
10	.3520	.3448	.9387	.3673	2.723	1.065	2.901	1.2188	50
20	.3549	.3475	.9377	.3706	2.699	1.066	2.878	1.2159	40
30	.3578	.3502	.9367	.3739	2.675	1.068	2.855	1.2130	30
40	.3607	.3529	.9356	.3772	2.651	1.069	2.833	1.2101	20
50	.3636	.3557	.9346	.3805	2.628	1.070	2.812	1.2072	10
21°00′	.3665	.3584	.9336	.3839	2.605	1.071	2.790	1.2043	69°00′
10	.3694	.3611	.9325	.3872	2.583	1.072	2.769	1.2014	50
20	.3723	.3638	.9315	.3906	2.560	1.074	2.749	1.1985	40
30	.3752	.3665	.9304	.3939	2.539	1.075	2.729	1.1956	30
40	.3782	.3692	.9293	.3973	2.517	1.076	2.709	1.1926	20
50	.3811	.3719	.9283	.4006	2.496	1.077	2.689	1.1897	10
22°00′	.3840	.3746	.9272	.4040	2.475	1.079	2.669	1.1868	68°00′
10	.3869	.3773	.9261	.4074	2.455	1.080	2.650	1.1839	50
20	.3898	.3800	.9250	.4108	2.434	1.081	2.632	1.1810	40
30	.3927·	.3827	.9239	.4142	2.414	1.082	2.613	1.1781	30
40	.3956	.3854	.9228	.4176	2.394	1.084	2.595	1.1752	20
50	.3985	.3881	.9216	.4210	2.375	1.085	2.577	1.1723	10
23°00′	.4014	.3907	.9205	.4245	2.356	1.086	2.559	1.1694	67°00′
10	.4043	.3934	.9194	.4279	2.337	1.088	2.542	1.1665	50
20	.4072	.3961	.9182	.4314	2.318	1.089	2.525	1.1636	40
30	.4102	.3987	.9171	.4348	2.300	1.090	2.508	1.1606	30
40	.4131	.4014	.9159	.4383	2.282	1.092	2.491	1.1577	20
50	.4160	.4041	.9147	.4417	2.264	1.093	2.475	1.1548	10
24°00′	.4189	.4067	.9135	.4452	2.246	1.095	2.459	1.1519	66°00′
10	.4218	.4094	.9124	.4487	2.229	1.096	2.443	1.1490	50
20	.4247	.4120	.9112	.4522	2.211	1.097	2.427	1.1461	40
30	.4276	.4147	.9100	.4557	2.194	1.099	2.411	1.1432	30
40	.4305	.4173	.9088	.4592	2.177	1.100	2.396	1.1403	20
50	.4334	.4200	.9075	.4628	2.161	1.102	2.381	1.1374	10
		Cos	Sin	Cot	Tan	Csc	Sec	Radians	Degrees

TABLE III (*Continued*)

Degrees	Radians	Sin	Cos	Tan	Cot	Sec	Csc		
25°00′	.4363	.4226	.9063	.4663	2.145	1.103	2.366	1.1345	65°00′
10	.4392	.4253	.9051	.4699	2.128	1.105	2.352	1.1316	50
20	.4422	.4279	.9038	.4734	2.112	1.106	2.337	1.1286	40
30	.4451	.4305	.9026	.4770	2.097	1.108	2.323	1.1257	30
40	.4480	.4331	.9013	.4806	2.081	1.109	2.309	1.1228	20
50	.4509	.4358	.9001	.4841	2.066	1.111	2.295	1.1199	10
26°00′	.4538	.4384	.8988	.4877	2.050	1.113	2.281	1.1170	64°00′
10	.4567	.4410	.8975	.4913	2.035	1.114	2.268	1.1141	50
20	.4596	.4436	.8962	.4950	2.020	1.116	2.254	1.1112	40
30	.4625	.4462	.8949	.4986	2.006	1.117	2.241	1.1083	30
40	.4654	.4488	.8936	.5022	1.991	1.119	2.228	1.1054	20
50	.4683	.4514	.8923	.5059	1.977	1.121	2.215	1.1025	10
27°00′	.4712	.4540	.8910	.5095	1.963	1.122	2.203	1.0996	63°00′
10	.4741	.4566	.8897	.5132	1.949	1.124	2.190	1.0966	50
20	.4771	.4592	.8884	.5169	1.935	1.126	2.178	1.0937	40
30	.4800	.4617	.8870	.5206	1.921	1.127	2.166	1.0908	30
40	.4829	.4643	.8857	.5243	1.907	1.129	2.154	1.0879	20
50	.4858	.4669	.8843	.5280	1.894	1.131	2.142	1.0850	10
28°00′	.4887	.4695	.8829	.5317	1.881	1.133	2.130	1.0821	62°00′
10	.4916	.4720	.8816	.5354	1.868	1.134	2.118	1.0792	50
20	.4945	.4746	.8802	.5392	1.855	1.136	2.107	1.0763	40
30	.4974	.4772	.8788	.5430	1.842	1.138	2.096	1.0734	30
40	.5003	.4797	.8774	.5467	1.829	1.140	2.085	1.0705	20
50	.5032	.4823	.8760	.5505	1.816	1.142	2.074	1.0676	10
29°00′	.5061	.4848	.8746	.5543	1.804	1.143	2.063	1.0647	61°00′
10	.5091	.4874	.8732	.5581	1.792	1.145	2.052	1.0617	50
20	.5120	.4899	.8718	.5619	1.780	1.147	2.041	1.0588	40
30	.5149	.4924	.8704	.5658	1.767	1.149	2.031	1.0559	30
40	.5178	.4950	.8689	.5696	1.756	1.151	2.020	1.0530	20
50	.5207	.4975	.8675	.5735	1.744	1.153	2.010	1.0501	10
30°00′	.5236	.5000	.8660	.5774	1.732	1.155	2.000	1.0472	60°00′
10	.5265	.5025	.8646	.5812	1.720	1.157	1.990	1.0443	50
20	.5294	.5050	.8631	.5851	1.709	1.159	1.980	1.0414	40
30	.5323	.5075	.8616	.5890	1.698	1.161	1.970	1.0385	30
40	.5325	.5100	.8601	.5930	1.686	1.163	1.961	1.0356	20
50	.5381	.5125	.8587	.5969	1.675	1.165	1.951	1.0327	10
31°00′	.5411	.5150	.8572	.6009	1.664	1.167	1.942	1.0297	59°00′
10	.5440	.5175	.8557	.6048	1.653	1.169	1.932	1.0268	50
20	.5469	.5200	.8542	.6088	1.643	1.171	1.923	1.0239	40
30	.5498	.5225	.8526	.6128	1.632	1.173	1.914	1.0210	30
40	.5527	.5250	.8511	.6168	1.621	1.175	1.905	1.0181	20
50	.5556	.5275	.8496	.6208	1.611	1.177	1.896	1.0152	10
32°00′	.5585	.5299	.8480	.6249	1.600	1.179	1.887	1.0123	58°00′
10	.5614	.5324	.8465	.6289	1.590	1.181	1.878	1.0094	50
20	.5643	.5348	.8450	.6330	1.580	1.184	1.870	1.0065	40
30	.5672	.5373	.8434	.6371	1.570	1.186	1.861	1.0036	30
40	.5701	.5398	.8418	.6412	1.560	1.188	1.853	1.0007	20
50	.5730	.5422	.8403	.6453	1.550	1.190	1.844	.0977	10
33°00′	.5760	.5446	.8387	.6494	1.540	1.192	1.836	.9948	57°00′
10	.5789	.5471	.8371	.6536	1.530	1.195	1.828	.9919	50
		Cos	Sin	Cot	Tan	Csc	Sec	Radians	Degrees

TABLE III (*Continued*)

Degrees	Radians	Sin	Cos	Tan	Cot	Sec	Csc		
20	.5818	.5495	.8355	.6577	1.520	1.197	1.820	.9890	40
30	.5847	.5519	.8339	.6619	1.511	1.199	1.812	.9861	30
40	.5876	.5544	.8323	.6661	1.501	1.202	1.804	.9832	20
50	.5905	.5568	.8307	.6703	1.492	1.204	1.796	.9803	10
34°00′	.5934	.5592	.8290	.6745	1.483	1.206	1.788	.9774	56°00′
10	.5963	.5616	.8274	.6787	1.473	1.209	1.781	.9745	50
20	.5992	.5640	.8258	.6830	1.464	1.211	1.773	.9716	40
30	.6021	.5664	.8241	.6873	1.455	1.213	1.766	.9687	30
40	.6050	.5688	.8225	.6916	1.446	1.216	1.758	.9657	20
50	.6080	.5712	.8208	.6959	1.437	1.218	1.751	.9628	10
35°00′	.6109	.5736	.8192	.7002	1.428	1.221	1.743	.9599	55°00′
10	.6138	.5760	.8175	.7046	1.419	1.223	1.736	.9570	50
20	.6167	.5783	.8158	.7089	1.411	1.226	1.729	.9541	40
30	.6196	.5807	.8141	.7133	1.402	1.228	1.722	.9512	30
40	.6225	.5831	.8124	.7177	1.393	1.231	1.715	.9483	20
50	.6254	.5854	.8107	.7221	1.385	1.233	1.708	.9454	10
36°00′	.6283	.5878	.8090	.7265	1.376	1.236	1.701	.9425	54°00′
10	.6312	.5901	.8073	.7310	1.368	1.239	1.695	.9396	50
20	.6341	.5925	.8056	.7355	1.360	1.241	1.688	.9367	40
30	.6370	.5948	.8039	.7400	1.351	1.244	1.681	.9338	30
40	.6400	.5972	.8021	.7445	1.343	1.247	1.675	.9308	20
50	.6429	.5995	.8004	.7490	1.335	1.249	1.668	.9279	10
37°00′	.6458	.6018	.7986	.7536	1.327	1.252	1.662	.9250	53°00′
10	.6487	.6041	.7969	.7581	1.319	1.255	1.655	.9221	50
20	.6516	.6065	.7951	.7627	1.311	1.258	1.649	.9192	40
30	.6545	.6088	.7934	.7673	1.303	1.260	1.643	.9163	30
40	.6574	.6111	.7916	.7720	1.295	1.263	1.636	.9134	20
50	.6603	.6134	.7898	.7766	1.288	1.266	1.630	.9105	10
38°00′	.6632	.6157	.7880	.7813	1.280	1.269	1.624	.9076	52°00′
10	.6661	.6180	.7862	.7860	1.272	1.272	1.618	.9047	50
20	.6690	.6202	.7844	.7907	1.265	1.275	1.612	.9018	40
30	.6720	.6225	.7826	.7954	1.257	1.278	1.606	.8988	30
40	.6749	.6248	.7808	.8002	1.250	1.281	1.601	.8959	20
50	.6778	.6271	.7790	.8050	1.242	1.284	1.595	.8930	10
39°00′	.6807	.6293	.7771	.8098	1.235	1.287	1.589	.8901	51°00′
10	.6836	.6316	.7753	.8146	1.228	1.290	1.583	.8872	50
20	.6865	.6338	.7735	.8195	1.220	1.293	1.578	.8843	40
30	.6894	.6361	.7716	.8243	1.213	1.296	1.572	.8814	30
40	.6923	.6383	.7698	.8292	1.206	1.299	1.567	.8785	20
50	.6952	.6406	.7679	.8342	1.199	1.302	1.561	.8756	10
40°00′	.6981	.6428	.7660	.8391	1.192	1.305	1.556	.8727	50°00′
10	.7010	.6450	.7642	.8441	1.185	1.309	1.550	.8698	50
20	.7039	.6472	.7623	.8491	1.178	1.312	1.545	.8668	40
30	.7069	.6494	.7604	.8541	1.171	1.315	1.540	.8639	30
40	.7098	.6517	.7585	.8591	1.164	1.318	1.535	.8610	20
50	.7127	.6539	.7566	.8642	1.157	1.322	1.529	.8581	10
41°00′	.7156	.6561	.7547	.8693	1.150	1.325	1.524	.8552	49°00′
10	.7185	.6583	.7528	.8744	1.144	1.328	1.519	.8523	50
20	.7214	.6604	.7509	.8796	1.137	1.332	1.514	.8494	40
30	.7243	.6626	.7490	.8847	1.130	1.335	1.509	.8465	30
		Cos	Sin	Cot	Tan	Csc	Sec	Radians	Degrees

TABLE III (*Continued*)

Degrees	Radians	Sin	Cos	Tan	Cot	Sec	Csc		
40	.7272	.6648	.7470	.8899	1.124	1.339	1.504	.8436	20
50	.7301	.6670	,7451	.8952	1.117	1.342	1.499	.8407	10
42°00′	.7330	.6691	.7431	.9004	1.111	1.346	1.494	.8378	48°00′
10	.7359	.6713	.7412	.9057	1.104	1.349	1.490	.8348	50
20	.7389	.6734	.7392	.9110	1.098	1.353	1.485	.8319	40
30	.7418	.6756	.7373	.9163	1.091	1.356	1.480	.8290	30
40	.7447	.6777	.7353	.9217	1.085	1.360	1.476	.8261	20
50	.7476	.6799	.7333	.9271	1.079	1.364	1.471	.8232	10
43°00′	.7505	.6820	.7314	.9325	1.072	1.367	1.466	.8203	47°00′
10	.7534	.6841	.7294	.9380	1.066	1.371	1.462	.8174	50
20	.7563	.6862	.7274	.9435	1.060	1.375	1.457	.8145	40
30	.7592	.6884	.7254	.9490	1.054	1.379	1.453	.8116	30
40	.7621	.6905	.7234	.9545	1.048	1.382	1.448	.8087	20
50	.7650	.6926	.7214	.9601	1.042	1.386	1.444	.8058	10
44°00′	.7679	.6947	.7193	.9657	1.036	1.390	1.440	.8029	46°00′
10	.7709	.6967	.7173	.9713	1.030	1.394	1.435	.7999	50
20	.7738	.6988	.7153	.9770	1.024	1.398	1.431	.7970	40
30	.7767	.7009	.7133	.9827	1.018	1.402	1.427	.7941	30
40	.7796	.7030	.7112	.9884	1.012	1.406	1.423	.7912	20
50	.7825	.7050	.7092	.9942	1.006	1.410	1.418	.7883	10
45°00′	.7854	.7071	.7071	1.000	1.000	1.414	1.414	.7854	45°00′
		Cos	Sin	Cot	Tan	Csc	Sec	Radians	Degrees

TABLE IV *Natural Logarithms of Numbers—0.00 to 99*

(Base $e = 2.718 \cdots$)*

N	0	1	2	3	4	5	6	7	8	9
0.0		5.395	6.088	6.493	6.781	7.004	7.187	7.341	7.474	7.592
0.1	7.697	7.793	7.880	7.960	8.034	8.103	8.167	8.228	8.285	8.339
0.2	8.391	8.439	8.486	8.530	8.573	8.614	8.653	8.691	8.727	8.762
0.3	8.796	8.829	8.861	8.891	8.921	8.950	8.978	9.006	9.032	9.058
0.4	9.084	9.108	9.132	9.156	9.179	9.201	9.223	9.245	9.266	9.287
0.5	9.307	9.327	9.346	9.365	9.384	9.402	9.420	9.438	9.455	9.472
0.6	9.489	9.506	9.522	9.538	9.554	9.569	9.584	9.600	9.614	9.629
0.7	9.643	9.658	9.671	9.685	9.699	9.712	9.726	9.739	9.752	9.764
0.8	9.777	9.789	9.802	9.814	9.826	9.837	9.849	9.861	9.872	9.883
0.9	9.895	9.906	9.917	9.927	9.938	9.949	9.959	9.970	9.980	9.990
1.0	0.0 0000	0995	1980	2956	3922	4879	5827	6766	7696	8618
1.1	9531	*0436	*1333	*2222	*3103	*3976	*4842	*5700	*6551	*7395
1.2	0.1 8232	9062	9885	*0701	*1511	*2314	*3111	*3902	*4686	*5464
1.3	0.2 6236	7003	7763	8518	9267	*0010	*0748	*1481	*2208	*2930
1.4	0.3 3647	4359	5066	5767	6464	7156	7844	8526	9204	9878
1.5	0.4 0547	1211	1871	2527	3178	3825	4469	5108	5742	6373
1.6	7000	7623	8243	8858	9470	*0078	*0682	*1282	*1879	*2473
1.7	0.5 3063	3649	4232	4812	5389	5962	6531	7098	7661	8222
1.8	8779	9333	9884	*0432	*0977	*1519	*2058	*2594	*3127	*3658
1.9	0.6 4185	4710	5233	5752	6269	6783	7294	7803	8310	8813
2.0	9315	9813	*0310	*0804	*1295	*1784	*2271	*2755	*3237	*3716
2.1	0.7 4194	4669	5142	5612	6081	6547	7011	7473	7932	8390
2.2	8846	9299	9751	*0200	*0648	*1093	*1536	*1978	*2418	*2855
2.3	0.8 3291	3725	4157	4587	5015	5442	5866	6289	6710	7129
2.4	7547	7963	8377	8789	9200	9609	*0016	*0422	*0826	*1228
2.5	0.9 1629	2028	2426	2822	3216	3609	4001	4391	4779	5166
2.6	5551	5935	6317	6698	7078	7456	7833	8208	8582	8954
2.7	9325	9695	*0063	*0430	*0796	*1160	*1523	*1885	*2245	*2604
2.8	1.0 2962	3318	3674	4028	4380	4732	5082	5431	5779	6126
2.9	6471	6815	7158	7500	7841	8181	8519	8856	9192	9527
3.0	9861	*0194	*0526	*0856	*1186	*1514	*1841	*2168	*2493	*2817
3.1	1.1 3140	3462	3783	4103	4422	4740	5057	5373	5688	6002
3.2	6315	6627	6938	7248	7557	7865	8173	8479	8784	9089
3.3	9392	9695	9996	*0297	*0597	*0896	*1194	*1491	*1788	*2083
3.4	1.2 2378	2671	2964	3256	3547	3837	4127	4415	4703	4990
3.5	5276	5562	5846	6130	6413	6695	6976	7257	7536	7815
3.6	8093	8371	8647	8923	9198	9473	9746	*0019	*0291	*0563
3.7	1.3 0833	1103	1372	1641	1909	2176	2442	2708	2972	3237
3.8	3500	3763	4025	4286	4547	4807	5067	5325	5584	5841
3.9	6098	6354	6609	6864	7118	7372	7624	7877	8128	8379
4.0	8629	8879	9128	9377	9624	9872	*0118	*0364	*0610	*0854
4.1	1.4 1099	1342	1585	1828	2070	2311	2552	2792	3031	3270
4.2	3508	3746	3984	4220	4456	4692	4927	5161	5395	5629
4.3	5862	6094	6326	6557	6787	7018	7247	7476	7705	7933
4.4	8160	8387	8614	8840	9065	9290	9515	9739	9962	*0185
4.5	1.5 0408	0630	0851	1072	1293	1513	1732	1951	2170	2388
4.6	2606	2823	3039	3256	3471	3687	3902	4116	4330	4543
4.7	4756	4969	5181	5393	5604	5814	6025	6235	6444	6653
4.8	6862	7070	7277	7485	7691	7898	8104	8309	8515	8719
4.9	8924	9127	9331	9534	9737	9939	*0141	*0342	*0543	*0744
5.0	1.6 0944	1144	1343	1542	1741	1939	2137	2334	2531	2728
5.1	2924	3120	3315	3511	3705	3900	4094	4287	4481	4673
5.2	4866	5058	5250	5441	5632	5823	6013	6203	6393	6582
5.3	6771	6959	7147	7335	7523	7710	7896	8083	8269	8455
5.4	8640	8825	9010	9194	9378	9562	9745	9928	*0111	*0293
5.5	1.7 0475	0656	0838	1019	1199	1380	1560	1740	1919	2098
5.6	2277	2455	2633	2811	2988	3166	3342	3519	3695	3871
5.7	4047	4222	4397	4572	4746	4920	5094	5267	5440	5613
5.8	5786	5958	6130	6302	6473	6644	6815	6985	7156	7326
5.9	7495	7665	7834	8002	8171	8339	8507	8675	8842	9009
N	0	1	2	3	4	5	6	7	8	9

Take tabular value −10 (applies to rows 0.0–0.9)

$$\log_e 0.10 = 7.69741\ 49070 - 10$$

* From Richard Stevens Burington, *Handbook of Mathematical Tables and Formulas*, Third Edition. Handbook Publishers, Inc., Sandusky, Ohio, 1954.

TABLE IV (*Continued*)

N	0	1	2	3	4	5	6	7	8	9
6.0	1.7 9176	9342	9509	9675	9840	*0006	*0171	*0336	*0500	*0665
6.1	1.8 0829	0993	1156	1319	1482	1645	1808	1970	2132	2294
6.2	2455	2616	2777	2938	3098	3258	3418	3578	3737	3896
6.3	4055	4214	4372	4530	4688	4845	5003	5160	5317	5473
6.4	5630	5786	5942	6097	6253	6408	6563	6718	6872	7026
6.5	7180	7334	7487	7641	7794	7947	8099	8251	8403	8555
6.6	8707	8858	9010	9160	9311	9462	9612	9762	9912	*0061
6.7	1.9 0211	0360	0509	0658	0806	0954	1102	1250	1398	1545
6.8	1692	1839	1986	2132	2279	2425	2571	2716	2862	3007
6.9	3152	3297	3442	3586	3730	3874	4018	4162	4305	4448
7.0	4591	4734	4876	5019	5161	5303	5445	5586	5727	5869
7.1	6009	6150	6291	6431	6571	6711	6851	6991	7130	7269
7.2	7408	7547	7685	7824	7962	8100	8238	8376	8513	8650
7.3	8787	8924	9061	9198	9334	9470	9606	9742	9877	*0013
7.4	2.0 0148	0283	0418	0553	0687	0821	0956	1089	1223	1357
7.5	1490	1624	1757	1890	2022	2155	2287	2419	2551	2683
7.6	2815	2946	3078	3209	3340	3471	3601	3732	3862	3992
7.7	4122	4252	4381	4511	4640	4769	4898	5027	5156	5284
7.8	5412	5540	5668	5796	5924	6051	6179	6306	6433	6560
7.9	6686	6813	6939	7065	7191	7317	7443	7568	7694	7819
8.0	7944	8069	8194	8318	8443	8567	8691	8815	8939	9063
8.1	9186	9310	9433	9556	9679	9802	9924	*0047	*0169	*0291
8.2	2.1 0413	0535	0657	0779	0900	1021	1142	1263	1384	1505
8.3	1626	1746	1866	1986	2106	2226	2346	2465	2585	2704
8.4	2823	2942	3061	3180	3298	3417	3535	3653	3771	3889
8.5	4007	4124	4242	4359	4476	4593	4710	4827	4943	5060
8.6	5176	5292	5409	5524	5640	5756	5871	5987	6102	6217
8.7	6332	6447	6562	6677	6791	6905	7020	7134	7248	7361
8.8	7475	7589	7702	7816	7929	8042	8155	8267	8380	8493
8.9	8605	8717	8830	8942	9054	9165	9277	9389	9500	9611
9.0	9722	9834	9944	*0055	*0166	*0276	*0387	*0497	*0607	*0717
9.1	2.2 0827	0937	1047	1157	1266	1375	1485	1594	1703	1812
9.2	1920	2029	2138	2246	2354	2462	2570	2678	2786	2894
9.3	3001	3109	3216	3324	3431	3538	3645	3751	3858	3965
9.4	4071	4177	4284	4390	4496	4601	4707	4813	4918	5024
9.5	5129	5234	5339	5444	5549	5654	5759	5863	5968	6072
9.6	6176	6280	6384	6488	6592	6696	6799	6903	7006	7109
9.7	7213	7316	7419	7521	7624	7727	7829	7932	8034	8136
9.8	8238	8340	8442	8544	8646	8747	8849	8950	9051	9152
9.9	9253	9354	9455	9556	9657	9757	9858	9958	*0058	*0158
10.0	2.3 0259	0358	0458	0558	0658	0757	0857	0956	1055	1154
N	0	1	2	3	4	5	6	7	8	9

N	0	1	2	3	4	5	6	7	8	9
1	2.30259	39790	48491	56495	63906	70805	77259	83321	89037	94444
2	99573	*04452	*09104	*13549	*17805	*21888	*25810	*29584	*33220	*36730
3	3.40120	43399	46574	49651	52636	55535	58352	61092	63759	66356
4	68888	71357	73767	76120	78419	80666	82864	85015	87120	89182
5	91202	93183	95124	97029	98898	*00733	*02535	*04305	*06044	*07754
6	4.09434	11087	12713	14313	15888	17439	18965	20469	21951	23411
7	24850	26268	27667	29046	30407	31749	33073	34381	35671	36945
8	38203	39445	40672	41884	43082	44265	45435	46591	47734	48864
9	49981	51086	52179	53260	54329	55388	56435	57471	58497	59512

$$\log_e 10 = 2.30258\ 50930$$

TABLE V *Values of e^x and e^{-x}*

x	e^x	e^{-x}	x	e^x	e^{-x}	x	e^x	e^{-x}
0.00	1.000	1.000	0.1	1.105	0.905	1	2.72	0.368
.01	1.010	.990	.2	1.221	.819	2	7.39	.135
.02	1.020	.980	.3	1.350	.741	3	20.09	.0498
.03	1.030	.970	.4	1.492	.670	4	54.60	.0183
.04	1.041	.961	.5	1.649	.607	5	148.4	.00674
.05	1.051	.951	.6	1.822	.549	6	403.4	.00248
.06	1.062	.942	.7	2.014	.497	7	1097.	.000912
.07	1.073	.932	.8	2.226	.449	8	2981.	.000335
.08	1.083	.923	.9	2.460	.407	9	8103.	.000123
.09	1.094	.914	1.0	2.718	.368	10	22026.	.000045

Note. $e^{x+y} = e^x \cdot e^y$.

Example. $e^{2.81} = e^2 \cdot e^{0.8} \cdot e^{0.01} = (7.39)(2.226)(1.01) = 16.6$.

TABLE VI *Table of Integrals*

In the following table u stands for any differentiable function of x and can, of course, be x itself. The constant of integration is to be added in each case. The reduction formulas are in many cases valid for values of the constants other than those indicated, but this table does not give the variety of special cases.

1. $\displaystyle \int u^n \, du = \frac{u^{n+1}}{n+1}$

2. $\displaystyle \int \frac{du}{u} = \log |u|$

3. $\displaystyle \int a^u \, du = \frac{a^u}{\log a}, \qquad a > 0, \, a \neq 1$

4. $\displaystyle \int e^u \, du = e^u$

5. $\displaystyle \int \sin u \, du = -\cos u$

6. $\displaystyle \int \cos u \, du = \sin u$

7. $\displaystyle \int \tan u \, du = \log |\sec u|$

8. $\displaystyle \int \cot u \, du = \log |\sin u|$

9. $\int \sec u \, du = \log |\sec u + \tan u| = \log \left| \tan \left(\frac{u}{2} + \frac{\pi}{4} \right) \right| = \cosh^{-1} (\sec u)$

10. $\int \csc u \, du = \log |\csc u - \cot u| = \log \left| \tan \frac{u}{2} \right| = -\sinh^{-1} (\cot u)$

11. $\int \frac{du}{u^2 + a^2} = \frac{1}{a} \tan^{-1} \frac{u}{a}, \qquad a \neq 0$

12. $\int \frac{du}{a^2 - u^2} = \frac{1}{2a} \log \left| \frac{u + a}{u - a} \right| = \begin{cases} \frac{1}{2a} \log \frac{a + u}{u - a} = \frac{1}{a} \coth^{-1} \frac{u}{a}, & u^2 > a^2 \\ \frac{1}{2a} \log \frac{a + u}{a - u} = \frac{1}{a} \tanh^{-1} \frac{u}{a}, & u^2 < a^2 \end{cases}$

13. $\int \frac{du}{\sqrt{a^2 - u^2}} = \sin^{-1} \frac{u}{|a|}, \qquad u^2 < a^2$

14. $\int \frac{du}{u(a + bu)} = \frac{1}{a} \log \left| \frac{u}{a + bu} \right|, \qquad a \neq 0, \, b \neq 0$

15. $\int \frac{du}{u^2(a + bu)} = -\frac{1}{au} + \frac{b}{a^2} \log \left| \frac{a + bu}{u} \right|, \qquad a \neq 0, \, b \neq 0$

16. $\int \frac{du}{u(a + bu)^2} = \frac{1}{a(a + bu)} - \frac{1}{a^2} \log \left| \frac{a + bu}{u} \right|, \qquad a \neq 0, \, b \neq 0$

Forms Involving $\sqrt{a + bu}, \, u > -\dfrac{a}{b}$

17. $\int u\sqrt{a + bu} = \frac{2(3bu - 2a)\sqrt{(a + bu)^3}}{15b^2}, \qquad a \neq 0, \, b \neq 0$

18. $\int \frac{u \, du}{\sqrt{a + bu}} = \frac{2(bu - 2a)\sqrt{a + bu}}{3b^2}, \qquad a \neq 0, \, b \neq 0$

19. $\int u^2\sqrt{a + bu} = \frac{2(15b^2u^2 - 12abu + 8a^2)\sqrt{(a + bu)^3}}{105b^3}, \qquad a \neq 0, \, b \neq 0$

20. $\int \frac{u^2 \, du}{\sqrt{a + bu}} = \frac{2(3b^2u^2 - 4abu + 8a^2)\sqrt{a + bu}}{15b^3}, \qquad a \neq 0, \, b \neq 0$

21. $\int \frac{du}{u\sqrt{a + bu}} = \begin{cases} \dfrac{1}{\sqrt{a}} \log \left| \dfrac{\sqrt{a + bu} - \sqrt{a}}{\sqrt{a + bu} + \sqrt{a}} \right|, & a > 0, \, b \neq 0 \\ \dfrac{2}{\sqrt{-a}} \tan^{-1} \sqrt{\dfrac{a + bu}{-a}}, & a < 0, \, b \neq 0 \end{cases}$

22. $\int \frac{\sqrt{a + bu}}{u} \, du = 2\sqrt{a + bu} + a \int \frac{du}{u\sqrt{a + bu}}, \qquad a \neq 0, \, b \neq 0$

23. $\displaystyle\int \frac{du}{u^2\sqrt{a+bu}} = -\frac{\sqrt{a+bu}}{au} - \frac{b}{2a}\int \frac{du}{u\sqrt{a+bu}}, \qquad a \neq 0, b \neq 0$

24. $\displaystyle\int \sqrt{\frac{a+u}{b+u}}\, du = \sqrt{(a+u)(b+u)} + (a-b)\log\left(\sqrt{a+u} + \sqrt{b+u}\right)$

25. $\displaystyle\int \sqrt{\frac{a-u}{b+u}}\, du = \sqrt{(a-u)(b+u)} + (a+b)\sin^{-1}\sqrt{\frac{b+u}{a+b}}$

Forms Involving $\sqrt{a^2 - u^2},\, u^2 < a^2$

We use $\dfrac{u}{|u|} = \begin{cases} 1 \text{ for } u > 0 \\ 0 \text{ for } u = 0 \\ -1 \text{ for } u < 0 \end{cases}$

26. $\displaystyle\int \sqrt{a^2 - u^2}\, du = \frac{1}{2}\left(u\sqrt{a^2 - u^2} + a^2 \sin^{-1}\frac{x}{|a|}\right)$

27. $\displaystyle\int u\sqrt{a^2 - u^2}\, du = -\tfrac{1}{3}(a^2 - u^2)^{3/2}$

28. $\displaystyle\int u^2\sqrt{a^2 - u^2}\, du = \frac{u}{8}(2u^2 - a^2)\sqrt{a^2 - u^2} + \frac{a^4}{8}\sin^{-1}\frac{u}{|a|}$

29. $\displaystyle\int \frac{u\, du}{\sqrt{a^2 - u^2}} = -\sqrt{a^2 - u^2}$

30. $\displaystyle\int \frac{u^2\, du}{\sqrt{a^2 - u^2}} = -\frac{u}{2}\sqrt{a^2 - u^2} + \frac{a^2}{2}\sin^{-1}\frac{u}{|a|}$

31. $\displaystyle\int (a^2 - u^2)^{3/2}\, du = \frac{u}{8}(5a^2 - 2u^2)\sqrt{a^2 - u^2} + \frac{3a^4}{8}\sin^{-1}\frac{u}{|a|}$

32. $\displaystyle\int \frac{du}{(a^2 - u^2)^{3/2}} = \frac{u}{a^2\sqrt{a^2 - u^2}}$

33. $\displaystyle\int \frac{u^2\, du}{(a^2 - u^2)^{3/2}} = \frac{u}{\sqrt{a^2 - u^2}} - \sin^{-1}\frac{u}{|a|}$

34. $\displaystyle\int \frac{du}{u\sqrt{a^2 - u^2}} = \frac{1}{|a|}\log\left|\frac{|a| - \sqrt{a^2 - u^2}}{u}\right| = -\frac{1}{|a|}\frac{u}{|u|}\operatorname{sech}^{-1}\left|\frac{u}{a}\right|$

35. $\displaystyle\int \frac{du}{u^2\sqrt{a^2 - u^2}} = -\frac{\sqrt{a^2 - u^2}}{a^2 u}$

36. $\displaystyle\int \frac{\sqrt{a^2 - u^2}}{u}\, du = \sqrt{a^2 - u^2} + |a|\log\left|\frac{|a| - \sqrt{a^2 - u^2}}{u}\right|$

37. $\displaystyle \int \frac{\sqrt{a^2 - u^2}}{u^2}\, du = -\frac{\sqrt{a^2 - u^2}}{u} - \sin^{-1}\frac{u}{|a|}$

Forms Involving $\sqrt{u^2 \pm a^2}$.

It is understood that $u^2 > a^2$ in the case of $\sqrt{u^2 - a^2}$.

Moreover, $\displaystyle \frac{u}{|u|} = \begin{cases} 1 & \text{for } u > 0 \\ 0 & \text{for } u = 0 \\ -1 & \text{for } u < 0 \end{cases}$

38. $\displaystyle \int \frac{du}{\sqrt{u^2 + a^2}} = \log|u + \sqrt{u^2 + a^2}| = \sinh^{-1}\frac{u}{a}$

39. $\displaystyle \int \frac{du}{\sqrt{u^2 - a^2}} = \log|u + \sqrt{u^2 - a^2}| = \cosh^{-1}\left|\frac{u}{a}\right|$

40. $\displaystyle \int \sqrt{u^2 \pm a^2}\, du = \frac{u}{2}\sqrt{u^2 \pm a^2} \pm \frac{a^2}{2}\log|u + \sqrt{u^2 \pm a^2}|$

41. $\displaystyle \int u\sqrt{u^2 \pm a^2}\, du = \tfrac{1}{3}(u^2 \pm a^2)^{3/2}$

42. $\displaystyle \int u^2\sqrt{u^2 \pm a^2}\, du = \frac{u}{8}(2u^2 \pm a^2)\sqrt{u^2 \pm a^2} - \frac{a^4}{8}\log|u + \sqrt{u^2 \pm a^2}|$

43. $\displaystyle \int \frac{u^2\, du}{\sqrt{u^2 \pm a^2}} = \frac{u}{2}\sqrt{u^2 \pm a^2} \mp \frac{a^2}{2}\log|u + \sqrt{u^2 \pm a^2}|$

44. $\displaystyle \int (u^2 \pm a^2)^{3/2}\, du = \frac{u}{8}(2u^2 \pm 5a^2)\sqrt{u^2 \pm a^2} + \frac{3a^4}{8}\log|u + \sqrt{u^2 \pm a^2}|$

45. $\displaystyle \int \frac{du}{(u^2 \pm a^2)^{3/2}} = \frac{\pm u}{a^2\sqrt{u^2 \pm a^2}}$

46. $\displaystyle \int \frac{u\, du}{\sqrt{u^2 \pm a^2}} = \sqrt{u^2 \pm a^2}$

47. $\displaystyle \int \frac{u^2\, du}{(u^2 \pm a^2)^{3/2}} = -\frac{u}{\sqrt{u^2 \pm a^2}} + \log|u + \sqrt{u^2 \pm a^2}|$

48. $\displaystyle \int \frac{du}{u^2\sqrt{u^2 \pm a^2}} = \mp\frac{\sqrt{u^2 \pm a^2}}{a^2 u}$

49. $\displaystyle \int \frac{du}{u^3\sqrt{u^2 - a^2}} = \frac{\sqrt{u^2 - a^2}}{2a^2 u^2} + \frac{1}{|a|^3}\frac{u}{|u|}\sec^{-1}\frac{u}{|a|}$

50. $\displaystyle \int \frac{\sqrt{u^2 - a^2}}{u}\, du = \sqrt{u^2 - a^2} - |a|\frac{u}{|u|}\sec^{-1}\frac{u}{|a|}$

51. $\displaystyle \int \frac{\sqrt{u^2 \pm a^2}}{u^2}\, du = -\frac{\sqrt{u^2 \pm a^2}}{u} + \log |u + \sqrt{u^2 \pm a^2}|$

52. $\displaystyle \int \frac{du}{u\sqrt{u^2 + a^2}} = \frac{1}{|a|} \log \left| \frac{\sqrt{u^2 + a^2} - |a|}{u} \right| = -\frac{1}{|a|} \frac{u}{|u|} \operatorname{csch}^{-1} \left| \frac{u}{a} \right|$

53. $\displaystyle \int \frac{du}{u\sqrt{u^2 - a^2}} = \frac{1}{|a|} \frac{u}{|u|} \sec^{-1} \frac{u}{|a|}$

54. $\displaystyle \int \frac{du}{u^3\sqrt{u^2 + a^2}} = -\frac{\sqrt{u^2 + a^2}}{2a^2u^2} - \frac{1}{2\,|a|^3} \log \left| \frac{|a| - \sqrt{u^2 + a^2}}{u} \right|$

55. $\displaystyle \int \frac{\sqrt{u^2 + a^2}}{u}\, du = \sqrt{u^2 + a^2} + |a| \log \left| \frac{|a| - \sqrt{u^2 + a^2}}{u} \right|$

Forms Involving $\sqrt{2au \mp u^2}$

It is understood that $2a > u$ when the minus sign holds and $2a < -u$ when the plus sign holds.

56. $\displaystyle \int \sqrt{2au - u^2}\, du = \frac{u - a}{2} \sqrt{2au - u^2} + \frac{a^2}{2} \sin^{-1} \frac{u - a}{|a|}$

57. $\displaystyle \int \frac{du}{\sqrt{2au - u^2}} = \sin^{-1} \frac{u - a}{|a|}$

58. $\displaystyle \int \frac{u^n\, du}{\sqrt{2au - u^2}} = \frac{-u^{n-1}\sqrt{2au - u^2}}{n} + \frac{a(2n - 1)}{n} \int \frac{u^{n-1}}{\sqrt{2au - u^2}},$

$\qquad\qquad\qquad\qquad\qquad\qquad n$ integral and ≥ 1

59. $\displaystyle \int \frac{du}{u^n\sqrt{2au - u^2}} = \frac{\sqrt{2au - u^2}}{a(1 - 2n)u^n} + \frac{n - 1}{(2n - 1)a} \int \frac{du}{u^{n-1}\sqrt{2au - u^2}},$

$\qquad\qquad\qquad\qquad\qquad\qquad n$ integral and ≥ 1

60. $\displaystyle \int u^n\sqrt{2au - u^2}\, du = \frac{-u^{n-1}(2au - u^2)^{3/2}}{n + 2} + \frac{(2n + 1)a}{n + 2}$

$\qquad\qquad\qquad \times \displaystyle \int u^{n-1}\sqrt{2au - u^2}\, du, \qquad n$ integral and ≥ 1

61. $\displaystyle \int \frac{\sqrt{2au - u^2}}{u^n}\, du = \frac{(2au - u^2)^{3/2}}{(3 - 2n)au^n} + \frac{n - 3}{(2n - 3)a} \int \frac{\sqrt{2au - u^2}}{u^{n-1}}\, du,$

$\qquad\qquad\qquad\qquad\qquad\qquad n$ integral and ≥ 1

62. $\displaystyle \int \frac{du}{(2au - u^2)^{3/2}} = \frac{u - a}{a^2\sqrt{2au - u^2}}$

63. $\displaystyle \int \frac{du}{\sqrt{2au + u^2}} = \log |u + a + \sqrt{2au + u^2}|$

Forms Involving $a + bx \pm cx^2$

The condition below on the discriminant $4ac - b^2$ can be relaxed if x is limited to values for which the radicand is positive.

64. $\displaystyle\int \frac{du}{a + bu + cu^2} = \frac{2}{\sqrt{4ac - b^2}} \tan^{-1} \frac{2cu + b}{\sqrt{4ac - b^2}}$,

$$4ac - b^2 > 0, c > 0$$

65. $\displaystyle\int \frac{du}{a + bu - cu^2} = \frac{1}{\sqrt{b^2 + 4ac}} \log \left| \frac{\sqrt{b^2 + 4ac} - b + 2cx}{\sqrt{b^2 + 4ac} + b - 2cx} \right|$,

$$4ac + b^2 > 0, c > 0$$

66. $\displaystyle\int \frac{du}{\sqrt{a + bu - cu^2}} = \frac{1}{\sqrt{c}} \sin^{-1} \frac{2cu - b}{\sqrt{b^2 + 4ac}}$, $\qquad 4ac + b^2 > 0, c > 0$

67. $\displaystyle\int \frac{du}{\sqrt{a + bu + cu^2}} = \frac{1}{\sqrt{c}} \log |2cu + b + 2\sqrt{c}\sqrt{a + bu + cu^2}|$,

$$4ac - b^2 > 0, c > 0$$

68. $\displaystyle\int \sqrt{a + bu + cu^2} \, du = \frac{2cu + b}{4c} \sqrt{a + bu + cu^2} - \frac{b^2 - 4ac}{8c^{3/2}}$

$\qquad \times \log |2cu + b + 2\sqrt{c}\sqrt{a + bu + cu^2}|$, $\qquad 4ac - b^2 > 0, c > 0$

69. $\displaystyle\int \sqrt{a + bu - cu^2} \, du = \frac{2cu - b}{4c} \sqrt{a + bu - cu^2} + \frac{b^2 + 4ac}{8c^{3/2}}$

$\qquad \times \sin^{-1} \frac{2cu - b}{\sqrt{b^2 + 4ac}}$, $\qquad 4ac + b^2 > 0, c > 0$

70. $\displaystyle\int \frac{u \, du}{\sqrt{a + bu - cu^2}} = -\frac{\sqrt{a + bu - cu^2}}{c} + \frac{b}{2c^{3/2}} \sin^{-1} \frac{2cu - b}{\sqrt{b^2 + 4ac}}$,

$$4ac + b^2 > 0, c > 0$$

71. $\displaystyle\int \frac{u \, du}{\sqrt{a + bu + cu^2}} = \frac{\sqrt{a + bu + cu^2}}{c} - \frac{b}{2c^{3/2}}$

$\qquad \times \log |2cu + b + 2\sqrt{c}\sqrt{a + bu + cu^2}|$, $\qquad 4ac - b^2 > 0, c > 0$

Trigonometric Forms

72. $\displaystyle\int \sin^n u \, du = -\frac{\sin^{n-1} u \cos u}{n} + \frac{n - 1}{n} \int \sin^{n-2} u \, du$,

$$n \text{ integral and } \geq 2$$

73. $\displaystyle\int \cos^n u\, du = \frac{\cos^{n-1} u \sin u}{n} + \frac{n-1}{n}\int \cos^{n-2} u\, du,$

n integral and ≥ 2

74. $\displaystyle\int \tan^n u\, du = \frac{\tan^{n-1} u}{n-1} - \int \tan^{n-2} u\, du,$ n integral and ≥ 2

75. $\displaystyle\int \cot^n u\, du = -\frac{\cot^{n-1} u}{n-1} - \int \cot^{n-2} u\, du,$ n integral and ≥ 2

76. $\displaystyle\int \sec^n u\, du = \frac{\tan u \sec^{n-2} u}{n-1} + \frac{n-2}{n-1}\int \sec^{n-2} u\, du,$

n integral and ≥ 2

77. $\displaystyle\int \csc^n u\, du = -\frac{\cot u \csc^{n-2} u}{n-1} + \frac{n-2}{n-1}\int \csc^{n-2} u\, du,$

n integral and ≥ 2

78. $\displaystyle\int \cos^m u \sin^n u\, du = \frac{\cos^{m-1} u \sin^{n+1} u}{m+n} + \frac{m-1}{m+n}\int \cos^{m-2} u \sin^n u\, du,$

m and n integral, $m \geq 2$, $n \geq 0$

$\displaystyle = -\frac{\sin^{n-1} u \cos^{m+1} u}{m+n} + \frac{n-1}{m+n}\int \cos^m u \sin^{n-2} u\, du,$

m and n integral, $m \geq 0$, $n \geq 2$

$\displaystyle = -\frac{\sin^{n+1} u \cos^{m+1} u}{m+1} + \frac{m+n+2}{m+1}\int \cos^{m+2} u \sin^n u\, du,$

m and n integral, $m \geq 0$, $n \geq 0$

$\displaystyle = \frac{\sin^{n+1} u \cos^{m+1} u}{n+1} + \frac{m+n+2}{n+1}\int \cos^m u \sin^{n+2} u\, du,$

m and n integral, $m \geq 0$, $n \geq 0$

79. $\displaystyle\int \sin au \sin bu\, du = \frac{\sin (a-b)u}{2(a-b)} - \frac{\sin (a+b)u}{2(a+b)},$ $|a| \neq |b|$

80. $\displaystyle\int \cos au \cos bu\, du = \frac{\sin (a-b)u}{2(a-b)} + \frac{\sin (a+b)u}{2(a+b)},$ $|a| \neq |b|$

81. $\displaystyle\int \sin au \cos bu\, du = -\frac{\cos (a-b)u}{2(a-b)} - \frac{\cos (a+b)u}{2(a+b)},$ $|a| \neq |b|$

82. $\displaystyle\int u^n \sin u\, du = -u^n \cos u + n\int u^{n-1} \cos u\, du,$ n integral and ≥ 1

83. $\displaystyle\int u^n \cos u\, du = u^n \sin u - n\int u^{n-1} \sin u\, du,$ n integral and ≥ 1

84. $$\int \frac{du}{a + b \cos u} = \begin{cases} \dfrac{2}{\sqrt{a^2 - b^2}} \tan^{-1} \dfrac{\sqrt{a^2 - b^2} \tan \dfrac{u}{2}}{a + b}, & a^2 - b^2 > 0 \\[4ex] \dfrac{1}{\sqrt{b^2 - a^2}} \log \left| \dfrac{a + b + \sqrt{b^2 - a^2} \tan \dfrac{u}{2}}{a + b - \sqrt{b^2 - a^2} \tan \dfrac{u}{2}} \right|, & \\[4ex] & b^2 - a^2 > 0 \end{cases}$$

85. $$\int \frac{du}{a + b \sin u} = \begin{cases} \dfrac{2}{\sqrt{a^2 - b^2}} \tan^{-1} \dfrac{a \tan \dfrac{u}{2} + b}{\sqrt{a^2 - b^2}}, & a^2 - b^2 > 0 \\[4ex] \dfrac{1}{\sqrt{b^2 - a^2}} \log \left| \dfrac{a \tan \dfrac{u}{2} + b - \sqrt{b^2 - a^2}}{a \tan \dfrac{u}{2} + b + \sqrt{b^2 - a^2}} \right|, & \\[4ex] & b^2 - a^2 > 0 \end{cases}$$

86. $$\int \frac{du}{a^2 \cos^2 u + b^2 \sin^2 u} = \frac{1}{ab} \tan^{-1} \frac{b \tan u}{a}, \qquad ab \neq 0$$

Inverse Trigonometric Forms, Principal Values Understood

87. $$\int \sin^{-1} u \, du = u \sin^{-1} u + \sqrt{1 - u^2}, \qquad u^2 < 1$$

88. $$\int \cos^{-1} u \, du = u \cos^{-1} u - \sqrt{1 - u^2}, \qquad u^2 < 1$$

89. $$\int \tan^{-1} u \, du = u \tan^{-1} u - \tfrac{1}{2} \log (1 + u^2)$$

90. $$\int \operatorname{ctn}^{-1} u \, du = u \operatorname{ctn}^{-1} u + \tfrac{1}{2} \log (1 + u^2)$$

91. $$\int \sec^{-1} u \, du = u \sec^{-1} u - \log |u + \sqrt{u^2 - 1}|, \qquad u^2 > 1$$

92. $$\int \csc^{-1} u \, du = u \csc^{-1} u + \log |u + \sqrt{u^2 - 1}|, \qquad u^2 > 1$$

93. $$\int u \sin^{-1} u \, du = \tfrac{1}{4}[(2u^2 - 1) \sin^{-1} u + u\sqrt{1 - u^2}], \qquad u^2 < 1$$

94. $$\int u \tan^{-1} u \, du = \tfrac{1}{2}[(u^2 + 1) \tan^{-1} u - u]$$

Forms Involving Exponential and Logarithmic Functions

95. $\displaystyle\int u^n e^{au}\, du = \frac{u^n e^{au}}{a} - \frac{n}{a}\int u^{n-1} e^{au}\, du,$ n integral and ≥ 1, $a \neq 0$

96. $\displaystyle\int u^n \log u\, du = u^{n+1}\left[\frac{\log u}{n+1} - \frac{1}{(n+1)^2}\right],$ n integral and ≥ 1

97. $\displaystyle\int u^n \log^m u\, du = \frac{u^{n+1}\log^m u}{n+1} - \frac{m}{n+1}\int u^n \log^{m-1} u\, du,$

m and n integral and ≥ 1

98. $\displaystyle\int e^{au} \sin nu\, du = \frac{e^{au}(a \sin nu - n \cos nu)}{a^2 + n^2},$ $a^2 + n^2 \neq 0$

99. $\displaystyle\int e^{au} \cos nu\, du = \frac{e^{au}(n \sin nu + a \cos nu)}{a^2 + n^2},$ $a^2 + n^2 \neq 0$

100. $\displaystyle\int \frac{du}{a + be^{nu}} = \frac{1}{an}[nu - \log|a + be^{nu}|],$ $an \neq 0$, $a + be^{nu} \neq 0$

101. $\displaystyle\int \frac{du}{ae^{nu} + be^{-nu}} = \begin{cases} \dfrac{1}{n\sqrt{ab}} \tan^{-1}\left(e^{nu}\sqrt{\dfrac{a}{b}}\right), & ab > 0 \\[3mm] \dfrac{1}{2n\sqrt{-ab}} \log\left|\dfrac{ae^{nu} - \sqrt{-ab}}{ae^{nu} + \sqrt{-ab}}\right|, & ab < 0 \end{cases}$

102. $\displaystyle\int \frac{ue^u\, du}{(1+u)^2} = \frac{e^u}{1+u}$

103. $\displaystyle\int \sin(\log u)\, du = \frac{u}{2}[\sin(\log u) - \cos(\log u)]$

104. $\displaystyle\int \cos(\log u)\, du = \frac{u}{2}[\sin(\log u) + \cos(\log u)]$

Forms Involving Hyperbolic Functions

105. $\displaystyle\int \sinh u\, du = \cosh u$

106. $\displaystyle\int \cosh u\, du = \sinh u$

107. $\displaystyle\int \tanh u\, du = \log \cosh u$

108. $\int \operatorname{sech} u \, du = 2 \tan^{-1} e^u$

109. $\int \sinh^2 u \, du = -\tfrac{1}{2}u + \tfrac{1}{4} \sinh 2u$

110. $\int \cosh^2 u \, du = \tfrac{1}{2}u + \tfrac{1}{4} \sinh 2u$

111. $\int \operatorname{sech}^2 u \, du = \tanh u$

112. $\int \operatorname{csch}^2 u \, du = -\coth u$

113. $\int \operatorname{sech} u \tanh u \, du = -\operatorname{sech} u$

114. $\int \operatorname{csch} u \coth u \, du = -\operatorname{csch} u$

Miscellaneous Integrals

115. $\int u^m(a + bu^n)^p \, du =$

$$
\begin{cases}
\dfrac{u^{m-n+1}(a + bu^n)^{p+1}}{b(np + m + 1)} - \dfrac{(m - n + 1)a}{b(np + m + 1)} \\
\qquad\qquad \times \displaystyle\int u^{m-n}(a + bu^n)^p \, du \\[2mm]
\dfrac{u^{m+1}(a + bu^n)^p}{np + m + 1} + \dfrac{npa}{np + m + 1} \\
\qquad\qquad \times \displaystyle\int u^m(a + bu^n)^{p-1} \, du \\[2mm]
\dfrac{u^{m+1}(a + bu^n)^{p+1}}{a(m + 1)} - \dfrac{b(np + n + m + 1)}{a(m + 1)} \\
\qquad\qquad \times \displaystyle\int u^{m+n}(a + bu^n)^p \, du \\[2mm]
\dfrac{-u^{m+1}(a + bu^n)^{p+1}}{na(p + 1)} + \dfrac{np + n + m + 1}{na(p + 1)} \\
\qquad\qquad \times \displaystyle\int u^m(a + bu^n)^{p+1} \, du,
\end{cases}
$$

m, n, p integral and > 0 in all four forms

116. $\displaystyle\int_0^\pi \sin^2 nu \, du = \int_0^\pi \cos^2 nu \, du = \frac{\pi}{2}$

117. $\displaystyle\int_0^{\pi/2} \sin^n u \, du = \int_0^{\pi/2} \cos^n u \, du$

$$= \begin{cases} \dfrac{(n-1)(n-3)(n-5)\cdots 4\cdot 2}{n(n-2)(n-4)\cdots 5\cdot 3} \\ \qquad\qquad \text{for } n \text{ an odd integer and } > 1 \\[2ex] \dfrac{(n-1)(n-3)(n-5)\cdots 3\cdot 1}{n(n-2)(n-4)\cdots 4\cdot 2}\cdot\dfrac{\pi}{2} \\ \qquad\qquad \text{for } n \text{ an even integer and } > 0 \end{cases}$$

118. $\displaystyle\int_0^{\pi/2} \sin^m u \cos^n u \, du = \begin{cases} \dfrac{(n-1)(n-3)(n-5)\cdots 4\cdot 2}{(m+n)(m+n-2)\cdots(m+5)(m+3)(m+1)} \\ \qquad\qquad \text{for } n \text{ an odd integer } > 1 \\[2ex] \dfrac{(m-1)(m-3)(m-5)\cdots 4\cdot 2}{(n+m)(n+m-2)\cdots(n+5)(n+3)(n+1)} \\ \qquad\qquad \text{for } m \text{ an odd integer } > 1 \\[2ex] \dfrac{(m-1)(m-3)\cdots 1\cdot(n-1)(n-3)\cdots 1}{(m+n)(m+n-2)\cdots 4\cdot 2}\cdot\dfrac{\pi}{2} \\ \qquad\qquad \text{for } m \text{ and } n \text{ both even integers and } > 0 \end{cases}$

Index